INTERNATIONAL MOLAR MASSES

NAME	SYMBOL	ATOMIC NUMBER	MOLAR MASS	NAME	SYMBOL	ATOMIC NUMBER	MOLAR MASS
Actinium	Ac	89	(227)	Mercury	Hg	80	200.6
Aluminum	Al	13	27.0	Molybdenum	Mo	42	95.9
Americium	Am	95	(243)	Neodymium	Nd	60	144.2
Antimony	Sb	51	121.8	Neon	Ne	10	20.2
Argon	Ar	18	39.9	Neptunium	Np	93	(237)
Arsenic	As	33	74.9	Nickel	Ni	28	58.7
Astatine	At	85	(210)	Niobium	Nb	41	92.9
Barium	Ba	56	137.3	Nitrogen	N	7	14.01
Berkelium	Bk	97	(247)	Nobelium	No	102	(255)
Beryllium	Be	4	9.01	Osmium	Os	76	190.2
Bismuth	Bi	83	209.0	Oxygen	O	8	16.00
Boron	B	5	10.8	Palladium	Pd	46	106.4
Bromine	Br	35	79.9	Phosphorus	P	15	31.0
Cadmium	Cd	48	112.4	Platinum	Pt	78	195.1
Calcium	Ca	20	40.1	Plutonium	Pu	94	(244)
Californium	Cf	98	(251)	Polonium	Po	84	210
Carbon	C	6	12.01	Potassium	K	19	39.1
Cerium	Ce	58	140.1	Praseodymium	Pr	59	140.9
Cesium	Cs	55	132.9	Promethium	Pm	61	(145)
Chlorine	Cl	17	35.5	Protactinium	Pa	91	(231)
Chromium	Cr	24	52.0	Radium	Ra	88	(226)
Cobalt	Co	27	58.9	Radon	Rn	86	(222)
Copper	Cu	29	63.5	Rhenium	Re	75	186.2
Curium	Cm	96	(247)	Rhodium	Rh	45	102.9
Dysprosium	Dy	66	162.5	Rubidium	Rb	37	85.5
Einsteinium	Es	99	(254)	Ruthenium	Ru	44	101.1
Erbium	Er	68	167.3	Samarium	Sm	62	150.4
Europium	Eu	63	152.0	Scandium	Sc	21	45.0
Fermium	Fm	100	(257)	Selenium	Se	34	79.0
Fluorine	F	9	19.0	Silicon	Si	14	28.1
Francium	Fr	87	(223)	Silver	Ag	47	107.9
Gadolinium	Gd	64	157.2	Sodium	Na	11	23.0
Gallium	Ga	31	69.7	Strontium	Sr	38	87.6
Germanium	Ge	32	72.6	Sulfur	S	16	32.1
Gold	Au	79	197.0	Tantalum	Ta	73	180.9
Hafnium	Hf	72	178.5	Technetium	Tc	43	(97)
Helium	He	2	4.00	Tellurium	Te	52	127.6
Holmium	Ho	67	164.9	Terbium	Tb	65	158.9
Hydrogen	H	1	1.008	Thallium	Tl	81	204.4
Indium	In	49	114.8	Thorium	Th	90	232.0
Iodine	I	53	126.9	Thulium	Tm	69	168.9
Iridium	Ir	77	192.2	Tin	Sn	50	118.7
Iron	Fe	26	55.8	Titanium	Ti	22	47.9
Krypton	Kr	36	83.8	Tungsten	W	74	183.9
Lanthanum	La	57	138.9	Uranium	U	92	238.0
Lawrencium	Lr	103	(260)	Vanadium	V	23	50.9
Lead	Pb	82	207.2	Xenon	Xe	54	131.3
Lithium	Li	3	6.94	Ytterbium	Yb	70	173.0
Lutetium	Lu	71	175.0	Yttrium	Y	39	88.9
Magnesium	Mg	12	24.3	Zinc	Zn	30	65.4
Manganese	Mn	25	54.9	Zirconium	Zr	40	91.2
Mendelevium	Md	101	(258)	(unnamed)*	?	104	(261)

*Discovery reported in 1964.
Molar masses based on $^{12}C = 12.000$.
Numbers in parentheses give the mass number of the most stable isotope.

Chemistry

Experiments and Principles

THE CANDLE-
ILLUMINATING CHEMISTRY

Chemistry

Experiments and Principles

Paul R. O'Connor
Professor of Chemistry
University of Minnesota
Minneapolis, Minnesota

Joseph E. Davis, Jr.
Head of Science Department
Campolindo High School
Moraga, California

Edward L. Haenisch
Professor of Chemistry
Wabash College
Crawfordsville, Indiana

W. Keith MacNab
Head of Science Department
Sir Francis Drake High School
San Anselmo, California

A. L. McClellan
Senior Research Associate
Chevron Research Company
Richmond, California

HEATH D. C. HEATH AND COMPANY
Lexington, Massachusetts   Toronto

Acknowledgment

Frontis-piece	The Candle— *Illuminating Chemistry,* by Bernard Abramson, courtesy Chemical Education Material Study.	86	Daniel S. Brody/Editorial Photocolor Archives	245	Fredrick D. Bodin
		87	Herb Taylor/Editorial Photocolor Archives	252	courtesy of Raytheon Company
Page		92	Fredrick D. Bodin	262	Joyce R. Wilson/Sports Camera West
1	Willard Chase	98	Fredrick D. Bodin	273	General Electric Company
6	M. C. Escher, NIGHT AND DAY, Escher Foundation-Haags Gemeentemuseum-The Hage	117	Laurence Lowry	288	James Carroll/Editorial Photocolor Archives
		128	courtesy of Professor Neil Bartlett, University of California, Berkeley	289	D. C. Heath Staff
9	Marion Bernstein/Editorial Photocolor Archives (top), courtesy of Taylor Instrument, Sybron Corp. (bottom center), Smithsonian Institution, Photo #59,483 (bottom right)	138	M. H. Kellicutt/Editorial Photocolor Archives	297	courtesy of Central Scientific Company
		142	courtesy of Raytheon Company	310	Bohdan Hrynewych
		149	courtesy of Perkin-Elmer Corporation	329	courtesy of Sebring Vanguard, Inc.
		163	Centre National de la Recherche Scientifique	331	Utah Copper Division, Kennecott Copper Corporation
13	Marion Bernstein/Editorial Photocolor Archives	193	Laurence Lowry	332	
25	Authenticated News International	205	courtesy of Harvard University News Office	333	courtesy of Reed and Barton Silversmiths
30	Wide World Photos	206	courtesy of Eastern Mountain Sports, Inc.	347	Mark Chester
39	courtesy of Morton Salt Company, Division of Morton-Norwich Products, Inc.	221	Authenticated News International	371	Bayer Company
		222	Daniel S. Brody/Editorial Photocolor Archives	377	courtesy of F. S. Werblin
50	courtesy of Raytheon Company	227	Complex calorimeter, courtesy Morganite Research and Development Ltd.	380	Dr. Alexander Rich, M.I.T.
54	courtesy of Union Carbide Corporation, Linde Division			387	Museum of Science, Boston, Massachusetts
55	courtesy of Caloric Corporation	231	Bruce Anspach/Editorial Photocolor Archives	402	Chemical Education Material Study, by Charles L. Finance
65	courtesy of NASA	235	courtesy of Pacific Gas and Electric Company News Bureau	416	Fredrick D. Bodin
67	Wide World Photos (left), Robert Rapelye/Editorial Photocolor Archives (right)			427	courtesy of Bethlehem Steel Corporation
		238	Andrew Sacks/Editorial Photocolor Archives	438	courtesy of Bethlehem Steel Corporation
72	courtesy of Pacific Gas and Electric Company News Bureau	243	Paul K. Landfried/Sports Camera West	440	U.S. Steel
				443	courtesy of Luray Caverns, Virginia
84	Mark Chester/Editorial Photocolor Archives			Color Plate I & II	Chemical Education Material Study, by Charles L. Finance

Illustrations by Anco Technical Service

Published simultaneously in Canada.

Printed in the United States of America.

International Standard Book Number: 0-669-00382-4

Library of Congress Catalog Card Number: 76-13344

A Note to the Student

Chemistry deals with all the substances that make up our environment. It also deals with the changes that take place in these substances—changes that make the difference between a cold and lifeless planet and one that teems with life and growth. Chemistry helps us understand and benefit from nature's wondrous ways.

Chemistry is an important part of science. Since every phase of our daily life is affected by the fruits of scientific activity, everyone should know what scientific activity is, what it can do, and how it works. The study of chemistry will help you learn these things.

CHEMISTRY: EXPERIMENTS AND PRINCIPLES presents chemistry as it is today. It does so with emphasis upon the most enjoyable part of chemistry—experimentation. A clear and valid picture of the steps by which scientists proceed is carefully presented and repeatedly used. Unifying principles are developed, with the laboratory work providing the basis for the development. The experimental theme is supported by a number of films to provide experimental evidence that is needed but not readily available in the classroom because of inherent danger or expense. When you become familiar with these widely applicable principles, you no longer need to memorize innumerable chemical facts. To see these principles grow out of observations you have made in the laboratory gives you a valid picture of how all scientific advances begin. It permits you to engage in scientific activity and to start becoming a scientist yourself.

At the end of this course you will not know all of chemistry. You will know enough chemistry and enough about science to feel that the part you do not know is understandable, not mysterious. You will appreciate the great power of scientific methods and appreciate their limitations. You will have become practiced in making observations, in weighing facts, and in framing valid conclusions. You will have formed the habit of questioning and of seeking understanding rather than being satisfied with blind acceptance. You will be able to share in the excitement of science and feel the pleasure that comes with discovery. When you achieve these things, you will have had a thorough introduction to science through chemistry. Nothing could be a more important part of your education at a time when science is molding our age.

Preface

The title CHEMISTRY: EXPERIMENTS AND PRINCIPLES emphasizes the theme of this book. A clear and valid picture of the steps by which scientists proceed is carefully presented and repeatedly used. Observations and measurements lead to the development of unifying principles, and then these principles are used to interrelate diverse phenomena.

The initial set of experiments and the first seven chapters provide a foundation for this course. The elements of scientific activity are immediately displayed, including the role of uncertainty. The atomic theory, the nature of matter in its various phases, chemical periodicity, and the mole concept are developed early. After presentation of the experimental evidence that led scientists to postulate different models for the atom (Chapters 8 and 9), six chapters are devoted to the extraction of important chemical principles from relevant laboratory experience. The principles considered include energy, rate and equilibrium characteristics of chemical reactions, acid-base behavior, oxidation-reduction, and chemical bonding in gases, liquids, and solids. The book concludes with four chapters of descriptive chemistry (16-19) in which the applicability and worth of the principles developed earlier are seen again and again.

This book places emphasis on chemical principles to represent properly the change that has taken place in chemistry over the last decades. Descriptive chemistry is found in the examples illustrating the principles, and then, in the later chapters, in the application of these principles. Less obvious, but perhaps more important, is the systematic development of the relation between experiment and theory. Chemistry is gradually and logically unfolded, not presented as a collection of facts, dicta, and dogmas. We hope to convey an awareness of the significance and capabilities of scientific activities that will help each future citizen assess calmly and wisely the growing impact of technological advances on his social environment. Finally, we have tried to achieve closer continuity of subject matter and pedagogy between high school and modern introductory college and university courses for those students who will continue their science training.

This book follows the pace-setting work of the Chemical Education Material Study. That program, usually called CHEM Study, was one of the curriculum improvement projects supported by the National Science Foundation. This agency of our federal government provided support to the creative effort for three years (1960-63) during which time about 30 contributors produced three trial versions and a final set of materials. The contributors were drawn from across the United States and included, about equally, high school teachers and university professors, with industry also represented. All the professors had previously written textbooks or research treatises. The material was modified by the experience gained in nearly 500 high schools where the trial versions were used. The CHEM Study books and films have been generally available since 1963, and they have earned a place in schools throughout the nation. Test results, now becoming numerous enough for valid conclusion, suggest that CHEM Study pupils do better in selective college chemistry classes and are not at a disadvantage in regular ones.

This book, with the accompanying Laboratory Manual and the associated Teacher's Guides, is a descendant of the CHEM Study project. As one of the authorized revisions of those materials, the present work reflects the talents and dedication of the original CHEM Study team. We are grateful for the opportunity to build on their outstanding effort.

During the revisions following CHEM Study we have made changes. They are based on reactions from our students in high school, university, and teacher institute classes. The principal ones are:

- a completely rewritten text, modified to bring fundamental understanding of bonding earlier in the course and to provide somewhat easier reading.
- more descriptive material in the chapters that develop chemical principles.
- about 30 essays, many marginal comments, and 100 or so career statements representing new additions designed to stimulate student interest and initiate class discussion.
- a completely reworked laboratory manual in which approximately one-fourth of the experiments are new ones.
- the support material split into two parts: a Teacher's Guide for the text, and a Teacher's Laboratory Guide for the Laboratory Manual.
- a number of demonstrations added to the Laboratory Guide.
- all problems and exercises reconsidered and new ones added to give about 40 per chapter.

These changes are designed to facilitate learning by the beginner; to give him real understanding of the process by which new knowledge is gained; to highlight the distinction between facts, interpretations, and proof; and, of course, to instill some chemical information in an easier way.

P. R. O'Connor
J. E. Davis, Jr.
E. L. Haenisch
W. K. MacNab
A. L. McClellan

Acknowledgments

We have gained help and encouragement from our co-workers in chemistry teaching. In particular

Janet Campbell	Campolindo High School Moraga, California
Margaret Nicholson	Acalanes High School Lafayette, California
Nina Tychinin	Sir Francis Drake High School San Anselmo, California
John Girton	Redwood High School Larkspur, California
Don Olds	Woodbridge High School Woodbridge, Ontario
Leigh Wilson	Lynbrook High School Cupertino, California

deserve our thanks. There have been numerous benefits from the teachers who were the "students" in the institutes we have conducted. Finally, we appreciate the many teachers and some students who have written to help us clarify specific problems. We would welcome continuation of this direct communication.

Contents

Chemistry: An Experimental Science 1

What is the nature of science?

What is the nature of chemistry?

We will develop the answers to these questions, not through words alone but through experience. No one can completely convey through words the excitement of scientific discovery. We will see the nature of science by engaging in scientific activity. We will see the nature of chemistry by considering problems which interest chemists.

Our starting point, then, will be the activities of science. We will *perform* these activities, beginning on familiar ground. On such ground, where *you* know the answer, you will best see the steps by which science advances.

1-1 The Activities of Science

Every form of life interacts with its surroundings in one way or another. Some plants require bright direct sunlight for maximum growth. Other plants grow best in dim light. Birds and animals maintain constant body temperatures by balancing heat gains and heat losses. Feathers and fur are important in retaining heat energy. When the colder temperatures of winter come, many birds migrate to warmer climates. Other animals, like the chipmunk, hibernate through the winter. The body temperature of the chipmunk drops during his long winter nap. The food requirements for the hibernating animal are much less than during his active period in the warm summer months. It is no coincidence that an animal hibernates during the months when food is most difficult to find.

People are aware of their surroundings and respond in most complex ways. Their eyesight and hearing warn them of dangers. They have learned by experience that certain plants are harmful and that some pools of water are poisonous. Their intellects permit them to respond to their environment in many ways.

To help you see how people have developed one of the most useful ways of looking at their environment, we will use a non-chemical example so that there will be no new technical terms or unfamiliar ideas. You have probably had dreams and know how strange things can happen in them. Often both time and space become distorted in dreams. Consider this description of a dream:

"... those sciences are vain and full of errors which are not born from experiment, the mother of all certainty ..."
Leonardo da Vinci
1452–1519

Figure 1-1
The person in the dream.

You find yourself floating silently over a forest. You can see clearly what is happening below. At first you see only the trees of the forest, but suddenly there is a clearing with the remains of a deserted village. A closer look shows an old log cabin with the roof half caved in. It is a desolate area, cold and uninhabited. Wait. There is a campfire near the cabin. And there is a person shivering with cold while searching through the forest. You see the figure stop at a fallen tree, break off a dead branch, and drag it along. As you drift silently overhead, the person picks up many other things to take back to the campfire. In your dream you drop lower and see the person standing by the fire warming hands and feet. It is quite cold. Nearby there is a large pile of the things which have been brought in from the forest.

Then there starts a strange routine. The figure takes something from the pile and holds it in the fire. If it catches fire, it is quickly blown out and placed in a smaller pile to the left. There are many objects there: branches from dead trees; handles from hoes, brooms, and mops; a few chair legs; and a fence post or two. If something does not burn, it is placed on another pile to the right. You can see an old flat-iron, some rocks, and a rusty shovel blade. After trying all the objects and putting each one either to the right or to the left, the person sits down. In that funny way of dreams you are watching the person writing out a list. Or rather two lists.

Things that burn	Things that do not burn
Tree branches	Rocks
Broom handles	Shovel blades
Chair legs	Flatirons

Just as you wonder about this, the writer gets up and goes off into the forest again while studying the list, perhaps to decide what to bring back. Clever! No energy wasted on any more rocks and shovels. But it is awkward to carry the list and to check each time against it. Then, too, the searcher finds some things that are not on the list: a big door from the cabin, some books, and a box of old newspapers. What about them? They are passed by.

In camp considerable time is spent looking at the list and at the piles of material that have been gathered. Slowly a smile comes. The person writes three words that summarize the findings.

Cylindrical objects burn.

Now there is one of those weird time jumps you find only in dreams. It is the next day and you find

Crisis

The combination of trial, observation, and deduction gives a method to meet changing conditions. Currently there is much talk of energy shortage. The scientific method will probably help as it did in Pilgrim days. In 1615, James I of England found that his navy was short of wood and the supply was running out. He decreed that wood could no longer be used to stoke the glassmakers' furnaces. This ruling seemed to mean the end of an industry. Actually, the glassmakers soon learned to use coal, an innovation at the time.

But coal produced smoke and gases that were bad for the glass. A covered melting pot kept the smoke away from the molten glass and produced a bonus, higher temperature. This made it possible for George Ravenscroft to make glass with a larger percentage of lead oxide in it. His lead, or flint, glass was clearer and easier to carve and mold. English glassmaking improved instead of dying.

your friend looking for more material for the fire. But there is no list. Instead a rule is being used. You know this, for you hear: "cylindrical objects burn; cylindrical objects burn, . . ." More trees and limbs are collected, as well as a cane, and three baseball bats. Tested in the fire, they all burn just as the rule predicted. What's more, the person recalls happily the piece of chain and the large door that were left in the forest. There was no reason to expect them to burn. *They were not cylindrical.*

The rule was helping to solve the problem of keeping warm. It worked so well that it gave confidence in using it. The next day the rule led the searcher to bring back three pieces of metal pipe, two soda bottles, and the axle from an old car. A large cardboard box of newspapers and some shingles that had blown off the cabin were left in the forest. It was a long, cold night! None of these objects burned. The next morning there were some new thoughts.

Perhaps the cylindrical shape of an object is not related to burning.

Even though the "cylindrical" rule did not always work, the original lists were still true. Tree limbs, broom handles, and chair legs DO burn. That information is still usable.

You watch again. The person is writing a new rule.

Wooden objects burn.

Now let's leave the dream and interpret what it means. We will do that in terms of the character's activities and then relate them to what scientists do, to what you will be doing as you study chemistry.

First, notice that the person was cold. The first thought was so natural that we might not realize how important it is. The problem was defined. The person was cold. This led to a practical question: What to do? Every scientific study starts with these steps: define the problem and choose a way to solve it. The lost searcher thought of a fire just as you would, but there was a strange limitation to this dream. The person didn't know what would burn. However, the actions were well suited to the situation. The person used the experimental way of testing things. The *first* activity directed toward solving the problem of getting warm was *observation*. This is the active, physical part of science. Like the cold character in the forest, the scientist collects and sorts observations. *Second, the information is organized into lists or patterns and studied for regularities.*

The dream character's *third activity* was one that involved thinking. As the person got warm by the fire, the lists were studied trying to find an answer to a simple looking question, *Why*? Why were there two piles? What property caused all objects in one pile to burn but was absent from the other? In the forest, after one false start, the rule was found that made it easier to look for things that would burn: wooden objects burn. In real life the scientist looks for regularities for the same reason, to make the job of remembering easier. The *third* activity is *to wonder why the rule exists.*

Fourth, the scientist and our friend in the forest write down what they learn, both the experimental results and the rules they devise. This makes it easier to tell others. *They communicate their findings.*

The third activity leads us deeper into underlying causes. It is to wonder why the rule exists. Why does the rule work? The figure in the dream didn't ask a question like that. But someone afterwards would probably reach that point sooner or later. The second rule led to abandoning shape as important to burning and moving on to composition. Later, perhaps even after several generations, someone would probably find that a box of papers also burns. Then the rule would have to be changed again. The new rule might be "Objects made of wood or derived from wood burn."

Let us summarize what our dream showed us. The scientific method has several steps. Some steps involve tangible things you can see and feel and do: carrying out experiments, making observations, and communicating to others. Other steps require mental efforts: seeking a rule and wondering why the rule exists. You may object to the dream. You know that the first rule was *wrong.* "Cylindrical objects burn" is a silly rule. It doesn't matter whether something is flat or round or pointed. It might still burn. "Wooden objects burn" is a better rule, but only partly right. Wood burns, but so do paper, gasoline, sugar, bread, and many other objects.

There is an important point here. The cold person by the fire made a rule that *fitted the data.* In the real situation the scientist has *only* the data (plus that communicated from others), and doesn't have the advantage that you had in the dream story. *The scientist doesn't know the answer.* In this book you will see some examples of rules in science that have been shown to be wrong. They have been replaced by new rules. Someday these new rules may have to be changed too. This method of trying to create explanations that fit all the facts has led to such wonderful successes as polio vaccine and the propulsion of rockets to the moon.

One final comment: Most of the students in your chemistry class will not become scientists. But all of you live in a world greatly influenced by science. You will read the newspapers about many scientific advances, and sometimes you will be asked to vote on important technical subjects. You will be asked to consider the effect of aerosol sprays on the earth's atmosphere, cancer-producing chemicals in water supplies, the bad effects of industrial wastes, and the advantages and possible dangers of nuclear power production. All these are important problems that require two major efforts. First, scientists and engineers must collect *enough good* information so that the real dangers and possible solutions are known. Second, a political decision has to be made about what society wants. Each citizen should be involved in the second effort. For this reason it is important to understand how scientists go about solving problems. Then you will know, like our dream character, that too little information can lead to rules that require changing. Further, when changes do come, you can understand why. Probably more and better information is available, or a better rule has been made by someone. Now let's return to chemistry. To review, a scientist tries to understand the world by these steps:

Does experiments and gathers information through
    observation.
Organizes this information and looks for regularities.
Wonders why the regularities exist.
Communicates the findings to others.

These are the basic **activities of science**. Observation is the starting point. Observation is most useful when the conditions which affect the observation are controlled carefully. A condition is controlled when it is fixed, known, and can be varied deliberately. All science is built upon the results of experiments performed under controlled conditions.

1-2 Observation and Description

We will start to learn chemistry by considering what might be observed about a high school chemistry stockroom. It is easy to make a number of observations that describe what we see. Some observations are not as important as others.

Vulcanization of Rubber

In February 1838 Charles Goodyear had a lucky accident when a mixture of sulfur and India rubber was brought carelessly into contact with a hot stove. He saw it melt and react to form the product he had been trying to make for seven years. By this act and observation he discovered how to vulcanize rubber.

Observation may involve looking for patterns that are not always obvious.

The stockroom is on the second floor.
The door to the stockroom is kept locked.
There is a list of all the supplies on the bulletin board
near the door.

Once inside we find a number of shelves with beakers, flasks, and test tubes in one section of the stockroom. Other shelves are full of bottles of chemicals arranged in alphabetical order (a regularity that is easy to understand). A number of observations could be listed:

Many bottles contain solids.
Most of the solids are white, but a few are colored.
All the bottles have labels; most have chemical names and symbols.
On the bottom shelf, in a metal tray, there are large bottles of colorless liquids.
Chained against the wall there are some tall metal cylinders with valves on top. These have labels with names such as ammonia, chlorine, hydrogen, hydrogen chloride, nitric oxide, nitrogen dioxide, and oxygen.

More observations could be made if we opened the bottles to smell the chemicals (always do this cautiously!). One of the first things you are likely to observe is the different behavior of solids, liquids, and gases. Everyone realizes that a solid has a definite shape and volume, whereas a liquid takes on the shape of the container it is in. The volume of the liquid does not change as it is put in various containers. A gas, on the other hand, expands to fill any container it is in. Gases have neither definite shape nor volume. Let's take samples of the various gases from the cylinders we saw in the stockroom. We want to make more observations and to do some experiments with them, to see if we can find any regularity about gases.

In alphabetical order the names of these gases are ammonia, chlorine, hydrogen, hydrogen chloride, nitric oxide, nitrogen dioxide, and oxygen. Two of these gases can be recognized by their color. Chlorine is greenish yellow, and nitrogen dioxide is reddish brown. The other five gases are colorless. The colorless gases can be further sorted according to how well they dissolve in water. Figure 1-2 shows what happens if a stoppered test tube full of each gas is opened with the mouth of the test tube under water. In the tubes containing ammonia and hydrogen chloride the water rises rapidly, filling the tubes. These two gases dissolve readily in water. In the other three test tubes the liquid levels rise only a little, showing that these gases are not very soluble in water. Ammonia and hydrogen chloride are colorless gases which dissolve readily in water. These two gases can be distinguished by their effect on the moistened dye, litmus. This dye turns red if it is placed in hydrogen chloride. The dye turns blue if it is placed in ammonia.

We have not yet identified the gases nitric oxide, hydrogen, and oxygen. Nitric oxide has its own personality. Immediately upon exposure to air this colorless gas becomes reddish brown, exactly

The word *gas* was first used in chemistry by the Belgian scientist Jan van Helmont during the early 1600's.

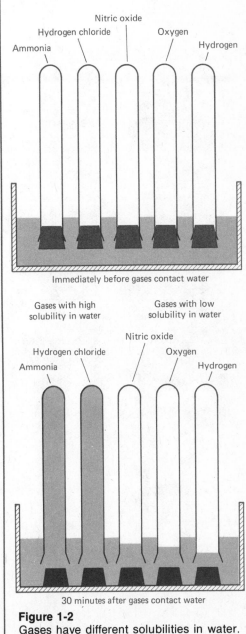

Figure 1-2
Gases have different solubilities in water.

the color of nitrogen dioxide. Neither oxygen nor hydrogen behaves this way.

Oxygen and hydrogen are readily distinguished by their combustion properties. When a glowing splint is plunged into oxygen, the splint bursts into flame. When a glowing splint is plunged into hydrogen, the splint is either extinguished or, if air has mixed with the hydrogen, a small explosion is produced.

Like the character in the forest, we can make a list of our observations on the behavior of these seven gases. Looking at Table 1-1, we notice some blank spaces. We did not carry out all the experiments with each gas. However, it would be easy to tell each of these gases from the others by making use of the observations in this table.

Table 1-1

Experiments and Observations to Show the Differences Between Seven Gases

Gas	Color	Solubility in Water	Color Change of Litmus	Glowing Splint Test
Chlorine	Greenish yellow			
Nitrogen dioxide	Reddish brown			
Ammonia	Colorless	High	Red to blue	
Hydrogen chloride	Colorless	High	Blue to red	
Nitric oxide	Colorless	Low		On contact with air a reddish-brown gas forms.
Oxygen	Colorless	Low		Glowing splint bursts into flame.
Hydrogen	Colorless	Low		Glowing splint goes out.

1-3 The Search for Regularities

While studying gases, we noticed that each gas filled its container, regardless of the shape or size of the container. Any gas we may select has the property of expanding to fill its container. You know this from your own experience. If there is a gas leak in your kitchen stove, you can soon smell the gas everywhere in the room. When you enter a bakery, the pleasant aroma of fresh-baked bread seems to be everywhere.

This property, expanding to fill a container, holds true for colored gases and for colorless ones, for those that dissolve readily in water and for those that do not. This regularity of gases is in marked contrast to what we find for liquids and solids. A solid object has a definite shape and volume. A liquid has a definite volume but takes the shape of its container. Only a gas has the property of expanding to fill any container, regardless of its shape or volume. All gases exhibit this regularity.

Another important property of a gas is the pressure it exerts. We have all had many experiences that help us understand what is meant by gas pressure. If we inflate a car tire with air, the pressure in the tire increases. The tire can now support its share of the weight of the car. If we drive up to the top of a mountain, the air pressure on our eardrums changes.

1-4 Measurement of Gas Pressure

Air pressure is measured with an instrument called a **barometer**. Several are illustrated in Figure 1-3. A barometer can be made by filling a long closed tube with mercury and inverting the tube in a dish of mercury. The mercury level in the tube drops until the mercury column exerts a pressure on the mercury in the dish which is exactly balanced by the pressure of an air column which reaches from the mercury surface in the dish to the top of the earth's atmosphere. Air pressure, then, can be expressed in terms of the height of the mercury column. In this illustration the air pressure is 760 millimeters of mercury. Exercise 1-1 shows how it is possible to determine pressure by measuring the height of a mercury column without considering its diameter.

Meteorologists use barometers to help predict weather.

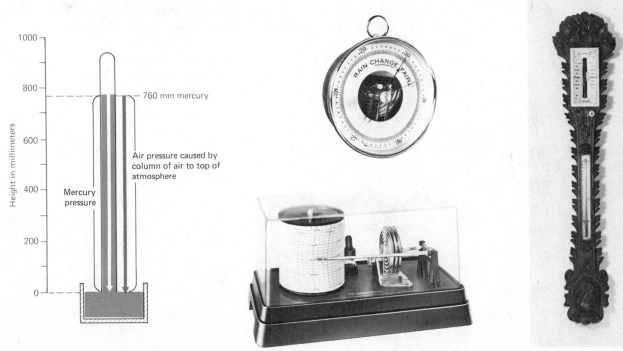

Figure 1-3
Various forms of barometers.

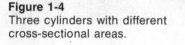

Cross-sectional area

1 cm²   10 cm²   100 cm²

10 cm

Figure 1-4
Three cylinders with different
cross-sectional areas.

EXERCISE 1-1

Figure 1-4 shows three cylinders with different cross-sectional areas. Mercury is poured into each of these cylinders to a depth of 10.0 cm. Calculate the pressure in grams/cm² at the bottom of each cylinder. The density of mercury is 13.5 grams/cm³.

$$P = \frac{g}{cm^2} = cm \times \frac{g}{cm^3} = height \times density$$

Temperature is another condition that is often important in chemical experiments. Both air temperature and pressure change from day to day and from place to place. Consequently, chemists usually control and measure these conditions. In addition, it is useful to refer many experimental results to a standard set of temperature and pressure conditions. The temperature 0 °C (degrees Celsius) is easy to obtain with an ice-water bath. This temperature is one at which thermometers are calibrated. A temperature that is easy to obtain and easy to measure makes a good standard temperature. By international agreement *the value of 0 °C has been accepted as the* **standard temperature** *for gas volumes.*

By international agreement *a* **standard pressure** *of one atmosphere (1 atm) is represented by a height of 760 millimeters (mm) of mercury.* Chemists use both units, **millimeters of mercury** and **atmospheres**, in reporting pressures.* At times one unit is more convenient than the other. There are many familiar examples where different units mean the same thing. Sometimes we state the cost of something as 50 cents, but other times we may say half a dollar or "four bits." Athletes compete in the 880-yard or half-mile run.

Chemists have accepted 0 °C and one atmosphere pressure as convenient standard conditions. These conditions are called **standard temperature** and **pressure**, and the abbreviation **STP** is used.

A device similar to a barometer can be used to measure the pressure of a gas. This device is called a **manometer**. In the

Average human blood pressure is 120/80. This means a maximum pressure of 120 mmHg is produced when the heart contracts and forces blood through the arteries. A minimum pressure of 80 mmHg exists when the heart relaxes and takes in blood. Some diseases can double blood pressure.

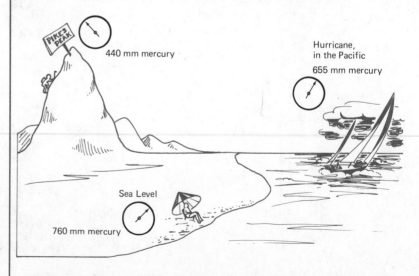

PIKE'S PEAK
440 mm mercury

Hurricane,
in the Pacific
655 mm mercury

Sea Level

760 mm mercury

*Pressure is also measured in pascals, which have the units newtons/meter²,
but we will not use this unit.

closed-end manometer, Figure 1-5, there is a balance between the pressure of the gas in the flask and the pressure caused by the mercury column. The gas pressure in the flask is 105 mm of mercury. Gas pressure is stated in terms of mercury height. In the open-end manometer, Figure 1-6A, the external atmospheric pressure balances the sum of two pressures, that of the mercury column plus that of the gas. In Figure 1-6B the gas pressure balances the sum of the mercury column plus the atmosphere.

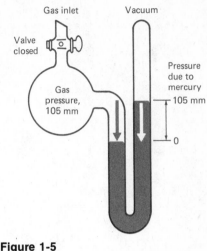

Figure 1-5
Closed-end manometer.

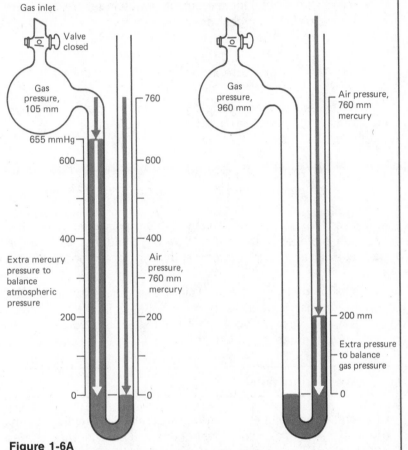

Figure 1-6A
Open-end manometer, gas pressure **less** than atmospheric.

Figure 1-6B
Open-end manometer, gas pressure **greater** than atmospheric.

The lowest recorded atmospheric pressure at sea level was 65.5 cmHg in the center of Typhoon June during November 1975.

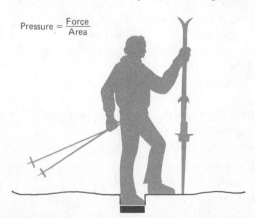

$$Pressure = \frac{Force}{Area}$$

Man on foot sinks on soft snow.

Same man on skis does not sink.
The downward force is the same in both cases.
What about pressure?

A

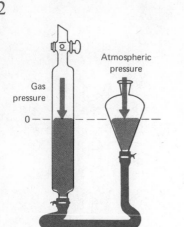

Gas pressure = atmospheric pressure

B

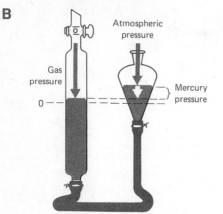

Gas pressure = atmospheric pressure
plus pressure due to mercury above upper reference line

C

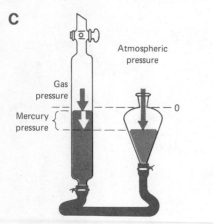

Gas pressure plus pressure due to mercury above
lower reference line = atmospheric pressure
Gas pressure = atmospheric pressure
minus pressure due to mercury above lower reference line

Figure 1-7

Let us look at the experiment illustrated in Figure 1-7. (All of our measurements will be made at the same temperature in this experiment.) A fixed amount of a gas is confined in a calibrated measuring tube which is called a **gas buret**. Mercury is in the flexible rubber tube attached to a reservoir or leveling bulb. If we adjust the bulb so that the mercury levels are the same in the gas buret and in the reservoir, the pressure of the gas is equal to the external atmospheric pressure.

As we raise the bulb, the mercury levels change. We can make an observation and suggest an interpretation:

> The gas volume decreases. (Observation)
> The gas pressure increases. (Interpretation)

The gas pressure increases to balance the mercury height plus the atmospheric pressure. Now if we lower the bulb, the mercury levels change again.

> The gas volume increases. (Observation)
> The gas pressure decreases. (Interpretation)

As long as the gas does not react with mercury, it does not matter what gas is placed in the buret. We always find this regularity in gas behavior at constant temperature and fixed amount of gas.

> As the pressure on a gas is increased, the volume of the gas is decreased.
> As the pressure on a gas is decreased, the volume of the gas is increased.

1-5 Wondering Why

Undoubtedly many questions have been raised in the discussions of the experiments and demonstrations you have already carried out in this course. Are some of them in this list?

> Why is a candle flame colored?
> Why is heat liberated when a candle burns?
> What happens if you try to burn a candle in a carbon dioxide-oxygen mixture?
> Why does aluminum metal cause the blue color of the copper solution to disappear?
> What happens if iron metal is placed in the copper solution?
> What is the gas that forms when aluminum metal is placed in the copper solution?
> What gases besides chlorine and nitrogen dioxide are colored?
> Why does a gas expand to fill its container?
> Why does a gas exert pressure?

Perhaps you have never asked yourself questions like these before. A scientist learns to ask questions, and part of the excitement in science comes in trying to find answers. Often the questions start with the words "What happens if?" These questions can be answered by doing experiments and making careful observations. The result is a fact or a description of what happened. Other questions are phrased "Why does something happen?" These are more difficult to answer. In trying to answer questions that start with "Why?" people have been led to ideas that could be developed and tested. The answers often suggest new regularities, new experiments, and new ideas. Questions that start with "Why?" are answered by explanations. Often we explain the new in terms of what is already familiar to us. Let us see what it means to search for an explanation to the following question:

Why does the volume of a gas decrease when pressure on the gas is increased?

Perhaps a gas is made up of tiny particles that are moving around and colliding with each other. These particles are too small for us to see. To test this idea, we will first look at a system we can see. Scientists call such a system a **model** or an **analogy**.

All scientists make up mental pictures of matter and its actions.

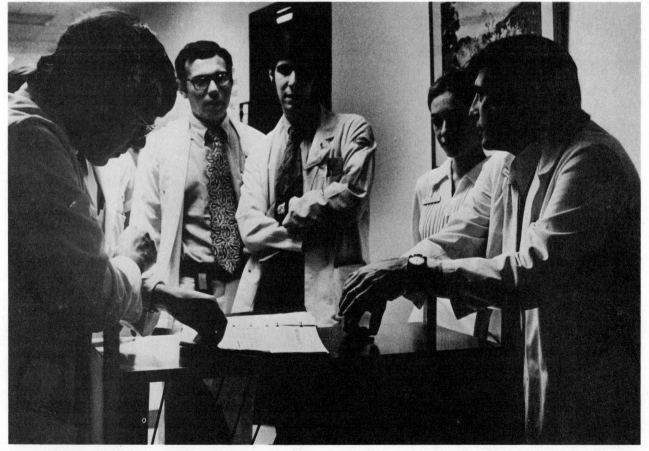

All scientists must communicate in many ways.

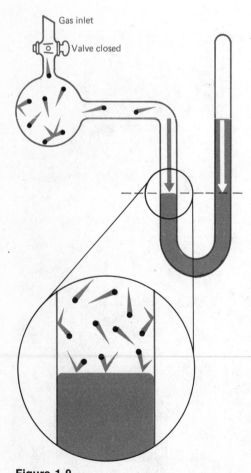

Figure 1-8
Ping-pong balls shaken in a plastic box.

Gas inlet
Valve closed

Figure 1-9
Gas particles pushing against a mercury surface.

Suppose we shake a plastic box containing some ping-pong balls. Of course, you know what you would see. The balls begin to fly around, colliding with each other and with the walls of the box. Figure 1-8 illustrates what is happening. The balls seem to fill the entire box. If we place our hands on the box, we might feel the ping-pong balls bounce off the sides. Each time one rebounds from the wall, there is a push or force exerted on the box.

Perhaps, then, a gas is made up of particles that behave like the ping-pong balls in our example. As the gas particles rebound from the container wall, they push on the wall and exert force. In Figure 1-5 we saw the balance between gas pressure and the pressure of a column of mercury. Our picture of a gas would look like Figure 1-9 now, with gas particles pushing against the mercury surface in the manometer. Doesn't it seem reasonable that the mercury column would be supported if every second a large number of gas particles was pushing against it?

How does our analogy of gas particles and moving ping-pong balls agree with some of the observations we have already made? If we take the stopper from a test tube containing reddish-brown nitrogen dioxide gas, the colored gas moves out into the room. We also notice a sharp, biting odor. If we take the top off the vibrating box containing ping-pong balls, some of the balls bounce out. If we increase the volume available to a sample of gas, its pressure decreases. Similarly, if we made the box containing ping-pong balls larger without changing the number of ping-pong balls, the number of collisions on the wall every second would decrease. Our ping-pong ball model seems to be good.

Starting with a "Why?" question is a common way to search for an explanation about a process that is not well understood. An answer is presented as a description of a similar system that is familiar. If we want to explain a regularity in gas behavior, we describe gas behavior as resulting from gas particles that behave like ping-pong balls moving in a plastic box. Ping-pong balls can be seen and studied easily. Although all gases have some properties that are the same, gases also have properties that make them different from each other. If gases are made up of particles, the particles must be different in each gas. It seems reasonable that the particles of one gas—for example, ammonia—are not the same as the particles in other gases. The particles that make up a gas determine its properties, such as color, odor, and solubility in water. These particles are so important that chemists have given them a special name. The particles making up a gas are called **molecules**.

The molecules of nitric oxide gas cannot be the same as the molecules that make up nitrogen dioxide. There must be differences in these molecules to account for the observation that nitric oxide is a colorless gas and nitrogen dioxide is reddish brown. Yet, they are related, for when nitric oxide and air are mixed, a reddish-brown gas appears. This color suggests that a change has occurred.

To explain observations like this, we assume that molecules are built of still smaller particles called **atoms**. Now we can explain the differences between two gases in terms of the atoms present in each molecule of the gas. Nitric oxide and nitrogen dioxide differ in the number or the arrangement of atoms. We will see many times in this course that the properties of a substance depend on the kinds of atoms it contains and on their arrangement.

1-6   Communicating Scientific Information

We can use our experiment on the pressure and volume of a gas to learn how scientists communicate with each other.

We observed a regularity in gas behavior. As the pressure on any gas increases, the volume decreases. This description, or qualitative statement, is the simplest way to express a regularity. In some respects a qualitative statement is most useful because it is so easy to remember. It serves as a guide in thinking about gases. During this course you will be furnished with many guides like this one.

We can investigate this regularity further by making careful measurements on gases. Let us use a gas buret like the one shown in Figure 1-7 to make quantitative measurements. We will place 32.0 grams of oxygen gas in the apparatus. The temperature of the gas will be held constant, at $t = 0\,°C$, throughout our measurements. (In the next chapter you will see why we have chosen 32.0 grams of oxygen. The important point here is that we have controlled our system.) By raising and lowering the mercury leveling bulb, we can change the gas volume. At the same time, of course, the gas pressure changes. The numerical values for pressure and volume are listed in Table 1-2.

Technical writers combine their word skill and scientific knowledge.

TABLE 1-2

The Pressure and Volume
of 32.0 Grams of Oxygen at $t = 0\,°C$

Pressure (atmospheres)	Volume (liters)	Pressure $\times$ Volume (liter-atmospheres)
1.00	22.4	22.4
0.90	24.7	22.2
0.90	24.6	22.1
0.77	29.9	23.0
0.75	29.9	22.4
0.50	44.4	22.2
1.10	20.4	22.4
1.25	17.5	21.9
2.00	11.3	<u>22.6</u>
	Average	22.4

These numbers are also presented in a graph in Figure 1-10. The values for pressure are plotted on the y-axis and the values for volume are plotted on the x-axis.

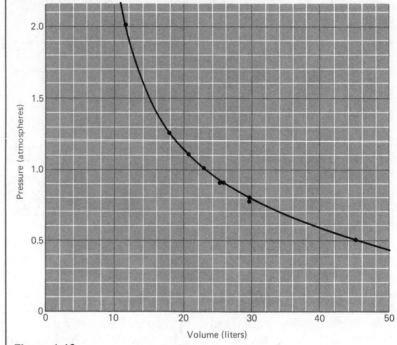

Figure 1-10
Pressure *vs* volume data for a gas.

Here are two quantitative ways that scientists use to communicate a regularity. The first is the listing of the experimental data in a table. The second is the visual presentation of the data in a graph. There is still another way that scientists communicate. A mathematical statement of a regularity is sometimes the most useful way to pass on information. It is the most compact way of stating a regularity. Let us see how to arrive at a mathematical statement of our experimental values.

In the third column of Table 1-2 each value for gas pressure has been multiplied by the corresponding gas volume. We see that this product is approximately the same for all our measurements. Our statement of regularity in gas behavior can be expressed in mathematical form:

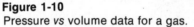

$$P \times V = 22.4 \text{ (at } t = 0\,°C)$$
P is the pressure in atmospheres and
V is the volume in liters

This equation can be put back into words. If P increases, V must decrease to give a constant product. If P decreases, V must increase to give a constant product.

There is some variation in the product of pressure times volume. Every PV product did not give the same number. An average of all the values is given in Table 1-2. There is some scatter of the points around the smooth curve in Figure 1-10. This scatter in the data represents the uncertainty that arises in all measurements.

1-7   Uncertainty in Science

Perhaps you have already noticed in Table 1-2 that the pressure, 0.90 atmosphere, appears twice. However, the gas volumes for each of these measurements are not the same. This situation is typical of experimental data. Repetition of measurements often gives a series of values that are close to each other. Every measuring device has limitations that fix its precision. Scientists report their experimental values in ways which indicate how carefully they have made their measurements. When a scientist sees a number which comes from an experimental measurement, it has a special meaning. The way in which the number is written is an indication of how carefully the measurement was made.

Suppose three people measure a gas volume using different measuring devices. Each makes a report of his measurement.

> Report 1. The volume is 22 liters.
> Report 2. The volume is 22.4 liters.
> Report 3. The volume is 22.414 liters.

What does a scientist think of these measurements? What does each report mean?

Report 1.   The volume is 22 liters.
"This measurement was made in a rather approximate fashion. The volume lies closer to 22 liters than it does to either 21 liters or 23 liters. Although this is not a very precise measurement, it may be good enough for many uses. I could use some simple equipment like that in Figure 1-11A to duplicate this measurement."

Report 2.   The volume is 22.4 liters.
"This measurement has been made much more carefully than the one in Report 1. The value lies between 22.3 liters and 22.5 liters. To duplicate this measurement, I would choose an apparatus like that in Figure 1-11B. I have to be able to estimate the volume reading to the nearest tenth of a liter."

Report 3.   The volume is 22.414 liters.
"This measurement is the result of a very carefully performed experiment. I would have to use equipment like that in Figure 1-11C to make such a precise measurement. In addition, I recognize that other conditions, such as temperature, must be carefully controlled. The person who made this measurement is telling me that the volume lies between 22.413 and 22.415 liters."

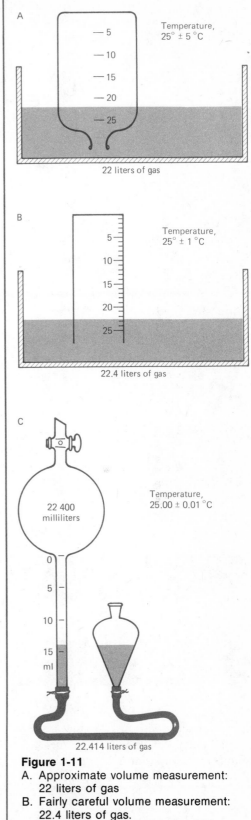

Figure 1-11
A. Approximate volume measurement: 22 liters of gas
B. Fairly careful volume measurement: 22.4 liters of gas.
C. Very careful volume measurement: 22.414 liters of gas.

The scientists giving Reports 1, 2, and 3 used **significant figures** to tell us how much care they took in their measurements. They report different degrees of certainty for the gas volumes. Report 1 (22 liters) has two significant figures, Report 2 has three, and Report 3 has five.

Most of the values that you will obtain in your laboratory work in this course will be like the one in Report 2. Some examples are given in Table 1-3. Usually three significant figures are determined in our laboratory work.

TABLE 1-3
Some Typical Measurements

Quantity Measured	Value of Measurement	Equipment Used to Make Measurements
Volume	18.3 milliliters	25 ml-graduated cylinder, marked in 1 ml divisions
Mass	3.06 grams	Centigram balance
Temperature	24.4 °C	Thermometer calibrated in 1° intervals

For each of the measurements in Table 1-3 the last digit has been estimated. So in writing down any measurements, a scientist records those digits that can be read with certainty *and* estimates one more digit. An example is shown in the margin. With the first meter stick you *know* the length is between 5 cm and 6 cm, and you *estimate* the length as 5.4 cm, two significant figures. For the second meter stick you *know* the value is between 5.4 cm and 5.5 cm. Estimating one more digit, you record the length as 5.47 cm, three significant figures.

1-8 Significant Figures and Derived Quantities

Often scientists want to combine values from experimental measurements to obtain other values which are not measured directly. Such a value is called a **derived quantity**. You have already encountered a combination of measured values in this course. In Experiment 4 on density you divided values for mass by volume to get density, a derived quantity. In the gas behavior demonstration you multiplied pressure times volume to get a *PV* product, another derived quantity. There will be many more examples.

Since any experimental measurement has a definite number of significant figures, it is important to know how many significant figures there should be in a derived quantity. We will give you some rules to follow. Remember that the significant figures in a derived quantity will be determined by the number of significant figures in the values combined. A derived quantity can be no more precise than the separate measurements used in getting it.

Chemical technicians set up and carry out these and many other experiments. There are about 750 000 scientific technicians in the United States.

l = 5.4 cm

l = 5.47 cm

The two scales in the figures above show a measurement with two different instruments. The figure indicates how the number of significant figures in a measurement depends on the equipment used.

Addition and Subtraction

When metallic aluminum reacts with a copper chloride solution, the temperature of the solution increases. If we want to know the temperature change, we subtract the initial temperature from the final temperature. The change in temperature is called "delta *t*" and is written Δt. It is the result of two measurements. The change in temperature is a derived quantity.

$$\text{Final temperature} = 88.4\,°\text{C}$$
$$\text{Initial temperature} = 26.2\,°\text{C}$$
$$\Delta t = 62.2\,°\text{C}$$

Both the initial and final temperatures have three significant figures. The value of Δt also has three significant figures.

But now suppose you wanted to combine the two lengths, 5.4 cm and 5.47 cm, in the example in the margin:

$$\text{Length No. 1} = 5.4\ \text{cm}$$
$$\text{Length No. 2} = 5.47\ \text{cm}$$
$$\text{Total length} = \quad ? \quad \text{cm}$$

The rule to follow in addition and subtraction is:

Round off the values to be combined so that they all have the same number of digits after the decimal point.

Length No. 2 then becomes 5.5 cm, and the total length would be 10.9 cm, not 10.87 cm.

EXERCISE 1-2

Round off each of the following numbers to show three significant figures:

a. 0.47 036   d. 0.004 962 3
b. 1.765   e. 10 000.95
c. 3.055   f. 24 820 000

EXERCISE 1-3

Three students measure out different volumes of water into the same beaker, using a 25 ml graduated cylinder. The three volumes are

22.517 ml
18.0   ml
25   ml

What is the total volume of water in the beaker? Use the correct number of significant figures for your answer.

Multiplication and Division

To handle quantities derived by multiplying or dividing measured values, we use a slightly different way to get the correct answer.

Zeros used only to position a decimal point are not significant figures. For example: 0.001 23 has three significant figures, but 0.001 230 00 has six. The last three zeros are not needed to place the decimal point. Also zeros which are needed because units are changed are not significant. For example, if a measurement is 12 cm, the distance could be expressed as 120 mm or 0.12 m or 0.000 12 km. In each case there are two significant figures. To show three significant figures in a number like 120, it would have to be written 1.20×10^2. We say each temperature has three significant figures; that is, the value 88.4 means that we *know* the temperature is between 88° and 89° and we estimate it is about 0.4° above 88°. **Significant figures** are those that are known for certain plus one more that is estimated.

For example, how would we estimate the number of significant figures in this PV product?

$$P = \quad 1.25 \quad \text{atmospheres}$$
$$V = 17.534 \text{ liters}$$
$$PV = \quad ? \quad \text{ liter-atmospheres}$$

We will adopt some rules to obtain the number of significant figures in a derived quantity obtained by multiplication or division.

(a) Look for the experimental number with the smallest number of significant figures. Round off all other numbers to the same number of digits. For example, if you want to combine the values 1.25 and 17.534, round off the second one to 17.5. Both numbers now have the same number of digits, three.

(b) Carry out the multiplication or division. Keep the same number of significant figures in the derived quantity. In our example we would not write the PV product as 21.875. Instead we would round this off to three digits, 21.9.

There are more complicated schemes for estimating the uncertainty of a product or quotient. One is to take the same percent uncertainty for the answer as is present in the least certain factor. The simple use of significant figures accomplishes the same goal with less work for you. The main points are that all measured quantities have some error *and* that derived quantities have even more.

EXERCISE 1-4

An engineer wished to determine the density of a new alloy of magnesium. The sample weighed 33.35 g and occupied 18.6 ml. Calculate the density and show the proper number of significant figures.

1-9   Review

This chapter began with the statement that you would find through experience what science is all about. You have already had opportunities to do this in the laboratory program for this course. Let us review some of the experiments and demonstrations with emphasis on the activities of science.

Gathering Information Through Observation

Many observations can be made of a burning candle. Undoubtedly some members of your class recorded observations that others did not see. Some may have included interpretations in their list. Careful study and attention to details are needed to observe any system. If you repeated this experiment at home, you were able to make observations that you missed the first time you tried it. It takes practice to become a good observer.

A variety of observations can be made when metallic aluminum is placed in a copper chloride solution. Were you a better observer when you performed this experiment? Don't be discouraged if you missed the observation that a classmate recorded. Some of the greatest scientific discoveries have been overlooked for years. And yet when someone finally makes the vital observation, it is difficult to understand how anyone could have missed it for so long.

There are ways to help yourself become a good observer. One of the most important is to keep a careful record in your notebook of everything you see at the moment you see it. Try to make your notebook as neat, legible, and complete as possible. Organization makes your notebook more valuable. You will find that planning ahead for an experiment saves you time, time that you can use in making observations. Remember that chemistry is built on the results of experiments. And a good experimentalist is a good observer.

Organizing Information and Looking for Regularities

There is more to science than making a list of observations. If scientists did no more than that, we would soon be overwhelmed by the large number of recorded observations. We look for some way to organize our information. It is natural to look for patterns or regularities. Perhaps that is why the search is so interesting and why scientists gain so much satisfaction from their work. Perhaps you may experience the same sort of pleasure when you carry out the experiments in this course.

In this chapter we described some experiments that could be used to tell one gas from another. Our observations brought out the differences in properties of the gases we studied. There was one property that all the gases displayed. They expanded to fill any container. Liquids and solids do not behave in this manner. When we carried out a careful experiment with oxygen gas, we found the regularity that a change in gas volume brings about a change in gas pressure.

Regularities provide an efficient way to summarize the results of many experiments. Regularities also allow us to predict the results of experiments that we have not carried out before.

Wondering Why

It is a short step from finding a regularity to asking why the regularity exists. Scientists seek explanations for "wondering why" questions. Often the explanation is presented as an analogy between a system that we understand and the system that we are trying to explain. An explanation is always tentative. It leads us to further experiments to test the explanation. An explanation, in this sense, is often called a **theory**.

An explanation has been suggested for the regularity in pressure-volume behavior of oxygen gas. A gas was compared with a system that we can see and study directly, ping-pong balls moving about in a plastic box. More experiments with gases will be outlined in the next chapter. Perhaps we will be in the same predicament as the character in the dream who said "cylindrical objects burn." Then, like the character, we will search for a new explanation.

Chemists are often detectives; molecules are their suspects.

Wondering why is the most rewarding activity of science. Learn to ask yourself questions beginning with "Why?" when you make observations, in and out of the chemistry laboratory.

Communicating with Others

The fourth activity of science is, in many ways, the most important one of all. It is only through communicating ideas to others that a strong framework can be provided for science. Experimental results must be confirmed and explanations must be tested by others. If it were not for this aspect of science, each generation of scientists would have to start from the beginning.

In this chapter we have discussed several ways that scientists communicate. No matter which way is chosen, the objective is always the same: to tell others what experiments you have performed, what the results were, and how carefully you have made the measurements. In this course try to develop skill in scientific communication. A carefully kept notebook is essential. Recognize that errors are part of any scientific measurement and try to communicate how large these errors may be. Test yourself by asking what your report of an experiment means. It takes practice to become a good observer. It takes practice to learn how to communicate. Remember that in this course you are learning about the nature of chemistry through your own experience.

Questions and Problems for Chapter 1

1

Name some conditions that should be controlled if you wish to determine how many miles different cars will travel per gallon of gasoline.

2

Name some conditions that should be controlled if you want to determine the effectiveness of various laundry detergents.

3

Write two brief descriptions of a party. In one include only qualitative items and in the other only quantitative.

4

Which of the following statements are interpretations rather than observations?

(a) Gases are made of tiny particles in random motion.
(b) Gases fill their container.
(c) A gas can be compressed.
(d) Some gases are colored.
(e) The particles that make up a gas are far apart.

5

Make each of the following qualitative observations into a quantitative observation:

(a) A burning candle warms an object held above the flame.
(b) When aluminum foil reacts with a copper chloride solution, the system becomes warm.
(c) When Alka-Seltzer reacts with water, gas bubbles form.

6

Make a list of the regularities and the differences that you can observe among the various cars you know.

7

Make a list of the regularities and differences that you can observe among the various soft drinks you know.

8

A man jogs along the street doing his daily mile. He sees a car stopped with the hood up and a man looking inside with his hands on his hips.

Smoke is coming from the hood in small wisps. The jogger runs on to the nearby firehouse and reports a car owner in trouble with a burning car. What did the jogger observe and what did he interpret?

9

State a regularity that fits these numbers: 1, 9, 25, 49, 81.

10

The following list contains several regularities. Express as many as you can: apple, peach, lemon, berry, grape.

11

State a regularity to fit these numbers: 2, 5, 10, 17, 26, 37, 50, 65, 82.

(a) Do the numbers 100 and 226 fit the regularity?
(b) Express the regularity in a mathematical relation.

12

Write an equation connecting the total score of a professional football team with the number of touchdowns, conversions, and field goals. (6 points per touchdown, 1 point per conversion, and 3 points per field goal.)

13

What do you think will happen to the mercury column in a barometer (Figure 1-3) if you do these things?

(a) Tip the glass barometer tube away from its vertical position, about 20°.
(b) Carry the barometer up a high mountain.
(c) Lower the barometer to the bottom of a swimming pool.

14

Gas is slowly added to the empty chamber of a closed-end manometer (see Figure 1-5). Draw a picture of the manometer mercury levels, showing the difference in heights in millimeters of the two mercury levels:

(a) before any gas has been added to the empty gas chamber.
(b) when the gas pressure in the chamber is 300 mmHg.
(c) when the gas pressure in the chamber is 760 mmHg.
(d) when the gas pressure in the chamber is 865 mmHg.

15

Repeat Problem 14 with an open-end manometer (see Figure 1-6). Use a value of 760 mmHg for atmospheric pressure.

16

List three different units that could be used to express the speed of a spaceship.

17

The heel of a man's shoe is about 10 in²; that on a woman's high-heeled shoe is about 0.50 in². Calculate the pressure on the floor if each weighs 120 pounds and uses only one heel for support.

18

Hydrogen, helium, and carbon dioxide are gases at room temperature. What differences among the properties of these gases account for the following?

(a) Hydrogen and helium are used in balloons but carbon dioxide is not.
(b) Helium is less dangerous to use.

19

In studying the effect of pressure on the volume of a gas, why is it necessary to keep the temperature constant?

20

The balloons that are used for weather study are quite large. When they are released at the surface of the earth, they contain a relatively small volume of gas compared to the volume they have when aloft. Explain.

21

Give several examples of two variables that are related so that when one variable increases, the other decreases, for example, the pressure and volume of a gas. This is called an inverse relation.

22

Express mathematically the relation between the number of days you have lived and your age in years. Ignore the number of leap years that may have occurred during your lifetime. How could you modify your mathematical equation to take into account leap years?

23

In 1970 a ten-year census of the United States was carried out. The population of a large city was stated to be 3 325 263. How do you react to that figure? How would you have reacted before you began to study chemistry?

24

Which do you think would cost more, a cube of iron 3 centimeters on each edge or a cube of iron 3.000 centimeters on each edge? Why?

25

Suppose you wanted to measure the distance between two city halls. What kind of equipment would you need to arrive at each of the following results?

(a) 35 miles (b) 184 800 feet

26

Convert each of these numbers to three significant figures:

(a) 314 713 (d) 4.075 00
(b) 0.010 101 (e) 0.000 223 3
(c) 3.1249

27

Work out the following problems to the proper number of significant figures:

(a) 31.14 (b) $\dfrac{41.55 \times 3.0}{6.003}$ (c) 4.113×0.005
  2.211
  8.3

28

Record the following readings to the proper number of significant figures:

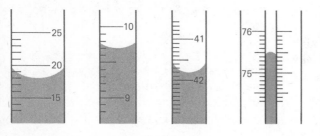

29

A regularly shaped object has the following dimensions:

$$\begin{aligned}
\text{width} &= 6.50 \text{ cm} \\
\text{height} &= 2.30 \text{ cm} \\
\text{length} &= 12.30 \text{ cm}
\end{aligned}$$

(a) It has a mass of 497 grams. Calculate the density of the object.
(b) If weighed in water what would its apparent mass be?

30

A rectangular box was found to have edges of 12, 22, and 8.0 cm. What is the volume of the box?

31

A liquid that occupies 12.6 ml has a mass of 11.2 grams. What is the density of the liquid?

32

A small boat weighs 80 grams. What is the minimum volume for the boat if it just barely floats in water?

33

A pure, solid, silver football weighs 50.0 grams. The density of silver is 10.5 grams/milliliter. What is the volume of the miniature football?

34

A pure gold bracelet weighs 315 grams. Calculate the volume it occupies. The density of gold is 19.3 g/ml.

35

An Aztec amulet claimed to be pure solid gold weighs 29.0 grams in air and 27.4 grams in water. Is the amulet both pure and solid gold? The density of gold is 19.3 g/ml.

36

A rock has a mass of 42.0 grams when weighed in air. When it is weighed in liquid carbon tetrachloride, the mass of the rock is 34.0 grams. Carbon tetrachloride has a density of 1.59 g/ml.

(a) What is the volume of the rock?
(b) What is the density of the rock?

37

Calculate the density of an irregularly shaped object using these data. Water displacement was used to determine the volume of the object. Express your answer to the correct number of significant figures. (Use the value of 1.00 g/ml for the density of water.)

Volume of water in the graduated cylinder before the object was immersed.	20.0 ml
Volume of water in the graduated cylinder after the object was immersed.	32.6 ml
Mass of the object in air	34.0 g

The Atomic Theory 2

One of the activities of science is the search for regularities. Regularities have daily practical use. For example, many definitions express such regularities. We say metals are usually hard, dense, malleable, with a typical luster. Although you may never have heard of ruthenium metal, at least you know it is probably a shiny, hard, dense material that can be deformed by hammering or other pressure. The word **law** is sometimes applied to the older scientific generalizations. For example, the gas behavior described by the equation $PV = a\ constant$ is called Boyle's law. Robert Boyle published this regularity in 1660. Today scientists do not like to use the word *law* in talking of regularities or generalizations. It is easy to see why. Most people think of a law as something that is permanent, with penalties if the "law is broken."

25

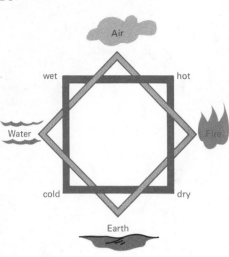

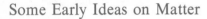

Some Early Ideas on Matter

Anaxagoras (Greek, born 500 B.C.) suggested every substance had its own kind of "seeds" that clustered together to make the substance, much as our atoms cluster to make molecules.

Empedocles (Greek, born in Sicily, 490 B.C.) suggested there were only four basic seeds—earth, air, fire, and water. The elementary substances (atoms to us) combined in various ways to make everything.

Democritus (Thracian, born 470 B.C.) actually proposed the word *atom* (indivisible) because he believed that all matter consisted of such tiny units with voids between, an idea quite similar to our own beliefs. It was rejected by Aristotle and thus lost for 2000 years.

Aristotle (Greek born 384 B.C.) added the idea of "qualities"—heat, cold, dryness, moisture—as basic elements which combined as shown in the diagram— hot + dry made fire; hot + wet made air, and so on.

Scientists are continually testing generalizations, by making more precise measurements and by devising new experiments. New techniques and new instrumental methods are developed each year. The person in the forest described the observations with the regularity "Wooden objects burn." But someday other generations would have to expand the rule to include such things as paper and gasoline and many other materials that burn. In the same way new observations that a scientist can make frequently show that the original generalizations apply only over a limited range of experimental conditions. Somehow changing a "generalization" seems less drastic than changing a "law." As science progressed, the word *law* was avoided more and more.

When seeking an explanation, we sometimes test out more than one model or theory. The most useful model or theory is retained. One test of a useful theory is that it often suggests new directions of thought which guide us to new experiments. Additional experimental facts come to light. Sometimes the new facts require growth of the theory. The metal pipe contradicted the "Cylindrical objects burn" theory. Then the theory must be abandoned in favor of another ("Wooden objects burn"). Even so, we should not forget that studying a very simple generalization often leads to a better one. The history of science has many examples like the dream described in the first chapter. Both the growth and replacement of theories come from the increase in our understanding of the experiments we perform.

This chapter will show how a theory grows.

2-1 Implications and Growth of a Scientific Theory

We can explore our explanation that gas behavior results from randomly moving molecules. To do this we ask a "Why?" question. Why does the gas pressure increase when the gas volume is decreased?

Recall the proposal that a gas contains many molecules that are in constant motion. As the molecules rebound from the walls of their container, they push on the walls. Since there are many molecules striking the wall each second, we must combine all the individual pushes. This is the cause of gas pressure. What if the same number of molecules is put in a container that is half as big? Now there are twice as many molecules per unit volume. With twice as many molecules per unit volume, the frequency of wall collisions will be doubled. Doubling the wall collisions will double the pressure. Our model is consistent with the equation:

$$PV = \text{a constant} = (2P)\left(\frac{1}{2}V\right)$$

For 32.0 grams of oxygen at $t = 0\,°C$, we found experimentally that

$$PV = 22.4 \text{ liter-atmospheres}$$

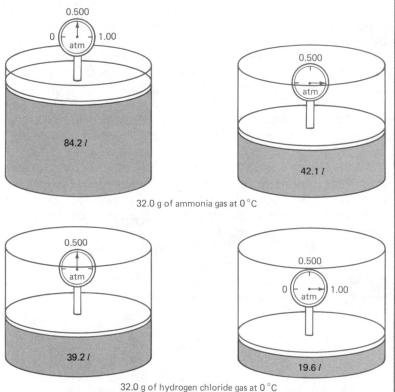

32.0 g of ammonia gas at 0 °C

32.0 g of hydrogen chloride gas at 0 °C

Two other common gases are ammonia and hydrogen chloride. Does our theory apply to them as well as to oxygen? We must perform experiments to find out. We duplicate the conditions used in the study of oxygen. Table 2-1 shows pressure-volume measurements for 32.0 grams of ammonia at 0 °C. Table 2-2 shows the same type of data for 32.0 grams of hydrogen chloride at the same temperature.

TABLE 2-1
Pressure and Volume of 32.0 Grams of
Ammonia Gas at $t = 0$ °C

Pressure (atmospheres)	Volume (liters)	Pressure $\times$ Volume (liter-atmospheres)
0.100	421	42.1
0.500	84.2	42.1
1.00	42.1	42.1

TABLE 2-2
Pressure and Volume of 32.0 Grams of
Hydrogen Chloride Gas at $t = 0$ °C

Pressure (atmospheres)	Volume (liters)	Pressure $\times$ Volume (liter-atmospheres)
0.100	196	19.6
0.500	39.2	19.6
1.00	19.6	19.6

Every day during 1974
United States industry made
86 million pounds (40 million kg) of
ammonia
13 million pounds (6 million kg) of
hydrogen chloride

We see that for these gases $PV =$ a constant at $0\,°C$. Our theory should be useful for these gases as well as for oxygen. However, the value of the constant varies from one gas to another if the same mass of gas is considered. We have seen that 32.0 grams of oxygen at $0\,°C$ and one atmosphere pressure occupy 22.4 liters. The same mass of ammonia gas also at STP occupies 42.1 liters. The same mass of hydrogen chloride gas at STP occupies only 19.6 liters. Did we do the right thing in taking 32.0 grams of each gas? Less ammonia and more hydrogen chloride would have led to 22.4 liters for all three gases. Is it more important to take the same amount of each gas or to have the same volume at STP? The answer to this question occupied many chemists for several decades in the 1800's.

Chemists have found it more useful to consider a different mass for each gas. They select the amount of gas that gives the same PV product as 32.0 grams of oxygen gas. Consider, first, ammonia gas. At $0\,°C$ and a pressure of one atmosphere, 32.0 grams of ammonia occupy 42.1 liters. Less ammonia is needed to occupy 22.4 liters. The mass of ammonia needed to occupy only 22.4 liters at this pressure is smaller by a factor of 22.4/42.1.

$$\text{mass of ammonia} = 32.0 \text{ g} \times \frac{22.4}{42.1} = 17.0 \text{ g}$$

Pressure-volume data for this mass of ammonia are shown in Table 2-3.

TABLE 2-3
Pressure and Volume of 17.0 Grams of
Ammonia Gas at $t = 0\,°C$

Pressure (atmospheres)	Volume (liters)	Pressure × Volume (liter-atmospheres)
0.100	224	22.4
0.500	44.8	22.4
1.00	22.4	22.4

EXERCISE 2-1

If 32.0 grams of hydrogen chloride gas (at $0\,°C$ and one atmosphere) occupy 19.6 liters, then a larger mass of hydrogen chloride is needed to occupy the larger volume, 22.4 liters. Show that the mass needed is 36.5 grams.

Now the regularity between pressure and volume of these three gases can be expressed as follows:

For $0\,°C$ and 1 atmosphere $PV = 22.4$ liter-atmospheres if we take

32.0 grams of oxygen or 17.0 grams of ammonia

or 36.5 grams of hydrogen chloride

Each of the gas samples is now consistent with the regularity $PV = 22.4$ liter-atmospheres. However, as shown in Figure 2-1, a different amount or mass of gas is needed for each substance.

Some chemists devote their life to studying the details of molecular structure.

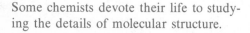

At $0\,°C$ and one
atmosphere pressure

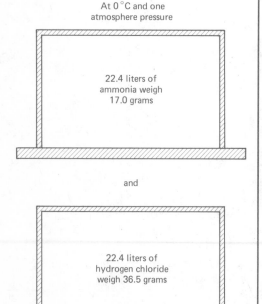

22.4 liters of
ammonia weigh
17.0 grams

and

22.4 liters of
hydrogen chloride
weigh 36.5 grams

Why?

Figure 2-1
SEARCH FOR AN EXPLANATION:
Why do equal volumes of ammonia and
hydrogen chloride have different masses?

This is another indication, like color, solubility, and behavior to litmus, that these molecules are different.

How do the molecules differ? Why is it that 32.0 grams of oxygen give the same *PV* product as 17.0 grams of ammonia and 36.5 grams of hydrogen chloride (all at 0 °C)? We wonder, why do 22.4 liters of ammonia weigh 17.0 grams when the same volume of hydrogen chloride weighs 36.5 grams? Do molecules have different masses?

There are two factors to consider. These are the same factors we would think about if we were to ask why a bag full of marbles weighs 36.5 grams while the same bag full of ping-pong balls weighs 17.0 grams. The explanation would be found by comparing the number of marbles in the bag and the mass per marble to the number and mass of individual ping-pong balls in a similar bag. In our gas problem we make the same kind of comparison. The mass and number of ammonia molecules in 22.4 liters must be compared to the mass and number of hydrogen chloride molecules in 22.4 liters. Here are two possibilities, illustrated in Figure 2-2:

(a) Perhaps:
    (1) Equal volumes of these two gases contain the same number of molecules, and
    (2) one ammonia molecule weighs less than one hydrogen chloride molecule by the factor 17.0/36.5.

(b) Perhaps:
    (1) Equal volumes of these two gases contain different numbers of molecules, ammonia containing fewer by the factor 17.0/36.5, and
    (2) an ammonia molecule weighs exactly the same as a hydrogen chloride molecule.

These two possibilities are attractive because they are simple. One factor alone is held responsible in each case. We must be prepared, however, for disappointment. There is the third possibility that neither (a) nor (b) accounts for the properties of gases. We need more information to decide whether either proposal (a) or proposal (b) applies to gases. More information is obtained by observing how some gases behave when mixed. As our model grows, we are led again to new experiments.

2-2 Reacting Volumes of Gases

Chemists talk of molecules in graphic terms. They speak of the size of molecules and they describe how molecules and atoms move. Yet, they have not *seen* any of these things. Let us expand the example we used in Section 1-5, where gases were pictured as ping-pong balls in a box. This time we want to take a box with two compartments. In one compartment the ping-pong balls represent oxygen molecules. The other compartment has ping-pong balls to represent carbon monoxide molecules. Just to mark them for observation, let us make the carbon monoxide ping-pong balls blue and the oxygen ping-pong balls red.

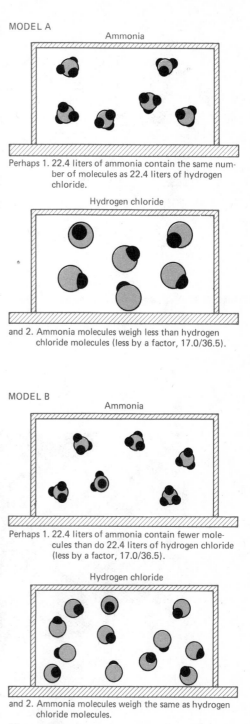

MODEL A

Ammonia

Perhaps 1. 22.4 liters of ammonia contain the same number of molecules as 22.4 liters of hydrogen chloride.

Hydrogen chloride

and 2. Ammonia molecules weigh less than hydrogen chloride molecules (less by a factor, 17.0/36.5).

MODEL B

Ammonia

Perhaps 1. 22.4 liters of ammonia contain fewer molecules than do 22.4 liters of hydrogen chloride (less by a factor, 17.0/36.5).

Hydrogen chloride

and 2. Ammonia molecules weigh the same as hydrogen chloride molecules.

Figure 2-2
Two simple models to explain the masses of equal volumes of gases.

Now the box is shaken. We can see red ping-pong balls on one side moving around rapidly, colliding with one another and with the walls. Their direction of motion changes and so does their velocity. In the other compartment blue ping-pong balls do the same thing. What would happen if the section separating the two compartments somehow could be taken away? There would be one large box. The random motion mixes the two kinds of balls.

Looking to the real chemistry again, we note that oxygen and carbon monoxide react to form a new substance, carbon dioxide. Somehow the two molecules we started with have changed. We can add to our model to account for this. As the red and blue ping-pong balls mix together, there will be several kinds of collisions. If red hits red or blue hits blue, the balls bounce off each other. But if red hits blue or blue hits red, the ping-pong balls stick together. A new "substance" is formed. At first the chance of red finding blue is fairly good. But after some time most of the ping-pong balls are joined together and only a few separate red and blue remain. It is going to take much longer for these "unreacted" balls to find each other.

With this model in mind let's do a real experiment. When hydrogen chloride and ammonia gases are mixed, a white powder forms. Something new is present, and chemists say that a chemical reaction has occurred. A quantitative study of this process is informative.

Probably a spark ignited the hydrogen in the *Hindenburg,* a German zepplin.

Figure 2-3 shows an apparatus suitable for measurement of gas volumes. Thirty milliliters of ammonia have been admitted to the left tube from an ammonia storage tank. Next, 50 milliliters of hydrogen chloride have been admitted to the right tube. The leveling bulbs are used to adjust the pressure of each gas to one atmosphere. The temperature of both gases is, of course, the same. We are ready to carry out the experiment. The hydrogen chloride sample can be transferred slowly into the tube containing the ammonia. Figures 2-4 and 2-5 show the progress of the experiment.

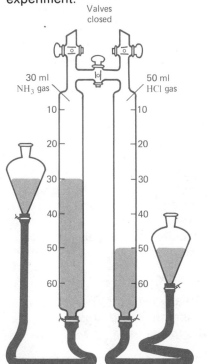
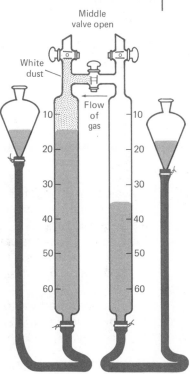
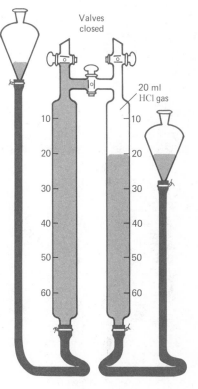

Figure 2-3
An apparatus to measure volume changes when gases react.
Figure 2-4
Ammonia gas reacting with hydrogen chloride gas.
Figure 2-5
Completion of reaction between ammonia gas and hydrogen chloride gas. 30 ml of ammonia has reacted with 30 ml of hydrogen chloride.

A cloud of the white solid forms in the left tube where the gases react. Twenty milliliters of hydrogen chloride combine with 20 milliliters of ammonia, forming the white solid. Ten milliliters more of hydrogen chloride are just enough to react with the last of the ammonia.

We have an important result. Thirty milliliters of hydrogen chloride combine with just 30 milliliters of ammonia, measured at the same temperature and pressure. Therefore, one liter of hydrogen chloride would combine with one liter of ammonia. Though a given volume of ammonia weighs less than the same volume of hydrogen chloride (less by the factor 17.0/36.5), equal volumes of these gases combine. This simple situation suggests that we should seek a simple explanation. Proposal (a) fits nicely. If we propose that equal gas volumes contain equal numbers of molecules, then 30 milliliters of ammonia and 30 milliliters of hydrogen chloride contain the same number of molecules. Proposal (a) leads us to conclude that one molecule of ammonia combines with one molecule of hydrogen chloride to form the white solid. Through proposal (a) the combining volumes tell us the numbers of molecules that combine. In contrast, there is no correspondingly simple way to explain the new data with proposal (b).

Proposal (a) works very well for the two gases, ammonia and hydrogen chloride. Will it work with other gases? Other experiments show that all gases react in simple whole-number volume ratios. For example,

$$\begin{array}{ccc} \text{1 liter} \\ \text{hydrogen} \end{array} + \begin{array}{c} \text{1 liter} \\ \text{chlorine} \end{array} \longrightarrow \begin{array}{c} \text{2 liters} \\ \text{hydrogen chloride} \end{array}$$

$$\begin{array}{c} \text{1 liter} \\ \text{oxygen} \end{array} + \begin{array}{c} \text{2 liters} \\ \text{carbon} \\ \text{monoxide} \end{array} \longrightarrow \begin{array}{c} \text{2 liters} \\ \text{carbon} \\ \text{dioxide} \end{array}$$

$$\begin{array}{c} \text{2 liters} \\ \text{hydrogen} \end{array} + \begin{array}{c} \text{1 liter} \\ \text{oxygen} \end{array} \longrightarrow \begin{array}{c} \text{2 liters} \\ \text{gaseous water} \end{array}$$

These integer volume ratios confirm the usefulness of proposal (a): equal volumes of gases contain equal numbers of molecules. This proposal was first made in 1811 by an Italian scientist, Amedeo Avogadro. It is called **Avogadro's hypothesis**. It has been used successfully in explaining the properties of gases for more than a century and a half.

> *Avogadro's hypothesis: Equal volumes of gases, measured at the same temperature and pressure, contain equal numbers of molecules.*

2-3 Relative Masses of Molecules

Avogadro's hypothesis is important because it furnishes a basis for weighing molecules. Two equal volumes of gas (at the same temperature and pressure) are weighed. If we assume these two volumes contain the same numbers of molecules, then we must also conclude that the gas that weighs more must have heavier molecules. Furthermore, the ratio of the masses of the molecules must be the ratio of the masses of the two gas samples.

For example, in Table 1-1, page 8, data were given that show that 32.0 grams of oxygen at 0 °C and one atmosphere pressure occupy 22.4 liters. The same volume of ammonia (also at 0 °C and one atmosphere pressure) weighs 17.0 grams. By Avogadro's hypothesis these two volumes contain equal numbers of molecules. Each ammonia molecule must weigh less than an oxygen molecule by the factor 17.0/32.0. By the same argument each hydrogen chloride molecule must weigh more than an oxygen molecule by 36.5/32.0.

By many such weighings scientists have learned the relative masses of many gases. The experiment is fairly simple. A carefully

Physicists can often use logic to deduce properties of particles they cannot see just as doctors use a person's symptoms to deduce the causes of illness.

measured volume of oxygen is weighed at a fixed pressure and temperature. Then the same volume of another gas is weighed, at the same pressure and temperature. The relative masses of the gas samples indicate the relative masses of the molecules. Neither the pressure nor the temperature need be measured, provided they are held constant.

Look at the sample data that would be obtained from such an experiment. The air is removed from a one-liter flask and the flask is weighed. In turn, the flask is filled with different gases and weighed again. We must be sure that the temperature and pressure of the gases are the same in this experiment. The conditions chosen for this experiment are 25 °C and one atmosphere pressure. The experimental results are summarized in Table 2-4.

TABLE 2-4

Masses of One Liter of Gases at 25 °C and One Atmosphere Pressure

Gas	Mass of Evacuated Flask (grams)	Mass of Flask + Gas (grams)	Mass of One Liter of Gas (grams)	Mass of Molecule Relative to Oxygen (arbitrary units)
Oxygen	157.35	158.66	1.31	32.0
Ammonia	157.35	158.05	0.70	17.1
Hydrogen chloride	157.35	158.84	1.49	36.4
Nitrogen	157.35	158.50	1.15	28.1
Carbon dioxide	157.35	159.15	1.80	44.0
Nitrogen dioxide	157.35	159.23	1.88	46.0
Nitric oxide	157.35	158.58	1.23	30.0

EXERCISE 2-2

At 25 °C and 1 atm pressure, one liter of neon gas weighs 0.83 gram. What is the mass of a neon molecule relative to the mass of an oxygen molecule (32.0)? See Table 2-4 for the mass of one liter of oxygen.

2-4 The Number of Atoms in a Molecule

Assumed mass of oxygen molecule $\times \left(\dfrac{\text{mass of ammonia}}{\text{mass of oxygen}}\right)$

$$= \text{mass of ammonia molecule}$$

$$32.0 \times \left(\frac{0.70}{1.31}\right) = 17.1$$

Recall the reaction between the two colorless gases, nitric oxide and oxygen. When nitric oxide reacts with oxygen, a reddish-brown gas forms. The color is identical to that of another gas, nitrogen dioxide. All the properties of the reddish-brown gas are consistent with the conclusion that nitrogen dioxide has been formed. How can this change be discussed in terms of our theory for gas behavior?

Since we find that nitrogen dioxide can be formed from the reaction of nitric oxide and oxygen, we can conclude that the atoms in nitrogen dioxide must have come from those in nitric oxide together with those in oxygen. Also, we find from an experiment that two volumes of nitric oxide combine with one volume of oxygen. Two volumes of nitrogen dioxide are formed. Avogadro's hypothesis proposes that equal volumes of gases have equal numbers of molecules.

Since

$$\begin{array}{c} \text{2 volumes} \\ \text{nitric oxide} \end{array} + \begin{array}{c} \text{1 volume} \\ \text{oxygen} \end{array} \longrightarrow \begin{array}{c} \text{2 volumes} \\ \text{nitrogen dioxide} \end{array}$$

then

$$\begin{array}{c} \text{2 molecules} \\ \text{nitric oxide} \end{array} + \begin{array}{c} \text{1 molecule} \\ \text{oxygen} \end{array} \longrightarrow \begin{array}{c} \text{2 molecules} \\ \text{nitrogen dioxide} \end{array}$$

The oxygen molecule must have split into two equal parts. We can say "two" because two molecules of nitrogen dioxide are formed. We can say "equal" because all nitrogen dioxide molecules are alike. The oxygen molecule must contain an even number of atoms. In addition, no one has ever reported an experiment in which one volume of oxygen formed more than two volumes of an oxygen-containing compound. Chemists have concluded from this and other experiments that there are two oxygen atoms in an oxygen molecule. The oxygen molecule is diatomic. Since the letter O represents an atom of oxygen, the molecule is shown as O_2.

A diatomic molecule

EXERCISE 2-3

One volume of hydrogen gas reacts with one volume of chlorine gas to form two volumes of hydrogen chloride gas. What can you say about the number of atoms in one molecule of hydrogen? Of chlorine? Of hydrogen chloride?

Now we want to make a slight change in our ping-pong ball model. The oxygen molecule should be represented as two ping-pong balls stuck together. The drawing in the margin shows how chemists draw a picture of the diatomic oxygen molecule. There are seven common elements that have two atoms per molecule: H_2, N_2, O_2, F_2, Cl_2, Br_2, and I_2.

2-5 Substances: Elements and Compounds

Molecules are clusters of atoms. Two types of molecules are possible. A few molecules are clusters of atoms in which all the atoms are identical. Most molecules contain two or more different kinds of atoms. Substances made of these two kinds of molecules are given different names.

> An **element** is a pure substance containing only one kind of atom.
>
> A **compound** is a pure substance containing two or more kinds of atoms combined in definite proportions.

There are over 100 different elements known today. Some elements occur pure in nature and have been known for thousands of years. Elements like iron, silver, gold, mercury, and sulfur were known to the ancients. They were given Latin names by the early chemists. For example, iron was called **ferrum**, silver was called **argentum**, and gold was called **aurum**.

During the 19th century there was an increase in the number of elements discovered as chemists began to adopt quantitative methods. Thirty-one elements were known at the beginning of the 19th century. One hundred years later over 81 elements were known. Almost twice as many elements were discovered in that one century as were discovered up to that time. Credit for proof of elemental character goes to scientists in England, France, Sweden, Germany, Portugal, and the United States. Three of those scientists were; Marie Sklodowska Curie (radium, polonium), Marguerite Perey (francium), and Ida Tacke (rhenium). Each element has a name and has been given a shorthand symbol of one or two letters. The element carbon is symbolized by the letter C, the element neon by the letters Ne. Ten of the elements have symbols derived from the capitalized first letter of the Latin name of the element and, if necessary, by a second letter. The ten include seven common metals known to the ancients. The symbol for the element tungsten comes from the German word **wolfram**. Except for the 11 elements listed in Table 2-5, all the

List of elements with single letter symbols:
H, B, C, O, N, F, P, S, K, V, Y, I, U, W

Chemists, whatever their native language, use the same chemical symbols and equations.

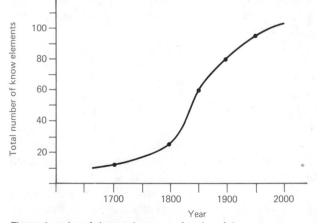

The total number of elements known as a function of time.

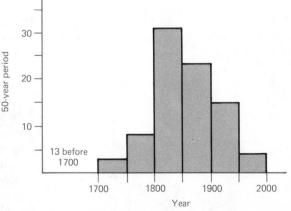

The number of elements discovered in each half-century since 1700.

elements have symbols that can be derived from their English names. For example, the symbols for hydrogen (H), helium (He), carbon (C), nitrogen (N), oxygen (O), calcium (Ca), and chlorine (Cl) are easily obtained from the names. Notice that He is used for helium to distinguish it from H for hydrogen. Since C is used for carbon, the symbols for calcium and chlorine have a second letter added to the first. The table of elements, inside the front cover of this book, contains a complete list of the chemical symbols.

TABLE 2-5

Chemical Symbols That Are Not Derivable from the English Name of the Element

English Name	Symbol	Symbol Source	English Name	Symbol	Symbol Source
Antimony	Sb	stibium	Potassium	K	kalium
Copper	Cu	cuprum	Silver	Ag	argentum
Gold	Au	aurum	Sodium	Na	natrium
Iron	Fe	ferrum	Tin	Sn	stannum
Lead	Pb	plumbum	Tungsten	W	wolfram
Mercury	Hg	hydrargyrum			

Chemists use many methods to find the formulas of compounds. Many thousands are determined every year.

But now consider a substance like water. Water can be identified by its properties: color, taste, melting and boiling temperatures, and ability to dissolve sugar and salt. A demonstration of electrolysis can easily show that water can be changed into two other substances, hydrogen gas and oxygen gas. The hydrogen and oxygen are produced in definite amounts. Since water can be decomposed into two other substances, water must contain at least two kinds of atoms. *Water is a compound.*

Sugar is another substance that you know. One property of sugar is its sweetness. Another property is that it dissolves in water. Still another is the way it behaves when heated. At a definite temperature sugar not only begins to melt to a liquid but it also begins to decompose. The liquid darkens and water bubbles off. Finally, a black solid remains in the container. We recognize the black solid as a form of carbon called charcoal. Sugar can be decomposed to form water and charcoal in definite amounts. *Sugar is a compound.*

Water and sugar are compounds. What about hydrogen and oxygen? Hydrogen is a gas at normal conditions. It can be liquefied at a characteristic temperature by cooling. It becomes a solid at a second characteristic temperature. It is a pure substance. No treatment, however, forms two other substances from it. Hydrogen, then, must contain only one kind of atom. *Hydrogen is an element.* Oxygen, too, has characteristic properties. It cannot be decomposed into two other substances. *Oxygen is an element.* It contains only one kind of atom.

Now we can return to the decomposition of water. Water can be decomposed to give only hydrogen and oxygen. Since hydrogen contains only hydrogen atoms and oxygen contains only oxygen atoms, water molecules must contain some hydrogen atoms and some oxygen atoms but no other kind of atom.

Finding what atoms are present in a given substance is one of the most important experiments in chemistry. How important this is can be seen by comparing the three substances water, oxygen, and hydrogen. Both water and oxygen contain oxygen atoms, but these substances are very different in their properties. Both water and hydrogen contain hydrogen atoms, but these substances are no more alike than are water and oxygen. The properties of water are determined by the combination of the two kinds of atoms in a definite ratio and arrangement. These properties are distinctive.

EXERCISE 2-4

What differences between water, oxygen, and hydrogen can you point out from your own experience? For example, consider

(a) boiling and melting temperatures.
(b) role in combustion.
(c) role in supporting life.

Sugar contains both oxygen and hydrogen atoms, but it contains carbon atoms as well. The three kinds of atoms, their number, and their arrangement account for the distinctive properties which identify sugar. In any substance the atoms present, their numbers, and their arrangement fix the properties of that substance.

2-6   Chemical Formulas

Molecules are made up of atoms in definite numbers and definite arrangements. Experiments show that the water molecule contains two atoms of hydrogen and one atom of oxygen. In a water molecule each of the two hydrogen atoms is connected to the oxygen atom in an angular arrangement. How the shape is determined and how important it is in chemistry will be discussed later.

The number and kinds of atoms in a molecule can also be shown in a **molecular formula**. Symbols for the elements aid us in showing the composition of a molecule. For example, the water molecule is symbolized as H_2O. In this molecular formula H means a hydrogen atom and O means an oxygen atom. The subscript following H indicates that there are two hydrogen atoms in the molecule. The lack of a subscript on O means there is only one oxygen atom per molecule. The molecular formula of ammonia is NH_3. This indicates that one molecule of ammonia contains one atom of nitrogen (N) and three atoms of hydrogen (H). Experiments show that oxygen is diatomic. Each oxygen molecule contains two atoms. Its molecular formula is O_2. Hydrogen gas is diatomic. Its formula is H_2.

EXERCISE 2-5

Carbon dioxide has the formula CO_2. Remembering that the prefix "di" means two and "tri" means three, write the formula

SYMBOLS FOR GOLD AND MERCURY

1500

1600

1700

1800

1814-present   Au   Hg

In 1973, 88 000 000 pounds (40 000 000 kg) of oxygen were liquefied from air each day in the United States.

Kinds of atoms shown by symbols

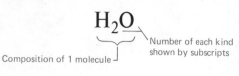

$$H_2O$$

Composition of 1 molecule — Number of each kind shown by subscripts

$$Al_2Cl_6$$

One molecule of aluminum chloride has 2 aluminum atoms and 6 chlorine atoms

Technical draftsmen must be able to draw chemical formulas and diagrams of molecules.

A spectroscopist uses a spectroscope to help deduce the structure of molecules.

for each of the following substances: carbon disulfide, sulfur dioxide, sulfur trioxide. (If you do not know the symbol for an element, use the table inside the front cover of the book.)

Both the numbers and the arrangement of the atoms in the molecule can be shown by a **structural formula**. Structural formulas show which atoms are attached to each other. The lines indicate the connections between the atoms and represent **chemical bonds**. Water has the structural formula

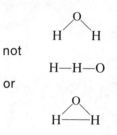

not

or

We see that each hydrogen atom is bound to the oxygen atom. The alternative arrangements,

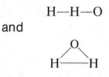

and

agree with the molecular formula H_2O. However, we know from experiments that the atoms are not bonded in these ways.

No written formula is quite as effective as a molecular model to help us visualize molecular shape. Since chemists find that the shape of a molecule strongly influences its chemical behavior, molecular models are important aids. Various molecular models are commonly used, depending upon the emphasis needed. Figure 2-6 shows some representations of molecules of hydro-

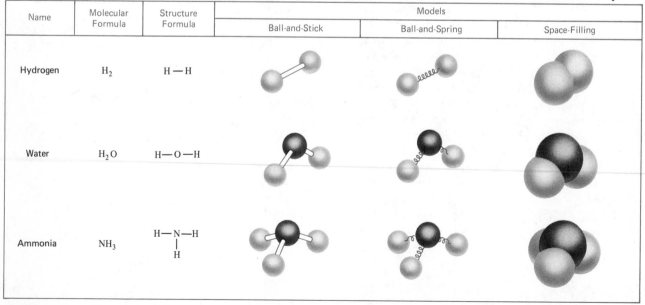

Name	Molecular Formula	Structure Formula	Models		
			Ball-and-Stick	Ball-and-Spring	Space-Filling
Hydrogen	H_2	H—H			
Water	H_2O	H—O—H			
Ammonia	NH_3	H—N—H | H			

Figure 2-6
Different representations of the molecules H_2, H_2O, and NH_3.

gen, water, and ammonia. The ball-and-stick and ball-and-spring models display clearly the atoms and their bonds. The space-filling models provide a more realistic view of the spatial relationships and crowding among atoms.

Model makers have become more important as more complex chemicals are studied. Computers now draw stereoscopic views of molecules.

2-7 The Mole

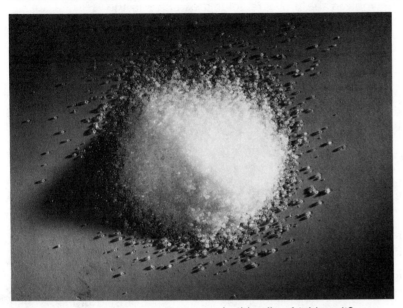

How many moles do you suppose are in this pile of table salt?

Whenever you weigh a substance or whenever you measure the volume of a gas, your sample contains a very large number of atoms. Chemists have found it convenient to choose a unit much larger than a single atom or molecule for comparing amounts of different materials. This unit, called the **mole**, contains a huge number of particles, 6.0×10^{23}. A mole of oxygen atoms or a mole of hydrogen atoms or a mole of copper atoms contains 6.0×10^{23} atoms of the specified kind. A mole of oxygen molecules, O_2, contains 2 moles of oxygen atoms [$2 \times (6.0 \times 10^{23})$ oxygen atoms] because each oxygen molecule contains two atoms. Chemists have determined that the molecular formula for phosphorus is P_4. There are four atoms in each molecule. A mole of P_4 molecules contains [$4 \times (6.0 \times 10^{23})$] phosphorus atoms, that is, four moles of phosphorus atoms.

A baker counts biscuits in dozens, a convenient number. Money is counted in dollars. How did chemists choose to count in terms of moles? The number 6.0×10^{23} seems an odd choice. There is a reason. Chemists prefer a definition in terms of a quantity that can be measured readily and with high precision. Weighing is much easier than counting when the number of particles is so large. Consequently, chemists based the definition of the mole upon a chosen mass rather than a chosen number of particles. During the 19th century chemists decided that the number of molecules in a sample of oxygen gas weighing exactly 32 grams would be taken as the standard number of molecules. A mole was defined as the number of oxygen molecules in 32

A modern computer can make about 3 000 000 additions per minute. If such a computer had been started when the Earth began (about 4.5×10^9 years ago), the computer would by now have made 7.1×10^{21} additions. Avogadro's number is a hundred times larger.

grams of oxygen gas. (Thus one mole of oxygen molecules (O_2) weighs 32 g; one mole of oxygen atoms (O) weighs 16 g.) The significance of a mole is more usefully connected with this number of particles rather than with the mass. The number 6.0×10^{23} is called **Avogadro's number**. This number occurs so many times in chemistry that it is often represented by the letter N. Do you see now why we chose to talk about 32.0 grams of oxygen in the pressure-volume example in the last chapter? In doing that, we were dealing with one mole of oxygen molecules.

In 1961 chemists and physicists agreed to redefine a mole as the number of carbon atoms in exactly 12 grams of one particular isotope of carbon, ^{12}C. The change does not affect our discussion.

Avogadro's number is
$6.022\,045 \pm 0.000\,031 \times 10^{23}$.

EXERCISE 2-6

Since a mole of oxygen molecules weighs 32.0 grams, how much would one million oxygen molecules weigh? Why was a mole not defined as one million molecules?

2-8 Molar Mass

Although a chemist can calculate that the mass of a single oxygen atom is 2.67×10^{-23} gram, it is much more convenient to know that a mole of oxygen atoms has a mass of 16.0 grams and that a mole of oxygen molecules has a mass of 32.0 grams. These amounts can be easily weighed in the laboratory. The mass of one mole of a substance is a useful number. We will call it the **molar mass**.

Chemical technicians and chemical engineers both use molar masses, sometimes called molecular weights.

*The **molar mass** of an element in the atomic state is the mass in grams of 6.0×10^{23} atoms.*

There is a table inside the front cover of this book which lists the molar masses for elements in the atomic state. For example, the molar masses of oxygen, copper, and silver are 16.0 grams, 63.5 grams, and 107.9 grams respectively.

*The **molar mass** of a compound or of an element in the molecular state is the mass in grams of 6.0×10^{23} molecules.*

A dozen,   12, apples weighs about 2 kg.

A gross,   144, of pencils weighs about 0.7 kg.

A mole, 6×10^{23}, of H atoms weighs 0.001 kg, or 1 g.

A mole, 6×10^{23}, of O atoms weighs 0.016 kg, or 16 g.

A mole, 6×10^{23}, of H_2 molecules weighs 0.002 kg, or 2 g.

A mole, 6×10^{23}, of H_2SO_4 molecules weighs 0.098 kg, or 98 g.

A mole, 6×10^{23}, of electrons weighs 5.5×10^{-7} kg, or 0.000 55 g.

A chemist working with hydrogen chloride often needs to know its molar mass. The mass can be calculated from the molecular formula for hydrogen chloride, HCl, plus the molar masses of the two kinds of atoms, H and Cl.

If we know the molecular formula for a substance, we can calculate its molar mass. This mass contains 6.0×10^{23} molecules.

Study Figure 2-7 carefully to understand the logic used in getting molar mass.

one molecule of HCl	contains	one atom of hydrogen	and	one atom of chlorine
one dozen molecules of HCl	contains	one dozen atoms of hydrogen	and	one dozen atoms of chlorine
one mole of HCl molecules	contains	one mole of hydrogen atoms	and	one mole of chlorine atoms
the mass of one mole of HCl molecules	is the same as	the mass of one mole of hydrogen atoms	+	the mass of one mole of chlorine atoms
molar mass of HCl	=	molar mass of atomic hydrogen	+	molar mass of atomic chlorine
molar mass of HCl	=	1.01 g	+	35.5 g
molar mass of HCl	=	36.5 g		
molar mass of HCl	=	36.5 g and contains 6×10^{23} molecules		

Figure 2-7
The relation between molecules, atoms, moles, and molar mass.

EXERCISE 2-7

Show that the mass of a mole of NO_2 is 46.0 grams and that the mass of a mole of SO_2 is 64.1 grams.

EXERCISE 2-8

What is the molar mass of each of the following molecular sub-

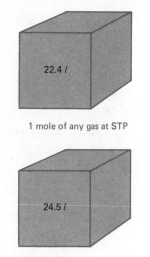

22.4 *l*

1 mole of any gas at STP

24.5 *l*

1 mole of any gas at 25 °C and 1 atmosphere

Each time you breathe, about 7×10^{21} oxygen molecules enter your lungs.

$$1.0 \text{ mile} \times \frac{5280 \text{ ft}}{\text{mi}} \times \frac{12 \text{ in.}}{\text{ft}} \times \frac{2.54 \text{ cm}}{\text{in.}}$$

$$= 1.6 \times 10^5 \text{ cm}$$

$$1.0 \text{ year} \times \frac{365 \text{ days}}{\text{yr}} \times \frac{24 \text{ h}}{\text{d}} \times \frac{60 \text{ min}}{\text{h}}$$

$$\times \frac{60 \text{ s}}{\text{min}} = 3.2 \times 10^7 \text{ s}$$

stances: sulfur (S_8), ammonia (NH_3), and nitrogen (a diatomic molecule)?

EXERCISE 2-9

Calculate the mass of 6.0×10^{23} molecules of carbon monoxide, CO.

2-9   Molar Volume

The 6.0×10^{23} molecules in one mole occupy a volume called the **molar volume**. Molar mass is constant for any substance; its molar volume is not. The volume increases somewhat as a solid substance is heated. Consequently, the molar volume will change as temperature changes. The volume usually increases more when a change from solid to liquid occurs. However, a change from liquid to gas causes a much larger increase in volume. In general, a gas will have a volume about 1000 times the liquid volume. The calculation of molar volume is a good example of the use of units as a guide to a correct solution of a problem. This is shown in the next section.

2-10   Units

All measured values have a *unit name* which is every bit as important as the numerical part. A football field is 100 *yards* long, not just 100 long. A soft drink costs 25 *cents*, not 25. A molar mass is 18 g, not 18, and so on. Therefore, units must be included for all measurements and for all derived quantities. In many calculations units "cancel," so the final answer has fewer or different units than the values that went into the computation. Some familiar examples are shown in the margin.

1. How many grams are there in 3.0 moles of water?

$$3.0 \text{ moles} \times \frac{18 \text{ grams water}}{1 \text{ mole}} = 54 \text{ grams of water}$$

2. If there are 3×10^{19} molecules of a gas per cubic centimeter, how many molecules would there be in 2 cubic centimeters?

$$3 \times 10^{19} \frac{\text{molecules}}{\text{cm}^3} \times 2 \text{ cm}^3$$

$$= 6 \times 10^{19} \text{ molecules in 2 cm}^3$$

3. If the density of oxygen gas is 1.43 grams per liter at STP, what would the volume of one mole of oxygen be?

$$\frac{32.0 \text{ grams oxygen}}{1 \text{ mole}} \times \frac{1 \text{ liter oxygen}}{1.43 \text{ grams oxygen}} = \frac{22.4 \text{ liters}}{\text{mole}}$$

If you sometimes have difficulty in knowing how to set up a problem, the use of units will often lead you to the correct method and answer. Consider this problem:

Al_2O_3 weighs 4.0 g/cm³. How many cm³ will 24 g occupy?

Correct	Incorrect

$$24 \cancel{g} \times \frac{1 \text{ cm}^3}{4.0 \cancel{g}} = 6.0 \text{ cm}^3 \qquad 24 \text{ g} \times \frac{4.0 \text{ g}}{1 \text{ cm}^3} = \frac{96 \text{ g}^2}{\text{cm}^3}$$

The units are wrong.
The problem specified cm³.

2-11 Calculations Based on the Mole

If we take a certain mass of a substance, we can calculate the number of moles that we have of that substance. We can also calculate how many molecules we have. Here is an example to help you understand these calculations:

How many moles and how many molecules are contained in 2.2 grams of carbon dioxide? The molecular formula CO_2 tells us that its molar mass is the mass of one mole of C atoms plus the mass of two moles of O atoms.

$$\text{molar mass of } CO_2 = \text{molar mass of C} + (2 \times \text{molar mass of O})$$

$$= 12.0 + (2 \times 16.0)$$

$$= 44.0 \text{ grams}$$

$$3 \cancel{\text{drinks}} \times \frac{30\cancel{c}}{\cancel{\text{drink}}} = 90\cancel{c} \text{ for drinks}$$

$$1.5 \cancel{\text{hours}} \times 50 \frac{\text{miles}}{\cancel{\text{hour}}} = 75 \text{ miles}$$

In our example we have taken a smaller mass than 44.0 grams. We have less than 1.0 mole. If we have less than 1.0 mole of carbon dioxide, then we should have fewer than 6.0×10^{23} molecules. We will use these guides to check our answers.

$$\text{number of moles of } CO_2 = 2.2 \cancel{\text{grams}} \times \frac{1 \text{ mole}}{44 \cancel{\text{grams}}}$$

$$= 0.050 \text{ mole}$$

We have two very quick checks on our problem-solving. The first was our guess that the answer would be less than 1.0 mole. The answer 0.050 mole confirms our guess. The second check is observing that the units combine to give an answer which has the units asked for in the problem. We can write out the units to show the combination needed to give the correct answer:

$$\text{number of moles} = \cancel{\text{grams}} \times \frac{\text{mole}}{\cancel{\text{grams}}} = \text{mole}$$

Now let us find out how many molecules we have in 2.2 grams of CO_2. We will use units to check our calculation.

number of molecules of CO_2

$$= 0.050 \cancel{\text{mole}} \times 6.0 \times 10^{23} \frac{\text{molecules}}{\cancel{\text{mole}}}$$

$$= 3.0 \times 10^{22} \text{ molecules}$$

This number is less than 6.0×10^{23} molecules, which agrees with our guess.

EXERCISE 2-10

How many moles of iron atoms are present in 1.67 grams of iron? How many iron atoms are present in 1.67 grams of iron?

2-12 Determining the Formula of a Compound

Analytical chemists determine the composition of chemicals by many methods.

By the middle of the 19th century chemists had developed methods that allowed them to determine how much of an element was present in a pure compound. Using this information and molar masses, they were able to determine chemical formulas. Let us look at some examples of how this is done.

A compound containing only carbon and oxygen is analyzed. For each 12 grams of carbon there are 32 grams of oxygen. What is the formula for this oxide? To answer this, we must find how many moles of carbon atoms and how many moles of oxygen atoms there are in the sample.

$$\text{number of moles of carbon atoms} = 12 \text{ grams carbon} \times \frac{1 \text{ mole}}{12 \text{ grams carbon}}$$

$$= 1.0 \text{ mole carbon atoms}$$

$$\text{number of moles of oxygen atoms} = 32 \text{ grams oxygen} \times \frac{1 \text{ mole}}{16 \text{ grams oxygen}}$$

$$= 2.0 \text{ moles oxygen atoms}$$

This tells us that the ratio of moles of carbon to moles of oxygen is 1 to 2 in this compound. There are twice as many moles of oxygen as carbon and therefore twice as many oxygen atoms as carbon atoms in each molecule. The chemical formula is CO_2. The compound is carbon dioxide.

EXERCISE 2-11

Suppose a smaller sample was taken, one containing 6 grams of carbon and 16 grams of oxygen. Convince yourself that the formula for this substance is CO_2.

Another oxide of carbon was analyzed. For 12 grams of carbon in this compound there were 16 grams of oxygen. As in the first example, calculation of the number of moles of each element will lead us to the chemical formula.

$$\text{number of moles of carbon atoms} = 12 \text{ grams carbon} \times \frac{1 \text{ mole}}{12 \text{ grams carbon}}$$

$$= 1.0 \text{ mole carbon atoms}$$

$$\text{number of moles} \atop \text{of oxygen atoms} = 16 \text{ grams oxygen} \times \frac{1 \text{ mole}}{16 \text{ grams oxygen}}$$

$$= 1.0 \text{ mole oxygen atoms}$$

This compound contains 1.0 mole of carbon atoms for 1.0 mole of oxygen atoms. Its formula is CO, carbon monoxide.

EXERCISE 2-12

Convince yourself that a larger sample of carbon monoxide, one containing 24 grams of carbon atoms and 32 grams of oxygen atoms, will still have the formula CO.

Hydrogen and oxygen also form two compounds. If 1.00 gram of water is decomposed, 0.11 gram of hydrogen and 0.89 gram of oxygen are obtained. What is the formula for water? Calculation of the number of moles of hydrogen and oxygen will lead to the answer.

$$\text{number of moles} \atop \text{of hydrogen atoms} = 0.11 \text{ g hydrogen} \times \frac{1 \text{ mol}}{1.0 \text{ g hydrogen}}$$

$$= 0.11 \text{ mol hydrogen atoms}$$

$$\text{number of moles} \atop \text{of oxygen atoms} = 0.89 \text{ g oxygen} \times \frac{1 \text{ mol}}{16 \text{ g oxygen}}$$

$$= 0.056 \text{ mol oxygen atoms}$$

The ratio of moles of hydrogen atoms to moles of oxygen atoms is 0.11 to 0.056, or 2 to 1. The formula is H_2O.

When the other compound of hydrogen and oxygen, hydrogen peroxide, is analyzed, a 1.00 gram sample yields 0.059 gram of hydrogen and 0.94 gram of oxygen. The formula is found in the same way as before.

$$\text{number of moles} \atop \text{of hydrogen atoms} = 0.059 \text{ g hydrogen} \times \frac{1 \text{ mol}}{1.0 \text{ g hydrogen}}$$

$$= 0.059 \text{ mol hydrogen atoms}$$

$$\text{number of moles} \atop \text{of oxygen atoms} = 0.94 \text{ g oxygen} \times \frac{1 \text{ mol}}{16 \text{ g oxygen}}$$

$$= 0.059 \text{ mol oxygen atoms}$$

The ratio of moles of hydrogen atoms to moles of oxygen atoms is 1 to 1. The formula is HO. However, this is not the formula for hydrogen peroxide that is given in a chemical handbook. The formula given there is H_2O_2. Now why should we get the wrong answer? The method we used gave the correct formulas in the first three examples. Why does our method break down with hydrogen peroxide?

Do you see that the ratio of H atoms to O atoms is 1 to 1 in both HO and H_2O_2? Then why do we accept H_2O_2 but not HO? The decision is based on additional evidence from experiments similar to those presented in Section 2-3. A molar volume of hydrogen peroxide weighs 34 grams. The formula H_2O_2 is in agreement with this.

Both formulas are useful for describing our environment. They have different names. HO is the **empirical formula** for hydrogen peroxide. It shows the simplest ratio in which the atoms combine. H_2O_2 is the **molecular formula** for hydrogen peroxide. It shows the number and kind of atoms present in one molecule. Both HO and H_2O_2 are examples of chemical formulas.

In our first three examples, the empirical formulas happened to be the same as the molecular formulas. The molar masses of carbon dioxide, carbon monoxide, and water are 44, 28, and 18 grams respectively. The empirical formula in each accounts for all the mass. The empirical formula and molecular formula are the same for many compounds.

EXERCISE 2-13

A chemist made 32.0 grams of a compound called hydrazine. Analysis shows there are 28.0 grams of nitrogen and 4.0 grams of hydrogen. The molar mass is found to be 32.0 grams. What is the empirical formula for hydrazine? What is the molecular formula for hydrazine?

2-13   Review

The explanation for the regularity in gas behavior, $PV = a$ constant, in terms of molecular particles, is called a **theory**. We make use of a **model system**, ping-pong balls moving in a box, in arriving at this explanation. In this chapter we have seen the theory grow.

Gases differ in properties like color, odor, and solubility in water. The masses of molecules of different gases also are different. The idea that equal volumes of gases (at the same temperature and pressure) contain equal numbers of molecules is called **Avogadro's hypothesis**. This proposal offers a simple explanation for the integral ratios observed for the reacting volumes of different gases. Moreover, this idea leads to an experimental method for measuring the relative masses of molecules of different gases.

Chemists have found it useful to choose a particular number of molecules, 6.0×10^{23}, as the unit in comparing one substance with another. This number is called **Avogadro's number**. Chemists use the word **mole** when referring to 6.0×10^{23} particles.

In the 19th century the value of 32.0 grams was chosen for the mass of one mole of oxygen molecules. Since the oxygen molecule is diatomic, the molar mass of atomic oxygen is 16.0 grams. The molar mass for atoms of other elements could be established by comparison with the molar mass of atomic oxygen.

In this chapter you have been introduced to chemical symbols and formulas as well as the mole, molar mass, and molar volume.

The use of the mole in chemical calculations was introduced, and in the next chapter we will see how important the idea of the mole can be when we begin to study chemical reactions.

Questions and Problems for Chapter 2

1

How could you make money buying helium gas at $1.25 per liter and selling it for $0.50 per liter?

2

Four grams of helium gas at 1.00 atm and 0 °C occupy a volume of 22.4 liters. What would the volume be at 1.75 atm and 0 °C?

3

The most important step in converting atmospheric nitrogen into fertilizers or explosives is the combination of one volume of nitrogen gas with three volumes of hydrogen gas to form two volumes of ammonia. From these data alone and Avogadro's hypothesis, how many molecules of hydrogen combine with one molecule of nitrogen? How many molecules of ammonia are produced for each molecule of nitrogen used? What is the chemical formula for ammonia?

4

Gaseous uranium hexafluoride is used in the preparation of uranium as a source of nuclear energy. A flask filled with this gas is weighed under certain conditions of temperature and pressure. The mass of the gas is found to be 3.52 grams. The same flask is then filled with oxygen gas and weighed under the same conditions. The mass of the oxygen is found to be 0.32 gram.

(a) What is the ratio of the mass of one uranium hexafluoride molecule to the mass of an oxygen molecule?
(b) State any guiding principles needed in answering the question.

5

A white substance, on heating, forms a colorless gas and a purple solid. Is the substance an element or a compound? Why do you think so?

6

What do the following symbols represent? K, Ca, Co, CO, Pb, Hf, HF

7

Here are the names of some common chemicals and their formulas. What elements does each compound contain?

(a) hydrogen peroxide H_2O_2
(b) jeweler's rouge Fe_2O_3
(c) light-bulb filament W
(d) tetraethyl lead $Pb(C_2H_5)_4$
(e) baking soda $NaHCO_3$
(f) octane C_8H_{18}
(g) household gas (methane) CH_4

8

For each of the following substances, give the name of each kind of atom present and the total number of atoms represented in the formula.

(a) graphite (pencil lead) C
(b) diamond C
(c) sodium chloride (table salt) NaCl
(d) sodium hydroxide (lye) NaOH
(e) calcium hydroxide $Ca(OH)_2$
(f) potassium nitrate KNO_3
(g) magnesium nitrate $Mg(NO_3)_2$
(h) sodium sulfate Na_2SO_4
(i) calcium sulfate $CaSO_4$

9

All the following substances are called *acids*. What element do they have in common?

(a) nitric acid HNO_3
(b) hydrochloric acid HCl
(c) acetic acid $HC_2H_3O_2$
(d) sulfuric acid H_2SO_4
(e) phosphoric acid H_3PO_4

10

What does the molecular formula CI_4 mean? What additional information is provided by the structural formula?

11

Write formulas for these compounds:

(a) hydrogen chloride
(b) sulfur dichloride
(c) nitrogen trifluoride
(d) aluminum trifluoride
(e) dinitrogen difluoride
(f) sulfur hexafluoride
(g) dinitrogen pentasulfide
(h) carbon disulfide
(i) phosphorus pentachloride
(j) zinc dichloride

12

Write formulas for these compounds:

(a) silicon dioxide
(b) hydrogen bromide
(c) hydrogen iodide
(d) boron trichloride
(e) carbon tetrachloride
(f) nitrogen trifluoride
(g) oxygen dichloride
(h) iron dichloride
(i) diphosphorus pentoxide
(j) tungsten hexachloride

13

How many particles are in one mole?

14

How many moles of oxygen atoms are in one mole of nitric acid molecules? Of sulfuric acid molecules? See Problem 9 for formulas.

15

If we had one mole of pennies to divide among all the people in the world, how many dollars would each of the 4 billion inhabitants receive?

16

How many moles of people are on the Earth?

17

If there were a mole of people evenly distributed over the surface of the Earth, including both land and sea, how many square inches would be allotted to each person?

18

A liter of fluorine gas is 1.19 times as heavy as a liter of oxygen gas when both are measured at room temperature and pressure. Calculate the molar mass of fluorine. How does this value com-

pare with the molar mass of atomic fluorine found in the table of molar masses? What is the formula of a molecule of fluorine gas?

19

Calculate the mass of each of the following:

(a) One water molecule (H_2O)
(b) One oxygen molecule (O_2)
(c) One hydrogen atom (H)
(d) One uranium atom (U)
(e) One silver atom (Ag)
(f) One gold atom (Au)

20

If 2.5 moles of hydrogen gas (H_2) react in a given experiment, how many grams of hydrogen does this represent?

21

If you were to process one cubic kilometer of seawater in one year, how many liters would you have to process each minute? Assume you work 250 eight-hour days. (10^3 cm^3 equals 1 liter)

22

Calculate the molar mass for each of these substances: SiF_4, HF, Cl_2, Xe, NO_2.

23

Write the formulas for these compounds and calculate the mass of one mole of each:

(a) carbon disulfide
(b) sulfur hexafluoride
(c) nitrogen trichloride
(d) osmium tetroxide

24

How many grams in each of the following?

(a) 3.0 moles of oxygen molecules
(b) 1.5 moles of sulfuric acid (H_2SO_4)
(c) 10.0 moles of water molecules
(d) 2.5 moles of phosphoric acid (H_3PO_4)
(e) 1000 moles of nitric acid (HNO_3)

25

Consider the following data:

Element	Molar Mass of Atoms
A	12.01 g
B	19.00 g

A and B combine to form a new substance, X. If four moles of B combine with one mole of A to give one mole of X, then the mass of one mole of X is:

(a) 31.0 g   (c) 67.0 g   (e) 124.0 g
(b) 38.0 g   (d) 88.0 g

26

A flask of gaseous CCl_4 was weighed at a certain temperature and pressure. The flask was flushed and filled with oxygen gas at the same temperature and pressure. The mass of CCl_4 vapor will be about:

(a) the same as that of the oxygen
(b) one-fifth as heavy as the oxygen
(c) five times as heavy as the oxygen
(d) twice as heavy as the oxygen
(e) one-half as heavy as the oxygen

27

In Experiment 7 you calculated the ratio of the mass of carbon dioxide to the mass of the same volume of oxygen. Molecular oxygen has been assigned a molar mass of 32.0 grams. From the molar mass of oxygen and your measured ratio, calculate the molar mass of carbon dioxide. Compare the value you obtain with the molar mass of CO_2 calculated on page 43.

28

A glass bulb weighs 108.11 grams after all the gas has been removed from it. When filled with oxygen gas at atmospheric pressure and room temperature, the bulb weighs 109.56 grams. When filled, at the same pressure and temperature, with a gas sample obtained from the mouth of a volcano, the bulb weighs 111.01 grams. Which of the following molecular formulas for the volcano gas could account for the data?

CO_2, SO_3, COS, S_8, Si_2H_6, SO_2,
A gas mixture, half CO_2 and half Kr.

29

A chemist weighs out 10.0 grams of chlorine gas and 10.0 grams of sulfur dichloride. How many moles of each substance does he have?

30

How many moles of atoms are there in 9.0 grams of aluminum? In 0.83 gram of iron?

31

How many moles are there in 53 grams of phosphoric acid, H_3PO_4?

32

The most delicate balance can detect a change of about 10^{-8} gram. How many gold atoms would there be in such a sample?

33

A stone about the size of a softball weighs roughly one kilogram. How many moles of such stones would be needed to account for the entire mass of the Earth, about 6×10^{27} grams?

34

How many atoms are in a copper penny (mass 2 grams)?

35

How many grams of table sugar $(C_{12}H_{22}O_{11})$ are needed to supply one molecule for each of the 4×10^9 people on the Earth?

36

Acetylene gas is used in welding. Acetylene contains 30 grams of carbon for each 2.5 grams of hydrogen. What is the empirical formula for acetylene? At the same temperature and pressure, 26 grams of acetylene are needed to occupy the same volume as 32 grams of oxygen gas. What is the molecular formula of acetylene?

37

There are two common oxides of sulfur. One contains 32 grams of sulfur for each 32 grams of oxygen. The other oxide contains 32 grams of sulfur for each 48 grams of oxygen. What are the empirical formulas of these oxides?

38

A variety of phosphorus called red phosphorus is used in match heads. When 0.062 gram of red phosphorus burns, 0.142 gram of phosphorus oxide is formed. What is the empirical formula of this oxide?

39

There are two known compounds containing only tungsten and carbon. One is the very hard alloy tungsten carbide, used for the edges of cutting tools. Analysis of the two compounds gives, for one, 1.82 grams of tungsten per 0.12 gram of carbon, and for the other compound, 3.70 grams of tungsten per 0.12 gram of carbon. What are the empirical formulas for these compounds?

 # Principles of Chemical Reactions

You have already studied several chemical reactions in the laboratory experiments for this course. Copper wire reacts with a solution of silver nitrate to form metallic silver. Aluminum metal dissolves in a copper chloride solution forming metallic copper. Chemical changes are taking place in each of these experiments.

We do not have to be in a laboratory to observe chemical reactions. There are many occurring around us every day. A candle burning in air produces carbon dioxide and water. Eggs cooking undergo change. Something must be happening when green leaves grow on trees in the spring or a bud turns into a beautiful flower. We know that gasoline is burned to water and carbon dioxide in an automobile engine, providing energy to make the automobile move. Growing plants convert carbon dioxide and water into complex chemical substances and release oxygen to the atmosphere. When we push a flashlight button, a beam of light is produced because chemical reactions take place in the dry cells. Important structural materials like aluminum and steel are produced through chemical reactions. Drugs like penicillin and synthetic fibers such as nylon are known to all of us. These, and hundreds of others, are examples of important substances made through chemical reactions.

A chemist wants to understand and control chemical reactions. In this chapter we will examine some simple ones. We will find that certain principles apply to all chemical reactions. Suppose we begin with a reaction that forms a familiar substance, water.

Cooks are chemists of a very practical kind.

3-1   Formation of Water from Hydrogen and Oxygen

Water is produced when two volumes of hydrogen gas combine with one volume of oxygen gas. The properties of water are very different from the properties of the starting materials, hydrogen and oxygen.

Try to imagine what is happening at the molecular level. Suppose that you could shrink in size so that you were about as big as a molecule of hydrogen or oxygen. You would be smaller then by a factor of about 5 billion. You could see hydrogen and oxygen molecules whizzing past you, occasionally colliding and rebounding from each other. Every once in a while collisions would break the bonds between atoms in hydrogen and oxygen molecules. New chemical bonds would form as the atoms rearrange to form water molecules.

Two hydrogen molecules and one oxygen molecule are represented on the left of Figure 3-1. When these molecules react to form water, the bonds between the atoms in the oxygen molecule and in the hydrogen molecules must be broken. As water molecules form, the molecular models show clearly that new chemical bonds form. A chemical change has taken place. Although the atoms regroup to form two water molecules, the total number of atoms does not change. Chemists have developed molecular models to help visualize these changes.

Distribution of Water on the Earth
(in million million cubic meters)

Oceans	1 350 000
Glaciers, polar ice	29 000
Underground aquifers	8 400
Lakes and rivers	2 000
Atmosphere	13
Biosphere	0.6

 react with to form + energy

Figure 3-1
Molecular models. $2 H_2 + O_2 \longrightarrow 2 H_2O$ + energy.

EXERCISE 3-1

Suppose ten hydrogen molecules and ten oxygen molecules are mixed. How many molecules of water could be formed? What would be left over?

EXERCISE 3-2

One million oxygen molecules react with sufficient hydrogen molecules to form water molecules. How many water molecules are formed? How many hydrogen molecules are required?

Production of 100 water molecules requires 100 hydrogen molecules to react with 50 oxygen molecules. We would need 6.0×10^{23} hydrogen molecules to react with 3.0×10^{23} oxygen molecules to produce 6.0×10^{23} water molecules. To make one mole of water, one mole of hydrogen gas must react with one-half mole of oxygen gas. These results are summarized in Table 3-1.

TABLE 3-1
Amounts of Hydrogen and Oxygen Reacting to Form Water

Hydrogen	Oxygen	Water
(In terms of molecules)		
2	1	2
100	50	100
6.0×10^{23}	3.0×10^{23}	6.0×10^{23}
(in terms of moles)		
1	$\frac{1}{2}$	1
2	1	2
10	5	10

A large amount of heat is given off during this reaction, 68 300 calories* for each mole of H_2O formed. Two moles of hydrogen react with one mole of oxygen. Two moles of water would be produced and $2 \times 68\,300$ calories, or 136.6 kilocalories, of heat energy would be released. This heat energy must come from the reactants, hydrogen and oxygen, since no heat energy was supplied from the outside after the reaction started. We may conclude that water has less energy than the reactants used to make it. *A chemical reaction in which energy is released is called an* **exothermic reaction**.

EXERCISE 3-3

How much heat energy is released when ten moles of hydrogen gas burn? When one-tenth of a mole burns?

3-2 Decomposition of Water

We can decompose the water in a solution of water and sulfuric acid by passing an electric current through the solution. The way to do this is shown in Figure 3-2. Two pieces of metal called electrodes are placed in the solution. When the electrodes are con-

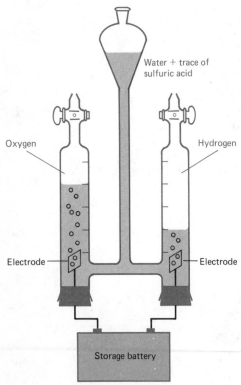

Water + trace of sulfuric acid

Oxygen

Hydrogen

Electrode

Electrode

Storage battery

(Source of DC electricity)

Figure 3-2
Electrolytic decomposition of water.

*A calorie is the unit of heat energy that chemists use. It is the amount of heat energy needed to raise the temperature of one gram of water one degree on the Celsius scale. Another unit of heat energy is the joule, equal to 4.18 calories. The joule is the internationally accepted unit of heat energy used by physicists, but United States chemists have not yet switched over from calories to joules.

nected to a source of energy, hydrogen gas appears at one electrode and oxygen gas at the other. If we operate the apparatus until one mole of water has decomposed, one mole of hydrogen gas and one-half mole of oxygen gas are produced. Electrical energy causes the decomposition of water. *If energy is absorbed in a chemical reaction, we call it an* **endothermic reaction**.

A calorie (4.2 joules) is a small unit. One ordinary kitchen match, burned completely, liberates about 850 calories (3600 joules).

Let us compare the formation and decomposition of water. We can show with molecular models, Figure 3-3, that the chemical change in the formation of water is exactly the reverse of the chemical change in water decomposition. Simple rules describe these changes. In each drawing we find two oxygen atoms on the left and two oxygen atoms on the right. We can see four hydrogen atoms on the left and four on the right. Atoms are neither gained nor lost. *Atoms are conserved in chemical reactions.*

Rocket designers use exothermic reactions to power rockets.

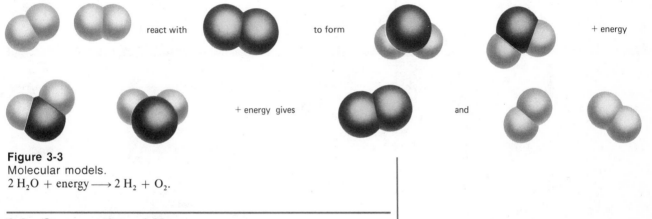

Figure 3-3
Molecular models.
$2 H_2O + energy \longrightarrow 2 H_2 + O_2$.

3-3 Conservation of Mass

Belief in the conservation of atoms is based upon a generalization that has stood the test of many experiments. There is no detectable increase or decrease in the quantity of matter during a chemical change. Since we often measure a quantity of matter in terms of its mass, we may say that mass is conserved. One mole of liquid water weighs 18.0 grams. When this amount of water is decomposed, 2.0 grams of hydrogen and 16.0 grams of oxygen are produced:

Pollution fighters, sanitation engineers, and garbage collectors are all struggling with conservation of mass. Whatever comes into an area has to go out—or accumulate.

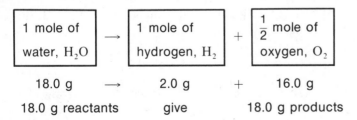

1 mole of water, H_2O	$\longrightarrow$	1 mole of hydrogen, H_2	+	$\frac{1}{2}$ mole of oxygen, O_2
18.0 g	$\longrightarrow$	2.0 g	+	16.0 g
18.0 g reactants		give		18.0 g products

In chemical reactions:
(a) Mass is conserved.
   The mass of the reactants is equal to the mass of the products.
(b) Atoms are conserved.
   Each atom appears both in a reactant and in a product.

(c) The chemical bonding changes.

The arrangement of atoms is different in the reactants from what it is in the products of a chemical equation.

The number of moles of molecules may not be conserved in chemical reactions. We can understand this by recognizing that molecules undergo change or rearrangement in a chemical reaction. In our example of water decomposition

$$1 \text{ mole of molecules} \longrightarrow 1\frac{1}{2} \text{ moles of molecules}$$

$$\text{(reactant)} \qquad\qquad\qquad \text{(product)}$$

Moles of molecules are not necessarily conserved in a chemical reaction.

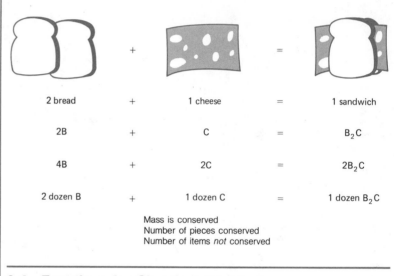

2 bread	+	1 cheese	=	1 sandwich
2B	+	C	=	B_2C
4B	+	2C	=	$2B_2C$
2 dozen B	+	1 dozen C	=	1 dozen B_2C

Mass is conserved
Number of pieces conserved
Number of items *not* conserved

3-4 Equations for Chemical Reactions

The molecular models we have used in representing chemical reactions help us visualize the rearrangement of atoms in the reactions. By a slight change we can show the results in a less detailed but simpler way. Chemical formulas can be used rather than drawings of the atoms and molecules. The formula for hydrogen gas is H_2, the formula for oxygen gas is O_2, and the formula for water is H_2O. By using the formulas to represent the molecules, we can write

$$2\,H_2 + 1\,O_2 \longrightarrow 2\,H_2O$$

This is called a **chemical equation**. Notice that we show two molecules of a substance by writing the coefficient 2 before the formula. The coefficient 2 before the formula H_2O means two molecules of water. In two molecules of water there are four hydrogen atoms and two oxygen atoms. We can also show with an equation that using twice as much hydrogen and oxygen will produce twice as much water.

$$4\,H_2 + 2\,O_2 \longrightarrow 4\,H_2O$$

The heat of the reaction of oxygen and acetylene is enough to melt steel.

The equation for the decomposition of water into hydrogen and oxygen would be written:

$$2\,H_2O \longrightarrow 2\,H_2 + 1\,O_2$$

In all chemical equations atoms are conserved. Every symbol, when multiplied by the subscript after it and the coefficient before the formula, must appear as often on the left side of the equation as on the right.

Let us consider another example. Natural gas contains a large amount of methane, CH_4. The chemical equation for methane burning in oxygen is:

$$1\,CH_4 + 2\,O_2 \longrightarrow 1\,CO_2 + 2\,H_2O$$

There is the same number of each kind of atom in the reactants as there is in the products. One carbon atom, four hydrogen atoms, and four oxygen atoms are represented on each side of the equation. Because a mole is a fixed number of particles, we can read this equation in two ways:

Molecular Interpretation
one molecule of methane + two molecules of oxygen $\longrightarrow$ one molecule of carbon dioxide + two molecules of water

Molar Interpretation
one mole of methane + two moles of oxygen $\longrightarrow$ one mole of carbon dioxide + two moles of water

3-5 Writing Equations for Reactions

Let us practice writing equations for chemical reactions. First, we have to know what the reactants and products are. Then we follow two simple steps:

  (a) We have to write the correct molecular formula for each reactant and each product.

  (b) We must show that atoms are conserved.

When magnesium metal is burned in oxygen, a new substance, magnesium oxide, is formed. The formulas needed are Mg, O_2, and MgO. When writing chemical equations, we write the formulas for the reactants on the left and the products on the right:

$$Mg + O_2 \longrightarrow MgO$$

This is not yet a proper chemical statement. There are two moles of oxygen atoms on the left side of the equation and only one mole on the right. We must find numerical coefficients to place before each correct chemical formula to obtain the same number of moles of atoms for each element on the left side of the equation as there are on the right. That is, our statement must show conservation of atoms. The process of finding these coefficients is called **balancing the equation**.

Dieticians create tasty, healthful meals by combining the proper chemicals.

A kitchen stove burner mixes methane and air, which then react and produce heat.

Plaster of Paris is a dehydrated form of gypsum with the formula $CaSO_4 \cdot \frac{1}{2}H_2O$ that is produced when gypsum is heated to about 100 °C. It is used in the production of wallboard and for plaster. It sets, after the addition of water, by the re-forming of crystalline gypsum, $CaSO_4 \cdot 2H_2O$.

Engineering clerks make chemical calculations of many kinds.

First, suppose one mole of oxygen gas is consumed in the reaction.

$$Mg + 1\ O_2 \longrightarrow MgO$$

One mole of oxygen gas, with its two moles of oxygen atoms, forms two moles of magnesium oxide.

$$Mg + 1\ O_2 \longrightarrow 2\ MgO$$

But two moles of magnesium oxide require two moles of magnesium metal.

$$2\ Mg + 1\ O_2 \longrightarrow 2\ MgO$$

Atoms are conserved in the last statement; the equation is balanced.

We could have decided to begin balancing the equation by choosing one mole of magnesium metal as the amount of reactant consumed in the reaction.

Suppose one mole of magnesium is consumed in the reaction.

$$1\ Mg + O_2 \longrightarrow MgO$$

One mole of magnesium will form one mole of magnesium oxide

$$1\ Mg + O_2 \longrightarrow 1\ MgO$$

One mole of magnesium oxide contains one mole of oxygen atoms, the number in one-half mole of oxygen molecules.

$$1\ Mg + \frac{1}{2} O_2 \longrightarrow 1\ MgO$$

This statement is also a balanced equation. (Remember that we are now talking about one half of a mole of O_2 molecules, not one half of an O_2 molecule). Atoms are conserved.

Either way of writing the chemical equation for the burning of magnesium is acceptable:

$$2\ Mg + 1\ O_2 \longrightarrow 2\ MgO$$

$$1\ Mg + \frac{1}{2} O_2 \longrightarrow 1\ MgO$$

We can multiply all the coefficients in the second equation by 2 to obtain the first equation. We can always multiply or divide all coefficients in a balanced chemical equation by the same number and obtain an equally valid equation. It just means we are considering a different number of moles. In writing equations the coefficient 1 is often dropped. However, it is never wrong to write it in the equation.

This example shows you that it does not matter where you start in balancing a chemical equation. The important thing is that you start! A few more examples will help you learn to balance equations.

Hydrogen gas, H_2, and chlorine gas, Cl_2, react to form hydrogen chloride gas, HCl.

Suppose we assume one mole of H_2 reacts. Conservation of hydrogen atoms requires that two moles of HCl be produced.

$$1\ H_2 + Cl_2 \longrightarrow 2\ HCl$$

There are two moles of chlorine atoms in the product, hydrogen chloride. One mole of Cl_2 is required.

$$1\,H_2 + 1\,Cl_2 \longrightarrow 2\,HCl$$
$$\text{or}$$
$$H_2 + Cl_2 \longrightarrow 2\,HCl$$

   Another example is the reaction of formaldehyde with oxygen to form CO_2 and H_2O. Formaldehyde has the formula H_2CO. What would the equation for this reaction be? We will start with one mole of formaldehyde. One mole of carbon atoms and two moles of hydrogen atoms in one mole of formaldehyde must appear in the products. We can write

$$1\,H_2CO + \underline{\quad?\quad}\,O_2 \longrightarrow 1\,CO_2 + 1\,H_2O$$

Notice that we have not yet determined the coefficient of O_2. The question mark is to remind us of this. Experiments show us that oxygen atoms are conserved. Since three moles of oxygen atoms appear in the products of this reaction, three moles of oxygen atoms must have been present in the reactants. One mole of oxygen atoms can be counted in one mole of formaldehyde. Two more moles of oxygen atoms must be supplied by one mole of molecular oxygen. The question mark is replaced by the coefficient 1.

$$1\,H_2CO + 1\,O_2 \longrightarrow 1\,CO_2 + 1\,H_2O$$
$$\text{or}$$
$$H_2CO + O_2 \longrightarrow CO_2 + H_2O$$

We deliberately left oxygen as the last element to balance. This is often wise when an element shows up in more than two places in an equation. Leave the most difficult balancing act until last. Remember that all oxygen atoms in both compounds on the left side of the equation must be balanced with all oxygen atoms in the two compounds on the right.

EXERCISE 3-4

Ammonia, NH_3, reacts with oxygen, O_2, to give nitrogen, N_2, and water, H_2O. Follow each step in balancing this reaction:

$$NH_3 + O_2 \longrightarrow N_2 + H_2O$$
$$NH_3 + O_2 \longrightarrow 1\,N_2 + H_2O$$
$$2\,NH_3 + O_2 \longrightarrow 1\,N_2 + H_2O$$
$$2\,NH_3 + O_2 \longrightarrow 1\,N_2 + 3\,H_2O$$
$$2\,NH_3 + \frac{3}{2}O_2 \longrightarrow 1\,N_2 + 3\,H_2O$$

State briefly what was done in each step.

A 707 jet airplane during takeoff burns 4 tons of fuel in the first 3 minutes.

EXERCISE 3-5

A paraffin candle burns in air to form water and carbon dioxide. Paraffin is made up of molecules of several sizes. We will use the molecular formula $C_{25}H_{52}$ as representative of the molecules present.

Formulas of Reactants	Formulas of Products

$$C_{25}H_{52} + O_2 \longrightarrow H_2O + CO_2$$

Suppose one mole of paraffin is burned. We can write

$$1\ C_{25}H_{52} + \underline{\quad ?\quad} O_2 \longrightarrow 26\ H_2O + 25\ CO_2$$

We still have not determined the coefficient for O_2. Since 76 oxygen atoms are required for the products $[26 + (2 \times 25) = 76]$, they must have been present in the reactants. Show that the coefficient for O_2 must be 38.

$$C_{25}H_{52} + 38\ O_2 \longrightarrow 26\ H_2O + 25\ CO_2$$

Usually it is easier to think of chemical equations in terms of molecules rather than moles. However, in practical terms it is more useful to think in terms of moles. The reason for this is that single molecules are much too small to measure individually. Look back at Problem 2-32. The best balances cannot detect less than 30 million million gold atoms. When we deal with amounts of chemicals that can be weighed, it is more useful to think of moles rather than molecules.

3-6 Calculations Based on Chemical Equations

Balanced equations give the information needed for finding the masses of substances consumed or produced in chemical reactions. It is not only chemists who make use of equations this way. In medicine one may have to determine how much antidote is needed to counteract a poison. Space scientists need to know how much oxygen must be supplied to keep the astronauts alive. The balanced chemical equation is as important to a chemist as a map is to a navigator or a blueprint to an engineer.

Suppose we wish to know how many moles of water are produced when 68 grams of ammonia are burned. We balanced the equation for this reaction in Exercise 3-4.

$$2\ NH_3 + \frac{3}{2}O_2 \longrightarrow N_2 + 3\ H_2O$$

The molar mass of ammonia is 17 grams. In this problem 68 grams of NH_3 are burned. How many moles of NH_3 is this?

$$68\ \text{grams } NH_3 \times \frac{1\ \text{mole } NH_3}{17\ \text{grams } NH_3} = 4.0\ \text{moles } NH_3$$

The balanced equation tells us that

$$2 \text{ moles } NH_3 \longrightarrow 3 \text{ moles } H_2O$$

This must mean that

$$4 \text{ moles } NH_3 \longrightarrow 6 \text{ moles } H_2O$$

We see that 68 grams, or four moles, of ammonia produce six moles of water. Since the molar mass for water is 18.0 grams, 6×18.0, or 108, grams of water would be formed.

Let us review the steps we follow in this calculation.

First, balance the chemical equation.

Second, calculate the number of moles of ammonia that reacted. To do this, multiply the number of grams of ammonia by the mole-to-gram ratio for ammonia.

$$\begin{array}{l} \text{Number of moles} \\ \text{of ammonia} \end{array} = 68 \text{ grams } NH_3 \times \frac{1 \text{ mole } NH_3}{17 \text{ grams } NH_3}$$

$$= 4.0 \text{ moles } NH_3$$

Third, read from the balanced equation the relation between moles of water and moles of ammonia. From this relation we can determine the number of moles of water that are produced from 4.0 moles of ammonia.

This equation says:

$$2 \text{ moles } NH_3 \text{ form } 3 \text{ moles } H_2O$$

Therefore,

$$4.0 \text{ moles } NH_3 \times \frac{3 \text{ moles } H_2O}{2 \text{ moles } NH_3} = 6.0 \text{ moles } H_2O$$

Fourth, calculate the mass of water by multiplying the number of moles of water by the gram-to-mole ratio for water.

$$\text{mass of } H_2O = 6.0 \text{ moles } H_2O \times \frac{18.0 \text{ grams } H_2O}{1 \text{ mole } H_2O}$$

$$= 108 \text{ grams } H_2O$$

Another example will give us some practice in this kind of calculation. Suppose we want to know how many grams of chlorine, Cl_2, are required to make 730 grams of hydrogen chloride, HCl. Let us follow the steps we have discussed.

First, balance the equation

$$H_2 + Cl_2 \longrightarrow 2 \text{ HCl}$$

Second, calculate the number of moles of HCl to be produced:

number of moles HCl =

$$730 \text{ grams HCl} \times \frac{1 \text{ mole HCl}}{36.5 \text{ grams HCl}}$$

$$= 20.0 \text{ moles HCl}$$

Third, from the balanced equation, read the relation between number of moles of Cl_2 and the number of moles of HCl.

2 moles HCl can be made from 1 mole Cl_2.

$$20.0 \text{ moles HCl} \times \frac{1 \text{ mole } Cl_2}{2 \text{ moles HCl}} = 10.0 \text{ moles } Cl_2$$

Fourth, calculate the mass of chlorine required.

$$\text{mass } Cl_2 = 10.0 \text{ moles } Cl_2 \times \frac{71.0 \text{ grams } Cl_2}{1 \text{ mole } Cl_2}$$

$$= 710 \text{ grams } Cl_2$$

We would have to react 710 grams of chlorine with sufficient hydrogen to make 730 grams of hydrogen chloride.

EXERCISE 3-6

Show that 3.80 moles of oxygen gas are needed to burn 35.3 grams of paraffin by the reaction

$$C_{25}H_{52} + 38 O_2 \longrightarrow 26 H_2O + 25 CO_2$$

EXERCISE 3-7

How many moles of oxygen, O_2, are required to produce 242 grams of magnesium oxide by the following reaction?

$$2 Mg + O_2 \longrightarrow 2 MgO$$

EXERCISE 3-8

Iron burns in oxygen to form a black oxide, Fe_3O_4. Write a balanced equation for the reaction. If 0.558 gram of Fe is burned, how many moles of oxygen gas would be required and how many grams of Fe_3O_4 would be formed?

3-7 Review

Whether one is a research chemist investigating new chemical reactions in the laboratory, an engineer involved in the industrial preparation of important chemicals, or anyone else who must use chemical reactions, the same principles apply. In this chapter we have illustrated these principles.

In any chemical reaction several things happen. Bonds between atoms in molecules are broken. New bonds form to give molecular products. Energy is produced or consumed. *Atoms are conserved in chemical reactions*. This regularity is shown by the balanced chemical equations used to describe chemical reactions. Either molecular models or chemical formulas can be used to represent the reactants and products of a chemical reaction. The reactants are placed to the left of an arrow. The products are placed at the right of this arrow. The equation is said to be balanced when the number of each kind of atom is the same on both sides of the arrow.

The balanced equation is the key to the amounts of substances that react or form in the chemical reaction. The coefficients in the balanced equation tell us the relative number of moles of each substance in the reaction. Knowing the number of moles, one can readily calculate the mass of each substance that enters into the chemical reaction.

Questions and Problems for Chapter 3

1

If 3 grams of substance A combine with 4 grams of substance B to make 5 grams of substance C and some D, how many grams of D would you expect?

2

One volume of hydrogen gas combines with one volume of chlorine gas to give two volumes of hydrogen chloride gas. On the basis of many reactions, we have learned that the molecular formulas are H_2 for hydrogen, Cl_2 for chlorine, and HCl for hydrogen chloride. The reaction can be represented with this equation:

$$H_2 + Cl_2 \longrightarrow 2\,HCl$$

(a) According to this equation, how many molecules of hydrogen chloride can be formed using one molecule of hydrogen?
(b) How many moles of hydrogen chloride can be formed using one mole of hydrogen gas?
(c) How many molecules of hydrogen chloride can be formed using four molecules of chlorine?
(d) How many moles of chlorine gas are required to produce eight moles of hydrogen chloride?

3

The equation for the reaction between nitric oxide, NO, and oxygen, O_2, can be written

$$2\,NO + O_2 \longrightarrow 2\,NO_2$$

(a) How many molecules of nitrogen dioxide, NO_2, can be formed using two molecules of nitric oxide?

(b) How many moles of nitric oxide are needed to give four moles of nitrogen dioxide?
(c) How many moles of oxygen atoms are there in one mole of oxygen molecules?
(d) How many moles of oxygen atoms are there in two moles of nitric oxide?
(e) How many moles of oxygen atoms are there in two moles of nitrogen dioxide?
(f) Use the answers to parts (c), (d), and (e) to verify that oxygen atoms are conserved in the reaction.

4

Write the equation for the reaction between nitrogen gas and hydrogen gas to give ammonia gas. The molecular formulas are N_2, H_2, and NH_3 respectively.

(a) Verify that your equation conserves nitrogen atoms.
(b) Verify that your equation conserves hydrogen atoms.

5

Balance the equation for each of the following reactions. Use only one mole of the underlined substance.

(a) $Li + \underline{Cl_2} \longrightarrow LiCl$ (d) $Na + \underline{Br_2} \longrightarrow NaBr$
(b) $Na + \underline{Cl_2} \longrightarrow NaCl$ (e) $\underline{O_2} + Cl_2 \longrightarrow Cl_2O$
(c) $Na + \underline{F_2} \longrightarrow NaF$ (f) $O_2 + \underline{Cl_2} \longrightarrow Cl_2O$

Show that your answers to parts (e) and (f) contain the same information.

6

Balance the equation for each of the following

reactions involving oxygen. Use only one mole of the underlined substance.

(a) $\underline{Ni} + O_2 \longrightarrow NiO$
(b) $Ni + \underline{O_2} \longrightarrow NiO$
(c) $\underline{Li} + O_2 \longrightarrow Li_2O$
(d) With the rocket fuel hydrazine, N_2H_4:

$$N_2H_4 + O_2 \longrightarrow N_2 + H_2O$$

(e) With the important copper ore chalcocite, Cu_2S:

$$\underline{Cu_2S} + O_2 \longrightarrow Cu_2O + SO_2$$

(f) With the important ore iron pyrites, FeS_2: (This ore is sometimes referred to as "fool's gold" because of its bright golden luster.)

$$FeS_2 + O_2 \longrightarrow \underline{Fe_2O_3} + SO_2$$

7

When ammonia is decomposed into nitrogen gas and hydrogen gas, the reaction absorbs heat energy. The equation can be written this way:

$$2\,NH_3 + 22\ kcal \longrightarrow N_2 + 3\,H_2$$

(a) How many moles of nitrogen gas will be produced from two moles of ammonia?
(b) How much heat energy would be absorbed during the production of one mole of nitrogen gas?
(c) How much heat energy must be absorbed to produce nine moles of hydrogen gas?
(d) Calculate the mass of two moles of ammonia. Compare that number to the sum of the masses of one mole of nitrogen gas and three moles of hydrogen gas.

8

In the manufacture of nitric acid, HNO_3, nitrogen dioxide reacts with water as shown by this equation:

$$3\,NO_2 + H_2O \longrightarrow 2\,HNO_3 + NO$$

(a) Verify that the equation conserves oxygen atoms.
(b) How many molecules of nitrogen dioxide are required to form 25 molecules of nitric oxide?
(c) How many moles of nitric oxide are formed from 0.60 mole of nitrogen dioxide?

9

One step in the manufacture of sulfuric acid is the burning of sulfur, S_8, in air to form a colorless gas, SO_2, sulfur dioxide. On the basis of this information:

(a) Write a balanced equation for this reaction.
(b) Interpret the equation in terms of molecules.
(c) How many moles of sulfur dioxide can be produced from two moles of sulfur molecules?

10

When iron rusts, it combines with oxygen of the air to form iron oxide, Fe_2O_3. Which of the following statements is FALSE?

(a) The equation is $3\,O_2 + 4\,Fe \longrightarrow 2\,Fe_2O_3$
(b) There are five atoms represented by the formula Fe_2O_3.
(c) Atoms are conserved.
(d) The mass of the reactants equals the mass of the products.
(e) Molecules are conserved.

11

Chlorine, Cl_2, is one of the most important industrial chemicals. Each day many tons of chlorine are produced by the electrolysis of sodium chloride. Most of this chlorine is used to purify water supplies or to bleach paper and cloth. The other product of this electrolysis is metallic sodium.

(a) Write a balanced equation for this electrolysis reaction.
(b) How many grams of sodium chloride are required to make 1.00×10^6 grams of chlorine gas?
(c) How many kilograms of chlorine gas were produced in (b)?

12

Graphite is one form of carbon, C. It can be burned in air to produce carbon dioxide.

(a) Write a balanced equation for the reaction.
(b) If one mole of graphite is burned, how many moles of carbon dioxide are produced? What is the mass in grams for this amount of carbon dioxide?
(c) If five moles of graphite are burned in a vessel containing 10 moles of oxygen gas, what is the maximum number of moles of carbon dioxide that could be produced?

13

Large amounts of a very important metal, titanium (Ti), are made by reacting titanium tetrachloride with magnesium metal. Titanium metal and magnesium chloride, $MgCl_2$, are produced.

(a) Write a balanced equation for the reaction.

(b) How many grams of magnesium are required to produce 1000 grams of titanium?

14

Copper wire reacts with a silver nitrate solution to produce only silver metal and a solution of copper nitrate, $Cu(NO_3)_2$.

(a) Write a balanced equation for the reaction.
(b) How many grams of metallic silver would be produced if 2.37 grams of copper reacted?

15

When iron filings react with a copper sulfate solution ($CuSO_4$), only metallic copper and a solution of iron sulfate ($FeSO_4$) are produced.

(a) Write a balanced equation for the reaction.
(b) How many moles of copper would be produced if 2.45 grams of iron react with an excess of copper sulfate solution?
(c) How many grams of copper would be produced?

16

Write a balanced chemical equation for each of these reactions:

(a) $NH_4Cl + Ca(OH)_2$ gives $NH_3 + H_2O + CaCl_2$
(b) $Al_2(SO_4)_3 + KOH$ gives $Al(OH)_3 + K_2SO_4$
(c) $NaHCO_3 + H_2SO_4$ gives $Na_2SO_4 + CO_2 + H_2O$
(d) $AlCl_3 + LiH$ gives $AlH_3 + LiCl$
(e) $Na + S_8$ gives Na_2S

17

Write a balanced equation for the decomposition of ammonia, nitrogen trifluoride, and nitrogen trichloride into the elements of which they are composed. In each case show the production of one mole of nitrogen gas.

$$NH_3 \longrightarrow N_2 + H_2$$

$$NF_3 \longrightarrow N_2 + F_2$$

$$NCl_3 \longrightarrow N_2 + Cl_2$$

Change the equations to include the following information. Decomposition of ammonia and decomposition of nitrogen trifluoride are endothermic reactions, consuming 22 kcal and 54 kcal per mol of nitrogen, respectively. The decomposition of nitrogen trichloride is exothermic, giving off 109 kcal per mol of nitrogen. Which of these three compounds would you expect to be dangerously explosive?

18

Silver reacts with nitric acid as indicated by the equation:

$$Ag + 2\,HNO_3 \longrightarrow NO_2 + AgNO_3 + H_2O$$

(a) How many grams of nitric acid would be required to react with 5.00 grams of silver?
(b) How many grams of water would be formed?
(c) How many grams of nitrogen dioxide would be produced?

19

Hydrated copper sulfate, $CuSO_4 \cdot 5H_2O$, decomposes when heated to form anhydrous copper sulfate, $CuSO_4$, and water.

(a) Write a balanced equation for the reaction.
(b) How many grams of water would form if 5.00 grams of the hydrate were heated?
(c) How much hydrate must be decomposed to get 5.00 grams of water?

20

The large amounts of SO_2 needed to make H_2SO_4 are obtained by the reaction shown in Problem 6 (f). The Fe_2O_3 produced is also useful. It can be used in blast furnaces to produce iron (the compound FeS_2 cannot be used in blast furnaces).

(a) How many kilograms of FeS_2 are needed to produce 128 kilograms of SO_2?
(b) Does the Fe_2O_3 weigh more or less than the FeS_2 from which it is made?

21

Use the equation obtained in Problem 9 to answer these questions:

(a) How many kilograms of S_8 are needed to produce 641 kilograms of SO_2?
(b) SO_2 can be burned to form SO_3. How many kilograms of SO_2 are needed to produce 801 kilograms of SO_3?
(c) SO_3 reacts with water to form H_2SO_4. How many kilograms of sulfur are needed to produce 981 kilograms of sulfuric acid?

22

If a piece of sodium metal is lowered into a bottle of chlorine gas, a reaction takes place. Sodium chloride, table salt, is formed.

(a) Write an equation for this reaction.
(b) How many moles of sodium chloride could be formed using one mole of sodium?

(c) How many moles of sodium chloride could be formed using 2.30 grams of sodium?

23

Methane, the principal constituent of natural gas, has the formula CH_4. When it is burned in air, the combustion products are carbon dioxide and water.

(a) Write an equation for the combustion of methane.
(b) How many moles of water could be formed using one mole of methane?
(c) How many moles of water would be produced when 4.0 grams of methane are burned?

24

If potassium chlorate ($KClO_3$) is heated gently, the crystals will melt. When the temperature gets high enough, potassium chlorate decomposes to give oxygen gas and potassium chloride, KCl.

(a) Use the information above to write an equation for this decomposition.
(b) How many moles of $KClO_3$ are needed to give 1.5 moles of oxygen gas?
(c) How many moles of KCl would be formed when 0.33 mole of $KClO_3$ decomposes?

25

One gallon of gasoline can be considered to be about 25 moles of octane, C_8H_{18}.

(a) How many moles of oxygen gas must be used to burn one gallon of gasoline, forming carbon dioxide gas and water?
(b) How many moles of carbon dioxide are formed? How many grams? How many kilograms?
(c) How much carbon dioxide is released into the atmosphere when 10 gallons of gasoline are used in an automobile? Express your answer in pounds as well as in kilograms. (1 kilogram weighs 2.2 pounds)

26

Iron burns in air to form a black, solid oxide, Fe_3O_4.

(a) Write an equation for the reaction.
(b) How many moles of oxygen gas are needed to react with one mole of iron?
(c) How many grams of oxygen would this be?
(d) Can a piece of iron weighing 5.6 grams burn completely to Fe_3O_4 in a vessel containing 0.05 mole of O_2?

27

The reaction in Problem 8 relates to the manufacture of nitric acid.

(a) How many grams of nitric acid are formed from one mole of nitrogen dioxide, according to the equation in Problem 8?
(b) How many more grams of nitric acid could be made if the nitric oxide, NO, formed could be completely converted to nitric acid?

28

Hydrazine, N_2H_4, can be burned with oxygen to provide energy for rocket propulsion. The energy released is 150 kcal per mol of hydrazine burned.

(a) How much energy is released if 1.00×10^4 grams of hydrazine fuel are burned? Look at Problem 6 (d) for the reaction of hydrazine with oxygen.
(b) Compare the energy that would be released if the same mass of hydrogen molecules, 1.00×10^4 grams, was burned as fuel instead (see Section 3-1).

29

Although sodium carbonate is needed in the manufacture of glass, very little sodium carbonate is found in nature. It is made using two very abundant chemicals, calcium carbonate (limestone) and sodium chloride. The process involves several steps. The overall reaction can be expressed this way:

$$CaCO_3 + 2\,NaCl \longrightarrow Na_2CO_3 + CaCl_2$$

(a) How many grams of sodium chloride react with 1.00×10^3 grams of calcium carbonate?
(b) How many grams of sodium carbonate are produced?

30

A substance used in manufacturing gasoline consists of finely divided platinum supported on an inert solid. Suppose that the platinum is formed by the high-temperature reaction between platinum dioxide, PtO_2, and hydrogen gas to form platinum metal and water.

(a) How many grams of hydrogen are needed to produce 1.0 gram of platinum metal?
(b) How many moles of water are produced at the same time? How many grams of water?

31

Hydrazine, N_2H_4, and hydrogen peroxide, H_2O_2, are used together as a rocket fuel. The products of the reaction are nitrogen and water. How many grams of hydrogen peroxide are needed per 1.00×10^3 grams of hydrazine carried by the rocket?

The Gas Phase: An Introduction to the Kinetic Theory

The motion of atoms and molecules is a very important property of matter. Knowledge of this is necessary to understand how a chemical reaction takes place. The ideas concerning the motion of particles are described by the *kinetic theory*. The gaseous state is the simplest state of matter to understand. Molecules in a gas are relatively far apart and interact with one another much less than molecules in a liquid or solid.

Chemistry developed into a science when chemists in the 18th and 19th centuries made quantitative measurements on gases. We have already discussed how the regularity in pressure-volume behavior of gases led to the particle model of a gas. This model, in turn, suggested further experiments.

In this chapter we will explore some additional regularities in gas behavior. These regularities will help us to understand the meaning of temperature at the molecular level.

65

The Gas Phase

4-1 Partial Pressure of Gases

Operators of food drying plants monitor the partial pressure of water very carefully.

A simple experiment is shown in Figure 4-1. There are three one-liter bulbs at 25 °C. The first bulb contains 0.0050 mole of air. The manometer shows that the pressure is 93 mmHg. There is 0.0011 mole of water vapor in the second bulb, and the pressure is 20 mmHg. What happens when we combine the same amounts of air and water vapor in the same bulb? This is shown in the third bulb, and the pressure is 113 mmHg.

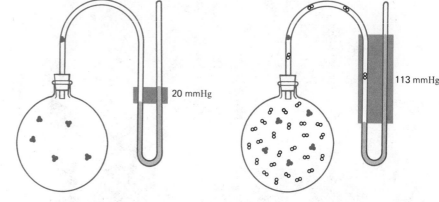

93 mmHg

20 mmHg

113 mmHg

0.0050 mole air in one liter at 25 °C

0.0011 mole water vapor in one liter at 25 °C

0.0050 mole air + 0.0011 mole water vapor in one liter at 25 °C

Figure 4-1
Pressure of a mixture of gases.

This experiment shows that the pressure of a mixture of gases is just the sum of the pressures of the gases.

Total pressure = 93 mmHg (air) + 20 mmHg (water vapor)

= 113 mmHg

The pressure exerted by each gas in a mixture is called the **partial pressure** *of that gas.* If the gas is collected over its liquid or solid phase, its partial pressure is called its vapor pressure. The partial pressure is the pressure that the gas would exert if it were the only gas in the container. Our model of a gas helps us understand why the total pressure equals the sum of the partial pressures of all gases in a container. There is so much space between molecules in a gas that molecules of another gas can readily share the space. Each gas behaves independently of the other and makes its own contribution to the total pressure.

Often in the laboratory gases are collected over water. The gas becomes saturated with water vapor. We can write an equation for the total pressure. Capital P is used to represent the total pressure in the system, and small $\bar{p}$ is used to represent the partial pressure of each gas.

To maintain our health, each of us needs:

13 kg (30 lbs) of air
2 kg (4½ lbs) of water
1.2 kg (2¾ lbs) of food per day

$$P = \bar{p}_{gas} + \bar{p}_{H_2O}$$

Now if we want to know the partial pressure of the gas, we can re-arrange the equation:

$$\overline{p}_{gas} = P - \overline{p}_{H_2O}$$

EXERCISE 4-1

A sample of nitrogen is collected over water at 18.5 °C. The vapor pressure of water at 18.5 °C is 16 mmHg. What are the partial pressures of nitrogen and of water if the total pressure is 756 mmHg?

4-2 The Volume Occupied by One Mole of a Gas

In Chapter 1 we found through a simple experiment at constant temperature that the pressure of a gas increases when the gas volume is decreased.

TABLE 4-1
The Pressure and Volume of One
Mole of Oxygen Gas at 0 °C

Pressure (atmospheres)	Volume (liters)	Pressure × Volume (liter-atmospheres)
2.00	11.3	22.6
1.00	22.4	22.4
0.90	24.7	22.2
0.75	29.9	22.4
	Average	22.4

This regularity for any gas can be expressed by the equation

$$P \times V = a$$

$$P = \frac{a}{V} \quad \text{or} \quad V = \frac{a}{P}$$

The volume of the gasoline-air mixture in the average car is reduced by compression about eight times before it is exploded. In a diesel engine the volume of the diesel oil-air mixture is reduced about 21 times before it is exploded. These numbers are called compression ratios.

where a is a constant that depends on the temperature and the amount of gas. The equation shows that pressure and volume are inversely related. As one goes up, the other goes down.

To help you understand what is meant by an inverse relation, consider a simple example. The area of a square or a rectangle is equal to its length times its width.

$$\text{length} \times \text{width} = \text{area}$$

At the right are several figures that have the same area. You can tell this by counting the squares. Since area is constant, length and width are inversely related. If one increases, the other must decrease. When the length is large, then the width must be small to give the same area. And when the width is large, the length must be small. The next two equations give the same information.

$$\text{length} = \frac{\text{area}}{\text{width}} \quad \text{or} \quad \text{width} = \frac{\text{area}}{\text{length}}$$

We can use the equation

$$P \times V = 22.4 \text{ liter-atmospheres (for one mole of gas at 0 °C)}$$

to solve for the volume of one mole of a gas at atmospheric pressure.

$$1 \text{ atmosphere} \times V = 22.4 \text{ liter-atmospheres}$$

$$V = 22.4 \text{ liters (at 0 °C and 1 atm)}$$

This is often referred to as the *molar volume* of a gas at STP. What happens to a gas as the temperature is increased? You undoubtedly know the answer. A gas expands when heated, and an experiment will give a quantitative measure of this. Table 4-2 gives the pressure-volume data for one mole of ammonia gas at 25 °C. We find the same regularity as before, $PV =$ a constant.

At sea level on an average day a cubic mile of air weighs 5.6×10^6 tons. At an elevation of 220 miles it weighs 2 ounces.

TABLE 4-2

Pressure and Volume of One Mole of Ammonia Gas
at a Constant Temperature of 25 °C

Pressure (atmospheres)	Volume (liters)	Pressure × Volume (liter-atmospheres)
0.1	245	24.5
0.20	123	24.6
0.50	48.2	24.1
1.00	24.7	24.7
2.00	12.1	24.2
		Average 24.4

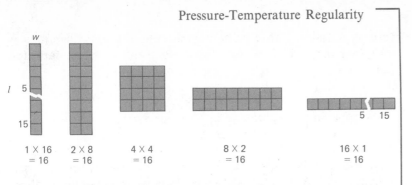

$l \times w$ = area = constant

This time the pressure-volume product is 24.4 liter-atmospheres for one mole of ammonia at 25 °C. This means that the molar volume of ammonia (and all other gases too) is 24.4 liters at 25 °C and 1 atmosphere pressure. The molar volume of a gas depends on the temperature. This is no surprise because we know that a gas expands when it is heated. So when we consider the molar volume of a gas, it is important that the temperature and pressure be specified.

4-3 Pressure-Temperature Regularity

Let us see what happens to the pressure of a gas as the temperature is changed. The gas volume will be kept constant in this experiment. We will take 17.0 grams of NH_3, one mole. Similar pressure values would be found for one mole of any gas.

Table 4-3

Pressure of One Mole of NH_3
at a Constant Volume of 22.4 Liters

Temperature (°C)	Pressure (atmospheres)
−25	0.91
0	1.00
25	1.09
100	1.37
200	1.74

When the volume remains constant, gas pressure increases as the temperature increases. An example that you may have observed often occurs on long automobile trips. The tires get warm and the air pressure in the tires increases.

Let us make a graph of the data in Table 4-3. The result shows another regularity of gas behavior. When pressure and temperature are plotted, the straight line in Figure 4-2 is obtained. The pressure of a gas, at constant volume, increases as the tempera-

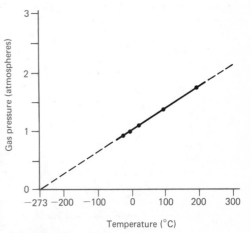

Figure 4-2
Pressure *vs.* temperature data for one mole of ammonia.

ture is increased. The mathematical equation that describes a straight-line graph is $y = mx + b$, where m and b are constants for any particular line. For our data we can write

$$P = mt + b$$

with P being the pressure in atmospheres and t being the temperature in degrees Celsius.

If we extend this line to higher temperatures, we see that the gas pressure at 273 °C is twice the gas pressure at 0 °C. On the other hand, extrapolation to lower temperatures suggests the surprising result that the gas pressure would become zero at −273 °C! (When we carry out the experiment of lowering the temperature of a gas more and more, we find the pressure does not go to zero. Before the temperature gets as low as −273 °C, gases liquefy and then change to solids.) The straight-line relation between P and t led scientists to wonder if there might not be a lowest possible temperature. This temperature would be really **zero, an absolute zero**. We can simplify the appearance of the equation that describes the pressure-temperature relation. Instead of assigning zero on the temperature scale to the temperature of melting ice (0 °C), let us assign zero to the temperature that would be needed to reduce the pressure of a gas to zero (−273 °C). This procedure establishes a new temperature scale, called the **absolute scale**. The temperature on this scale is indicated by K, kelvins. Scientists speak of temperature on the absolute scale as so many kelvins, not degrees kelvin. One degree on the Celsius scale is the same size as one kelvin on the absolute temperature scale. Temperatures on the two scales are related by the equation

$$T = t + 273$$

with T being kelvins and t being degrees on the Celsius scale.

The mathematical equation that describes the straight line in Figure 4-3 has the form

$$P = cT \quad \text{or} \quad \frac{P}{T} = c$$

where c is a proportionality constant. The regularity expressed in this equation can be stated in words:

> At constant volume the pressure of a gas is directly proportional to the absolute temperature (T).

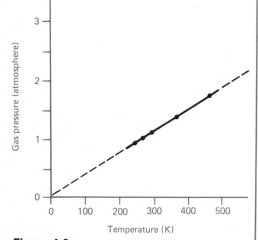

Figure 4-3
Pressure *vs.* temperature data for one mole of ammonia.

EXERCISE 4-2

Change the following temperatures from °C to kelvins.

a.   Standard room temperature, 25 °C.
b.   Normal boiling temperature of water, 100.0 °C.
c.   Boiling temperature of N_2, −196 °C.

d. Boiling temperature of O_2, $-183\,°C$.
e. Melting temperature of mercury, $-38.9\,°C$.
f. Melting temperature of pure aspirin, $135\,°C$.

4-4   Volume-Temperature Regularity

Figure 4-4 illustrates an experiment to measure changes in gas volume as the temperature is varied. A plug of mercury is supported by a sample of air in a long small-bore tube, closed at the bottom. The length of the air sample is a measure of the gas volume. As the temperature is changed, the mercury plug moves up or down, maintaining constant pressure. The gas volume increases as we increase the temperature. This is another important regularity for gases. All gases behave this way. Careful measurements of the molar volume of NH_3 gas at different temperatures are given in Table 4-4 and plotted in Figure 4-5. We would find similar values for one mole of any gas.

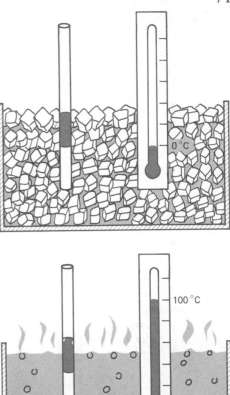

Table 4-4

Volume of One Mole of NH_3 at a
Constant Pressure of 1 Atmosphere

Temperature (°C)	Temperature (K)	Volume (liters)
−25	248	20.4
0	273	22.4
25	298	24.4
100	373	30.6
200	473	38.8

Figure 4-4
Apparatus for demonstrating the effect of temperature *on the volume of a gas.*

The straight line in Figure 4-5 can be expressed mathematically: $V = dT$, where d is a proportionality constant. At constant pressure the volume of gas is directly proportional to the absolute temperature, T. We have found another important regularity in gas behavior. That is

$$V = dT \quad \text{or} \quad \frac{V}{T} = d$$

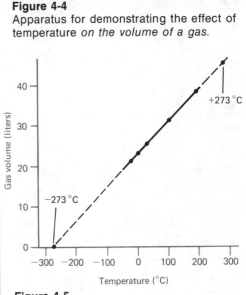

Figure 4-5
Volume *vs.* temperature data for one mole of ammonia.

4-5   The Meaning of Temperature

The equation $P = cT$ tells us that any factor that affects the pressure of gas must also affect the temperature of the gas as long as the volume is kept constant. Our ping-pong ball model will help us understand two factors that affect pressure.

Balloonists use heat to change gas density so that their hot-air balloons will float upward.

Temperature is a fundamental property used in many types of human activity. Doctors call it fever, jewelers and metallurgists measure it by the color of hot metal, and weathermen use it to help predict the weather.

Some wells at The Geysers geothermal field are being vented in some early testing. (California).

First, we can see that the velocity of a ping-pong ball determines the "push" in a collision. A fast-moving ping-pong ball exerts a much bigger "push" in a collision than a slow-moving ball would. Therefore, velocity of molecules is one factor that determines the pressure of a gas.

Second, let us include some solid ping-pong balls along with the usual hollow ones in our model. Now we would expect that the solid ping-pong ball would deliver a bigger "push" in a collision than would a hollow one moving at the same velocity. So the mass of a molecule is a second important factor determining the pressure of a gas. In the next paragraph we will discuss the way in which temperature is measured. We will then be able to understand how the mass and velocity of a molecule affect the pressure and temperature of a gas.

If someone asked you to measure the temperature of a gas, you would undoubtedly think first of using a thermometer. We can describe what is happening when we use the thermometer. If the thermometer is colder than the gas, heat energy flows into the thermometer until the gas and the thermometer are at the same temperature. We read the scale on the thermometer to determine what the gas temperature is. On the other hand, if the thermometer is hotter than the gas, heat energy would flow from the thermometer. When there is no net flow of heat energy, the gas and the thermometer are said to be in **thermal equilibrium**. They are at the same temperature.

There are many kinds of thermometers. Any substance can be used in a thermometer if it has some property that changes with temperature. The thermometer you use in the laboratory depends on the expansion or contraction of liquid mercury as the temperature is raised or lowered. Gas thermometers are often used in precise scientific measurements. Either a volume change (at constant gas pressure) or a pressure change (at constant gas volume) can serve as a basis for a gas thermometer.

Let us measure the temperature of gas A by placing it in thermal contact with a gas B, our thermometer. If A is initially at a higher temperature than B, heat energy flows from A to B. Our model of a gas helps us to understand what is happening. Molecules of gas A have higher energy than the molecules of gas B. Molecules of gas A collide with the wall separating the two gases. Some of their energy is transferred first to the wall and then to molecules of gas B on the other side of the wall. It is this transfer of energy which raises the temperature of gas B. At the same time the temperature of gas A goes down. It is as though molecules of gas A collide directly with molecules of gas B (the wall seems only to transfer energy). When the two gases are at the same temperature, no further net energy flow takes place. Thermal equilibrium exists.

It is easy to see that we are interested in the molecular motion that a molecule has as it moves about in space and up to the wall of the container. That kind of motion, moving up to a wall and bouncing off, is called **translation**. Later in this course we will see that there are several kinds of molecular motion: translation, vibration, and rotation. Right now we are interested only in translation.

The energy a molecule has because it is moving has been given the name **kinetic energy**. The kinetic energy (KE) associated with translation of a particle is related to its mass and to its velocity.

$$KE_{\text{translation}} = \frac{1}{2}mv^2$$

When a molecule of gas A is traveling with high velocity, it has high kinetic energy. If it transfers some of its energy through the wall to a molecule of gas B, two things must happen. The kinetic energy of gas B goes up and the kinetic energy of gas A goes down. The temperature of a gas must be directly related to the average translational kinetic energy of the gas. Two gases are at the same temperature when their average translational kinetic energies are equal.

Temperature is a measure of molecular translational energy.

EXERCISE 4-3

At a given temperature the average KE_{trans} of the molecules in two different gases will be the same. Using NH_3 and HCl as the two gases, explain why NH_3 molecules will have higher velocities than HCl molecules, on the average.

We can see that the absolute temperature scale has a new significance because of the relation between temperature and translational motion. The zero on the absolute scale is the temperature at which there is no longer any translational motion on the molecular level. This temperature is called **absolute zero**. Scientists have discovered methods to reach very low temperatures, within 10^{-6} kelvin of absolute zero.

Substances behave in unusual ways at very low temperatures. Investigations at temperatures within a few kelvins of absolute zero form one of the most exciting research areas in science today. It is easy to understand why. Until a substance reaches a very low temperature, the kinetic energy of molecular translation is often so great that it masks the energy effects of some other molecular behavior. Lowering the temperature of a substance minimizes the disturbances caused by molecular translation, making it possible to measure other effects.

Let us summarize what we have said so far by "going inside" our ping-pong ball model again. Remember that this means we get smaller by a factor of 5 000 000 000. As we stand on the bottom of the box, there would be molecules (ping-pong balls) flying around us. Some would move rather slowly past us. Others would really zing by. Naturally they would bump into each other, changing velocity and direction. Sometimes the collisions would be so violent that the molecules would break apart into atoms. What would happen if the temperature was slowly decreased to absolute zero? Gradually the motion of molecules would get less and less violent. There would be fewer and fewer molecules traveling at really high velocities. But occasionally a fast molecule would still move past us. As the temperature goes down, the molecular motion does too. Until, finally at absolute zero, there would be no

Writing with Gas Bubbles

Don't think $PV = constant$ is just part of the ancient history of chemistry and physics. It is the basis for a fast-growing modern method of duplication of printed material. This method uses a special film called *vesicular film*. A vesicle is a small cavity. An important feature of this method is that no silver is used, as in the usual photographic film. Silver prices are soaring today as it grows more scarce.

The basic principle is easy to illustrate. A layer of Mylar plastic film is coated with one or more layers of emulsion, much as photographic film is. But rather than containing silver salts, this emulsion has chemicals that react with light to release gas. These chemicals are called diazonium salts and contain the group —N≡N—. When this film is exposed to ultraviolet light, the diazonium salt breaks down and releases N_2 gas. The gas occurs as very tiny bubbles and at pressures greater than 1 atmosphere. At this stage there is no visible image. However, the emulsion is made so that the gas cannot leak out.

To develop the image, the film is heated to about 130 °C for a fraction of a second to soften the plastic. Here is where $PV = constant$ takes over. The high-pressure N_2 pushes back the soft plastic. The bubbles grow to about 0.001 millimeter in diameter. A single bubble does not scatter enough light for you to see; but when millions of them clump together, the cluster of bubbles does. The developed area appears opaque white. The foam on root beer or soapsuds in a bubble bath also appear white because light is scattered by thousands of tiny bubbles.

The method of duplication is quite fast. It is used for copying computer output, microfilms, and fingerprint records. Vesicular film copies can be made at 200 feet/minute. All this occurs because $PV = constant$. As the pressure goes down, the volume goes up.

On the average, the temperature increases about 1 degree Celsius for each 30 meters of descent into the Earth. At 6100 meters (20 000 ft) the temperature of one oil well was 168 °C.

Statisticians study distributions of all kinds—people, pollution, weather.

molecules moving at all. A very peaceful scene indeed! Now let's have the temperature go up again. The molecules go into action once more, slowly at first and then faster and faster. We would begin to see a range of velocities in molecular collisions. Some collisions are gentle bumps, but others are real tooth-rattlers. The collision energies are "distributed" over the energy scale just as velocities of molecules are.

4-6 Molecular Velocities

How fast do molecules move? Do all molecules in a sample of gas have the same velocity? At any instant some molecules will be colliding and others will be moving freely. We would expect a distribution of velocities with some high, some moderate, and some low values of velocity. A look at a familiar distribution may be helpful.

There probably are a few students in a typical chemistry class who are very tall. A few of the students are very short. Most students are intermediate in height. Let's count the number of students in each two-inch height interval. The graph in Figure 4-6 shows that there is quite a range of heights, from 4 feet 8 inches to 6 feet 3 inches. The students in the class are "distributed" over this height range. The bars drawn in this figure indicate the distribution of student heights.

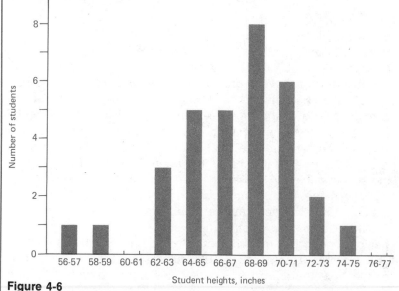

Figure 4-6
Distribution of student heights.

What is the distribution of molecular velocity in a sample of gas? The experiment illustrated in Figure 4-7 will provide the answer to this question. Two discs are fixed on the same axle and rotate rapidly. These discs are in a chamber evacuated to a low pressure so that molecules can move a long way before colliding with another molecule. The discs rotate in front of an oven containing molten tin. Some tin vaporizes and streams out of the small opening in the oven, striking the first rotating disc which acts as a

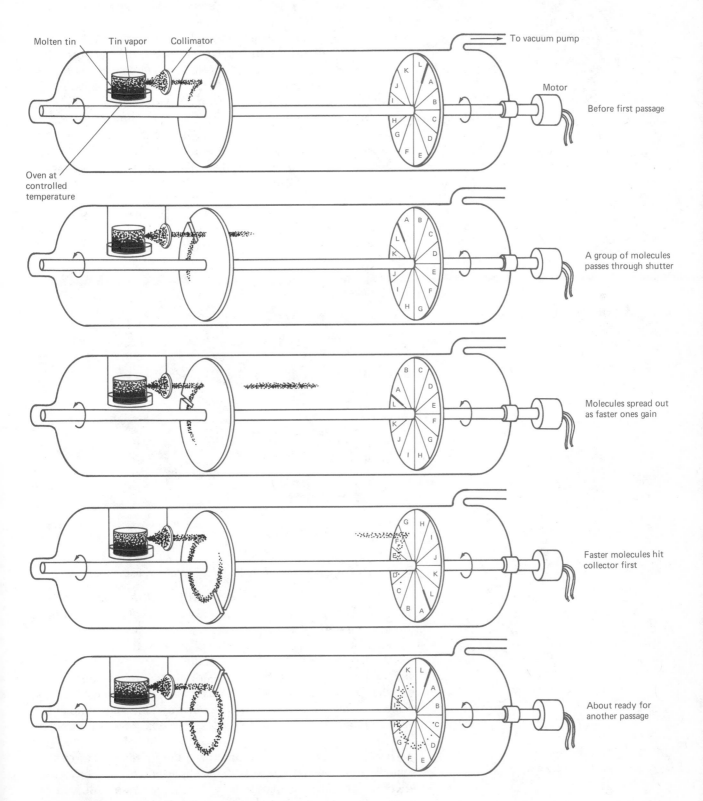

Figure 4-7
Rotating discs for measurement of molecular velocities.

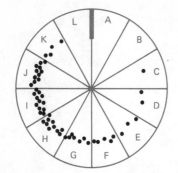

Figure 4-8
Schematic representation of
collector after many revolutions.

shutter. Once during every rotation the slot in this disc is in line with the hole of the oven. Then a small sample of tin molecules can pass through the slot and move on toward the collector. The faster-moving molecules lead the way. Slower-moving molecules begin to lag behind. As the molecules reach the collector, they condense on it. Since this disc also is rotating, fast-moving molecules would condense on sections *C*, *D*, and *E*. Slow-moving molecules take a longer time to reach the collector. The speed of the rotating discs is adjusted so that the slowest molecules condense on sections *I*, *J*, and *K*. Many different groups of tin molecules pass through the shutter each second. Soon a layer of metallic tin builds up on the collector. The amount of tin in each of the sections, *A* through *L*, can be determined. The results of such an experiment are shown in Figure 4-8. The largest amount of tin is found in section *I*. In our illustrative experiment no tin is deposited on the first or last sections, *A* and *L*. From such a disc the distribution curve shown in Figure 4-9 can be derived.

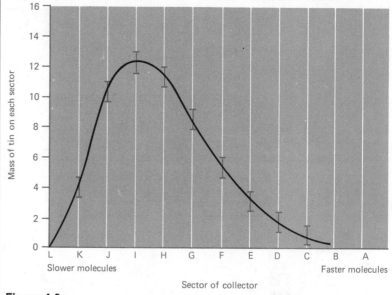

Figure 4-9
Distribution of molecular velocities from rotating disc experiment.

More information can be extracted from the experiment. We can calculate approximately what velocity a molecule must have to condense on a particular section of the collector. To do this, we must know how far apart the discs are and how fast they rotate. Now we can plot the molecular velocity rather than the section letter on the *x*-axis. The distribution curve we obtain tells us what fraction of the tin molecules have a particular velocity. A few molecules have very high velocities. A few molecules have very low velocities. Most molecules in a gas have intermediate velocities.

This experiment can be repeated at different temperatures. The results are shown in Figure 4-10 for 500 K and for 1500 K. At the lower temperature the distribution of molecular velocities is rather narrow. Not many molecules have high velocities. As the temperature is increased, more molecules move with high velocity. The distribution curve flattens out. We see that there are always some slow-moving molecules at any temperature. The distribution curves show that there is a smaller fraction of slow-moving molecules at 1500 K than at 500 K. At the same time the curves show that there is a larger fraction of fast-moving molecules at the higher temperature. From experiments like this we can get an idea of how fast molecules move. The peaks in the distribution curves tell us that the largest fraction of tin molecules have velocities of about 3×10^4 cm/s at 500 K and about 5×10^4 cm/s at 1500 K. Table 4-5 gives some numerical values of molecular velocities for several gases at different temperatures.

Sound Equals Pressure Change

Sound is perhaps the easiest sense to discuss. We hear by means of a device that detects pressure pulses. Intelligible sound frequently comes from a vibrating source: a guitar string, a trumpet player's lips, a clarinet reed, our vocal cords, or the column of air in an organ pipe. The vibration sets up a series of alternately higher and lower pressure regions in air. This pattern is transmitted through the air, but the air itself does not move from the source to the ear. These moving series of compressions strike our eardrum and cause it to vibrate. The three bones of the middle ear magnify the vibrations and transmit them to the cochlea, where the vibrations are converted into nerve impulses. Nerve cells carry the impulses to the brain for recognition. The ear is not only an extremely sensitive energy detector, but it can tolerate a wide range of energy. An impulse caused by as little as 10^{-18} calorie can be "heard." Up to 10^{12} times this minimum amount can be tolerated without pain. A balance with this range could weigh from one-millionth of a gram to one million grams (over a ton).

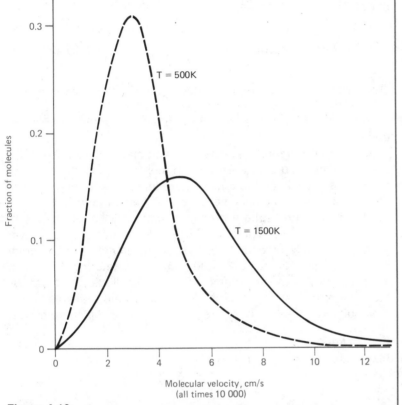

Figure 4-10
Molecular velocity distribution for tin at two temperatures.

TABLE 4-5
Molecular Velocities

Molecule	Temperature (K)	Most Common Velocity (cm/s)
H_2	273	18×10^4 (about 1 mi/s)
H_2	1500	42×10^4
NH_3	273	7.2×10^4
O_2	273	4.5×10^4
Sn	500	3×10^4 (about 1/6 mi/s)
Sn	1500	5×10^4
Escape velocity from Earth's gravitational field		(about 7 mi/s)
Jet airplane at 600 mi/h		(about 1/6 mi/s)

4-7 The Distance Between Molecules

We will conclude the discussion of the gas phase by considering the average distance between molecules. We can get an approximate idea of what these distances are by comparing the molar volume of ammonia in the solid, liquid, and gaseous states. Compare the volume of 17 grams of ammonia as a solid, liquid, and gas.

At $-79\,°C$ ammonia is a solid with a density of 0.81 gram per cubic centimeter. This means one mole would have a volume of about 21 cubic centimeters:

$$\text{Volume} = 17 \text{ grams } \text{NH}_3 \times \frac{1 \text{ cm}^3}{0.81 \text{ gram } \text{NH}_3} = 21 \text{ cm}^3$$

Just below the boiling temperature, $-33\,°C$, liquid ammonia has a density of 0.68 gram per cubic centimeter. The volume of 17 grams of liquid ammonia at this temperature is about 25 cubic centimeters.

Above the temperature $-33\,°C$ ammonia is a gas. We know that the temperature and pressure influence the volume of a gas, so we must decide on the temperature and pressure at which the density of ammonia gas is measured. At the standard conditions of $0\,°C$ and 1 atmosphere pressure, ammonia has a density of 7.7×10^{-4} gram per cubic centimeter. This value is much lower than the density of either solid or liquid ammonia. The molar volume of ammonia gas is 22 400 cubic centimeters at STP. Now if we divide the molar volume of the solid, liquid, and gas by 6.0×10^{23}, we can get an estimate of the volume available to one molecule. Table 4-6 summarizes the values for the three states.

Calculation of the molar volume of NH_3:

$$\frac{17.0 \text{ g}}{1.0 \text{ mol}} \times \frac{1 \text{ cm}^3}{0.81 \text{ g}} = 21 \frac{\text{cm}^3}{\text{mol}}$$

TABLE 4-6
Molar and Molecular Volumes of Ammonia

State	Density (g/cm³)	Molar Volume (cm³)	Volume Available per Molecule (cm³)
Solid	0.81	21	35×10^{-24}
Liquid	0.68	25	41×10^{-24}
Gas (at 0 °C, 1 atm)	0.000 77	22 400	$37\,000 \times 10^{-24}$

The volume available to a molecule in a gas is much greater than the volume of a molecule in either the solid or the liquid state. There is about 1000 times more space available for the molecule in the gaseous state. The molecule does not fill this space but moves about freely in it. We can understand now why it is easy to compress a gas and why it is very difficult to compress solids or liquids. A gas sample contains a great deal of space between molecules.

EXERCISE 4-4

Explain the experimental observation that diffusion occurs much more rapidly in a gas than in a solid or a liquid.

The numbers in Table 4-6 allow us to make another calculation that will give an idea of how far apart molecules are. Suppose we have a mole of ammonia in a cubical box and each molecule has a very small cube in which it moves. The numbers in the last column of Table 4-6 can be used to find the size of the small cube that each molecule occupies. The length of the side of a cube is related to volume by the equation

$$(length)^3 = volume$$

The lengths we calculate tell us approximately the distances between molecules in the solid, liquid, or gas:

Solid   length = 3.2 $\times$ 10^{-8} cm
Liquid   length = 3.4 $\times$ 10^{-8} cm
Gas   length = 33 $\times$ 10^{-8} cm

These numbers indicate that molecules in a solid or liquid are about the same distance apart. But molecules in a gas are about ten times as far from each other. A gas is "empty" when compared to a liquid or solid.

Pressures as low as 10^{-10} mmHg have been maintained in large containers (1500 liters) for several months. At this pressure a molecule travels about 2500 kilometers between collisions with other gas molecules.

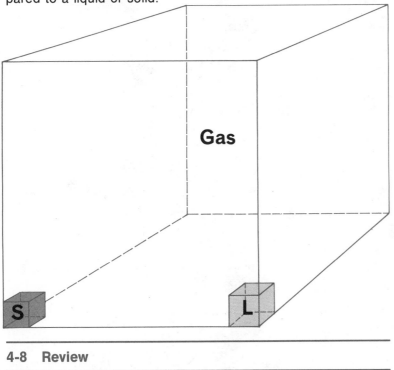

4-8   Review

We have seen our model for a gas grow as we carried out more experiments. The original suggestion that a gas might be compared with a group of ping-pong balls shaken in a box has proved very useful. Using this model, we can understand the regularities in the behavior of a gas.

Concentration of Atoms
(atoms/liter)

Average value
for outer space   100
Interstellar clouds   100 000
Best laboratory vacuum   3 600 000
Air at sea level 2.4×10^{22}

At constant temperature, $PV =$ (a constant) $= a$
At constant volume, $\quad P =$ (a second constant) $\times (T) = cT$
At constant pressure, $\quad V =$ (a third constant) $\times (T) \quad = dT$

Let us summarize the nature of a gas. In the next chapter we will see how these ideas can be extended to liquids and solids.

(a) A gas is made up of very small particles called *molecules*.
(b) Molecules in a gas have a range of velocities at any particular temperature. Some molecules have low velocity. Some molecules have very high velocity. *Average velocity* increases with temperature.
(c) Molecules collide with each other many times each second. We associate the pressure exerted by a gas with the collisions molecules make with the walls of their container.
(d) The volume of the molecules is small compared to the volume of the container except at extremely high gas pressures.
(e) The *absolute temperature* of the gas is a measure of the average kinetic energy of the molecules.

Table 4-7 summarizes some of the numerical values for a typical gas, NH_3.

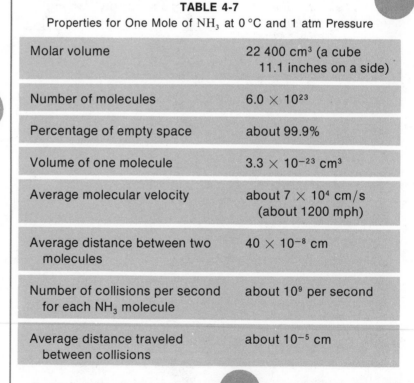

TABLE 4-7
Properties for One Mole of NH_3 at 0 °C and 1 atm Pressure

Molar volume	22 400 cm³ (a cube 11.1 inches on a side)
Number of molecules	6.0×10^{23}
Percentage of empty space	about 99.9%
Volume of one molecule	3.3×10^{-23} cm³
Average molecular velocity	about 7×10^4 cm/s (about 1200 mph)
Average distance between two molecules	40×10^{-8} cm
Number of collisions per second for each NH_3 molecule	about 10^9 per second
Average distance traveled between collisions	about 10^{-5} cm

A liquid and a gas at the same temperature will have the same distribution of molecular velocities. The difference is not in speed, it is in freedom of motion.

An idea of the distance between molecules in a gas is given by the circles on these pages. They represent ammonia molecules (about 4×10^{-8} cm across) separated by approximately 40×10^{-8} cm. Both dimensions are drawn 25 000 000 times larger than actual.

1

A sample of nitrogen gas is collected over water at 18.5 °C. The vapor pressure of water at 18.5 °C is 16 mmHg. What are the partial pressures of nitrogen and of water if the total pressure is 745 mmHg?

2

A student collects a volume of hydrogen gas over water. He determines that there is 2.00×10^{-3} mole of hydrogen and 6.0×10^{-5} mole of water vapor present. If the total pressure inside the collecting tube is 760 mmHg, what is the partial pressure of each gas?

3

A cylinder contains nitrogen gas and a small amount of liquid water at 25 °C. The vapor pressure of water at 25 °C is 23.8 mmHg. The total pressure is 600 mmHg. A piston is pushed into the cylinder until the volume is halved. What is the final total pressure?

Answer: 1176 mmHg.

4

What will be the pressure if we open:

(a) just valve A?
(b) just valve B?
(c) just valve C?
(d) any two valves?

5

A two-liter vessel contains gas at 0.8 atmosphere. If 400 ml of mercury is injected into the vessel, what is the pressure? There is no evidence of a chemical reaction.

6

Compressed oxygen gas is sold at a pressure of 130 atmospheres in steel cylinders of 40 liters volume. (Assume 25 °C.)

(a) How many moles of oxygen are in one of these cylinders?
(b) How many kilograms of oxygen are in one of these cylinders?

7

A 2.50-liter sample of dry air in a cylinder exerts a pressure of 3.00 atmospheres at 25 °C. Without change in temperature, a piston is moved until the pressure in the cylinder is reduced to 1.00 atmosphere. What is the volume of the gas?

8

In the reaction $NH_3 + O_2$ gives $NO + H_2O$, how many liters of oxygen are required to react with 4.48 liters of ammonia? All gases are measured at STP.

9

How many molecules are there in a molar volume of gas at 100 °C? At 0 °C?

10

The following reaction is carried out with all gas volumes measured at the same temperature and pressure:

$$C_4H_{10} + O_2 \text{ gives } CO_2 + H_2O$$

(a) How many liters of oxygen are required to produce 2.0 liters of CO_2?
(b) If 15 liters of oxygen are used, how many liters of butane, C_4H_{10}, will be burned?
(c) If 8.0 liters each of oxygen and butane are available for reaction, how many liters of CO_2 are produced?

11

A reaction involved in the production of iron from iron ore is:

$$Fe_2O_3 + CO \text{ gives } Fe + CO_2$$

(a) How many grams of CO are needed to produce 1.0×10^3 grams of Fe?
(b) How many liters of CO (at STP) are needed to produce 1.0×10^3 grams of Fe?

12

A gas mixture contains 20% CO, 60% CO_2, and 20% H_2 by volume. Consider a sample occupying 6.1 liters at 25 °C and 4 atmospheres pressure.

(a) How many moles of each gas are present?
(b) What is the percent of H_2 by mass which is present?

13

How many liters of air at STP are needed to burn 2.2 liters of methane, which is also at STP? Assume air is 20% oxygen by volume.

14

Kerosene is a mixture of hydrocarbons. A stove might burn 1.0 kg of kerosene per hour. Assume kerosene is the pure hydrocarbon decane, $C_{10}H_{22}$.

(a) How many liters of oxygen gas at STP are needed per hour?
(b) How many liters of carbon dioxide at STP are produced per hour?

15

How many grams of zinc metal are needed to react with hydrochloric acid to produce enough hydrogen gas to fill an 11.2-liter balloon at STP? What would the volume of this balloon be at 27 °C and 680 mmHg pressure? How many grams of zinc would be required if sulfuric acid were used instead of hydrochloric acid?

16

Imagine a 2.24-liter volume containing 0.1 mole of gas at STP. What would happen if the following changes were made on such a system?

(a) Double the pressure by changing volume.
(b) Double the absolute temperature.
(c) Double the mass of gas.

17

Surface conditions on Earth and Mars are

Earth	23 °C	760 mmHg
Mars	−23 °C	4.0 mmHg

Compare molar volumes of gas under each of these conditions.

18

What volume of Cl_2 gas at 37 °C and 753 mmHg pressure could be obtained from 58.4 liters of HCl, measured at the same temperature and pressure, if the following reaction takes place?

$$HCl + O_2 \text{ gives } H_2O + Cl_2$$

19

Suppose 105 liters of NH_3 and 285 liters of O_2 are allowed to react until this reaction is complete.

$$NH_3 + O_2 \text{ gives } H_2O + NO_2$$

All volume measurements are made at 200 °C and 0.30 atm pressure. Which gas, ammonia or oxygen, remains at the end of the reaction? How many moles of it would there be?

20

Combustion of gasoline, typical formula C_8H_{18}, provides the energy to propel an automobile. As the gasoline burns in the car cylinder, the pressure increases and forces the piston down. This motion in turn is transmitted to the wheels of the car. Oxygen reacts with the gasoline to form carbon dioxide and water, releasing enough energy to heat the gas from 300 K to about 1500 K.

(a) Write a balanced equation for the reaction.
(b) Decide whether the work done by the gas in the cylinder is mainly the result of pressure rise caused by the change in number of moles of gas or the result of pressure rise from heating.

21

A gas phase reaction between methane, CH_4, and oxygen, O_2, is carried out in a sealed container. Under the conditions used, the products are carbon dioxide and hydrogen. The reaction is exothermic, so the temperature rises during the reaction.

(a) Will the final pressure be greater or less than the original pressure?
(b) By what factor does the pressure change if one mole of methane and one mole of oxygen react (the temperature changes from 25 °C to 200 °C)?

Answer: 2.38.

22

A carbon dioxide fire extinguisher of 3 liters volume contains 4.4 kilograms of CO_2. What volume of gas could this extinguisher deliver at 25 °C and one atm pressure?

23

What is the molar mass of a gas if 1.00 liter of the gas weighs 2.00 grams at 0 °C and one atmosphere pressure?

24

Hydrogen for weather balloons is often supplied by the reaction between solid calcium hydride, CaH_2, and water to form solid calcium hydroxide, $Ca(OH)_2$, and hydrogen gas.

(a) Write a balanced equation for the reaction between water and calcium hydride.
(b) How many moles of CaH_2 would be required to fill a weather balloon with 250 liters of hydrogen at 25 °C and one atm pressure?
(c) What mass of water would be required to generate the hydrogen?

25

Why is it desirable to express all temperatures in kelvins when working problems dealing with gases?

26

The boiling and freezing temperatures of some pure liquids are listed below. Express these temperatures on the absolute temperature scale.

Liquid	F.T.	B.T.
Helium		$-269\,°C$
Hydrogen	$-259\,°C$	$-253\,°C$
Nitrogen	$-210\,°C$	$-196\,°C$
Oxygen	$-219\,°C$	$-183\,°C$
Hexane		$69\,°C$
Ethanol		$78.5\,°C$

27

If 1.00×10^2 ml of a gas at $10\,°C$ are heated to $20\,°C$, the volume of the gas will be approximately: (Pressure and number of molecules are kept constant.)

(a) 50 ml
(b) 100 ml
(c) 103 ml
(d) 200 ml
(e) 375 ml

28

Calculate the density of ammonia at 546 K.

29

Explain how a hot-air balloon works.

30

If a hot-air balloon has a volume of 224 000 liters and the average gas temperature is $100\,°C$, what total mass could be lifted on a winter day when the air temperature is $0\,°C$? Use 29 grams as the molar mass of air.

31

The temperatures of Venus and Jupiter are $480\,°C$ and $-150\,°C$ at the surface, which is visible to us with a telescope. Compare molar volumes on these planets if the pressure were 1 atmosphere (Earth).

32

Suppose steam begins to flow through a cold, bare steel pipe. After a while the pipe will be warm, then too hot to touch. Describe what happens to the atoms in the steel pipe.

33

A chemist collects two samples of N_2. One is pure and occupies 1.0 liter at 1 atm and $60\,°C$. The other sample is 1.1 liters and has water vapor in it (26 mmHg); the sample is at $27\,°C$ and 750 mmHg. Which sample has the greater mass of N_2 present?

34

Suppose the total pressure in an automobile tire is 30 pounds/inch^2 and we want to increase the pressure to 40 pounds/inch^2. What change in the amount of air in the tire must take place? Assume that the temperature and volume of the tire remain constant.

35

Why does the pressure build up in a tire on a hot day? Answer in terms of the kinetic theory.

36

Two glass containers have the same volume. One is filled with hydrogen gas, the other with carbon dioxide gas. Both containers are at the same temperature and pressure.

(a) Compare the number of moles of the two gases.
(b) Compare the number of molecules of the two gases.
(c) Compare the number of grams of the two gases.
(d) The temperature of the container of hydrogen gas is increased. Now compare the pressure, the volume, the number of moles, and the average molecular kinetic energy.

37

A vessel contains equal numbers of oxygen and hydrogen molecules. The pressure is 760 mmHg when the volume is 50 liters. Which of these statements is FALSE?

(a) On the average, the hydrogen molecules are traveling faster than the oxygen molecules.
(b) On the average, more hydrogen molecules strike the walls per second than oxygen molecules.
(c) If the oxygen were removed from the system, the pressure would drop to 190 mmHg.
(d) Equal numbers of moles of each gas are present.
(e) The average kinetic energies of oxygen and hydrogen molecules are the same.

Liquids and Solids: An Extension of the Kinetic Theory

Most of the things we encounter daily are solids. Some are liquids and a very few are gases. Air, carbon dioxide (in soft drinks), and the gas for stoves or Bunsen burners are the most commonly used gases. The number of different liquids is somewhat greater. For example: water, milk, ink, body fluids, gasoline, glue, paint, and oil are all liquids. But the number of solids we see daily is huge. In this chapter we will apply the kinetic theory to solids and liquids.

In the last chapter we proposed that the molecules in liquids and solids are very close together, whereas molecules in a gas are relatively far apart. Remember that one mole of water, 6.0×10^{23} molecules, occupies only 18 milliliters as a liquid. The same number of molecules for a gas at STP would occupy a volume about a thousand times greater. When the temperature is decreased, the molecules slow down and a gas condenses to a liquid. Formation of dew on the grass and condensation of hot shower vapor on the mirror are familiar examples of the gas-to-liquid **phase change**. In liquids, molecules are close to each other. However, they still have enough energy to move in a random fashion in the liquid phase. When the temperature of a liquid is lowered, the average kinetic energy decreases further. If enough energy is removed, a solid will form. The molecules in the solid take up the regular positions characteristic of a crystalline solid. Water freezing to ice is an example of the liquid-to-solid phase change.

Chemists are interested in phase changes for many reasons. If a substance can be vaporized, measurement of the gas volume provides a way to calculate the molar mass for the substance. The melting temperature of a substance often helps the chemist identify it or estimate its purity. Phase changes serve as relatively simple methods to separate one substance from another. The energy involved in phase changes may provide an important method of storing solar energy.

In this chapter phase changes of pure substances will be discussed. We have already discussed kinetic energy. Potential energy is important too. Let us see what scientists mean when they use the term *potential energy*.

5-1 Potential Energy

Which has more energy, a brick 1 ft up in the air or the same brick 6 ft up? If you drop each one on your foot, the answer would be all too obvious! Let us do a more careful experiment than that. Suppose we have two carts on the hills shown in Figure 5-1. When we move the carts over the edge of the plateau, they start to roll downhill. The carts gain kinetic energy. As you can tell from the illustration, cart 1 will acquire more kinetic energy than cart 2. Cart 1 moves faster and rolls farther than cart 2. But where does this energy come from?

Work must be done at the start of the experiment to raise the two carts to the tops of the hills. Energy is needed to do that work. Apparently this energy is "stored" in the carts until we let them roll back downhill. The energy is released as the carts move. The term **potential energy** is used to describe energy stored in this fashion.

Another experiment will help us understand potential energy. Suppose that we push the cart shown in Figure 5-2. The cart moves with constant speed toward a spring which is firmly attached to a very thick wall. The problem is simplified if we make two assumptions. First, there is no friction on this table and second, the wall is so massive that it does not move during the experiment. The cart moves in a straight line until it hits the spring. The cart slows down rapidly as the spring is compressed. For an instant there is no motion in the cart or the spring. Then everything reverses. The spring expands. The cart rebounds in the opposite direction, regaining its original speed.

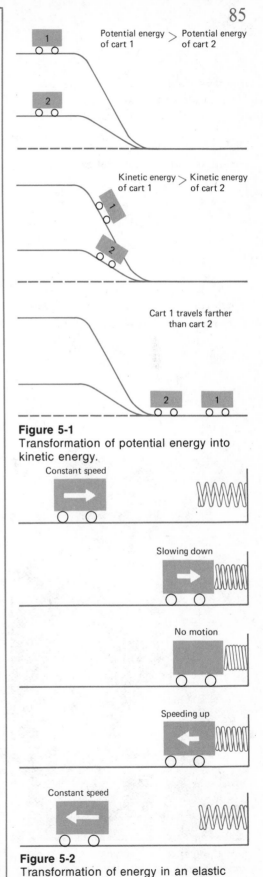

Figure 5-1
Transformation of potential energy into kinetic energy.

Figure 5-2
Transformation of energy in an elastic collision.

Energy—a much used word in recent years—stands for a concept that is not very old. It was introduced in 1808 but caught on slowly. The term *potential energy* was not invented until 1853 and *kinetic energy* not until 1867.

Engineers are interested in phase properties and phase changes. One problem in getting the energy from coal or oil shale is the difficulty of moving solids through a treatment plant.

Look only at the cart for a minute. It starts with a certain amount of kinetic energy. This energy disappears as the cart compresses the spring and comes to a stop. Then the cart gains back its original kinetic energy as it moves in the opposite direction. What can we say about energy changes in this experiment? Initially, the kinetic energy of the moving cart is some constant quantity, A. During the collision with the spring the cart rapidly slows down. The kinetic energy of the cart decreases from A to a to *zero* at the moment the spring is compressed its maximum amount. The original kinetic energy is stored as potential energy. Then everything operates in reverse. The spring expands; the cart moves in the opposite direction. The kinetic energy of the cart changes from *zero* to a and then to A, its original kinetic energy. Energy is being transformed from one type to another.

Figure 5-2 illustrates what happens at different times during the collision. We can represent the energy changes in this manner:

	Kinetic Energy of Cart	+	Potential Energy of Spring*	=	Total Energy of System
Initial constant speed	A	+	0	=	A
Cart slowing down	a	+	b	=	A
No motion	0	+	A	=	A
Cart speeding up	a	+	b	=	A
Final constant speed	A	+	0	=	A

*We neglect the very small kinetic energy of the spring as it is compressed or extended.

The cart striking the spring is similar to a molecule rebounding from a wall. As long as the wall does not move, the molecule rebounds with its original kinetic energy. We will encounter both kinetic energy and potential energy many times in this course. Now we want to find out how potential energy can help us understand phase changes.

5-2 Solid-Liquid Phase Changes

Solids and liquids are called **condensed phases**. You know that water molecules stick to each other fairly well in the liquid or solid phases. When you pour water from a pitcher, most of the molecules stay together and flow in a thin stream of liquid. And in an ice cube the water molecules are even more tightly bound to each other even though the density of ice is less than that of liquid water.

When the molecules in a solid are arranged in an orderly repeating pattern, we use the word **crystalline** to describe the solid. What happens when we add energy to a solid? At any temperature above 0 kelvin there is always some molecular motion in a crystal. The molecules move, to a slight extent, back and forth about their positions in the crystal. As energy is added to a solid, the temperature and the motion increase. When the temperature gets high

Liquid metal is being poured into a mold, where it will freeze into the desired shape.

Solid-Liquid Phase Changes

enough, the molecular motion disturbs the regular crystal pattern more and more. The solid melts.

$$H_2O \text{ (solid)} + \text{energy} \longrightarrow H_2O \text{ (liquid)}$$

or more simply $\quad H_2O(s) + \text{energy} \longrightarrow H_2O(l)$

In Experiment 13 you and your classmates determined the melting curve for several different pure substances. Similar diagrams would be found for other pure solids. The melting curve for water is shown in Figure 5-3. We can see that something unusual is happening during the melting of the solid phase. Even though we continue to add energy to the system, the temperature stays constant from the time the liquid appears until all the solid has melted. *This temperature is called the* **melting temperature** *of the solid.*

Foundrymen, jewelers, tinsmiths, electronic technicians, and many craftsmen must understand melting behavior in casting, plating, and soldering.

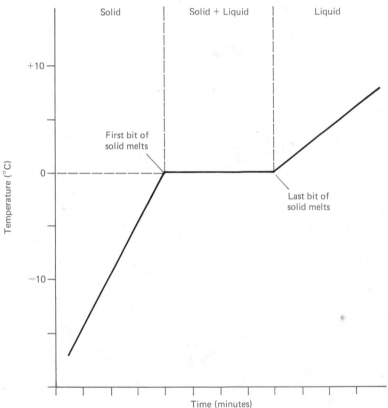

Figure 5-3
Phase change $H_2O(s) + \text{heat} \longrightarrow H_2O(l)$. Heat energy is being added slowly at a constant rate.

Where does the energy go? During the melting process the temperature of the liquid phase is the same as the temperature of the solid phase. The energy we supply is not increasing the temperature of either phase. This energy destroys the crystal lattice and is stored in the liquid phase as potential energy.

The amount of energy required to melt one mole of ice at 0 °C is known from experiments. We can show it in the equation

$$H_2O(s) + 1.44 \text{ kcal} \longrightarrow H_2O(l)$$

Water is present in all three phases.

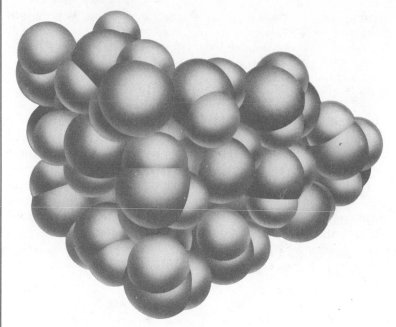

Liquid water lacks regular structure.

Few liquids expand on freezing. Water is one. A melted alloy of Pb, Sb, Sn, and Cu, called type metal, is another. This property causes the freezing alloy to fill the mold, forming a well-defined letter that prints a sharp image.

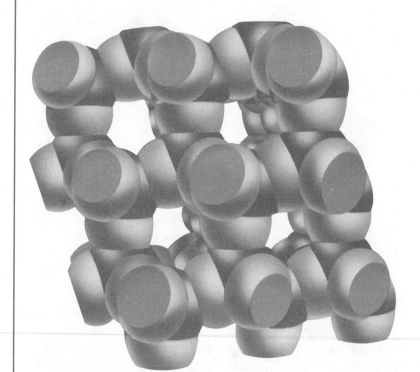

The crystal structure of ice.

This amount of energy is called the **molar heat of melting** or the **molar heat of fusion**. This is the energy required to overcome part of the forces that hold 6.0×10^{23} water molecules in their regular positions in the crystal. Heat is given back when the liquid changes to solid.

When we look at the different substances in Table 5-1, we find a range of energy values for molar heats of melting. In these examples the values vary from 0.080 kcal/mol for neon to 6.8 kcal/mol for sodium chloride, a change by a factor of 85. We interpret this large range to mean there are great differences in the forces that hold the particles together within these solids. These forces are important because they affect many properties of solids.

Table 5-1
The Temperature and Heat of Melting for
Some Pure Substances

	Melting Temperature		Molar Heat of Melting (kcal/mol)
Substance	K	°C	
Neon, Ne	24.6	−248.4	0.080
Chlorine, Cl_2	172	−101	1.53
Water, H_2O	273	0	1.44
Sodium, Na	371	98	0.63
Sodium chloride, NaCl	1081	808	6.8
Copper, Cu	1356	1083	3.11

5-3 Liquid-Gas Phase Change

We can continue to add energy to our sample of liquid water. The temperature rises. Molecules in the liquid acquire higher kinetic energy. Soon the water boils. The temperature stays constant as long as liquid water remains. We call this temperature the **boiling temperature** of the liquid.

$$H_2O \text{ (liquid)} + \text{energy} \longrightarrow H_2O \text{ (gas)}$$

or

$$H_2O(l) + \text{energy} \longrightarrow H_2O(g)$$

We can see in Figure 5-4 that addition of energy at 100 °C does not

Refrigeration engineers and air conditioning repairmen need to know about the liquid-gas phase changes used to transfer heat from one space to another.

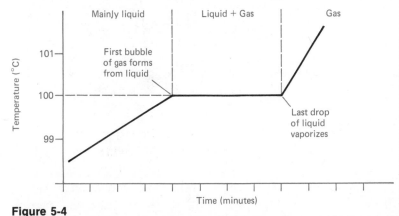

Figure 5-4
Phase change $H_2O(l) + \text{heat} \longrightarrow H_2O(g)$. Heat energy is being added slowly at a constant rate.

increase the temperature in our system as long as both liquid and vapor are present. The temperature of a system is directly related to the kinetic energy of the particles present. Since the temperature of both gas and liquid is 100 °C, the average kinetic energy of the molecules in both phases must be the same. The kinetic energy added to the liquid water during boiling causes the molecules to separate from each other. It is stored as potential energy in the separated gas molecules. Remember, potential energy is energy due to position of molecules. The **molar heat of vaporization** for water at 100 °C is 9.7 kilocalories.

$$H_2O(l) + 9.7 \text{ kcal} \longrightarrow H_2O(g)$$

When water vapor condenses to liquid water, the potential energy is released in the form of heat energy.

$$H_2O(g) \longrightarrow H_2O(l) + 9.7 \text{ kcal}$$

This phase change takes place when raindrops form. Just think of the energy that is released during a severe rainstorm!

EXERCISE 5-1

Calculate approximately how much energy is released when there is 1 cm of rain over an area of 10^{11} cm^2 (about 100 square miles). The density of water is 1 g/cm^3.

Answer. 5.4×10^{10} kcal

The boiling temperature and heat of vaporization for various liquids are given in Table 5-2. Again we find a wide range of energy values. In each example energy is absorbed as the liquid vaporizes.

Table 5-2
The Normal Boiling Temperature and Heat of Vaporization of Some Pure Substances

Substance	Boiling Temperature		Molar Heat of Vaporization (kcal/mol)
	K	°C	
Neon, Ne	27.2	−245.8	0.405
Chlorine, Cl$_2$	238.9	−34.1	4.88
Water, H$_2$O	373	100	9.7
Sodium, Na	1162	889	24.1
Sodium chloride, NaCl	1738	1465	40.8
Copper, Cu	2855	2582	72.8

Chemicals called *fatty alcohols*—for example, $C_{16}H_{33}OH$—spread as a thin film on water. A film only 5×10^{-7} cm (2×10^{-7} inches) thick can cut evaporation losses by 80 percent.

5-4   Vapor Pressure in Liquid-Vapor Equilibrium

The kinetic theory helps us understand the vaporization of a liquid at its boiling temperature. But liquids vaporize at all temperatures. Let us consider this behavior, beginning with liquid water again. If we place liquid water in an evacuated flask at 25 °C and close off the flask, we can measure the gas pressure with a manometer. The gas pressure rises rapidly from 0 mmHg to 23.8 mmHg. Then no further pressure change occurs as long as the temperature is kept at 25 °C. How can we interpret this experiment?

Water is the only substance in the flask. Some water molecules must leave the liquid phase and enter the vapor phase to account for the gas pressure. This explanation seems quite reasonable. Some molecules, near the surface of the liquid, would have enough energy to overcome attractions of nearby molecules and to move out of the liquid into the vapor phase. As the number of molecules in the vapor phase increases, the gas pressure rises. After a while the gas pressure reaches a constant value, 23.8 mmHg. Does this mean that water molecules no longer leave the liquid? This suggestion does not seem very reasonable. After all, there are still many molecules in the liquid moving with high velocities. If we look at the vapor phase, we know that the gas molecules are moving in a random fashion with many velocities. The distribution of velocities is the same in the gas and liquid phases, since the temperature is the same. Some gas molecules will return to the liquid. We can understand now why the gas pressure becomes constant. Molecules leave the liquid phase to enter the vapor. At the same time molecules leave the vapor phase to become part of the liquid again. Figure 5-5 shows what is happening. At first there are many more molecules leaving the liquid each second than are returning. The gas pressure goes up. The number of molecules in the vapor phase increases. The chance that a molecule will move back into the liquid phase also increases. Soon the two processes balance each other. The pressure stays constant. This pressure is called the **vapor pressure of water**. It remains at 23.8 mmHg as long as the temperature is kept at 25 °C. To give you some idea of the frenzied activity at the surface of a liquid when it evaporates, do Exercise 5-2.

Vapor pressure is an important factor in the cycle that moves water about the Earth. The sun distills vapor out of the oceans, clouds form, and the water is brought to Earth again. The drying of paint, ink, and glue depends on the vapor pressure of water—as does the preservation of food by drying. The control of body temperature is achieved in part by evaporation of water.

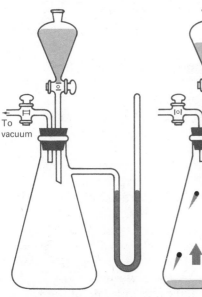

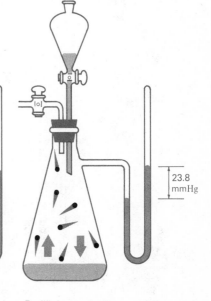

Evacuated   Water being added   Approaching equilibrium   Equilibrium attained

Figure 5-5
Equilibrium between liquid and vapor. Water at 25 °C.

92

Liquid water is constantly changing into water vapor, and vapor into liquid.

EXERCISE 5-2

Suppose one mole of water evaporates in one day. Approximately how many molecules leave the liquid each second?

The vapor pressure of a liquid is the same whether or not other gases are present. It is a property of the liquid. In our experiment, if the flask originally contained dry air at a pressure of 750.0 mmHg, liquid would evaporate until the pressure became 773.8 mmHg.

When a liquid is in contact with its vapor at a constant pressure, the liquid and gas are said to be in equilibrium.

This pressure is called the **vapor pressure** of the liquid.

At equilibrium, no measurable changes are taking place.

5-5 Change of Vapor Pressure with Temperature

The vapor pressure of water at 25 °C is 23.8 mmHg. At 40 °C the vapor pressure is 55.3 mmHg, as shown in Figure 5-6. At 60 °C it is 149.4 mmHg, and at 100 °C it is 760 mmHg. The vapor pressure of water increases with increasing temperature.

Ethyl alcohol is also a liquid at room temperature. Its vapor pressure at 25 °C is 59 mmHg. This value is higher than the vapor pressure of water at this temperature. Ethyl alcohol has a greater tendency to evaporate than water. At 40 °C ethyl alcohol has a vapor pressure of 135 mmHg. At 60 °C the vapor pressure is 353 mmHg. We find that the vapor pressure of ethyl alcohol also increases rapidly with increasing temperature. *The vapor pressure of every liquid increases as the temperature is raised.*

These results can be readily explained in terms of the kinetic theory. As the temperature increases, the average molecular velocity increases. We know from Figure 4-10 that the fraction of molecules in the liquid with sufficient energy to enter the vapor

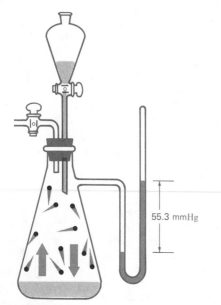

Figure 5-6
The equilibrium vapor pressure for water at 40 °C.

55.3 mmHg

phase would increase at higher temperatures and Figure 5-7 shows curves for 25 °C and 40 °C.

Molecules can escape from the surface of a liquid at any temperature to enter the gas phase as vapor. When the vapor pressure of the liquid just equals the atmospheric pressure, a new phenomenon occurs. At this temperature bubbles of vapor can form in the liquid. The liquid boils. We see that boiling is fixed by the external pressure. For example, if the pressure is 760 mmHg, water boils at 100 °C. This is the temperature at which the vapor pressure of water equals 760 mmHg. Figure 5-8 shows a bubble forming in water at 100 °C. The vapor pressure inside the bubble is equal to 760 mmHg balancing the external atmospheric pressure.

The **normal boiling temperature** of a liquid is *the temperature at which the vapor pressure of that liquid is exactly one standard atmosphere, 760 mmHg*. Suppose that the atmospheric pressure is 750 mmHg. Then bubbles of vapor could form in liquid water at 99.6 °C. The vapor pressure of water equals 750 mmHg at 99.6 °C. Water boils at this temperature when the atmospheric pressure is 750 mmHg.

EXERCISE 5-3

Compare the data for the vapor pressure of water and ethyl alcohol to estimate the boiling temperature of ethyl alcohol at atmospheric pressure.

5-6 Vapor Pressure in Solid-Vapor Equilibrium

Solid carbon dioxide is often called Dry Ice. At normal pressure Dry Ice evaporates without melting. The process of a solid going directly to the vapor without forming a liquid first is called **sublimation**. Another example of sublimation can be seen if you live in an area where the winters are very cold. Some snow disappears without the temperature ever rising to 0 °C.

Let us do an experiment to see if we can understand what might be happening. If we place some ice in an evacuated flask and keep the temperature below 0 °C, no liquid water forms. However, the gas pressure in the flask increases. If we keep the temperature at −10 °C, the pressure reaches 2.15 mmHg. Some water molecules leave the crystal surface and enter the gas phase. The vapor pressure for ice at −10 °C is 2.15 mmHg. Now let us increase the temperature to −5 °C. We should expect more water molecules would have enough energy to leave the solid. The equilibrium vapor pressure should go up. We find the vapor pressure for ice at −5 °C is 3.16 mmHg.

The kinetic theory provides an explanation for the vapor pressure of a liquid or a solid.

5-7 A Microscopic View of Phase Changes

Let us pretend again that we are 5 billion times smaller than we really are. We are standing in a large box filled with nitrogen gas

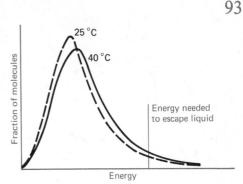

Figure 5-7
More molecules at 40 °C have enough energy to become gaseous. The vapor pressure is higher at 40 °C.

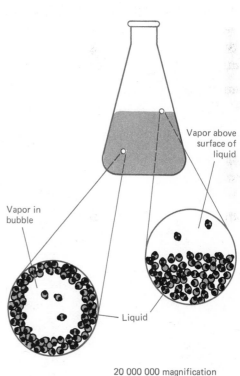

20 000 000 magnification

Figure 5-8
Formation of a bubble of water vapor at 100 °C.

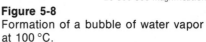

On Pikes Peak (14 000 ft, 2360 meters) water boils at 86 °C.

at room temperature. Most of the box is empty space, and we can see nitrogen molecules moving in all directions around us at a variety of velocities. Although there are plenty of collisions taking place, an individual molecule usually moves quite a long distance before it collides with another molecule. What happens if the temperature goes down? The picture is much the same, but it seems to be like a "slow motion" movie now. The kinetic energy, and therefore the velocity, of the molecules decreases as the temperature goes down.

But at −196 °C something new and startling happens to us. We are caught in a "rainstorm." Clusters of molecules are falling to the bottom of the box, crowding in close to us. As we struggle to swim up, we can see that the molecules have almost no space between them. Although they touch each other, we can easily push them past one another. They still move around violently in all directions. But now they are so close to one another that they travel only a short distance before colliding. And of course we get bounced back and forth too. When at last we swim high enough, we find ourselves floating at the top of this churning crowd of molecules. Most of the box above us is empty now, and only an occasional nitrogen molecule can be seen up there, darting by.

Every once in a while we can observe that a molecule seems to plunge from above to mix in with the crowded scene around us. And just as often, one leaves the sea of molecules, to move upwards into the almost empty space of the box.

As the temperature continues to drop below −196 °C, the molecular motion decreases. It is like the ocean calming down after a violent storm. At −210 °C we notice that another change is taking place. The molecules become firmly attached to each other in a regular pattern. We can jump around on top of the molecules and not sink down into them. They are about as far apart now as they were at −196 °C, but we can step from one to the next without too much trouble. They still move around a bit. If we want to, we can slide down and climb around the molecules, but at least we don't have to swim constantly as before.

There are still a few molecules high above us in the open space of the box. We can see a molecule move down from above to take a place in the regular pattern. Occasionally a molecule escapes from the pattern to move off towards the top of the box.

5-8 Review

In this chapter we have seen how the kinetic theory can be applied to condensed phases as well as to gases. The magnitude of the forces acting between molecules determines whether a substance is a solid, liquid, or gas at a particular temperature. The forces between molecules must be weak for a substance that is a gas at room temperature and very strong in solids with high melting temperature.

An understanding of the terms *potential energy* and *kinetic energy* lets us interpret phase changes at the molecular level. During any phase change the temperature stays constant. This

25

A sample of steam at 100 °C is condensed to give 1.80×10^2 grams of water, also at 100 °C. All the heat energy is used to vaporize benzene (C_6H_6). This procedure yields 1030 grams of gaseous benzene at its boiling temperature.

(a) Is the molar heat of vaporization of C_6H_6 greater or less than that of H_2O?
(b) What is the value for the molar heat of vaporization for benzene?

26

Use the data in Tables 5-1 and 5-2 to decide how many moles of sodium could be melted for every mole of steam condensed.

27

Find a regularity in the data on boiling temperature and molar heat of vaporization for the substances in Table 5-2.

28

Name at least two phase changes you have observed or know about that involve substances other than water.

29

The vapor pressure of ethyl ether is 537 mmHg at 25 °C. Estimate an approximate boiling temperature relative to water and ethanol.

30

A stoppered flask contains liquid mercury with water on top of the mercury. Floating on the liquid water is an ice cube (solid water). Also floating on the water is a piece of wood. Not counting the flask and the stopper, how many phases are present in the system? Name them.

31

Why is the boiling temperature for water lower in Denver, Colorado (altitude: 5280 ft) than in Boston, Massachusetts (at sea level)?

32

Both carbon tetrachloride, CCl_4, and mercury, Hg, are liquids whose vapors are poisonous to breathe. If CCl_4 is spilled, the danger can be removed merely by airing the room overnight. If Hg is spilled, it is necessary to pick up the liquid droplets with a "vacuum cleaner" device. Explain.

33

In an experiment a round-bottom flask is evacuated to near zero pressure. Some liquid alcohol is injected into the flask. Liquid alcohol remains in the flask after the pressure becomes constant. A pressure gauge attached to the flask indicates a pressure of 55 mmHg.

(a) What is the vapor pressure of the alcohol?
(b) If more liquid alcohol is injected into the flask, how will this affect the total pressure in the flask?
(c) What will happen to the vapor pressure of the alcohol if enough air is injected into the system to bring the total pressure to 760 mmHg? Explain.

34

A 50-50 mixture by weight of water and ethanol is heated to 60 °C at 500 mmHg pressure. Use the vapor pressure data in Section 5-5 to calculate the composition of the vapor.

35

How would the vapor pressure of water measured at 100 °C on the moon compare to the vapor pressure of water at the same temperature here on Earth?

36

Explain why leftover food placed in a refrigerator tends to dry out if left uncovered.

37

Why do some food production processes, such as the refining of sugar, make use of low-pressure evaporation?

38

The vapor pressure of a liquid increases as the temperature increases. State two causes for the increase in vapor pressure.

39

In an experiment, a 500 ml round-bottom flask was half-filled with water. The water was heated and boiled for a few minutes, filling the flask with water vapor. The flask was stoppered and quickly cooled under a stream of cold water. Explain why the water boiled as the flask was cooled.

40

A one-gallon can containing a small amount of water was heated. After the water had been boiling for a few minutes, to fill the can with water vapor, a stopper was used to seal the can. The can was then cooled and it collapsed. Explain.

6

Solutions, Solubility, and Ions

When sand and water are mixed in a beaker, the sand settles to the bottom of the beaker. There are distinct parts to the mixture. We use the word **heterogeneous** to describe this system. The properties change from one part of a heterogeneous mixture to another.

When a small amount of sugar and water are mixed, the sugar dissolves. The solid disappears, becoming part of the liquid. Mixtures of this type are called solutions. The word **homogeneous** describes such a system. The properties are the same every place within a homogeneous system. Both pure substances and solutions are homogeneous. However, a solution differs from a pure substance in that it has at least two different components and its properties vary, depending on the relative amounts and nature of the substances used in making it. There are three different types of solutions.

Gaseous Solutions

When two gases are put in the same container, the two kinds of molecules mix because molecules in a gas have large spaces between them. Therefore, all gaseous mixtures are homogeneous. All gaseous mixtures are solutions. Air is a good example of a gaseous solution. Table 6-1 shows the amounts of different gases in a typical sample of smog-free dry air.

Many technicians of all kinds will be needed to carry out pollution analyses.

Table 6-1
Composition of Smog-free Dry Air

Substance		Percent of Molecules
Name	Formula	
Nitrogen	N_2	78.08
Oxygen	O_2	20.95
Argon	Ar	0.93
Carbon dioxide	CO_2	0.03

Trace quantities of neon, helium, krypton, hydrogen, and xenon are present in air. Their total contribution is less than 0.003%.

The constituents of air can be separated by liquefaction. Large amounts of nitrogen for making fertilizers and of oxygen for the steel industry are obtained from air each year. The gases argon, neon, krypton, and xenon are also obtained from air. Helium occurs in some natural gas sources.

Solid Solutions

Many naturally occurring minerals, like the feldspars in clay or granite, are solid solutions. Metals often form solid solutions called *alloys*. For example, the alloys of gold and copper used in jewelry are solid solutions. Here the atoms of gold and copper are so similar in their chemical behavior and size that the atoms of one element can readily enter the crystals of the other element. Some solid metals dissolve hydrogen or carbon atoms. Steel is iron containing a small amount of dissolved carbon.

The American chemical industry annually spends over $500 million to operate and maintain environmental management facilities.

Liquid Solutions

In the laboratory work for this course you deal most often with liquid solutions. Liquid solutions can be made in many ways. Sometimes two liquids, such as water and ethyl alcohol, are mixed to form a solution. Some gases, such as NH_3 or CO_2, dissolve in water to give a liquid solution. Often, solutions are formed when a solid dissolves in water. In all these examples water is called the **solvent**. The substance dissolved in water is called the **solute**. At the molecular level we know that the molecules in a liquid are crowded close together, constantly jostling each other. When a solute molecule appears on the scene, it will be closely surrounded by solvent molecules that form a kind of cage. The solute molecule

Geologists study minerals—their formation, distribution, and recovery.

100

Metallurgists use their knowledge of alloys and the properties of alloys.

U.S. Production (1974)

Argon	246 000 tons
Nitrogen	8 550 000 tons
Oxygen	16 000 000 tons

will be hemmed in by jostling solvent molecules.

Solutions are very important because so many chemical reactions take place in them. Many of the reactions in living organisms occur in solution. We will begin our study of solutions by looking at their behavior during phase changes.

6-1 Behavior of Solutions During Phase Changes

When a pure substance such as water is heated, its vapor pressure increases. At 100 °C the vapor pressure of water is 760 mmHg. At one atmosphere pressure pure water boils at a constant temperature, 100 °C. Let's boil a sample of water until half of it has changed to steam. We can condense the steam to liquid water in a different vessel. If we repeat this experiment with two samples of water, they show identical behavior. Changing water from liquid to vapor and back to liquid again has not altered the water.

Pure water freezes at a constant temperature of 0 °C. We can freeze half of a water sample to ice, remove the ice, and melt it in another container. If we repeat this experiment with the two samples of water, once again we find that they behave in an identical manner.

What happens if we do the same experiments with a solution made by dissolving a solid in water? Figure 6-1 compares the results of heating pure water and a solution. We can observe several differences. The temperature at which boiling begins in the solution is higher than for pure water. Experiments show that the vapor pressure of an aqueous solution is less than the vapor pressure of pure water. It is necessary to heat the solution above 100 °C to reach a vapor pressure of 760 mmHg. At one atmosphere pressure the boiling temperature for the solution must be higher than 100 °C. This increase in boiling temperature depends both on how much solute is in solution and the nature of the solute. The more solute dissolved, the higher the boiling temperature.

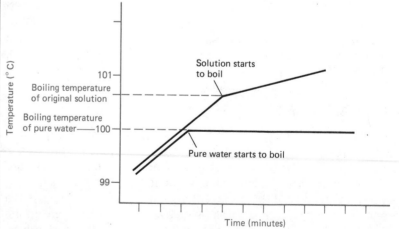

Figure 6-1
Heating curves for pure water and a solution. Heat energy is being added at a constant rate.

The temperature of the solution continues to rise during boiling. Let us see if we can find an explanation for this. We can condense the steam from the solution. The liquid we get has the properties of pure water. The solute remains behind in the boiling flask. As boiling continues, the relative amount of solute in the solution increases. The solution becomes more concentrated. The boiling temperature of the solution goes up. If we boil off all the water, solid solute remains behind. We can separate a pure liquid from a solution by evaporating the liquid and condensing the vapor that boils off. This process is called **distillation** and is illustrated in Figure 6-2. Distillation is one way to make fresh water from ocean water. The requirement of about 10 kcal of energy to vaporize one mole of water makes this a rather expensive method. Less expensive methods of obtaining pure water are being explored today. As the world's population continues to increase, the task of converting salty water to pure water becomes one of mankind's most important problems.

Now let us see what happens when a solution of a solid in water is cooled. In Figure 6-3 a solution is compared with pure water as the temperature is lowered. No solid appears until the solution is cooled below 0 °C. The freezing temperature of the solution is lower than the freezing temperature of pure water. This decrease in freezing temperature depends on how much solute is in the solution. The more solute dissolved, the lower the freezing temperature.

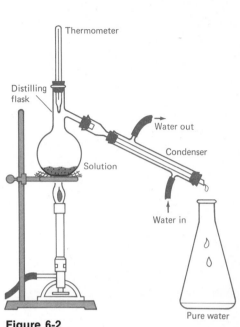

Figure 6-2
A distillation apparatus.

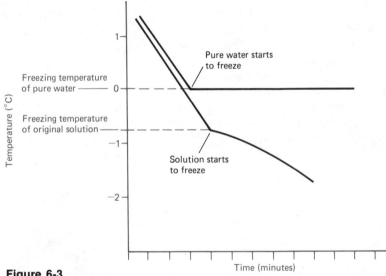

Figure 6-3
Cooling curves for pure water and a solution. Heat energy is being removed at a constant rate.

Chemical engineers may use phase changes to purify materials.

As freezing continues, the temperature of the solution continues to decrease. Perhaps we can find an explanation for this effect. To do this, separate the solid from the remaining liquid after about half of the solution has frozen. When we melt this solid, we obtain a liquid which behaves in the same way that pure water does on cooling. The solid that forms during the phase change contains no solute. The remaining solution must contain all the dissolved solute. The relative amount of solute in solution, and therefore the concentration, has increased. The temperature at which the solution freezes has decreased. "Antifreeze" substances added to an automobile radiator act this way. They dilute the water in the radiator and lower the temperature at which ice can crystallize from solution. The freezing temperature of the solution will depend on the relative amounts of water and antifreeze.

6-2   Expressing the Concentration of Solutions

The properties of solutions vary, depending on the relative amounts of solute and solvent used in making them up. The word **concentration** refers in general to the relative amount of solute and solution present. In this course you will use only one method for expressing concentration. The concentration of a solution is defined as the number of moles of solute divided by the number of liters of solution. The name for this unit of concentration is **molarity**. The symbol is M.

Nurses must understand the significance of the concentration of a solution.

$$M = \frac{\text{number of moles of solute}}{\text{number of liters of solution}} = \text{molarity} \qquad M = \frac{\text{moles}}{\text{liters}}$$

A one molar (1 M) solution contains 1 mole of solute in 1 liter of solution, or 0.5 mole in 0.5 liter, or any other combination that gives the ratio of $\frac{\text{moles}}{\text{liters}} = 1$. A two molar (2 M) solution contains two moles of solute in one liter of solution, or 1 mole in 0.5 liter, and so on. Notice that the concentration of the solvent water is not specified. Examples of how to make up some solutions will help you understand what is meant by molarity.

We can start to make a 1.000 M solution of NaCl by weighing out one mole of salt. From the formula, NaCl, we know that one mole weighs 58.5 grams (23.0 g + 35.5 g). We dissolve this salt in some water in a 1-liter volumetric flask as shown in Figure 6-4. This special flask holds 1.0000 liter when filled to the mark etched on the narrow neck. After the salt dissolves, more water is added until the water level almost reaches the etched mark. Now we

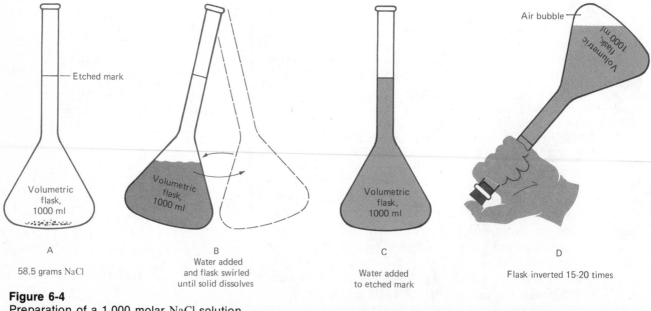

A
58.5 grams NaCl

B
Water added
and flask swirled
until solid dissolves

C
Water added
to etched mark

D
Flask inverted 15-20 times

Figure 6-4
Preparation of a 1.000 molar NaCl solution.

shake the flask to be sure that the solution is well mixed. Then we can add the last few milliliters of water to make the volume 1.0000 liter. The narrow neck makes it easier to do this.

We can also prepare a 1.00 M NaCl solution using a 100-ml volumetric flask. The final volume will be 0.1000 liter. We need only 0.100 mole of NaCl. We weigh 5.85 grams of NaCl, place it in the flask, dissolve it, and add water to the 100.0 ml mark. These examples show that

$$\text{Molarity} = \frac{\text{number of moles (solute)}}{\text{number of liters (solution)}}$$

EXERCISE 6-1

What mass of $AgNO_3$ is needed to make 1.0 liter of 1.0 M solution?

EXERCISE 6-2

What mass of $AgNO_3$ is needed to make 1.0×10^2 ml of 2.0 M solution?

EXERCISE 6-3

You have 8.4 grams of solid sodium hydrogen carbonate, $NaHCO_3$ (common name, sodium bicarbonate). How many moles of solid is this? How much 1.0 M solution can be made with this amount of $NaHCO_3$?

The words *dilute* and *concentrated* are often used in describing concentrations of solutions. They are adequate words when the exact value of the concentration is not required. Of course, they do not tell you how dilute or concentrated a solution is, but even so they are useful. The words *weak* and *strong* should not be used to describe concentration. These words are reserved to describe degree of ionization, which will be discussed in Chapter 14.

6-3 Solubility

Let us add a small amount of solid to a liquid, keeping the temperature constant. The solid begins to dissolve and the concentration of the solution rises. After all the solid has dissolved, the concentration remains constant, fixed by the amount of dissolved solid and the volume of the solution. If more solid is now added and dissolves, the concentration will rise further. Finally, however, the added solid does not dissolve. There is no further change in concentration. A solution that will not dissolve any more solute is said to be **saturated**. The word **solubility** refers to the amount of substance needed to make a saturated solution of specified volume at a given temperature.

The solubilities of solids in liquids vary widely. For example, sodium chloride dissolves in water at 25 °C until the concentration is about six moles per liter. The solubility of NaCl is 6 M at 25 °C. In contrast, only a small amount of sodium chloride dissolves in ethyl alcohol at 25 °C. The solubility is 0.009 M. Even in the same liquid solubilities differ over wide limits. The solids calcium chloride ($CaCl_2$) and silver nitrate ($AgNO_3$) have solubilities in water

Pharmacists (medical chemists) must understand the principles of solutions.

Deep-sea divers are very much concerned with the solubility of gases in blood.

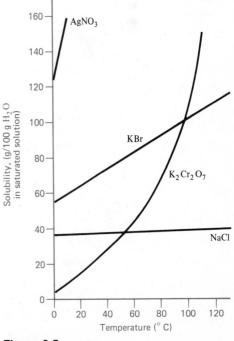

Figure 6-5
Solubility changes with temperature.

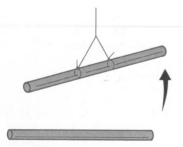

Figure 6-6
Salt solution conducts electricity; sugar solution does not.

exceeding one mole per liter. Solid, silver chloride (AgCl) has a solubility in water of only 10^{-5} mole per liter.

Temperature influences how much solid will dissolve and how fast. In general, the amount and rate of dissolving will go up as the temperature goes up. This is shown in Figure 6-5.

Because of this range of solubilities, the word *soluble* does not have a precise meaning. There is an upper limit to the solubility of the most soluble solid. On the other hand, even the least soluble solid furnishes a few dissolved particles per liter of solution. We use glass containers for much of our laboratory work in chemistry because glass has such low solubility in water. Yet in some experiments this solubility must be taken into consideration.

In this book we will use the word *soluble* to mean that more than 0.1 mole of a substance dissolves per liter.

6-4 Variations Among Properties of Solutions

The differences among solutions can be very great. We can demonstrate these differences with five substances: sodium chloride, sugar, iodine, ethyl alcohol, and water. Let us use the liquids, water and ethyl alcohol, as solvents in making up a set of solutions.

First, we can investigate the solubility of the three solids in each solvent. By adding a small crystal of each solid to one milliliter of liquid, we find that sugar dissolves in water and in ethyl alcohol. Sodium chloride dissolves readily in water but not in ethyl alcohol. Iodine, on the other hand, dissolves in ethyl alcohol but not appreciably in water. The solvent properties of the two liquids are different.

The experiment just described gives us four solutions containing a substantial amount of solute.

I	II	III	IV
Sugar in water	Sugar in ethyl alcohol	Sodium chloride in water	Iodine in ethyl alcohol

Of these four solutions, IV is readily distinguished. It has a dark brown color. The other three, like many solutions, are colorless. They can be distinguished by taste, but chemists have safer ways of telling them apart. Many solutions differ in the way they conduct

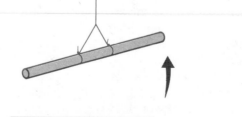

Two electrified glass rods repel each other

Two electrified plastic rods repel each other

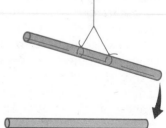

Electrified glass rod is attracted to electrified plastic rod

Figure 6-7
Electrical attraction and repulsion.

an electric current. Figure 6-6 shows this measurement. The two sugar solutions have almost the same electrical conductivity as the pure solvents. Their conductivity is very low. In marked contrast solution III conducts electric current much more readily than does pure water. Differences in electrical conductivity are used to distinguish one solution from another. The next two sections develop some ideas we need. Then in Section 6-7 we will apply them to chemical species in solution.

Dry cleaners use solvents and reactants of several kinds to clean clothes.

6-5 Electric Charge

You are familiar with many electrical devices. They surround you at home and at school. They furnish energy, light, and means of communication. Try to name several electrical phenomena that you have observed. Does your list include the following?

(a) The heat generated by an electric current passing through the heating element of an electric stove.

(b) The light emitted by the filament of an electric light bulb as electric current passes through it.

(c) The work done by an electric motor when electric current passes through its coils.

(d) The attraction of a comb for your hair on a dry day.

(e) A flash of lightning.

The interest of a chemist in the electrical nature of matter goes far deeper than this. We will find that an understanding of electrical behavior furnishes a key to the explanation of chemical properties. We will also find that electrical effects aid us in predicting molecular formulas, in explaining chemical reactions, and in understanding energy changes that accompany them. In order to understand the electrical behavior of matter, we must find out what is meant by electric charge. We begin with some simple experiments.

Rub a glass rod with a piece of silk and hang the rod up with a silk thread. Then rub a second glass rod and slowly bring it near to the first rod. As the two rods get close to each other, the suspended one moves away. The rods repel each other.

Now repeat this experiment with two plastic rods, rubbed with a piece of fur instead of silk. Once again, the rods move apart as they are brought near each other.

If we bring a plastic rod close to a suspended glass rod, the two rods move toward each other, not away. The two rods attract one another. These experiments are shown in Figure 6-7.

We use the word *electrified* to describe the condition of these rods after they have been rubbed vigorously. We can explore what happens with many different materials. Our experimental results always fall into two classes. Objects of the same material that have been electrified by the same procedure always repel each other. Objects of different materials may attract or repel each other. We find that electrified objects fall into two groups. Only two electrified states exist. One is like the electrified glass rod. The other is similar to the electrified plastic rod. We say that any object that behaves the way the glass rod does is **positively charged**. Any object that behaves the way the plastic rod does is **negatively charged**.

Electricians, electronic engineers, chemists, physicists, and other scientists deal with electric charge and its effects on matter.

Today it is easy to place an electric charge on different objects. You are familiar with the storage battery in an automobile or the dry cells in a flashlight. These are sources of electrical energy. A battery has two terminals, one marked "plus" and the other marked "minus." We can give an electric charge to an object by connecting it to one of the battery terminals.

A famous American physicist, Robert Millikan, carried out a very precise experiment to measure electric charge. This experiment is diagramed in Figure 6-8. Two plates are connected to opposite terminals of a battery. One plate acquires a positive electric charge. The other plate acquires a negative electric charge. Tiny droplets of oil or mercury are sprayed into the upper section of the apparatus. As these droplets fall through the air, some of them acquire an electric charge. If a charged droplet floats into the space between the charged plates, we can keep it from rising or falling by adjusting the charges on the two plates. This means a balance has been achieved between the gravitational forces which would make the particle fall and electrical forces which would make the particle move back to the upper plate.

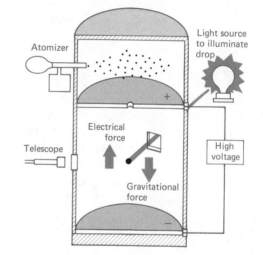

Figure 6-8
Cross-sectional view of apparatus for Millikan oil drop experiment.

Millikan carried out thousands of such experiments. He measured the electric charge that had to be placed on the parallel plates so that the droplets would be stationary. For some experiments the upper plate was given a positive electric charge and for others negative. Sometimes he found that the droplet had a positive charge. Sometimes it had a negative charge. He established that there is a smallest electric charge, either positive or negative. This is called the **unit electric charge**. We know that matter comes in packages called atoms. Electric charge also comes in packages. You can have one or two or any other whole number of electric charges. Particles with one half or three quarters of an electric charge are not found.

The electron charge is quite small. While you operate a flashlight for one second, 3 billion billion (3×10^{18}) electrons flow through the bulb.

6-6   The Electron-Proton Model

These new facts about electrical phenomena can be made part of our particle model. Let us propose that matter is made up of two kinds of particles which carry the property of electric charge. The particle which has one unit of negative electric charge is called the **electron**. The particle which has one unit of positive electric charge is called the **proton**. These two charges are equal in size but have opposite signs. One unit of negative charge will neutralize one unit of positive charge.

Let us see what our model looks like now. If an object has the same number of electrons and protons, then the amount of negative electric charge would be equal to the amount of positive electric charge. We say such an object is **electrically neutral**. It has **zero electric charge**.

Neutral atoms or molecules have zero electric charge. They have *equal numbers of electrons and protons*. The following examples will illustrate this point.

Each H atom, O atom, and H_2O molecule has a zero charge. Chemists know that the H atom is made up of one electron and one proton. The oxygen atom contains eight electrons and eight protons. These atoms can be shown as neutral particles made up of smaller particles, with e^- representing one electron and p^+ representing one proton.

1 H atom contains	1 electron 1 proton	or	$1\ e^-$ $1\ p^+$	a neutral atom with zero charge
1 O atom contains	8 electrons 8 protons	or	$8\ e^-$ $8\ p^+$	a neutral atom with zero charge

The H_2O molecule must have ten electrons and ten protons, coming from the two H atoms and one O atom. The H_2O molecule contains 2 H atoms + 1 O atom.

H	O	H
$1\ e^-$	$8\ e^-$	$1\ e^-$
$1\ p^+$	$8\ p^+$	$1\ p^+$

gives zero electric charge

The important point right now is the zero value for total electric charge. Particles having equal numbers of electrons and protons have zero electric charge. Such particles are electrically neutral.

It is easy to add an electron to some atoms or molecules. In other instances it is easy to remove an electron. When these processes take place, particles are formed with different numbers of electrons and protons. There is a net electric charge on these particles. Chemists have given the name **ion** to a charged particle. Here are two examples:

Chlorine atom   + electron ⟶   chloride ion

$$Cl\ +\ e^- \longrightarrow Cl^-$$

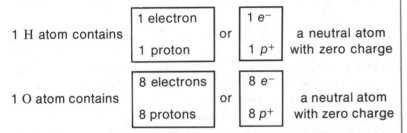

$$\boxed{\begin{array}{c} 17\ e^- \\ 17\ p^+ \end{array}}\ +\ e^- \longrightarrow \boxed{\begin{array}{c} 18\ e^- \\ 17\ p^+ \end{array}}^{1-}$$

Notice that the electric charge on the chloride ion is $1-$. The 17 protons plus 18 electrons give a net charge of $1-$.

Our Electrical Nerves

All the sensations we perceive are carried by electrical impulses. The exact manner in which this is done is not completely understood. The basic mechanism involves ions causing a voltage change that "ripples" along the nerve. Usually the voltage inside the nerve cell is lower (-0.07 volt) than that of the surrounding fluid. When the nerve is triggered by a sensing cell, the local voltage difference becomes $+0.04$ volt. This voltage change is accompanied by ion flow into and out of the nerve cell and moves as an impulse along the nerve "carrying" the message. Many impulses are needed to form a pattern that the brain can use. The process is quite fast. The impulse travels about 100 meters in a second or a bit over 200 mph! Your brain is sending impulses of this type while you move your eyes over these words and register their meaning.

Touch is one of our five senses. The impulses caused by touch come from several types of receptor cells located throughout your body. The nerve endings that pick up feeling are around the hair follicles, or roots of the hairs. On hairless skin there are special structures for touch reception.

The electrostatic force of repulsion between two electrons one centimeter apart is exceedingly small; the gravitational attraction between two electrons is even smaller. The ratio of these two forces is about 5×10^{42}!

Xerox—Charge at Work

In the Xerox process for copying written material, an unusual property of selenium metal is used. Selenium metal in the dark is a nonconductor of electricity and therefore holds an electrostatic charge. But in light selenium is a conductor of electricity, and the electrostatic charge rapidly leaks away. So in the Xerox process a positive electric charge is placed on a drum which is coated with a highly polished layer of selenium. The image of the material to be copied is focused onto the drum with bright lights and lenses. Where the page being copied is white, plenty of light strikes the selenium surface and the electric charge disappears. Where the page being copied is dark, no light hits the selenium and it stays charged. The drum now carries the image as a pattern of positive electric charge. As the drum turns, a fine black powder is given a negative charge and is sifted over the rotating drum. The powder sticks to the positively charged areas.

Next a piece of paper is positively charged and pressed against the drum. It "steals" the black powder by electrical attraction. Finally, the paper is heated so that the powder melts and fuses to the paper. The copy is made.

$$(17+) + (18-) = (1-)$$

The sodium atom loses an electron to become a sodium ion.

$$\text{Sodium atom} \longrightarrow \text{sodium ion} + \text{electron}$$
$$\text{Na} \longrightarrow \text{Na}^+ + e^-$$

11 e^-		10 e^- $^{1+}$	
11 p^+	$\longrightarrow$	11 p^+	$+ e^-$

The net electric charge for the sodium ion is $1+$.

6-7 Electric Properties of Liquids and Solids

Now let us go back to our four solutions (Section 6-4) and their behavior with the light and battery test. We are ready to investigate behavior of liquids and solids that show evidence of the presence and movement of electric charge. The movement of electric charge is called an **electric current**. When we say electric current flows through a solution, we mean there is a movement of electric charge through the solution. We want to see how this charge moves.

Pure water is a very poor conductor of electricity. So is solid NaCl, table salt. Yet when sodium chloride dissolves in water, the solution conducts readily. The dissolved sodium chloride must be responsible. How does the dissolved salt affect the solution so that electric charge can move through the liquid? Perhaps ions are present in the salt solution. The movement of these charged particles through the solution could account for the electric current. Salt has the formula NaCl. For every sodium atom there is one chlorine atom. Chemists have discovered that the ions Na^+ and Cl^- are present when NaCl is dissolved in water. We can write this as an equation:

$$NaCl \text{ (solid)} + \text{water} \longrightarrow Na^+ \text{ (in water)} + Cl^- \text{ (in water)}$$

Chemists usually omit the term *water* on the left side of this equation. Its presence is implied by the symbols on the right side of the equation. The expression "in water" is further shortened to "*aq*," meaning **aqueous**. The equation is usually written

$$NaCl(s) \longrightarrow Na^+(aq) + Cl^-(aq)$$

Electric charge always balances in a chemical equation. Here the zero charge of $NaCl(s)$ equals $+1$ on sodium ion plus -1 on chloride ion. The solid dissolves, forming the charged particles $Na^+(aq)$ and $Cl^-(aq)$. They can move about in the solution independently. Their attraction for each other is reduced because they are surrounded by a cage of many water molecules. Ions with positive charge are called **cations**. Ions with negative charge are called **anions**. An electric current can pass through the solution by means of the movement of these ions. The $Cl^-(aq)$ ions move in one direction, causing negative charge to move that way. The $Na^+(aq)$ ions move in the opposite direction, causing positive charge to move this way. These movements carry charge through the solution, and we say that electric current flows.

The electrical conductivity of an aqueous solution depends on how much solute is dissolved in the water. A solution containing 0.1 mole $NaCl$ per liter exhibits higher conductivity than a solution containing 0.01 mole $NaCl$ per liter. The amount of current conducted depends on the concentration of ions.

Sugar dissolves in water. The solution conducts electric current no better than does pure water. We conclude that no charged particles are present in a sugar solution. No ions are formed.

Calcium chloride ($CaCl_2$) is another crystalline solid that dissolves readily in water. The solution conducts electric current. Calcium chloride is, in this regard, like sodium chloride and unlike sugar. Ions are present in solution when calcium chloride dissolves in water. But how should the equation be written? An experiment like Experiment 16 shows that one mole of $CaCl_2$ forms three moles of ions in solution. This leads us to write the equation

$$CaCl_2(s) \longrightarrow Ca^{2+}(aq) + 2\ Cl^-(aq)$$

Again note that charges balance in this equation. The calcium ion, $Ca^{2+}(aq)$, has twice the positive charge of $Na^+(aq)$. The chloride ion that forms, $Cl^-(aq)$, behaves in the same way as the negative ion that is present in the sodium chloride solution. Because of that, we write $2\ Cl^-$ and not Cl_2^{2-} in the equation representing the dissolving of calcium chloride. A 1 M solution of calcium chloride contains two moles of chloride ion per liter of solution.

EXERCISE 6-4

A neutral calcium atom has 20 electrons and 20 protons. Show the formation of Ca^{2+} as an electron-loss process.

Silver nitrate ($AgNO_3$) is a third solid substance that dissolves in water to give a conducting solution. The ions formed are silver ions, $Ag^+(aq)$, and nitrate ions, $NO_3^-(aq)$. The reaction is

$$AgNO_3(s) \longrightarrow Ag^+(aq) + NO_3^-(aq)$$

The aqueous silver ion is a silver atom with the positive charge of a proton. It carries the same charge as an aqueous sodium ion. The aqueous nitrate ion carries the negative charge of an electron. It has the same charge as the aqueous chloride ion. This time, however, the negative charge is carried by a group consisting of one nitrogen atom and three oxygen atoms. Since this group, NO_3^-, remains together throughout many chemical reactions, acting as a unit, it has been given a distinctive name, *nitrate ion*. There are many other examples of such polyatomic ions.

EXERCISE 6-5

The solids listed below dissolve readily in water to give solutions that conduct electricity. For each substance write an equation to represent what happens. The four ions (sulfate, ammonium, carbonate, and hydrogen carbonate) act as units in the same

**Are
Negative
Ions
O
N
S**

110
Charge Cleans the Air

Frederick Cottrell discovered that static electric charge can be used to remove particles from smoke. An insulated wire in the center of a smokestack is given a charge of about 100 000 volts. Gas molecules are ionized and move to the wall of the smokestack, which is electrically grounded to the earth. Billions of collisions between the ions and the dust particles move the dust to the wall. There it clings until scraped off. Each year about 20 million metric tons of solids are removed from smokestacks in this fashion. Not only is pollution of the atmosphere decreased but often valuable chemicals can be recovered from the dust obtained using electrostatic precipitation.

way nitrate ion does. What electric charges would each of these ions have? Check Appendix 2 for confirmation.

Na_2SO_4	Sodium sulfate
NH_4Cl	Ammonium chloride
$(NH_4)_2CO_3$	Ammonium carbonate
$NaHCO_3$	Sodium hydrogen carbonate
$CuCl_2$	Cupric chloride

6-8 Ionic Solids Versus Molecular Solids

The solids sodium chloride, calcium chloride, and silver nitrate are similar. They all dissolve in water to form aqueous ions and give conducting solutions. These solids are called **ionic solids**. Let us see what that means.

The sodium chloride crystal contains an equal number of sodium ions and chloride ions. Salt molecules are not present in the crystal. On the basis of much experimental evidence, chemists have concluded that sodium chloride crystals are built up of sodium ions, Na^+, and chloride ions, Cl^-, rather than of neutral atoms or molecules. The numbers of Na^+ and Cl^- ions must be equal because the entire crystal is electrically neutral. There is electrical attraction between these oppositely charged particles. This attraction between positive and negative ions accounts for the bonding in an ionic solid.

We use the formula NaCl to represent the composition of such a solid. The formula NaCl shows only the simplest ratio of the number of atoms in the compound. It is called an **empirical formula**. Figure 6-9 shows the arrangement of the ions in the sodium chlo-

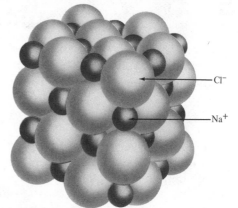

Figure 6-9
The face-centered cubic structure of Na^+Cl^-.

ride crystal. The ions are arranged in layers. A layer in the interior of a crystal has a similar layer in front of it and another behind it. These layers are displaced so that a Cl^- ion lies in front of each Na^+ ion and a Cl^- ion lies behind each Na^+ ion. Each ion is surrounded by six oppositely charged ions. We call this arrangement the **sodium chloride structure**. Many other ionic solids have the same crystal structure. Among them are LiF, KCl, and MgO. The bonding is strong because of the attraction between oppositely charged ions in this structure.

When an ionic solid such as sodium chloride is melted, the

molten salt conducts electric current. The conductivity is like that of an aqueous salt solution. Na^+ and Cl^- ions are present. The extremely high melting temperature (808 °C) shows that a large kinetic energy is needed to break down the NaCl crystalline arrangement to free the ions so that they can move. In contrast, at room temperature, solid sodium chloride dissolves readily in water and without a large heat effect. A reasonable interpretation is that the water interacts strongly with the ions, producing energy. But breaking the bonds in a solid requires a large amount of energy. The energy terms are about equal in this case. Aqueous ions are about as stable as ions in the crystal.

Many solids do not conduct when dissolved or melted. Apparently, ions do not form; rather, molecules are separated from the solid. Such substances are called **molecular solids**. Iodine is a typical example. The crystal structure, shown in Figure 6-10, reveals individual, diatomic I_2 molecules. This substance melts at a low temperature (113.5 °C).

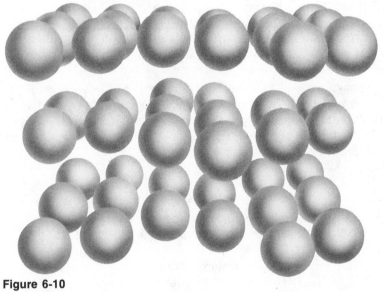

Figure 6-10
I_2, a molecular solid.

Industrial chemists make many important chemicals by the interaction of electricity with electrolyte solutions or liquids.

6-9 Types of Compounds That Are Electrolytes

Any substance that dissolves in water to give a conducting solution is called an **electrolyte**. We begin by looking for some regularities in the behavior of solutions of electrolytes. The observed properties suggest it is useful to make three classes of electrolytes. Chemists use the words **acid**, **base**, and **salt** to identify these three classes. Let us list the properties of aqueous solutions for each class of compound.

	Acids	Properties of All Acidic Solutions
HCl	Hydrochloric acid	1. Taste sour.
H_2SO_4	Sulfuric acid	2. React with many metals, with liberation of hydrogen.
CH_3COOH	Acetic acid	3. Turn litmus red.
H_3PO_4	Phosphoric acid	4. Conduct electricity.
		5. Neutralize bases.

For Litmus

ACID
RED

BASE
BLUE

Bases		Properties of All Basic Solutions
NaOH	Sodium hydroxide	1. Taste bitter, feel slippery.
KOH	Potassium hydroxide	2. Turn litmus blue.
NH_4OH	Ammonium hydroxide	3. Neutralize acids.
$Ca(OH)_2$	Calcium hydroxide	4. Conduct electricity.
$Ba(OH)_2$	Barium hydroxide	

We can write a general equation for an acid-base reaction:

$$acid + base \longrightarrow H_2O + salt$$

When the solution is heated, water can be driven off. A compound, called a **salt**, crystallizes from solution. Here are a few equations to show formation of water and a salt:

$$acid + base \longrightarrow water + salt$$
$$HCl(aq) + NaOH(aq) \longrightarrow H_2O + NaCl(aq)$$
$$H_2SO_4(aq) + KOH(aq) \longrightarrow H_2O + KHSO_4(aq)$$
$$H_2SO_4(aq) + 2\ KOH(aq) \longrightarrow 2\ H_2O + K_2SO_4(aq)$$
$$CH_3COOH(aq) + NH_4OH(aq) \longrightarrow H_2O + (NH_4)(CH_3COO)(aq)$$

We have chosen to write $NaOH(aq)$ and $NaCl(aq)$. It would be somewhat better to show that these compounds exist in water as hydrated ions, $Na^+(aq)$, $OH^-(aq)$, $Cl^-(aq)$. However, it is easier at this stage to see what happens in the reaction when empirical formulas are used instead of ionic formulas.

Salts		Properties of Salt Solutions
NaCl	Sodium chloride	1. Taste salty
$KHSO_4$	Potassium hydrogen sulfate	2. Conduct electricity
K_2SO_4	Potassium sulfate	
$(NH_4)(CH_3COO)$	Ammonium acetate	
$AgNO_3$	Silver nitrate	
$CaCl_2$	Calcium chloride	

Sulfuric acid, H_2SO_4, reacts with a base like KOH to give two different salts. The normal salt, K_2SO_4, forms when 2 moles of base react with 1 mole of acid. The acid salt, $KHSO_4$, called potassium hydrogen sulfate, forms when 1 mole of base reacts with 1 mole of acid. $KHSO_4$ and K_2SO_4 are white crystalline solids. Like crystalline NaCl, these salts have an ionic structure in the solid.

We will return to a more detailed discussion of acids and bases in Chapter 14. Now we finish this chapter by considering the solubility of ionic compounds.

6-10 Solubility of Ionic Compounds

Experiments show that some ionic compounds are very soluble in water, whereas other ionic compounds, such as AgCl, do not dissolve to any appreciable extent in water. We can summarize in a qualitative fashion the solubilities for a large number of substances. We will say that a substance is soluble if we can make an aqueous solution with concentration greater than 0.1 M. Table 6-2 summarizes the solubility in water of many ionic compounds that you are likely to encounter in your laboratory program. There is no simple theory to predict solubility. Therefore we have tried to emphasize the regularities you will find. An important use of these solubility guides is the separation of one substance with low solubility from a substance with high solubility. We will discuss this again in Chapter 13.

Some cations form soluble compounds with all the anions commonly found in the laboratory. These cations are the ammonium ion, NH_4^+, and the ions of the alkali metals, Li^+, Na^+, K^+, Rb^+, and Cs^+.

Some anions form soluble compounds with all the cations commonly found in the laboratory. Almost all compounds containing nitrate ions, NO_3^-, or acetate ions, CH_3COO^-, are soluble in water at room temperature.

Manufacturing chemists use solubility differences to separate materials.

In this book *soluble* means more than 0.1 mole of solute per liter of solution.

TABLE 6-2

Solubility of Some Ionic Compounds in Water

	Negative Ions (anions)	plus	Positive Ions (cations)	form	Compounds Which Are:
1.	All		Alkali ions (Li^+, Na^+, K^+, Rb^+, Cs^+)		Soluble, i.e., > 0.1 mole/liter
2.	All		Ammonium ion, NH_4^+		Soluble
3.	Nitrate, NO_3^-		All		Soluble
4.	Acetate, CH_3COO^-		All except Ag^+		Soluble
5.	Chloride, Cl^- Bromide, Br^- Iodide, I^-		Ag^+, Pb^{2+}, Hg_2^{2+}, Cu^+ All others		Not soluble Soluble
6.	Sulfate, SO_4^{2-}		Ca^{2+}, Sr^{2+}, Ba^{2+}, Ra^{2+}, Pb^{2+}, Ag^+ All others		Not soluble Soluble
7.	Sulfide, S^{2-}		Alkali ions and NH_4^+, Be^{2+}, Mg^{2+}, Ca^{2+}, Sr^{2+}, Ba^{2+}, Ra^{2+} All others		Soluble Not soluble
8.	Hydroxide, OH^-		Alkali ions and NH_4^+, Sr^{2+}, Ba^{2+}, Ra^{2+} All others		Soluble Not soluble
9.	Phosphate, PO_4^{3-} Carbonate, CO_3^{2-} Sulfite, SO_3^{2-}		Alkali ions and NH_4^+ All others		Soluble Not soluble

6-11 Review

Air pollution has caused much damage recently to marble structures that have survived for centuries; for example, the buildings on the Acropolis in Athens or statues in Venice. Marble is a form of calcium carbonate that is changed by SO_2 in the air into calcium sulfate. This compound is much more soluble in rainwater than is the carbonate. One remedy for this problem is to wash the marble with a Ba^{2+} solution, which converts $CaSO_4$ into $BaSO_4$. Barium sulfate is not soluble. The surface of the structure is better preserved.

Solutions are homogeneous mixtures of two or more pure substances. Although there are gaseous solutions and solid solutions, liquid solutions are by far the most common. In aqueous solutions water is usually considered to be the **solvent**. The substances dissolved in water are called **solutes**.

Comparison of the behavior of solutions and of pure substances during phase changes brings out some important differences. In most cases the boiling temperature of a solution is higher than the boiling temperature of the pure solvent. Similarly, in most cases the freezing temperature of a solution is lower than the freezing temperature of the pure solvent.

In this chapter we have considered experiments which show that some solutions are good conductors of electricity while others are poor conductors. In searching for an explanation for the results of these experiments, we have examined what the term *electric charge* means. Chemists have found that some substances dissolve in water to form electrically charged particles called **ions**. Other substances dissolve in water without forming ions. The conduction of electric charge through a solution can be accomplished by ions moving through the solution.

Substances that dissolve in water to give conducting solutions are called **electrolytes**. Chemists find it convenient to classify electrolytes as acids, bases, or salts.

Solubility of ionic compounds is summarized in Table 6-2.

Questions and Problems for Chapter 6

1

List three heterogeneous materials.

2

List three homogeneous materials.

3

Which of the following statements about seawater is FALSE?

(a) It boils at a higher temperature than pure water.
(b) It melts at a lower temperature than pure water.
(c) The boiling temperature rises as the liquid boils away.
(d) The melting temperature falls as the liquid freezes.
(e) The density is the same as that of pure water.

4

Early gold miners collected very fine gold dust from their sluice boxes by dissolving it in mercury.

How do you think the gold was then separated from the mercury?

5

Would ocean water in which ice has been formed and then removed be a better source of salt than untreated ocean water? Explain.

6

Explain why the boiling temperature of the solution increases in the fudge-making process.

7

Which of the following reactions is/are endothermic?

(a) $H_2O(s) \longrightarrow H_2O(l)$
(b) $H_2O(l) \longrightarrow H_2O(g)$
(c) $H(g) + H(g) \longrightarrow H_2(g)$
(d) $CuSO_4 \cdot 5H_2O(s) \longrightarrow CuSO_4(s) + 5H_2O(g)$
(e) $NaCl(g) \longrightarrow Na^+(g) + Cl^-(g)$

8

Homes heated by the sun need some way to store energy. In a University of Delaware experimental home, energy is stored in the phase change of sodium thiosulfate (commonly called hypo):

$$Na_2S_2O_3 \cdot 5H_2O(s) + 11.9 \, kcal \longrightarrow$$
$$Na_2S_2O_3 \cdot 5H_2O(l)$$

at a temperature of 48.5 °C (119 °F). How many liters of hypo are needed to store 10^5 kcal? This will keep a medium-sized house warm for 10 hours in freezing weather. The density of liquid hypo is 1.7 g/ml.

9

How many grams of methanol, CH_3OH, must be added to 2.00 moles of H_2O to make a solution containing equal numbers of H_2O and CH_3OH molecules? How many molecules (of all kinds) does the resulting solution contain?

10

How many grams of ammonium chloride, NH_4Cl, are present in 0.30 liter of a 0.40 M NH_4Cl solution?

11

How many liters of 0.250 M K_2CrO_4 solution contain 38.8 grams of K_2CrO_4?

12

Explain how a solution can be both dilute and saturated.

13

Describe what you would have to do to make 1.00×10^3 ml of 0.040 M Na_2SO_4 solution.

14

Calculate the moles of solute needed to make these solutions:

(a) 150 ml, 0.12 M $AgNO_3$
(b) 1.00 liter, 0.0035 M NaCl
(c) 3 ml, 2.50 M KOH

15

A chemist evaporated 25.0 ml of NaCl solution to dryness. He found 0.585 gram of NaCl. What was the original concentration?

16

Which has the greater solubility in water:

(a) pepper or salt?
(b) CO_2 or N_2?
(c) oil or molasses?
(d) limestone or granite?

17

One liter of saturated calcium carbonate solution contains 0.0153 gram at 25 °C. What is the solubility of $CaCO_3$ in moles/liter?

18

Name three chemicals that readily dissolve in water. Name three that scarcely dissolve at all.

19

List three properties of a solution you would expect to vary as the concentration of the solute varies.

20

Give two forces other than electrical that are felt at a distance.

21

Why do two electrically neutral objects with mass attract each other?

22

Why do scientists claim there are only two kinds of electric charge?

23

The following six measurements were obtained during a Millikan oil-drop experiment. They represent the electric charge on the drop.

4.83×10^{-19} coulomb	6.44×10^{-19} coulomb
3.24×10^{-19} coulomb	4.80×10^{-19} coulomb
9.62×10^{-19} coulomb	1.62×10^{-19} coulomb

(a) Might one of these values correspond to the unit electric charge? Which one? Why?
(b) Can you think of an argument to rule out the value 0.81×10^{-19} coulomb as the unit electric charge?

24

A neutral atom of barium has 56 electrons. Barium forms a 2+ ion. How many protons does a barium ion have? How many electrons in the 2+ ion? Show the formation of the ion as an electron loss process.

25

A neutral fluorine atom has 9 protons. Fluorine, F, forms an ion with 1− charge. How many electrons does a fluoride ion, F^-, have? Starting with F_2, show the formation of F^- as an electron gain process. Check to see that charge is balanced.

26

What would you expect the empirical formula for barium fluoride to be?

27

The salt ammonium sulfate, $(NH_4)_2SO_4$, dissolves in water to form a conducting solution containing ammonium ions, NH_4^+, and sulfate ions, SO_4^{2-}.

(a) Write the balanced equation for the reaction when this ionic solid dissolves in water.
(b) Verify the conservation of charge by comparing the charge of the reactant to the sum of the charges of the products.
(c) Suppose 1.32 grams of ammonium sulfate is dissolved to make 0.500 liter of solution. Calculate the concentrations of $NH_4^+(aq)$ and $SO_4^{2-}(aq)$.

28

Calculate the molarity of $Fe^{3+}(aq)$, $NH_4^+(aq)$, and $Cl^-(aq)$ in 1.00 liter of solution made by dissolving 0.100 mole of iron(III) chloride, $FeCl_3$, and also 0.100 mole ammonium chloride, NH_4Cl.

29

Assume the following compounds dissolve in water to form separate, mobile ions in solution. Write the formulas and the names for the ions that can be expected.

(a) HI   (d) $Ba(OH)_2$
(b) $CaCl_2$ (e) KNO_3
(c) Na_2CO_3 (f) NH_4Cl

30

Write the equation for the reaction that occurs when each of these electrolytes is dissolved in water:

(a) lithium hydroxide (solid)
(b) nitric acid (liquid)
(c) potassium sulfate (solid)
(d) sodium nitrate (solid)
(e) ammonium iodide (solid)
(f) potassium carbonate (solid)

31

A crude análysis of seawater gave these results for one liter of water: 1.90×10^4 milligrams of Cl^-, 1.00×10^4 milligrams of Na^+, and 0.120×10^4 milligrams of Mg^{2+}. What is the molarity for each of these ions in this water?

32

Seawater contains 6×10^{-6} milligrams of gold per liter. What is its molarity? At $4.50 per gram what is the value of gold in one cubic kilometer? (One cubic kilometer equals 1×10^{12} liters.)

33

What ion will all the acids listed on page 111 form?

34

Some of these solutions cannot be made because the solute is not soluble enough. Consult Table 6-2 to find which ones cannot be made.

(a) 0.25 M silver acetate
(b) 0.25 M nickel acetate
(c) 0.25 M $Ni(OH)_2$
(d) 0.25 M NiS

35

Describe two ways to produce a saturated solution of a solid in water.

36

Name and give the formula for the salt formed when the following acids and bases react:

(a) $H_2SO_4 + Ca(OH)_2$
(b) $HNO_3 + NaOH$
(c) $HCl + Al(OH)_3$
(d) $CH_3COOH + KOH$

37

Osmium chloride has the formula $OsCl_2$. Sodium iodate is $NaIO_3$. What is the formula for osmium iodate?

38

Write equations for the reactions between aqueous bromide ions and:

(a) aqueous lead ions
(b) aqueous silver ions

Use Table 6-2 to help you decide how to write these equations.

39

Predict what would happen if equal volumes of 0.2 M Na_2SO_3 and 0.2 M $MgSO_4$ were mixed. If a reaction takes place, write a net ionic equation.

40

Write an empirical formula for each of the following compounds and indicate which have low solubilities:

(a) silver sulfide
(b) potassium sulfide
(c) ammonium sulfide
(d) nickel sulfide
(e) ferrous sulfide
(f) ferric sulfide

Order Among Atoms

7

During the 19th century chemists made a large number of careful observations of the elements and their compounds. A major goal was to find an arrangement of the elements that would provide some organization for these observations. This search by chemists is in many ways like that of the person in the forest. Some of the first regularities proved too limited. Other proposals were shown to be incorrect. Step by step, better arrangements were achieved. One useful regularity that chemists recognized was the difference in the properties of metals and nonmetals. Table 7-1 contrasts the properties that can be observed for these two classes of materials.

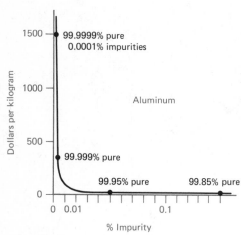

99.9999% pure
0.0001% impurities

Aluminum

99.999% pure

99.95% pure   99.85% pure

% Impurity

Dollars per kilogram

TABLE 7-1
Comparison of the General Properties of
Metals and Nonmetals

Metals	Nonmetals
Solids	Often gases and liquids
High density	Low density
High melting temperature	Low melting temperature
Shiny	Not shiny
Good conductors of heat and electricity	Poor conductors of heat and electricity
Oxides usually soluble in acid solutions	Oxides usually soluble in basic solutions

t2N8, m6N, t4N, m4N8

What strange numbers! They look like
football signals or a spy's code. Actually
these numbers and letters are a
shorthand way of indicating the purity
of metals. The N stands for nine, the
number before it tells how many nines,
and the number after N is the next digit
in the percent purity. Thus t2N8
means 99.8% pure; m6N means
99.9999% pure! The small m and t
indicate that the purity is in terms of
metallic elements only and total
impurity.

As you might guess, there is an
expense to purifying material. The
figure shows the relation for aluminum.

This same kind of steeply rising curve
occurs in all cases as purity increases.
Such curves must be considered in
pricing semiconductors for electronic
circuits as well as in deciding acceptable
pollution levels. When you want the
impurity level reduced to $\frac{1}{10}$ that
already attained in a given product, the
cost will be 5–10 times greater.

It was difficult to decide how to classify a few substances. Mercury
has many metallic properties, but it is a liquid at room temperature.
Carbon, in the form of graphite, is a good conductor of electricity,
but carbon in the form of diamond is a poor conductor. Even
though graphite and diamond have very high melting temperatures, chemists consider carbon to be a nonmetal.

By about 1800 chemists knew that many metals and nonmetals
reacted with oxygen in the air. They also could establish the
ratio between the number of moles of an element and the number
of moles of oxygen in the compounds that formed. A few examples
will help you see what this statement means.

TABLE 7-2
Formation of Oxides

Reaction	Moles of Atoms of First Element / Moles of Oxygen Atoms
$4\,Na\ +\ O_2 \longrightarrow 2\,Na_2O$	$\frac{4}{2} = \frac{2}{1}$
$2\,Mg +\ O_2 \longrightarrow 2\,MgO$	$\frac{2}{2} = \frac{1}{1}$
$4\,Al\ +\ 3\,O_2 \longrightarrow 2\,Al_2O_3$	$\frac{4}{6} = \frac{2}{3}$
$C\ +\ O_2 \longrightarrow\ CO_2$	$\frac{1}{2}$

Perhaps the elements could be divided into classes based on their
oxide formulas. This procedure worked well with many elements.
BeO, MgO, and CaO would form a group and so would be B_2O_3,
Al_2O_3, and Cr_2O_3. However, at this stage in the development of
chemistry there were too many confusing facts for chemists to
proceed with this scheme. For example, the element iron forms
several oxides—FeO, Fe_2O_3, and Fe_3O_4. Where would iron be
placed in the oxide grouping? Another example is even more
troublesome. Na_2O, K_2O, H_2O, and Cl_2O have the same type of

formula. But in many ways these compounds are quite different. Therefore, it is not reasonable to group the elements Na, K, H, and Cl together. It took chemists many years to unscramble some of these perplexing problems.

7-1 The Periodic Table

John Dalton proposed in his atomic theory that atoms of each element would have a characteristic mass. It was natural that chemists began to think of arranging the elements in the order of their molar masses. A number of the suggested regularities were similar to the statement by the person in the forest, "Cylindrical objects burn." Slowly, additional observations and more precise measurements resulted in an arrangement of the elements by the Russian chemist Dimitri Mendeleev. This arrangement is summarized in the periodic table of the elements. Mendeleev arranged the elements in groups according to their chemical properties. He noted that there were gaps in his arrangement. The regularities were so strong that the few irregularities must have some explanation. This led him to predict that new elements would be discovered. In addition, he even predicted the properties of these elements and of their compounds. Table 7-3 compares Mendeleev's predictions with the observed properties for scandium, gallium, and germanium.

Science historians trace the development of scientific ideas and relate them to the culture and events of the times.

TABLE 7-3

Properties of the Elements Scandium, Gallium, and Germanium

Property	Mendeleev's Predictions in 1871	Observed Properties
Scandium (Discovered in 1877)		
Molar mass	44 g	43.7 g
Oxide formula	M_2O_3	Sc_2O_3
Density of oxide	3.5 g/ml	3.86 g/ml
Solubility of oxide	Dissolves in acids	Dissolves in acids
Gallium (Discovered in 1875)		
Molar mass	68 g	69.4 g
Density of metal	6.0 g/ml	5.96 g/ml
Melting temperature	Low	30 °C
Oxide formula	M_2O_3	Ga_2O_3
Solubility of oxide	Dissolves in ammonia solution	Dissolves in ammonia solution
Germanium (Discovered in 1886)		
Molar mass	72 g	71.9 g
Density of metal	5.5 g/ml	5.47 g/ml
Color of metal	Dark gray	Grayish white
Melting temperature of metal	High	900 °C
Oxide formula	MO_2	GeO_2
Density of oxide	4.7 g/ml	4.70 g/ml
Chloride formula	MCl_4	$GeCl_4$
Density of chloride	1.9 g/ml	1.89 g/ml
Boiling temperature of chloride	Below 100 °C	86 °C

Rather than just duplicating the line of reasoning that led Mendeleev to his periodic table, we will also make use of the experimental information about the elements that is available to chemists today. Let us start by making a column of the elements, in order of increasing mass. A number of properties are placed beside each element in Table 7-4. The experimentally determined formulas for the hydride and fluoride are given for each element. Perhaps the first thing in this table that catches our eye concerns the elements He, Ne, and Ar. They are the only elements in our table that do not form hydrides and fluorides.

TABLE 7-4

Some Information About the First 21 Elements

Symbol for Element	Molar Mass (grams)	Numerical Order or Atomic Number	Physical State at 25 °C, 1 atm	Formula for Hydride	Ratio $\frac{H}{*}$	Formula for Fluoride	Ratio $\frac{F}{*}$	Ionization Energy (kcal/mol)
H	1.01	1	gas	H_2	1	HF	1	313.6
He	4.00	2	gas	—		—		567
Li	6.94	3	solid	LiH	1	LiF	1	124
Be	9.01	4	solid	BeH_2	2	BeF_2	2	215
B	10.8	5	solid	B_2H_6	3	BF_3	3	191
C	12.0	6	solid	CH_4	4	CF_4	4	260
N	14.0	7	gas	NH_3	3	NF_3	3	335
O	16.0	8	gas	H_2O	2	OF_2	2	314
F	19.0	9	gas	HF	1	F_2	1	402
Ne	20.2	10	gas	—		—		497
Na	23.0	11	solid	NaH	1	NaF	1	118
Mg	24.3	12	solid	MgH_2	2	MgF_2	2	175
Al	27.0	13	solid	Al_2H_6	3	AlF_3	3	138
Si	28.1	14	solid	SiH_4	4	SiF_4	4	188
P	31.0	15	solid	PH_3	3	PF_3	3	242
S	32.1	16	solid	H_2S	2	SF_2	2	239
Cl	35.5	17	gas	HCl	1	ClF	1	300
Ar	39.9	18	gas	—		—		363
K	39.1	19	solid	KH	1	KF	1	100
Ca	40.1	20	solid	CaH_2	2	CaF_2	2	141
Sc	45.0	21	solid	not known		ScF_3	3	151

*Other element in the compound.

Next, there seems to be a regularity in the combining ratios of the elements in hydrides and fluorides (1, 2, 3, 4, 3, 2, 1). Another important regularity can be seen in Table 7-4. When we reach Na, the set of chemical formulas is very much like the set for Li. The next element, Mg, has a set of chemical formulas like the set for Be. We can regroup these elements, starting with Na, placing each element directly below the element having similar formulas. The arrangement is shown in Table 7-5. The formula for the fluoride of each element is shown to help you recognize the similarity for each vertical group of elements. The word *periodicity* emphasizes that the formulas repeat themselves in a regular manner.

TABLE 7-5

Periodic Groups
for the Elements Helium to Scandium

							He 2
							—
Li 3 LiF	Be 4 BeF$_2$	B 5 BF$_3$	C 6 CF$_4$	N 7 NF$_3$	O 8 OF$_2$	F 9 F$_2$	Ne 10 —
Na 11 NaF	Mg 12 MgF$_2$	Al 13 AlF$_3$	Si 14 SiF$_4$	P 15 PF$_3$	S 16 SF$_2$	Cl 17 ClF	Ar 18 —
K 19 KF	Ca 20 CaF$_2$	Sc 21 ScF$_3$					

Chemical formulas and chemical properties across a row are very different as we move from one element to the next. On the other hand, formulas and properties of the elements in any vertical column are very similar. These vertical groups are called **chemical families** to emphasize similarities of the elements in each column.

You may be wondering why the first element, hydrogen, has been left out of our second arrangement of the elements. Compare the formulas H$_2$O and HF with the formulas Li$_2$O and LiF. The similarity in chemical formulas suggests that hydrogen should be in the same family with lithium. But now compare the formulas OH$_2$ and H$_2$ with formulas OF$_2$ and F$_2$. Perhaps hydrogen should be in the same family with fluorine. Chemists recognize that hydrogen is an unusual element. Some of its chemical properties indicate hydrogen should be placed with lithium. Other properties call for hydrogen to be grouped with fluorine. The problem is solved in the complete periodic table, presented in Figure 7-1, by giving the element hydrogen a separate box.

7-2 Predicted Properties of the Super-Heavy Elements

The periodic table is not a 100-year-old antique, interesting only as a historic step in science. It is in active daily use. For example, until 1939 uranium was the element with the highest known atomic number, 92. Since that time chemists and physicists have been able to make 14 new elements with atomic numbers 93 to 106, using nuclear reactions. The periodic table was of great help in these syntheses. There have been predictions that elements with atomic numbers around 114 may be stable enough that they can be synthesized. Scientists in the United States and Russia are attempting to make these super-heavy elements. To help in the search for them, their properties have been predicted in the same way that Mendeleev did for scandium, gallium, and germanium. Table 7-6 summarizes some of the predictions made by scientists at Oak Ridge National Laboratory in 1970.

H$_2$ is an important commercial chemical. It is used in the production of NH$_3$, in the conversion of oils to fats (Crisco and Spry), and in high-temperature welding. Some H$_2$ is made by the electrolysis of water and some from the water gas reaction:

steam + C $\longrightarrow$ CO + H$_2$.

Most comes from methane in several steps that can be summarized:

CH$_4$ + 2 H$_2$O $\longrightarrow$ CO$_2$ + 4 H$_2$.

Abundance of the Elements (percent of atoms)

Universe		Earth's Crust	
H	91	O	47
He	9.1	Si	28
O	0.057	Al	7.9
N	0.042	Fe	4.5
C	0.021	Ca	3.5
Si	0.003	Na	2.5
Ne	0.003	K	2.5
Mg	0.002	Mg	2.2
Fe	0.002	Ti	0.46
S	0.001	H	0.22
		C	0.19

Seawater		Human Body	
H	66	H	63
O	33	O	25.5
Cl	0.33	C	9.5
Na	0.28	N	1.4
Mg	0.033	Ca	0.31
S	0.017	P	0.22
Ca	0.006	Cl	0.03
K	0.006	K	0.06
C	0.0014	S	0.05
Br	0.0005	Na	0.03
		Mg	0.01

PERIODIC TABLE

Row																	
1	1 1.0080 H Hydrogen																	2 4.003 He Helium
2	3 6.941 Li Lithium	4 9.012 Be Beryllium											5 10.81 B Boron	6 12.011 C Carbon	7 14.007 N Nitrogen	8 15.999 O Oxygen	9 19.00 F Fluorine	10 20.179 Ne Neon
3	11 22.990 Na Sodium	12 24.30 Mg Magne- sium											13 26.98 Al Aluminum	14 28.09 Si Silicon	15 30.974 P Phos- phorus	16 32.064 S Sulfur	17 35.453 Cl Chlorine	18 39.948 Ar Argon
4	19 39.098 K Potassium	20 40.08 Ca Calcium	21 44.96 Sc Scandium	22 47.90 Ti Titanium	23 50.94 V Vanadium	24 52.00 Cr Chromium	25 54.94 Mn Manganese	26 55.85 Fe Iron	27 58.93 Co Cobalt	28 58.70 Ni Nickel	29 63.55 Cu Copper	30 65.38 Zn Zinc	31 69.72 Ga Gallium	32 72.59 Ge Germa- nium	33 74.92 As Arsenic	34 78.96 Se Selenium	35 79.904 Br Bromine	36 83.80 Kr Krypton
5	37 85.47 Rb Rubidium	38 87.62 Sr Strontium	39 88.91 Y Yttrium	40 91.22 Zr Zirconium	41 92.91 Nb Niobium	42 95.94 Mo Molyb- denum	43 (97) Tc Techne- tium	44 101.1 Ru Ruthe- nium	45 102.91 Rh Rhodium	46 106.4 Pd Palladium	47 107.868 Ag Silver	48 112.40 Cd Cadmium	49 114.82 In Indium	50 118.69 Sn Tin	51 121.75 Sb Antimony	52 127.60 Te Tellurium	53 126.90 I Iodine	54 131.30 Xe Xenon
6	55 132.90 Cs Cesium	56 137.34 Ba Barium	57-71 * La-Lu Below	72 178.49 Hf Hafnium	73 180.95 Ta Tantalum	74 183.85 W Tungsten	75 186.2 Re Rhenium	76 190.2 Os Osmium	77 192.2 Ir Iridium	78 195.09 Pt Platinum	79 197.0 Au Gold	80 200.59 Hg Mercury	81 204.37 Tl Thallium	82 207.2 Pb Lead	83 208.98 Bi Bismuth	84 (209) Po Polonium	85 (210) At Astatine	86 (222) Rn Radon
7	87 (223) Fr Francium	88 (226) Ra Radium	89-103 † Ac-Lr Below	104 (261)	105 (262)	106												

*LANTHANIDE SERIES 6	57 138.91 La Lantha- num	58 140.12 Ce Cerium	59 140.92 Pr Praso- dymium	60 144.24 Nd Neody- mium	61 (145) Pm Prome- thium	62 150.35 Sm Samarium	63 152.0 Eu Europium	64 157.25 Gd Gadoli- nium	65 158.93 Tb Terbium	66 162.50 Dy Dyspro- sium	67 164.93 Ho Holmium	68 167.26 Er Erbium	69 168.93 Tm Thulium	70 173.04 Yb Ytterbium	71 174.97 Lu Lutetium
†ACTINIDE SERIES 7	89 (227) Ac Actinium	90 232.04 Th Thorium	91 (231) Pa Protac- tinium	92 238.03 U Uranium	93 (237) Np Neptu- nium	94 (244) Pu Plutonium	95 (243) Am Ameri- cium	96 (247) Cm Curium	97 (247) Bk Berkelium	98 (251) Cf Califor- nium	99 (254) Es Einstei- nium	100 (257) Fm Fermium	101 (258) Md Mendele- vium	102 (255) No Nobelium	103 (260) Lr Lawren- cium

Figure 7-1
The periodic table.

Mendeleev and the Periodic Table, or "Wooden Tables Burn"

The person in the dream provided a nontechnical way to see how the conclusions drawn from experiment and observation can lead to a regularity. It also showed that often the first regularity is not the best. Mendeleev's struggle with the periodic table is a real example of a "wooden tables burn" rule. Here is Mendeleev's first version (March 1869):

```
1                         H                      Li
2                      Be  B   C   N   O   F  Na
3                      Mg  Al  Si  P   S   Cl  K  Ca  —  Er? Y? In?
4  Ti V Cr Mn Fe Ni,Co Cu Zn  —   —   As  Se  Br Rb  Sr Ce La Di Tb
5  Zr Nb Mo Rh Ru   Pd  Ag Cd  U   Sn  Sb  Te  I  Cs  Ba
6  —  Ta W  Pt Ir   Os  Hg  —  Au  —   Bi  —   —  Tl  Pb
```

Note the "errors" in terms of our modern table. How many can you find?

Early in 1870 Mendeleev published a different arrangement in which he folded the longer rows to get a narrower table:

```
1  Li  Be  B   C   N   O   F
2  Na  Mg  Al  Si  P   S   Cl
3  K   Ca  —   Ti  V        Cr Mn Fe Ni,Co
4  Cu  Zn  —   —   As  Se  Br
5  Rb  Sr  —   Zr  Nb       Mo Rh Ru   Pd
6  Ag  Cd  U   Sn  Sb  Te  I
7  Cs  Ba  —   —   —   —
8  —   —   —   —   Ta  W        Au Pt Os Ir,Hg?
9  Tl  Pb  Bi? —   —   —   —
```

This brings many of the correct elements together but introduces other problems. For example, Li, Na, K, Rb, and Cs are now in a column; but Cu, Ag, and Tl are also there. In December 1870 Mendeleev published yet another version.

Groups		I	II	III	IV	V	VI	VII	VIII
Typical Elements		H Li	Be	B	C	N	O	F	
Periods	Series								
1	1 2	Na K	Mg Ca	Al —	Si Ti	P V	S Cr	Cl Mn	Fe, Co, Ni, Cu
2	3 4	(Cu) Rb	Zn Sr	— Y?	— Zr	As Nb	Se Mo	Br —	Ru, Rh, Pd, Ag
3	5 6	(Ag) Cs	Cd Ba	In —	Sn Ce	Sb —	Te —	I —	
4	7 8	— —	— —	— —	— —	— Ta	— W	— —	Os, Ir, Pt, Au
5	9 10	(Au) —	Hg —	Tl —	Pb Th	Bi —	— U	— —	

Here he sets the "misfits" from the previous table to the right in each column. This table was used by chemists for over 50 years.

Finally, in 1871 Mendeleev proposed a table essentially as used in this book:

```
H                                           H
Li  Be                                      Li  Be  B   C   N   O   F
Na  Mg                                      Na  Mg  Al  Si  P   S   Cl
 K  Ca  –   Ti  V   Cr  Mn  Fe  Co  Ni  Cu  Zn  –   –   As  Se  Br
Rb  Sr  Y?  Zr  Nb  Mo  –   Ru  Rh  Pd  Ag  Cd  In  Sn  Sb  Te  I
Cs  Ba  Di? Ce  –   –   –   –   –   –   –   –   –   –   –   –   –
 –   –  Er  La? Ta? W   –   Os  Ir  Pt  Au  Hg  Tl  Pb  Bi  –   –
 –   –   –  Th  –   U   –   –   –   –   –   –   –   –   –   –   –
```

We have moved the five elements shown in color to heighten the correspondence. The only remaining errors are at Di?, Ce, Er, and La?.

Science really does grow by the same scheme as shown in the dream.

Chemists use the periodic table to predict properties of molecules.

Chemists have recently shown that part of a particular meteorite may have been produced by the radioactive decay of a super-heavy element.

TABLE 7-6
Predicted Properties of the
Super-Heavy Elements, 113 and 114

Property	Element 113	Element 114
Chemical properties	Like thallium	Like lead
Molar mass	297	298
Density of metal	16 g/ml	14 g/ml
Melting temperature of metal	700 K	340 K
Boiling temperature of metal	1400 K	420 K

The predictions that chemical properties of elements 113 and 114 will be very similar to the properties of thallium and lead should be of great help in trying to synthesize and identify these super-heavy elements.

7-3 Ionization Energy

Values for the first ionization energy are plotted in Figure 7-2 and listed in the last column of Table 7-4. This is a property that is different for each element. The **ionization energy** is the amount of energy for the reaction

$$M(g) + \text{ionization energy} \longrightarrow M^+(g) + e^-$$

All elements undergo ionization to form a positive ion if enough energy is supplied. As you can readily see, the ionization energy increases and decreases in a regular fashion as we proceed from one element to the next. We will now use ionization energy and other properties to examine some of the important chemical families in detail.

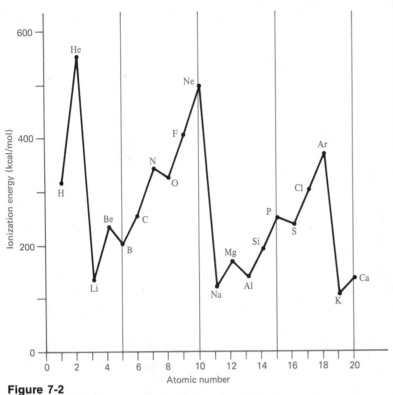

Figure 7-2
The relation between ionization energy and atomic number of the elements.

7-4 The Noble Gases

Almost two centuries ago an English scientist, Cavendish, tried to convert atmospheric nitrogen into nitric oxides. There was always a small amount of gas that would not react. He was not able to explain this result. When these experiments were repeated in 1894, other scientists found the same result. No matter what chemical tests were tried, some of the gas would not enter any chemical reactions. It was concluded that a new element had been discovered. It was given the name *argon* from the Greek word meaning "lazy." Additional careful experiments led to the isolation of four other gases from the atmosphere. The names *helium, neon, krypton,* and *xenon* were given to these elements. If you look back to Table 6-1, you can see that, with the exception of argon, the amount of each noble gas in the atmosphere is very small.

It is interesting to realize that almost thirty years earlier helium had been identified in the sun's atmosphere. When any substance is heated to a high enough temperature, light is emitted that is characteristic of the elements in the substance. During an eclipse of the sun in 1868 light in the sun's corona was observed that did not match any known element. On this basis a new element, called *helium*, was proposed in 1871. The noble gas elements precede each of the elements lithium, sodium, potassium, rubidium, and cesium. As we shall see in the next chapters, the noble gases supply an important key to understanding atomic structure. It is a curious quirk of nature that these gases are so

Ionization Energy Helps Discover New Compounds

Early in 1962 Professor Neil Bartlett, while working at the University of British Columbia, was experimenting with fluorides of heavy metals. One reaction was of special interest:

$$PtF_6(g) + O_2(g) \longrightarrow O_2^+PtF_6^-(s)$$

Analysis showed that the solid was ionic and the oxygen was in a positive oxidation state. This meant the PtF_6 was able to remove an electron from $O_2(g)$. Next, Bartlett made new use of some facts already known to many chemists. The ionization energy for $O_2(g)$ is 290 kcal/mol and for Xe is 278 kcal/mol. To Bartlett this meant PtF_6 should be able to take an electron away from Xe and consequently form a bond. This suggestion was contrary to the widely known fact that no inert gas compounds existed. Yet the ionization energy values seemed right for making some. The gases were mixed and the first inert gas compound was formed:

$$Xe(g) + PtF_6(g) \longrightarrow XePtF_6(s)$$

The inert gases were not so inert after all! Their name was changed to noble gases. Still today, only a few dozen compounds exist that contain a noble gas.

important in the organization of our chemical knowledge. Of all the elements the noble gases are the least reactive chemically. Until 1962 it was thought that the noble gases formed no chemical compounds.

Some of the properties of the noble gases are given in Table 7-7. Each of these elements exists as a monatomic gas at room temperature.

TABLE 7-7

Some Properties of the Noble Gases

Property	He	Ne	Ar	Kr	Xe	Rn
Atomic number	2	10	18	36	54	86
Molar mass of atoms, grams	4.00	20.0	39.9	83.7	131	222
Boiling temperature, K	4.2	27.2	87.3	120	165	211
Melting temperature, K	—	24.6	83.9	116	161	202
Ionization energy, kcal/mol	567	497	363	323	280	248

Boiling Temperatures

As a chemical family the noble gases have the lowest boiling temperatures known. The values are shown in Figure 7-3. Helium has the lowest boiling temperature of any substance, 4.2 K. Neon, argon, krypton, xenon, and radon have successively higher boiling temperatures. We interpret a higher boiling temperature to mean greater attractive forces between molecules.

Melting Temperatures

The melting temperatures for the noble gases are shown in Figure 7-4. These unusual elements form solids at temperatures only

Chemists use argon and helium to provide inert atmospheres to stop unwanted reactions. Helium welding (Heliarc welding) is an important commercial process for joining metals.

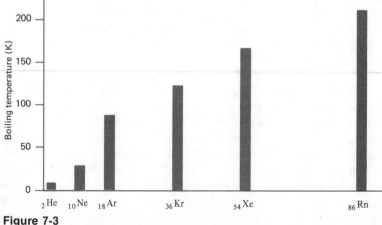

Figure 7-3

Trend in boiling temperature for the noble gases.

slightly below the temperatures at which they boil. The small temperature range in which these elements exist as liquids suggests that the forces holding the solids together are very much like the forces in the liquids. The forces between noble gas molecules in the liquid or the solid are quite small. No melting temperature for helium is listed in Table 7-6. Helium is the only substance, at one atmosphere pressure, that does not form a solid at any temperature. Helium becomes a solid at 1.1 K, at a pressure of 26 atmospheres. This fact indicates that the forces between helium molecules must be very weak.

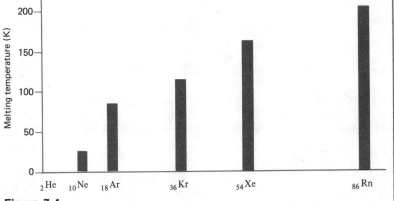

Figure 7-4
Trend in melting temperature for the noble gases.

Ionization Energy

The last property in Table 7-7 is the energy needed to ionize a mole of each noble gas. These energies form an important regularity. For the noble gases there is a decrease in ionization energy as we go from helium to neon to the others. These values are plotted in Figure 7-5. As we will see, within any row in the periodic table the ionization energy is highest for the noble gas element. The very stable atomic structures for these elements are indicated by the high ionization energies.

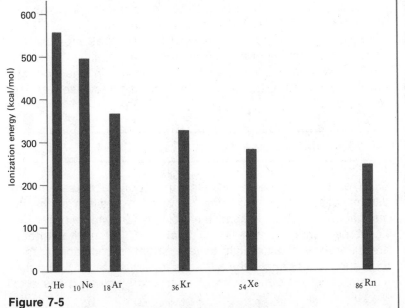

Figure 7-5
Trend in ionization energy for the noble gases.

Turning the Table on Refrigerants

The Freon compounds that are used to absorb heat in refrigerators and air conditioners were discovered in 1937 by Thomas Midgley, an American chemist. The following is his description of how the periodic table was used:

"What was wanted was obvious—a nontoxic, nonflammable refrigerant. The desired combination of properties was a boiling point between 0° and −40 °C, stability, nontoxicity, and nonflammability. I decided to bring into play the Periodic Table. Perhaps volatility could be related to it some way. It takes but a fraction of a second to see this is true. The elements on the right-hand side of the Periodic Table are the only ones which make compounds sufficiently volatile for the purpose in hand. In fact, only a certain number of these need to be considered. Volatile compounds of boron, silicon, phosphorus, arsenic, antimony, bismuth, selenium, tellurium, and iodine are all too unstable and toxic to consider. Now look over the remaining elements—carbon, nitrogen, oxygen, fluorine, sulfur, chlorine and bromine. Every refrigerant used has been made from combinations of these elements. Flammability decreases from left to right. Toxicity usually decreases from the heavy elements at the bottom to lighter elements at the top. These two trends focus on fluorine. It was an exciting deduction. Seemingly no one previously had considered it possible that fluorine might be nontoxic in some of its compounds."

Numerous Freons are now made to provide useful kinds of refrigerators, air conditioners and freezers for preparing or storing foods.

Chemical Properties

Another unique property of the noble gases lies in their very low chemical reactivity. This fact will be an important clue for us when we discuss atomic structure in Chapter 9. Compounds of these elements were made in 1962. Most of these compounds decompose readily to give the noble gas as one of the products. Some of the compounds are described in Table 7-8.

TABLE 7-8

Some Noble Gas Compounds

Compound	Melting Temperature °C	Properties
XeF_2	140	Reacts with H_2O to form Xe and O_2
XeF_4	114	Stable
XeF_6	48	Stable
XeO_3	—	Explosive; stable in aqueous solution
KrF_2	Sublimes below 0 °C	Decomposes spontaneously at room temperature

Everything that is known about the noble gases indicates that they have particularly stable atomic structures.

We turn now to the two chemical families that appear in the periodic table on either side of the noble gas family. In these two families we can see some of the regularities in chemical and physical properties that make the periodic table so valuable to chemists.

7-5 The Alkali Elements

Each of the **alkali elements**—lithium, sodium, potassium, rubidium, cesium, and francium—occupies a position in the numerical order of the elements immediately following a noble gas. These elements are metallic solids at 25 °C. When the surfaces are clean, the alkali metals have a bright, silvery appearance. Exposure to air causes the surfaces to tarnish rapidly. The metals are excellent conductors of heat and electricity. The alkali

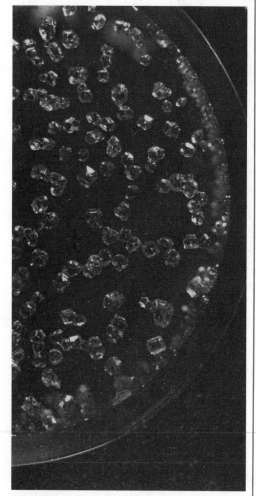

The crystals of two xenon compounds, XeF_2 and XeF_4, are here magnified ten times.

metals have very high chemical reactivity. Some of their properties are listed in Table 7-9. Francium is not included, since it is a very rare element.

TABLE 7-9
Some Properties of the Alkali Metals

Property	Li	Na	K	Rb	Cs
Atomic number	3	11	19	37	55
Molar mass of atoms (grams)	6.94	23.0	39.1	85.4	133
Boiling temperature (°C)	1326	889	757	700	670
(K)	1599	1162	1030	973	943
Melting temperature (°C)	180	98	63	39	29
(K)	453	371	336	312	302
Density at 20 °C (g/ml)	0.54	0.97	0.86	1.53	1.90
Ionization energy (kcal/mol)	124	119	100	96	90

Some Uses of Rarely Mentioned Elements

$_{60}$Nd	Neodymium	Its oxide, NdO, is the only chemical that makes a bright purple glass
$_{39}$Y	Yttrium	Used to make a suitable red in television tubes
$_{63}$Eu	Europium	
$_{61}$Pm	Promethium	Man-made element. ^{147}Pm produces electricity in batteries that last for five years even in extreme temperatures
$_{45}$Rh	Rhodium	Used to harden platinum in jewelry
$_{46}$Pd	Palladium	Used to face contact points in sealed electric switches
$_{58}$Ce	Cerium	Used in flints for gas lighters
$_{49}$In	Indium	Used to make mirrors that are more resistant to atmospheric corrosion than are silver mirrors
$_{64}$Gd	Gadolinium	All are used to make X-ray film more sensitive so that a suitable picture can be produced with less exposure time
$_{65}$Tb	Terbium	
$_{57}$La	Lanthanum	
$_{69}$Tm	Thulium	^{170}Tm emits gamma rays that can be used in portable X-ray machines to aid doctors and archaeologists in the field

---

Boiling and Melting Temperatures

The alkali metals are solids at room temperature. Cesium, however, melts at a few degrees above room temperature. Both melting and boiling temperatures decrease as the molar masses increase. This is opposite to the trend found for the noble gases.

130

Elements in You

Very common	H, C, N, O
Scarce	Na, Mg, P, S, Cl, K, Ca
Very scarce (but essential)	F, Si, V, Cr, Mn, Fe, Co, Cu, Zn, Se, Mo, Sn, I

The first four make up 63%, 25.5%, 9.5%, and 1.4% respectively, of your atoms. The other 20 account for the remaining 0.7%.

Order Among Atoms

Figure 7-6 and Figure 7-7 contrast the trends for these two families. Notice also the wide temperature range over which the alkali elements are liquids. Sodium, for instance, melts at 98 °C and boils at 889 °C, almost 800 °C higher. Contrast this with neon, which boils 2.6 °C higher than it melts. How different are the alkali elements from the noble gases!

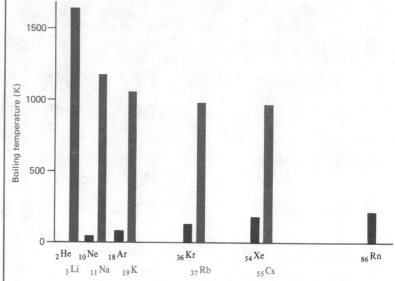

Figure 7-6
Comparison of boiling temperatures for the noble gases and the alkali metals.

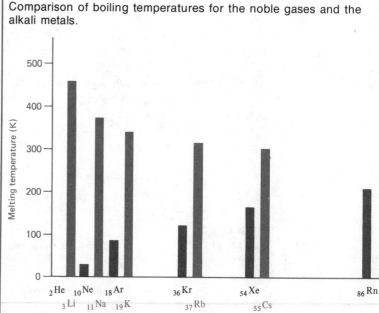

Figure 7-7
Comparison of melting temperatures for the alkali metals and the noble gases.

Ionization Energy

Very little energy is required to ionize the alkali elements. Again we see a great difference between the noble gases and the alkali metals. Figure 7-8 contrasts the ionization energies for these two chemical families. For each family the ionization energy decreases as the atomic number increases.

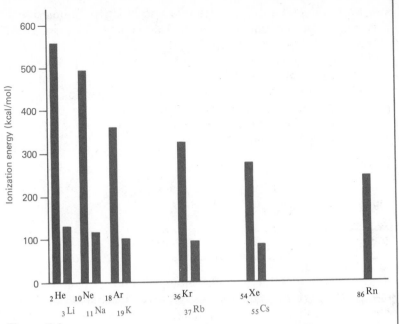

Figure 7-8
Comparison of ionization energies for the alkali metals
and the noble gases.

Electrical engineers have proposed the use of sodium-cored wire for long-distance power transmission.

Chemical Properties of the Alkali Metals

The alkali metals have high chemical reactivity. They react vigorously with oxygen, chlorine, or water. It will be interesting to investigate some of these reactions.

When chlorine gas is brought into contact with hot sodium metal, solid sodium chloride is formed.

$$2\,Na(l) + Cl_2(g) \longrightarrow 2\,NaCl(s) + energy$$

We have seen in Chapter 6 that solid NaCl has a regular arrangement of sodium ions (Na^+) and chloride ions (Cl^-) in the crystal. In the reaction between sodium and chlorine, ions are formed. The ions attract each other because they have opposite electric charge. The stability of the sodium chloride crystal depends on the electrical attraction of oppositely charged ions. The crystal is held together by ionic bonds. This chemical behavior is characteristic of all the alkali metals. Each alkali metal reacts with chlorine gas in a similar way. Ionic solids, which are soluble in water, form in these reactions.

EXERCISE 7-1

Write the four equations for the reactions between chlorine and lithium, potassium, rubidium, and cesium.

Reaction of the Alkali Metals with Water

Sodium metal reacts with water to form hydrogen gas and an aqueous solution of sodium hydroxide, NaOH.

$$2\,Na(s) + 2\,H_2O \longrightarrow 2\,Na^+(aq) + 2\,OH^-(aq) + H_2(g) + energy$$

Energy is liberated. The reaction often takes place so rapidly that the temperature rises and the hydrogen, mixing with air, explodes. Sodium metal is dangerous and must be handled with caution. Sodium is usually stored in oil so that moisture in air does not come into contact with the metal.

All the alkali metals react with water in a similar way. The reaction becomes more vigorous as we examine each metal from lithium to cesium. Two ions are formed in each reaction. The first is an alkali element ion with a charge of 1+. The other ion, $OH^-(aq)$, is called the **hydroxide ion**. The properties of basic solutions are attributed to this ion.

EXERCISE 7-2

Write the four equations for the reactions between water and lithium, potassium, rubidium, and cesium.

7-6   The Halogens

If we move across the periodic table, we find a column of elements called the **halogens**. They have the names *fluorine, chlorine, bromine, iodine,* and *astatine.* Astatine is a very rare element. It will not be part of our discussion.

Some of the physical properties of the halogens are given in Table 7-10. In the elemental state the halogens form stable diatomic molecules. At very high temperatures these diatomic molecules break down to form atoms. For example, it is known that chlorine near the surface of the sun is present as single chlorine atoms. At lower temperatures chlorine atoms react with each other to form molecules.

$$2 \ Cl(g) \longrightarrow Cl_2(g) + \text{energy}$$

TABLE 7-10
Some Properties of the Halogens

Property	Fluorine	Chlorine	Bromine	Iodine
Atomic number	9	17	35	53
Molar mass of atoms (grams)	19.0	35.5	79.9	127
Molecular formula at 25 °C	F_2	Cl_2	Br_2	I_2
Boiling temperature (K)	85	238.9	331.8	457
(°C)	−188	−34.1	58.8	184
Melting temperature (K)	55	172	265.7	387
(°C)	−218	−101	−7.3	114
Color	Pale yellow	Yellow green	Red	Black (purple vapor)
State at 25 °C	gas	gas	liquid	solid
Ionization energy (kcal/mol)	402	300	273	241

Boiling and Melting Temperatures

We have already compared the boiling and melting temperatures for the noble gases and the alkali metals. When we look at those temperatures for the halogens in Figures 7-9 and 7-10, there seems to be some similarity with noble gases. The melting and boiling temperatures of the halogens increase as the molar masses increase. The trend here is similar to the trend shown by the noble gases.

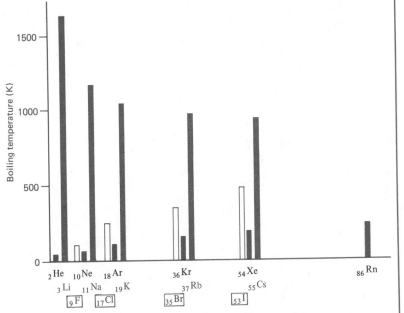

Figure 7-9
Boiling temperatures for the halogens, the alkali metals, and the noble gases.

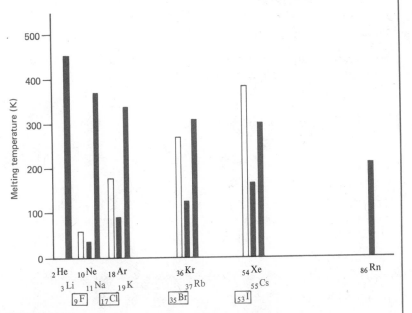

Figure 7-10
Comparison of melting temperatures for the halogens, the alkali metals, and the noble gases.

Terbium, Gadolinium, Yttrium, Europium

These are some of the rare-earth elements that are now serving us in hidden ways. One reason color TV screens are so bright is that yttrium oxide plus a little europium "activator" is used in phosphors. Phosphors absorb energy (from electron beams in the case of TV picture tubes) and emit visible light. The yttrium phosphors are 100% brighter than the older, weak red phosphors. They also allowed designers to use brighter greens and blues, so that the total picture was improved.

A less common example is the gadolinium and lanthanum phosphors with terbium activators. These materials are put in image-intensifying screens on X-ray machines. The practical result is less X-ray dosage for the patient. Thus there is less chance of damaging cells while making the X-ray picture.

Laboratory technicians in the textile and paper industries do many analyses of chlorine and its compounds in bleaching agents.

Order Among Atoms

Ionization Energy

The ionization energies for the halogens decrease as we go from fluorine to iodine. We have noticed this trend for the noble gases and for the alkali metals. Numerically, the ionization energies for the halogens are almost as large as the values for the noble gases. This fact indicates that it is difficult to remove an electron from the halogens. Figure 7-11 contrasts the ionization energies for the three families we have discussed in this chapter.

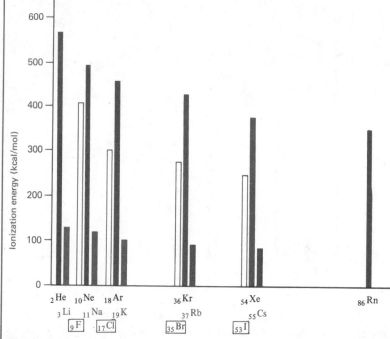

Figure 7-11
Comparison of ionization energies for the halogens, the alkali metals, and the noble gases.

The Chemistry of the Halogens

The reactions of the halogens with one of the alkali metals show similarity within this family.

$$2 K(s) + F_2(g) \longrightarrow 2 KF(s) + energy$$
$$2 K(s) + Cl_2(g) \longrightarrow 2 KCl(s) + energy$$
$$2 K(s) + Br_2(g) \longrightarrow 2 KBr(s) + energy$$
$$2 K(s) + I_2(g) \longrightarrow 2 KI(s) + energy$$

These reactions proceed readily. Ionic solids, with the general formula KX, form. Each of these white solids is crystalline, with the same structure that we saw for NaCl. The negative ions F^-, Cl^-, Br^-, and I^- are called **halide ions**.

EXERCISE 7-3

Write the equations for the reactions between each alkali metal and the halogen which is in the same row of the periodic table.

The halogens react with hydrogen gas to form the hydrogen halides:

$$H_2(g) + F_2(g) \longrightarrow 2\ HF(g) + energy$$
$$H_2(g) + Cl_2(g) \longrightarrow 2\ HCl(g) + energy$$
$$H_2(g) + Br_2(g) \longrightarrow 2\ HBr(g) + energy$$
$$H_2(g) + I_2(g) \longrightarrow 2\ HI(g) + energy$$

The hydrogen halides are gases at room temperature. The most important properties of the hydrogen halides are seen in their aqueous solutions. These compounds are very soluble in water. They give solutions that conduct electric current. This property suggests that ions are present. The reactions can be written in this way:

$$HF(g) + water \longrightarrow H^+(aq) + F^-(aq)$$
$$HCl(g) + water \longrightarrow H^+(aq) + Cl^-(aq)$$
$$HBr(g) + water \longrightarrow H^+(aq) + Br^-(aq)$$
$$HI(g) + water \longrightarrow H^+(aq) + I^-(aq)$$

These solutions have similar properties and are called acid solutions. The common ion in the solutions is the **aqueous hydrogen ion, $H^+(aq)$**. The properties of acid solutions are attributed to this ion. We will discuss acids and bases more extensively in Chapter 14.

7-7 Review

The periodic table proposed by the Russian chemist Mendeleev is one of the most important regularities in chemistry. By arranging the elements as in the diagram shown inside the back cover of this book, we can simplify the problem of understanding and remembering the large number of experimental observations made by chemists.

The elements grouped in vertical columns have very similar properties. In this chapter we have discussed three chemical families: the *noble gases*, the *alkali metals*, and the *halogens*. It is easy to see that general statements can be made about the chemical and physical properties of these elements and about the compounds they form. There will be many more examples in this book of the usefulness of the periodic table.

The search for an explanation of the periodic properties of the elements was a long one. The key was found to be an understanding of atomic structure, but this eluded scientists for many years. In the next two chapters we will outline the experiments and the interpretations that led to our present model of the atom.

Questions and Problems for Chapter 7

1

Use the periodic table to suggest formulas for compounds of these pairs of elements:

(a) antimony and bromine
(b) indium and sulfur
(c) tellurium and oxygen

2

Use the periodic table and your knowledge of chemicals to classify the following formulas as "probable," "possible," or "unlikely":

(a) IBr   (b) HSSSH
(c) $NeCl_2$ (d) $CH_3\overset{O}{\overset{\|}{C}}-O-O-H$ (e) NaO_2

3

Here is a list of chemicals: NaF, NaOH, H_2Se, CS_2, $AlCl_3$, Na_3PO_4. Use them and the periodic table to suggest values of x and y in the following formulas:

(a) $Al_x(OH)_y$ (c) Sn_xSe_y
(b) $Tl_x(PO_4)_y$ (d) $Ba_x(PO_4)_y$

4

Use Figure 7-2 to rationalize the fact that solid NaF contains Na^+ and F^- ions rather than neutral atoms.

5

Do the symbols used to represent the elements show any regularities as they are arranged in the periodic table?

6

Is there any regularity exhibited by the location of gaseous elements in the periodic table (at STP)?

7

Use the periodic table and your knowledge of experimental uncertainty to explain why early chemists could believe that elemental molar masses were multiples of the molar mass of hydrogen.

8

Write the molecular formulas of the hydrogen compounds of the second-row elements, Li, Be, B, C, N, O, F, and Ne. Indicate, for each compound, the H/M atom ratio.

9

Use Table 7-4 and the periodic table to suggest formulas for compounds of the following pairs of elements:

(a) strontium-sulfur   (d) chlorine-iodine
(b) gallium-fluorine   (e) arsenic-bromine
(c) beryllium-tellurium

10

The metallic elements Na, Mg, and Si in row 3 of the periodic table have atomic radii of 1.9, 1.60, and 1.3 Å. Estimate the size of an aluminum atom in a metal sample.

11

Consider these heats of vaporization of some elements in row 5 of the periodic table: Y, 94; Zr, 139; Mo, 142; Tc, 138; Rh, 118; and Ag, 61 kcal/mol. Estimate values for Nb, Pd, and Ru.

12

For the super-heavy element 114 predict:

(a) the formula of its chloride
(b) whether the sulfate is soluble
(c) whether the first ionization energy is less than 200 kcal/mol.

13

Use these values of metallic density to predict a value for lead: Ge 5.5g/ml, Sn 6.0g/ml, (114) 14g/ml (estimated).

14

If scientists continue to create elements beyond 106, what number do you predict for the next noble gas?

15

What is the significance of the trends in the boiling temperatures and melting temperatures of the noble gases in terms of attractions among the atoms?

16

Why is argon used in many electric lights?

17

Use the information in Table 7-9 to prepare a column listing the properties of element 87, francium. Give balanced equations for some chemical reactions expected for francium.

18

Use the information in Table 7-10 to prepare a column listing the properties of element 85, astatine. List some chemical reactions expected for astatine.

19

How do the trends in physical properties for the halogens compare with those for the noble gases? Compare boiling temperatures, melting temperatures, and ionization energies.

20

Chlorine is commonly used to purify drinking water. When chlorine dissolves in water, it forms hypochlorous acid,

$$Cl_2 + H_2O \longrightarrow HOCl(aq) + H^+(aq) + Cl^-(aq)$$

Predict what happens when iodine, I_2, dissolves in water. Write the chemical equation for the reaction.

21

The metals of the second column of the periodic

table combine with the halogens to form ionic solids. Write a general equation to represent these reactions, using M for the metals and X for the halogens.

22

The size of an atom can be expressed as the closest distance of approach by another atom. For the halogens the values are F, 1.35; Cl, 1.80; and Br, 1.95 Å. Estimate the value for iodine.

23

Which of the following is NOT a correct formula for a substance at normal laboratory conditions?

(a) $H_2S(g)$ (d) $NaNe(s)$
(b) $CaCl_2(s)$ (e) $Al_2O_3(s)$
(c) $He(g)$

24

From the following experimental information, identify which chemical family and which element are described. Answer each part separately.

Identify the specific element as soon as possible.

Element A:

(a) has an ionization energy of more than 400 kcal/mol.
(b) is a gas at room temperature.
(c) reacts readily with element number 11 to form an ionic solid.
(d) has the highest ionization energy of any element in the family.

Element B:

(a) has an ionization energy < 400 kcal/mol.
(b) has a boiling temperature above 800 °C.
(c) reacts with certain elements to form ionic solids.
(d) reacts with hydrogen in a one-to-one ratio.
(e) reacts with water to liberate hydrogen gas.
(f) has the lowest molar mass and density of any element in the family.

Element C:

(a) is not known to form a hydride.
(b) has a boiling temperature below 25 °C.
(c) has an ionization energy < 300 kcal/mol.
(d) forms compounds with both fluorine and oxygen.

25

Melting temperatures of some alkali metal chlorides are: KCl (772 °C), RbCl (717 °C), and CsCl (645 °C). Predict the melting temperature of NaCl.

26

In general, the molar mass of elements increases as the atomic number increases. Find several pairs of elements in the periodic table that are exceptions to this generalization.

27

Look up the origin of the names of two elements. The more unusual names might have the more interesting histories.

28

You know some of the properties of nickel and platinum. Predict some of the properties of palladium.

29

You know some of the properties of chromium and tungsten. Predict some of the properties of molybdenum.

30

Germanium is used in many transistors. Gallium is added to make an electron-deficient area in a transistor. Suggest another element that might serve this purpose.

31

You probably know that calcium occurs in your bones. Why is radioactive strontium 90 so dangerous to your health?

32

Give the symbol and location in the periodic table for the elements with the following characteristics:

(a) the largest ionization energy
(b) the lowest ionization energy
(c) the smallest atomic radius
(d) the element that reacts most vigorously with water to produce hydrogen gas

33

When fluorine gas, F_2, reacts with water, a violent reaction occurs. Oxygen gas, O_2, and hydrofluoric acid, $HF(aq)$, are produced. Write the equation for this reaction.

34

Zinc metal reacts with a solution of chlorine in water.

$$Zn(s) + Cl_2(aq) \longrightarrow Zn^{2+}(aq) + 2\,Cl^-(aq)$$

Use the idea of electron transfer to explain how the neutral atoms became ions.

8 Composition of the Atom and Radioactivity

The end of the 19th and the beginning of the 20th centuries was a time of turmoil in chemistry and physics. The concept of the atom proposed by John Dalton in 1803 was no longer able to explain the discoveries being made. But it had served a useful apprenticeship. Atoms during the 19th century were thought to be hard, indestructible spheres. Each element had a different kind of atom, and all atoms of a particular element were identical. Each kind of atom had a certain capacity to combine with other kinds of atoms. These ideas had been very useful to chemists who were able to analyze substances, to produce useful metals and alloys and other important chemicals, to synthesize colorful dyes and life-saving drugs, to discover 53 new elements that had not been known before 1800, and to bring order to the field of chemistry with the development of the periodic table.

At the same time many physicists were carrying out experiments on the conduction of electricity in gases. At first glance this might seem to have very little to do with chemistry. However, these experiments led to the discovery of X rays, radioactivity, the electron, and the proton. It became necessary to replace the Dalton model for the atom. "Cylindrical objects burn" was a useful regularity for a while; then the character in the dream changed it to "Wooden objects burn." In a similar way Dalton's model for the atom was used for a century and then replaced, in rapid succession, by the Thomson model, then the Rutherford model and Bohr models. These new models were proposed in the short space of ten years to provide explanations for new experiments. A true revolution in scientific thinking took place. This is a fascinating part of the history of science. In this chapter we will look briefly at the experiments that brought about this revolution. Their detailed treatment is presented in advanced chemistry and physics courses. For our purpose it is only necessary that you understand the general concepts, because these experiments provided the clues to the internal parts of atoms and eventually led to our present model for atomic structure.

The discussion in this chapter does not proceed in strict chronological fashion. First, we will outline some of the experiments that led to the nuclear model for the atom. Then in the next chapter the electronic structure around the nucleus will be discussed. Taken together, these provided chemists and physicists with a new model for the whole atom.

8-1 Conductivity of Electricity in Gases and the Discovery of the Electron

Look carefully at the apparatus outlined in Figure 8-1. Metal electrodes are sealed in each end of a long glass tube. Our main focus will be on the tube and what happens when a high voltage, about 10 000 volts, is applied to the electrodes. When the gas pressure in the tube is at one atmosphere, no electric current flows through the tube. When the gas pressure is decreased to about 0.01 atmosphere, an electric current flows. At the same time light is emitted by the gas. You have seen this phenomenon many times. The neon lights used in advertising signs operate this way.

Computer designers use cathode ray tubes to transfer pictorial information into and out of computers.

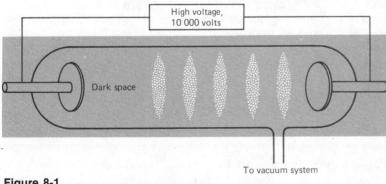

Figure 8-1
Gaseous discharge tube.

Tube designers, lighting experts, television repairmen, and X-ray and electronic technicians are among those who need to understand what is happening in gas discharge tubes.

As the gas pressure in the tube is decreased further to about 10^{-6} atmosphere, the light from the gas disappears. But a new phenomenon appears. The glass of the tube glows with a faint greenish light. We say that the glass fluoresces. In 1895 Wilhelm Röntgen noted something strange about this glow. It ionized the air around the gas discharge tube. Yet even when he blocked out the green light with an opaque screen, the air was still ionized. Röntgen named this new type of radiation X rays. Where did this radiation, which could pass through a piece of paper or metal, come from? Did the radiation result from some kind of change in the atoms in the glass? Was Dalton's idea of indestructible atoms beginning to fail? The experiments required a new model for the atom. The experiment illustrated in Figure 8-2 provides information to help answer these questions.

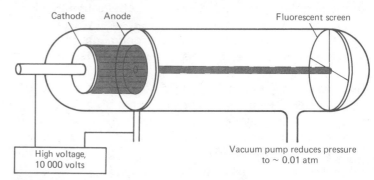

Cathode Anode   Fluorescent screen

High voltage, 10 000 volts

Vacuum pump reduces pressure to ~ 0.01 atm

Figure 8-2
Gaseous discharge tube. Cathode rays pass through hole in anode. Size and position of spot on screen suggest cathode rays travel in straight lines.

At low pressure, when electricity passes through the gas in a discharge tube, some sort of radiation moves from one electrode to the other. The electrode from which the radiation leaves has a negative electric charge and is called the **cathode**. The other electrode has a positive electric charge and is called the **anode**. Scientists spoke of cathode rays long before they understood what was happening in a discharge tube. Most of the cathode rays are stopped by the anode; but if the anode has a small hole in it, a narrow beam of cathode rays passes through the hole and strikes a fluorescent screen at the end of the discharge tube. (A modern TV tube operates in this manner.) The spot on the fluorescent screen lets us follow the behavior of cathode rays. First, the size of the spot on the screen compared to the size of the hole in the anode indicates that cathode rays travel in straight lines. Additional experiments showed that cathode rays carry negative electric charge. These experiments are illustrated in Figures 8-3 and 8-4. When a magnet is placed near the tube, the cathode rays are deflected. This behavior is like that of negatively charged particles and suggests that cathode rays carry a negative electric charge. Figure 8-4 shows the original apparatus with two additional electrodes sealed in the discharge tube. An electrical voltage can be applied to these electrodes. The cathode rays move toward the positively charged electrode. This result also indicates that cathode rays carry negative electric charge.

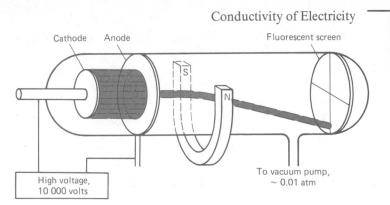

Figure 8-3
Gaseous discharge tube. Cathode rays deflected in magnetic field in same direction that negative electric charge is deflected.

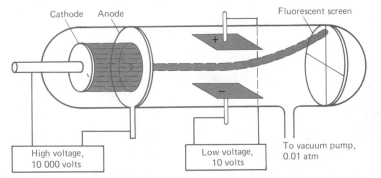

Figure 8-4
Gaseous discharge tube. Cathode rays deflected in electric field in same direction that negative electric charge is deflected.

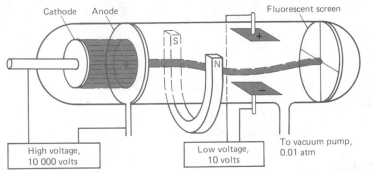

Figure 8-5
Gaseous discharge tube set up for the e/m experiment. Cathode rays deflected through magnetic and electric fields.

Roentgenographers (X-ray technicians) sometimes use a fluorescent screen to make the results of the examination visible.

In 1897 an English scientist, J. J. Thomson, combined the two experiments we have just described. He was able to study the behavior of cathode rays passing through both a magnetic field and an electric field. We can use Figure 8-5 to follow this experiment in stages. First, the cathode rays are deflected *down* as they pass through the magnetic field. Then the beam is deflected *up* as it passes through the electric field. It is possible to balance these fields so that the cathode rays strike the fluorescent screen at the same position they did when neither field was present. This experiment makes it possible to determine the ratio of the electric charge, *e*, to the mass, *m*, of the particles in the cathode rays.

Thomson used many different discharge tubes in his experiments. He changed the metal of the electrodes and placed different gases in the tube. For all experimental arrangements the charge-to-mass ratio (e/m) for cathode rays was always the same. Thomson concluded that the particles in cathode rays were always the same no matter what gas was in the discharge tube, and he used the name *electrons* for these particles. The e/m ratio for electrons is a large number. This tells us the charge is large compared to the mass. In Chapter 6 we discussed Millikan's experiment to measure the charge on the electron. He found it to be 1.6×10^{-19} coulomb. We can combine this result with Thomson's to obtain a numerical value for the mass of the electron:

Thomson experiment $e/m = 1.76 \times 10^8$ coulombs/gram

Millikan experiment $e = 1.60 \times 10^{-19}$ coulomb/electron

A simple calculation gives us the mass of the electron

$$m = 1.60 \times 10^{-19} \frac{\text{coulomb}}{\text{electron}} \times \frac{1}{1.76 \times 10^8} \frac{\text{gram}}{\text{coulomb}}$$

$$m = 9.1 \times 10^{-28} \frac{\text{gram}}{\text{electron}}$$

1 coulomb = 1.04×10^{-5} mole of electrons
= 6×10^{18} electrons

Notice that the value of electronic charge is about 2×10^8 times larger than the value of the mass.

We have talked in terms of molar masses for the elements. We can do the same for the electron.

$$\text{molar mass} = 9.1 \times 10^{-28} \frac{\text{gram}}{\text{electron}} \times 6.0 \times 10^{23} \frac{\text{electrons}}{\text{mole}}$$
(electron)

$$= 5.5 \times 10^{-4} \frac{\text{gram}}{\text{mole}}$$

The electron has much less mass than the lightest atom, the hydrogen atom.

$$\text{molar mass (hydrogen atom)} = 1.008 \text{ grams/mole}$$

EXERCISE 8-1

How many times heavier is a hydrogen atom than an electron?

A cathode-ray tube is often used to display computer information.

8-2 The Discovery of the Proton

In the early 1900's Thomson was able to carry out the same sort of measurement for another set of particles that are present in a gas discharge tube. If the cathode in a gas discharge tube has holes in it, careful observation shows that some kind of particle moves toward the cathode. (Remember that cathode rays, or electrons, travel *from* the cathode toward the anode.) Some of the particles moving toward the cathode pass through the holes as indicated in Figure 8-6. Their behavior in electric and magnetic fields indicates that they carry a positive electric charge. Thomson measured the charge-to-mass ratio, e/m, for these positive ions. This ratio was found to be much smaller than e/m for electrons. More important, the e/m values depended on the gas in the discharge tube. The charge-to-mass ratio for electrons did not depend on the nature of the gas. Comparison of the experiments that were made on these positive and negative particles is revealing.

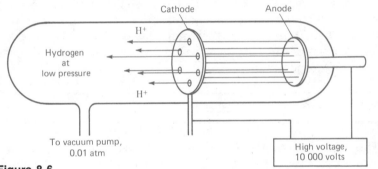

Figure 8-6
Positive rays when tube has hydrogen gas in it.

In a gas discharge tube electrons and positive ions are formed. The motion of these charged particles toward the electrodes is the electric current that passes through the gas. The charge-to-mass ratio for these ions can be measured by studying their behavior in electric and magnetic fields. Table 8-1 summarizes the experimental results.

TABLE 8-1
Experimental Results for the Positive and Negative Ions
Formed in Gas Discharge Tubes

Electric Charge of Particles	Charge-to-Mass Ratios (e/m)	Characteristics
Negative	A large number	Same values for all gases
Positive	Small numbers	Different values, depending on gas in discharge tube

Thomson interpreted these results in this manner. When sufficient energy is available in the gas discharge tube, molecules are broken into atoms and the atoms are ionized. We can illustrate this with some equations:

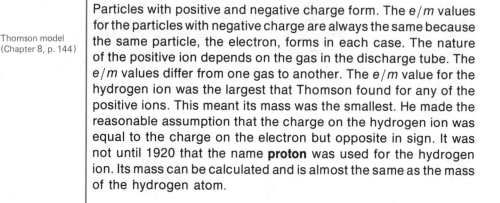

Molecules are broken $\quad H_2(g) + \text{ energy } \longrightarrow \quad 2\,H(g)$

Atoms ionize $\qquad\qquad H(g) + \text{energy} \longrightarrow \quad H^+(g) \quad + \quad e^-$

$\qquad\qquad\qquad\qquad He(g) + \text{energy} \longrightarrow \quad He^+(g) \quad + \quad e^-$

form anode   form cathode
rays with   rays with
different e/m constant e/m

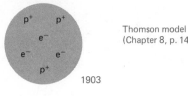

Dalton model
(Chapter 7, p. 119)

1807

Thomson model
(Chapter 8, p. 144)

1903

Particles with positive and negative charge form. The e/m values for the particles with negative charge are always the same because the same particle, the electron, forms in each case. The nature of the positive ion depends on the gas in the discharge tube. The e/m values differ from one gas to another. The e/m value for the hydrogen ion was the largest that Thomson found for any of the positive ions. This meant its mass was the smallest. He made the reasonable assumption that the charge on the hydrogen ion was equal to the charge on the electron but opposite in sign. It was not until 1920 that the name **proton** was used for the hydrogen ion. Its mass can be calculated and is almost the same as the mass of the hydrogen atom.

8-3   The Thomson Model for the Atom

Thomson was the first to propose an atomic model with internal structure. In 1903 he suggested that atoms were made of positively charged protons and negatively charged electrons. In the neutral atom there are equal numbers of these two kinds of particles. When energy is supplied to an atom, an electron is given up. The electron, or cathode ray, is always the same. The positive ion that is formed depends on the kind of atoms in the gas. Thomson's view of atomic structure is illustrated in Figure 8-7. A helium atom is used as the example. The molar mass for helium is very close to four grams, four times that of hydrogen atoms or protons. Thomson proposed that the helium atom contained four protons. Since each proton has one unit of mass, four protons would furnish the mass for helium. Thomson's atom also contained four electrons. Electrons have such low mass that they contribute little to the mass of an atom. However, they do provide negative electric charge. Figure 8-8 illustrates the ionization of a helium

Figure 8-7
Thomson model for He atom.

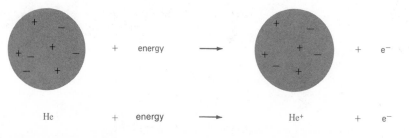

He $\qquad + \qquad$ energy $\qquad \longrightarrow \qquad$ He$^+$ $\qquad + \qquad e^-$

Figure 8-8
Ionization of helium atom (Thomson's model).

atom. Thomson's proposal was an important step in the growth of the atomic model. It was the first real change from Dalton's century-old view of atoms as hard spheres. Thomson's model later failed because it did not provide an explanation for the experiments that are described in the next section. Like the rule "Cylindrical objects burn," this model was helpful for a while but was replaced eight years later by a more useful model.

8-4   The Rutherford Model for the Atom

To explain how the Rutherford model for atoms was developed, we need to use alpha particles. These are high-energy helium nuclei emitted by some radioactive elements. We will discuss radioactivity and explain these particles in Sections 8-7 and 8-9. First, let us look at the experiment. Then perhaps we can appreciate Ernest Rutherford's interpretation. Once more we are following the activities of science: observation, a search for regularity, and wondering why.

Figure 8-9 shows the experiment that Rutherford carried out in 1911. A sample of radioactive material was placed in the lead box on the left of the diagram. A narrow beam of alpha particles escaped through the small hole in the side of the box. Thin metal foils of different elements were placed in the path of the beam of alpha particles. A fluorescent screen was set up around the foil. When an alpha particle hit the fluorescent screen, a flash of light could be seen. Most of the high-energy alpha particles passed straight through the metal foil to hit the fluorescent screen at point A. Occasionally an alpha particle would be deflected through a small angle to strike the screen at point B. Much to Rutherford's amazement a few alpha particles were deflected through very large angles. Some would strike the screen at point C. In a lecture that he gave in 1936 Rutherford described his astonishment by saying: "It was about as credible as if you had fired a 15-inch shell at a piece of tissue paper and it came back and hit you." In every experiment almost all the alpha particles passed straight through the foil. But there were always a few that were deflected through large angles.

Rutherford could not explain these results using Thomson's model of the atom. He knew that the positively charged alpha particles would be repelled by the positive charges that Thomson spread through his atoms. Small-angle deflections, as in Figure 8-10, would not be a surprise. Large-angle deflections could not be explained. Rutherford solved this problem by suggesting that the positive charge in an atom was contained in a very small nucleus. Most of the mass would also be in the nucleus. The electrons in the atom, with their negative charges, were imagined to surround the nucleus like a swarm of bees. The mass of an electron is so small that one could almost ignore it.

Let us use Rutherford's new idea of atomic structure to explain the alpha-scattering experiment. Figure 8-11 offers a schematic explanation of what happened. Since the nucleus of the atom is so small, few of the alpha particles would come very close to a nucleus. Most alpha particles would pass through the foil without

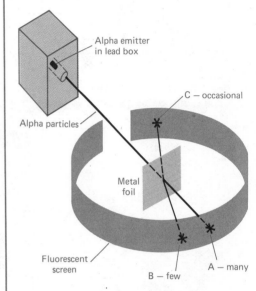

Figure 8-9
The Rutherford experiment.

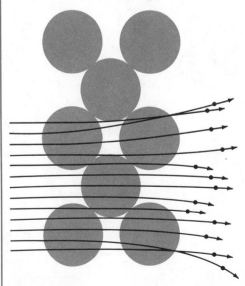

Figure 8-10
The scattering of alpha particles by a metallic crystal made up of Thomson atoms. Rutherford's results are *not* explained.

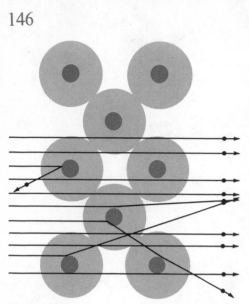

Figure 8-11
The scattering of alpha particles by a metallic crystal made up of Rutherford atoms. Rutherford's results *are* explained.

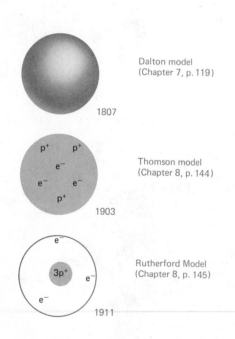

Dalton model
(Chapter 7, p. 119)

1807

Thomson model
(Chapter 8, p. 144)

1903

Rutherford Model
(Chapter 8, p. 145)

1911

much deflection. Some would pass near the positively charged nucleus. Repulsion between the positive nucleus and these particles would cause a small deflection. Every once in a while an alpha particle would collide almost head-on with a nucleus. These particles would change their directions through large angles. Rutherford was able to calculate from his model the fraction of alpha particles that should be deflected through a particular angle. The agreement between the experiments and his model was excellent. Rutherford, for his model, proposed that the mass of an atom and its positive charge are concentrated in a nucleus that is about one hundred thousandth of the diameter of the atom. The negative charge carried by electrons is spread throughout a much larger volume. Electrons define the size of an atom. The nucleus determines the mass.

Another important result of the scattering experiment was the determination of how much positive electric charge was on the nucleus. It is easy to understand how one can measure this positive charge, but the experiment requires great care and patience. As an alpha particle with its $2+$ charge passes through the metal foil, it is deflected through a large angle by a nucleus with a large positive charge. For a small nuclear charge the alpha particle would not be deflected as much. Rutherford's experiments also showed that the positive charge on the nucleus of an atom is always an integer. More important, the nuclear charge corresponds exactly to the position of an element in the periodic table. In talking about the periodic table in the last chapter, we referred to the atomic number of each element. The significance is now clear. *The **atomic number** of an element is equal to the number of positive charges in its nucleus.* For hydrogen this number is 1. The nucleus of a hydrogen atom carries a $1+$ charge. For calcium the atomic number is 20. The calcium nucleus has a charge of $20+$. The experiments described in this chapter led to a view of the atom with an internal structure. An atom is not the simple sphere that Dalton proposed 100 years earlier.

At various places in this book we imagined that we could decrease in size by a factor of 5 000 000 000. Then we would be about the same size as an atom. But we would still not be able to see the nucleus because it would be about 100 000 times smaller than the atom. Here is another way to give you some idea of the size of the nucleus and the atom for hydrogen. If the nucleus were as large as a ping-pong ball, the atom would be about two kilometers in diameter. The next two sections will help us describe the nucleus of an atom in more detail. Then in the next chapter we will see how the Rutherford model for the atom failed and had to be replaced by the Bohr model.

8-5 The Mass Spectrograph

In a gas discharge tube positive ions are separated according to mass as they pass first through an electric field and then a magnetic field. Because of this separation of masses, the instrument that Thomson developed was referred to as a mass spectrograph.

Electronic Numbers

Modern pocket calculators probably seem to have little connection with gas discharge tubes. The latter were used in the late 1800's to show the presence of electrons and other particles in atoms. But some calculators have gas discharge tubes to display the numbers produced in the calculation. These tubes are direct descendants of the devices used by J. J. Thomson. In these there is a back plate of glass, separated from a front glass plate by an insulated spacer. The space between the plates has low-pressure neon plus some mercury vapor. On the back plate is an array of metallic bars in the "7-stroke" pattern shown in Figure 1. These bars are connected so that all the top bars in a display are on one circuit, all the bottom bars on another, and so on for each of the 7 bars used for one digit. Figure 2 shows these circuit connections for a two-digit display.

The table shows the series of steps by which the number 12 could be formed. The sequence is repeated so fast and so many times per second that the last line, the sum line, is what we see.

There are other ways to make numerical displays visible, including light-emitting diodes (LED), liquid crystals, phosphors fluorescing in a vacuum, and light-emitting phosphors. These methods involve principles different from those in the gas discharge tube.

The two largest ice sheets in the world are in Greenland and in Antarctica. A vertical core of ice gives a chronological record of air contaminants. The older layers go back hundreds of years. One of the many studies carried out with these cores has been the analysis of the lead content. The amount of lead is building up more and more rapidly and probably represents pollution by man. In the upper layers there is about 0.2 microgram of Pb per kilogram of ice in Greenland and about 0.02 microgram of Pb per kilogram of ice in Antarctica. The difference may be due to the higher level of industrial technology in the Northern Hemisphere.

Figure 1
The 7-stroke array.

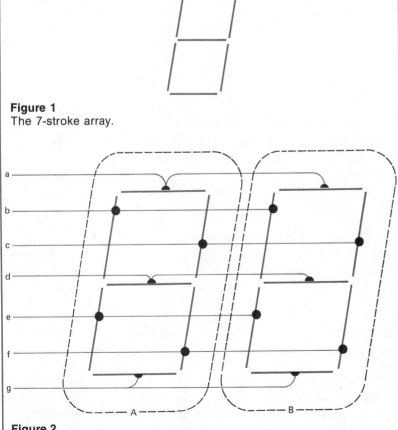

Figure 2
A 2-digit display. A and B represent separate transparent tin oxide electrodes, each above its entire 7-stroke array.

148

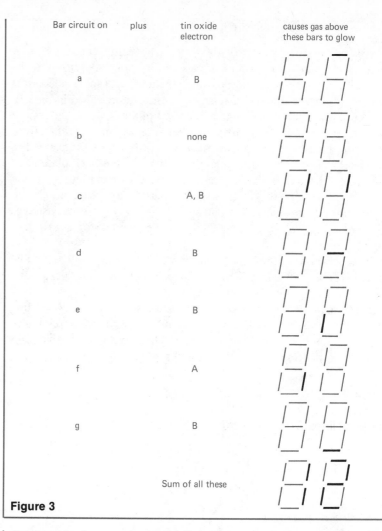

Bar circuit on	plus	tin oxide electron	causes gas above these bars to glow
a		B	
b		none	
c		A, B	
d		B	
e		B	
f		A	
g		B	
		Sum of all these	

Figure 3

One type is shown schematically in Figure 8-12. The left view shows the apparatus supported between the pole faces of a strong magnet. The right view is an enlargement of the spectrograph rotated so that the magnetic field is directed almost perpendicular to the page.

Positive ions are made by bombarding a gas with electrons. If the bombarding electrons have enough energy, positive ions form when electrons interact with gas molecules. Neon gas enters at the bottom of the apparatus (Figure 8-12). As the gas passes through the electron beam, some atoms absorb energy and then lose electrons to form neon ions, Ne^+. These ions are accelerated and pass through the slotted electrode. While each positive ion is in the magnetic field, it follows a circular path fixed by its mass, speed, and charge. For ions of the same speed a large mass leads to a large radius for the circle; a large charge leads to a small radius. After circling through an arc of 180°, the ions strike a photographic plate. The impact of the ions causes a reaction that darkens the plate. The slotted entry port causes ions to form lines on the plate. A line occurs for each type of ion at a position determined by the charge-to-mass ratio. Measurement of the position of each line permits calculation of the mass of the ion. The record on the photographic plate is called a **mass spectrum**.

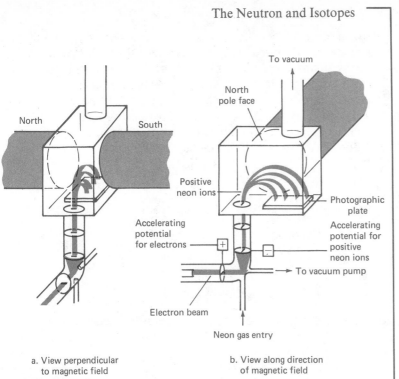

a. View perpendicular to magnetic field

b. View along direction of magnetic field

Figure 8-12
A mass spectrograph analyzing a neon sample.

The mass spectrum for neon consists of two widely separated groups of lines. The lines corresponding to large radii are caused by neon ions with a single positive charge, whereas the lines corresponding to small radii are caused by doubly charged ions. For each ionic charge there are two slightly separated lines which indicate that neon consists of atoms with different masses. The relative abundance of these atoms can be determined by measuring the intensity of the lines caused by each ion beam.

Thomson's experiments demonstrated that the element neon contained at least two kinds of atoms. One had a molar mass of approximately 20 grams, and the other approximately 22 grams. The line corresponding to mass 20 is about ten times as intense as that for mass 22. In a more refined instrument a third line for mass 21 can be detected, but its intensity is about three percent of the already weak mass 22 line. The best mass spectrographs in use today can determine masses to a precision better than one part in a billion. Automated mass spectrographs in rockets have been used to analyze the gases in the Earth's stratosphere. At the time this textbook was written, an automated mass spectrograph started on its long one-year trip in a space vehicle to Mars with the objective of measuring the composition of the atmosphere of the planet.

The name **isotope** was coined for atoms that have the same atomic number but different masses. We will gain a better understanding of isotopes after discussing the discovery of the neutron.

A technician operating a mass spectrometer to analyze drugs, atmospheric pollution, or flavor components in wine uses a device based on Thomson's gas tubes.

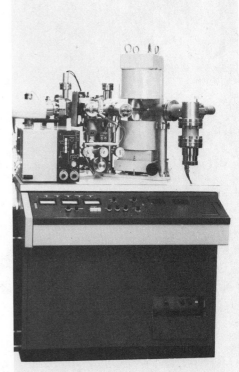

This is the part of a mass spectrograph which is shown in the diagram.

8-6 The Neutron and Isotopes

In 1932 a different type of scattering experiment was being studied by an English physicist, James Chadwick. If alpha particles are

Sir James Chadwick died July 25, 1974, at the age of 82.

allowed to strike beryllium metal, a very penetrating radiation is observed. And when this radiation passes through hydrogen gas, protons are formed and can be detected. These experiments could only be explained by postulating a new type of particle with zero electric charge. Its mass is close to the proton mass. It is called the **neutron**. Like the proton, the neutron is found in the nucleus. With the neutron we can build up atoms for all the elements. Table 8-2 describes the building blocks for all atoms.

TABLE 8-2

Charge and Mass of Electron, Proton, and Neutron

Particle	Charge	Approximate Mass Relative to Proton
Electron	1−	$\dfrac{1}{1840}$
Proton	1+	1
Neutron	0	1

Each atom except hydrogen has a nucleus made up of protons and neutrons. All atoms of a particular element have the same electric charge on the nucleus. This means *all atoms of a particular element have the same number of protons in the nucleus.*

The protons plus the neutrons account for the mass of the nucleus. The **mass number** of the nucleus equals the number of protons plus the number of the neutrons. The mass number is an integer which has approximately the same value as the molar mass. However, not all atoms of an element have the same mass number. *Isotopes of an element have the same number of protons but different numbers of neutrons in the nucleus.* An example will help make this statement clear.

Lithium is the element with atomic number three. All lithium atoms have three protons in their nuclei. Some lithium atoms have mass number of six. Other lithium atoms have mass number of seven. The isotope, ^{6}Li, has three protons and three neutrons in the nucleus. The isotope, ^{7}Li, has three protons and four neutrons in the nucleus. Each lithium isotope has three electrons in the neutral atom. The notations

$$^6_3\text{Li} \quad \text{and} \quad ^7_3\text{Li}$$

represent another way to describe these two isotopes of lithium. It is customary to write the atomic number at the lower left of the chemical symbol and the mass number at the upper left of the symbol.

EXERCISE 8-2

Write the notation for each of the three isotopes of oxygen, including the atomic numbers and the mass numbers. See Table 8-3.

EXERCISE 8-3

Use Table 8-3 to determine the number of protons and neutrons and the mass number for ^{235}U and ^{238}U. What would these numbers be for ^{239}U and ^{233}U?

Most chemical elements consist of a mixture of isotopes. For example, oxygen has three stable isotopes. The nuclear charge is 8+ for each isotope. The mass numbers are 16, 17, and 18. The kind of atom having mass number 16 is the most abundant. The chemical properties for these three isotopes depend almost entirely on the nuclear charge and not on the nuclear mass. Because of this it is not necessary to indicate which isotope of an element reacts in a chemical reaction. However, for a nuclear reaction the isotope must be specified. The molar mass you see in a periodic table is a weighted average derived from the masses of the isotopes, allowing for their relative abundance. Table 8-3 summarizes the structure of some common isotopes.

TABLE 8-3
Components of Some Common Isotopes

| Isotope | Abundance in Nature | Atomic Number | Mass Number | Nucleus | | Electric Charge | Mass of Atom $^{12}C = 12.0000$ | Number of Electrons in Neutral Atom |
				Number of Protons	Number of Neutrons			
Hydrogen 1	99.984%	1	1	1	0	1+	1.0078	1
Hydrogen 2	0.016	1	2	1	1	1+	2.0141	1
Helium 3	1.3×10^{-4}	2	3	2	1	2+	3.0160	2
Helium 4	100	2	4	2	2	2+	4.0026	2
Lithium 6	7.42	3	6	3	3	3+	6.0151	3
Lithium 7	92.58	3	7	3	4	3+	7.0160	3
Beryllium 9	100	4	9	4	5	4+	9.0122	4
Boron 10	19.61	5	10	5	5	5+	10.0129	5
Boron 11	80.39	5	11	5	6	5+	11.0093	5
Carbon 12	98.893	6	12	6	6	6+	12.0000	6
Carbon 13	1.108	6	13	6	7	6+	13.0034	6
Nitrogen 14	99.63	7	14	7	7	7+	14.0031	7
Nitrogen 15	0.37	7	15	7	8	7+	15.0001	7
Oxygen 16	99.76	8	16	8	8	8+	15.9949	8
Oxygen 17	0.04	8	17	8	9	8+	16.9991	8
Oxygen 18	0.20	8	18	8	10	8+	17.9992	8
Fluorine 19	100	9	19	9	10	9+	18.9984	9
Chlorine 35	75.53	17	35	17	18	17+	34.9689	17
Chlorine 37	24.47	17	37	17	20	17+	36.9659	17
Uranium 235	0.72	92	235	92	143	92+	235.0439	92
Uranium 238	99.27	92	238	92	146	92+	238.0508	92

8-7 Radioactivity

Now let us go backwards in time about 15 years before Rutherford's experiment to discuss the discovery of radioactivity.

In 1896 a French scientist, Henri Becquerel, discovered that uranium compounds have the unusual property of releasing energy spontaneously. Moreover the rate at which that energy is released could not be changed. Heating the sample, freezing the material, or carrying uranium through a series of chemical reactions does not slow down or speed up the rate at which the energy is released. Uranium was said to be **radioactive** and had the property of undergoing **radioactive decay**. Soon a number of scientists began to carry out experiments in their search for an explanation of this new phenomenon. The observation that some uranium ores had much higher levels of radioactivity than purified uranium compounds suggested that there might be new elements in those ores that were more radioactive than uranium. Marie Curie and her husband Pierre were the first to show that this indeed was true.

The method used by the Curies was relatively simple but at the same time very exacting. After dissolving the ore, different precipitating agents were added to the solution. In some instances the radioactive elements would concentrate in the precipitate. In other operations the radioactivity would remain in solution. The first element discovered by the Curies was similar in its chemical behavior to tellurium. The name **polonium** was chosen for this element, and it was placed below tellurium in the periodic table. The other element to be isolated by the Curies was **radium**. Radium showed chemical behavior like that of barium. Only after many fractional crystallizations was radium bromide separated from barium bromide. Radium was placed below barium in the second column of the periodic table.

8-8   Radioactive Decay

Early studies of natural radioactivity identified three ways energy was released. These were called alpha, beta, and gamma emission, or rays. Table 8-4 summarizes the characteristics of each radioactive decay process.

TABLE 8-4

Radioactive Rays

Name	Charge	Approximate Molar Mass (grams)	Description	Penetrating Power
α Alpha	2+	4	Nucleus of helium atom, ^4_2He	Short range; stopped by a piece of paper
β Beta	1−	$\frac{1}{1840}$	Electron $^0_{-1}e$	Intermediate range; stopped by a few centimeters of water
γ Gamma	0	0	High-energy radiation	Long range; stopped by a few centimeters of lead

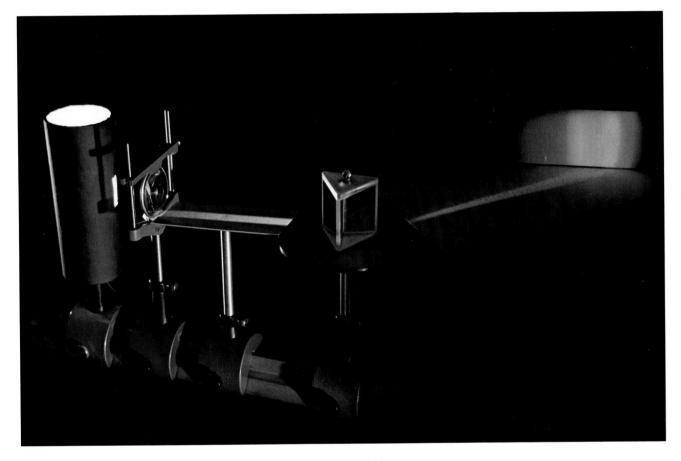

PLATE I A simple spectrograph and the spectrum of a hot tungsten ribbon.

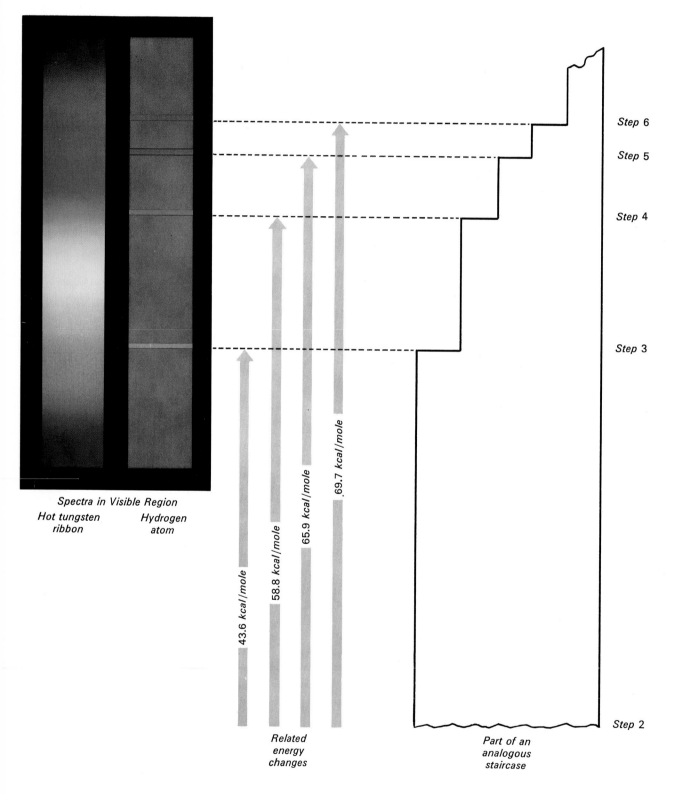

Spectra in Visible Region

Hot tungsten ribbon   Hydrogen atom

43.6 kcal/mole

58.8 kcal/mole

65.9 kcal/mole

69.7 kcal/mole

Related energy changes

Step 6

Step 5

Step 4

Step 3

Step 2

Part of an analogous staircase

PLATE II The hydrogen atom spectrum: a clue to energy levels.

All three of these rays are emitted by a uranium compound or by a piece of uranium ore. The behavior of these rays in an electric field is shown in Figure 8-13. It was a triumph of careful experimentation to demonstrate that there were many radioactive elements in the ore or in the supposedly pure compound. Eventually, these elements were separated and studied in detail by techniques similar to those used by the Curies.

Rutherford and Frederick Soddy demonstrated that an element which emitted an alpha particle changed spontaneously into another element (called a daughter element) whose atomic number was two less than the parent and whose mass number was four less. The daughter element fits in the periodic table two places to the left of the parent element. The alchemists' dream of changing one element to another took place. For one of the isotopes of radium we can write a nuclear equation

$$^{226}_{88}Ra \longrightarrow {}^{4}_{2}He + {}^{222}_{86}Rn$$

The alpha particle captures two electrons as it speeds through matter and becomes a neutral helium atom.

The same two scientists also found that beta emission corresponded to the spontaneous decay of an element into a daughter element whose mass number remained constant but whose atomic number increased by one. The daughter element is a member of the group in the periodic table one place to the right of the parent element. For one of the isotopes of thorium we can write

$$^{234}_{90}Th \longrightarrow {}^{0}_{-1}e + {}^{234}_{91}Pa$$

Since a new atom (protactinium) is produced, the electron must have come from the nucleus of the thorium atom as shown by this equation:

$$^{1}_{0}n \longrightarrow {}^{1}_{1}H + {}^{0}_{-1}e + \text{neutrino}$$

The symbol ${}^{1}_{1}H$ is used to designate the proton. The atomic number of the nucleus increases by one unit as a neutron changes into a proton and the electron (beta particle) is released. We will not discuss the neutrino in this book.

Gamma rays (high-frequency radiation) often accompany alpha or beta emissions. Gamma ray emission lowers the energy of the nucleus.

The details of the many steps whereby $^{238}_{92}U$ decays into the stable isotope $^{206}_{82}Pb$ are shown in Figure 8-14. These steps are called a *radioactive decay series*. Two other natural radioactive decay series are known. They involve the decay of $^{232}_{90}Th$ into $^{208}_{82}Pb$ and the change of $^{235}_{92}U$ into $^{207}_{82}Pb$.

An important characteristic of all radioactive species is that a constant fraction of the nuclei decomposes in a specified period of time. Normally, the time for one half of the nuclei to decay is chosen. This length of time, $T_{1/2}$, is known as the **half-life** of the nucleus. Thus, if we start with one gram of material whose half-life is 20 minutes, the following observations could be made:

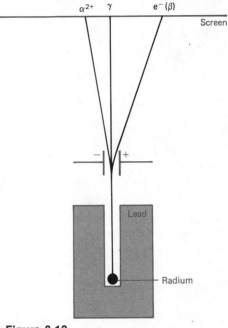

Figure 8-13
Radioactive decay products from radium.

Medical technicians use radioisotopes to study body processes in a method called "tagging" or "labeling."

Radiologists may treat cancer with
radioactive cobalt.

Beta rays are used to check wine for
added ethanol. Normally the alcohol
in wine is made by fermenting natural
sugars. To increase the alcohol content
or to increase the amount of wine available, pure ethanol that has been made
from crude oil can be added. The oil,
however, is so old that it contains very
little ^{14}C. If the beta-ray count is too
low, the wine has been adulterated.

Physicians and veterinarians treat some
diseases with man-made isotopes.

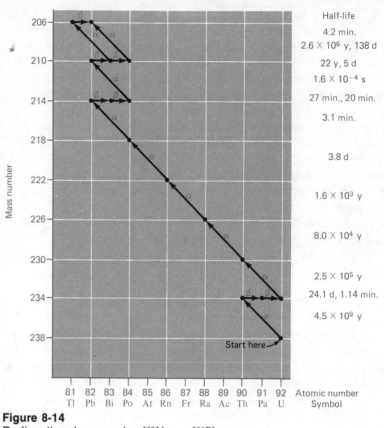

Figure 8-14
Radioactive decay series $^{238}_{92}U \longrightarrow \, ^{206}_{82}Pb$.

During 20 minutes
   ½ gram would decay; $(1 - ½) = ½$ gram would be left.
During the next 20 minutes (or 40 minutes total)
   $(½)(½$ gram) or ¼ gram would decay; $(½ - ¼) = ¼$ gram
   would remain.
During still another 20-minute period (or 60 minutes total)
   $(½)(¼$ gram) or ⅛ gram would decay; $(¼ - ⅛) = ⅛$ gram
   would be left.

The rate of decay of any radioactive species is shown in Figure
8-15, expressed in terms of its half-life.
   The half-lives of elements vary widely. For the alpha decay of
$^{238}_{92}U$ into $^{234}_{90}Th$, the half-life is 4.5×10^9 years. During 24.1 days half
of a $^{234}_{90}Th$ sample decomposes by beta decay. Half-lives as short
as microseconds have been observed. Note that the alpha decay
of $^{226}_{88}Ra$ is part of the $^{238}_{92}U$ decay series shown in Figure 8-14. In
any sample of uranium ore there will always be a small amount of
radium and all the other elements in the decay series. This is why
Madame Curie was able to find radium in uranium ores. $^{226}_{88}Ra$ has a
half-life of 1620 years. Since the age of the Earth is known to be
5×10^9 years, it is easy to understand why $^{238}_{92}U$ is found in the
Earth's crust. On the other hand, $^{226}_{88}Ra$ would have disappeared
soon after the Earth's formation, except that it is supplied continuously through the decay of $^{238}_{92}U$.

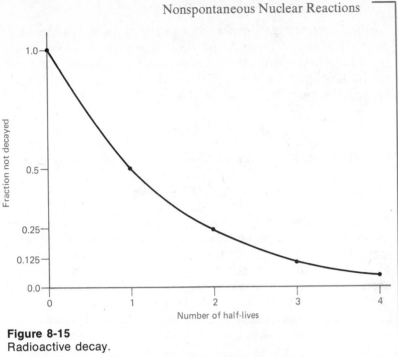

Figure 8-15
Radioactive decay.

Archeologists and chemists use natural radioactive decay for measuring the age of very old objects.

8-9 Nonspontaneous Nuclear Reactions

Rutherford was the first one to show that nonspontaneous nuclear reactions induced by collision or bombardment could occur. After many years of careful experiments he was able to prove in 1919 that an alpha particle with enough energy can combine with a nucleus instead of just being scattered by it. He showed that this reaction had occurred:

$$^{14}_{7}N + ^{4}_{2}He \longrightarrow ^{17}_{8}O + ^{1}_{1}H$$

During the years since Rutherford identified this nuclear reaction many others have been studied. With the advent of the high-energy accelerating machines such as the cyclotron, chemists and physicists have explored a variety of nuclear reactions.

Let us look at a few examples of nuclear changes induced by bombardment and some of the new particles discovered. In 1930 J. D. Cockroft and E. T. S. Walton accelerated protons so that they had enough energy to penetrate the $^{7}_{3}Li$ nucleus. Helium was produced, as represented by

$$^{1}_{1}H + ^{7}_{3}Li \longrightarrow 2 ^{4}_{2}He$$

In the same year a penetrating radiation was observed when beryllium compounds were bombarded with alpha particles. Chadwick interpreted the radiation by the reaction

$$^{4}_{2}He + ^{9}_{4}Be \longrightarrow ^{1}_{0}n + ^{12}_{6}C$$

This was the reaction in which the neutron was discovered.

In 1932 an American physicist named Anderson was studying

cosmic rays and found evidence for a particle like the electron but positively charged. He named it the **positron**, or positive electron ($_{+1}^{0}e$). Soon Madame Curie's daughter and her husband, Irène and Pierre Joliot-Curie, showed that the positron was emitted by a nitrogen isotope formed by the reaction

$$_{2}^{4}He + {}_{5}^{10}B \longrightarrow {}_{0}^{1}n + {}_{7}^{13}N$$

$_{7}^{13}N$ is radioactive and decays spontaneously according to

$$_{7}^{13}N \longrightarrow {}_{+1}^{0}e + {}_{6}^{13}C + \text{neutrino}$$

This was the first example of a radioactive species made by man. Radioactivity induced by bombardment is known as **artificial radioactivity**. Since then, hundreds of artificially radioactive nuclei have been produced. The neutron has proved to be very useful in causing nuclear reactions because it has zero electric charge. A neutron can approach close to and react with the positively charged nucleus.

Figure 8-16 will give you some idea about nuclear stability. The

Civil, mechanical, and chemical engineers working on nuclear power plants must know the properties of radioactive materials.

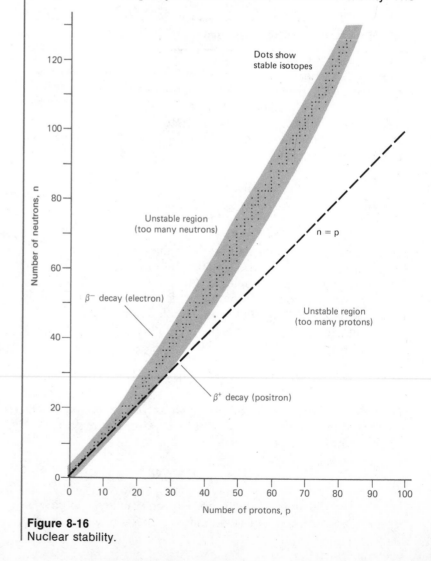

Figure 8-16
Nuclear stability.

stable, or nonreactive, isotopes are represented by black dots. The unstable radioactive isotopes that have long enough half-lives to be studied lie in the shaded region on either side of the stable isotopes. Any nucleus in this diagram that lies above the stable isotopes has too many neutrons for stability and spontaneously emits a beta particle. The nuclei below the stable region have too many protons for stability and spontaneously emit positrons.

We will discuss the energy from nuclear reactions in Chapter 11. However, it is appropriate to mention here two types of nuclear reactions that are possible energy resources to supplement coal, natural gas, and petroleum. The first is called the **fission** reaction and takes place in nuclear reactors. The second is called the **fusion** reaction.

When a neutron reacts with ^{233}U, ^{235}U, or ^{239}Pu, the nucleus is split into two fragments called **fission products** and two or three neutrons that can keep the reaction going. This is called a chain reaction. A large amount of energy is released in this kind of nuclear reaction. A number of nuclear reactors based on the fission reaction have already been built to generate electricity. A typical fission reaction can be written

$$^{235}_{92}U + ^{1}_{0}n \longrightarrow ^{90}_{38}Sr + ^{143}_{54}Xe + 3\ ^{1}_{0}n + \text{energy}$$

There are some 50 pairs of fission products known, including lanthanum/bromine and cerium/selenium. Each pair is such that the sum of their atomic numbers is 92. All the fission products are radioactive. One problem of great importance for future development of nuclear reactors is the safety hazard or possible pollution from the radioactivity of fission products.

The fusion process also produces a large amount of energy. A typical reaction is

$$^{2}_{1}H + ^{2}_{1}H \longrightarrow ^{3}_{2}He + ^{1}_{0}n + \text{energy}$$

To overcome the repulsive force as the two hydrogen nuclei approach each other, their collision energy must be of the order of 5×10^5 kcal/mol. Such kinetic energies are achieved when the temperature is around 200 million kelvins. At this temperature any gas is a collection of nuclei, ions, and electrons. Gas in this state is known as a **plasma**. Fusion reactions occur in the central regions of stars and give rise to the energy released by them.

8-10   Nuclear Stability

We will end this chapter by considering the isotopes of carbon as an example of nuclear stability. Some combinations of neutrons and protons lead to stable nuclei. Other combinations of neutrons and protons form nuclei that undergo radioactive decay. In Table 8-5 the known isotopes of carbon are listed. The two which are stable have approximately the same number of neutrons and protons. The isotopes with a greater proportion of either neutrons or protons are radioactive. The isotopes $^{12}_{6}C$ and $^{13}_{6}C$ are stable, whereas $^{10}_{6}C$, $^{11}_{6}C$, $^{14}_{6}C$, and $^{15}_{6}C$ are radioactive.

TABLE 8-5

Carbon Isotopes

Symbol	Number of Protons	Number of Neutrons	Type of Decay	Half-life $T_{1/2}$
$^{10}_{6}C$	6	4	Positron	19 seconds
$^{11}_{6}C$	6	5	Positron	20 minutes
$^{12}_{6}C$	6	6	Stable	—
$^{13}_{6}C$	6	7	Stable	—
$^{14}_{6}C$	6	8	Beta	5570 years
$^{15}_{6}C$	6	9	Beta	2.4 seconds

Unstable nuclei achieve stability by radioactive decay. ^{14}C is radioactive with a half-life of 5570 years. It emits a beta particle to form the stable isotope $^{14}_{7}N$.

$$^{14}_{6}C \longrightarrow \,^{14}_{7}N + \,_{-1}^{0}e \text{ (beta particle)} + \text{energy} + \text{neutrino}$$

8-11 Review

The search for an explanation for atomic structure is surely one of the best examples of how science grows. From an initial curiosity about the conductivity of electricity in gases at low pressure to the discovery of the neutron, one experiment led to another. Sometimes questions, answers, and more experiments followed rapidly on each other; sometimes answers did not appear for many years. In this chapter we have outlined briefly the most significant of the experiments. We can summarize this search with the block diagram in Figure 8-17. Some of the experiments seemed to be unrelated to the mainstream, only to provide an important link at a later date.

The important building blocks for atoms are electrons, protons, and neutrons. The electrons of an atom occupy a much larger volume than the nucleus and define the size of an atom. A neutral atom has the same number of protons in the nucleus as electrons in the volume around the nucleus. The **atomic number** for an atom is equal to the number of protons in the nucleus. Except for the simplest isotope of hydrogen ($^{1}_{1}H$) the nuclei of all atoms contain neutrons. The **mass number** for an atom is equal to the number of protons plus the number of neutrons. The mass number is approximately equal to the mass of the atom.

The mass spectrograph is an instrument that allows a very precise measurement of the mass of an atom.

All atoms of a particular element have the same number of protons in the nucleus. Atoms of the same element may have different mass numbers, that is, different numbers of neutrons in the nucleus. Atoms with the same atomic number but different mass numbers are called **isotopes**.

If a nucleus has too many protons or neutrons, it is not stable. It undergoes radioactive decay to reach a lower level of potential energy. There are many ways this can occur: emission of an alpha particle, which is a helium nucleus; emission of a beta particle, which can be either a negative or a positive electron; or emission of a gamma ray, which is high-energy invisible light. For elements with atomic number larger than 83 (bismuth), all isotopes are unstable and undergo radioactive decay. Many radioactive isotopes of the elements have been made by nuclear reactions. The neutron has proved to be very effective in causing nuclear reactions. Because it has zero electric charge, the neutron is not repelled by positively charged nuclei.

The question mark following the Rutherford model of the atom indicates that it was not the final answer. What prevented the negatively charged electrons from falling into the positively charged nucleus? Was there any relation between atomic structure and the simple patterns observed in line spectra? In the next chapter we will see how these questions were answered.

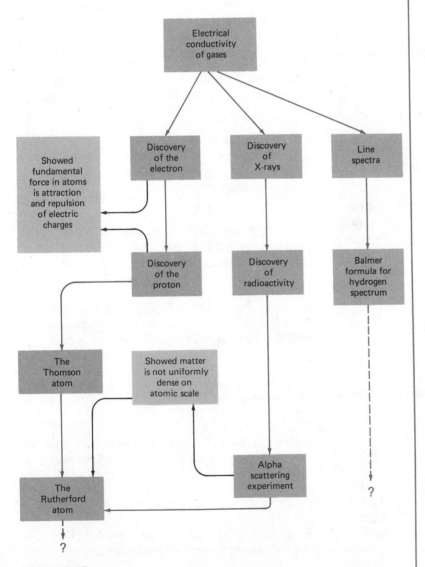

Figure 8-17
The search for experimental regularity that leads to an explanation of atomic structure.

Questions and Problems for Chapter 8

1

The pressure in a gaseous discharge tube is approximately 10^{-2} atmosphere when the glow appears. When the pressure is decreased to about 10^{-6} atmosphere, the gas stops glowing.
How many molecules would there be in one cubic centimeter of gas when the glow first appears? How many molecules would there be in one cubic centimeter of gas when the glow disappears?

2

How many electrons are needed to furnish a mass of one gram? What would be the mass of a mole of electrons?

3

How much electric charge is provided by one mole of electrons? By one mole of protons?

4

From the molar mass of the electron and the molar mass of the hydrogen atom, calculate the molar mass of the proton. Calculate the ratio of proton mass to electron mass.

5

Figure 8-5 shows the effects of a pair of electrodes on a beam of electrons. What is needed to make the beam move back and forth as well as side to side so that it covers the screen?

6

Which would have a larger charge-to-mass ratio, a Na^+ or a K^+ ion?

7

Elements numbers 9 and 17 both form one-minus ions, F^- and Cl^-. Will the e/m ratio for these ions be the same? The same as e/m for an electron? Explain.

8

Suppose, in the Thomson model for the atom, that the charge of the proton is uniformly spread throughout the volume for one hydrogen atom. Using the value 10^{-8} cm for the radius of the hydrogen atom and 1.6×10^{-19} coulomb for the unit electric charge, calculate the charge density in coulombs per cubic centimeter.

9

An aluminum atom has an average diameter of about 3×10^{-8} cm. The nucleus has a diameter of about 2×10^{-13} cm. Calculate the ratio of the diameters.

10

The radius of a carbon atom in many compounds is 0.77×10^{-8} cm. If the radius of a Styrofoam ball used to represent the carbon atom in a molecular model is 1.5 cm, how much of an enlargement is this?

11

Platinum and zinc have the same number of atoms per cubic centimeter. Would thin sheets of these elements differ in the way they scatter alpha particles? Explain.

12

Assume that the nucleus of the fluorine atom is a sphere with a radius of 5×10^{-13} cm. Calculate the density of matter in the fluorine nucleus.

13

An average dimension for the radius of an atom is 1×10^{-8} cm, and the radius of a nucleus is 1×10^{-13} cm. Determine the ratio of atomic volume to nuclear volume.

14

Repeat Problem 8 for the Rutherford model of the hydrogen atom. The proton is now the nucleus of the atom, with a radius of approximately 10^{-13} cm.

15

Use your answers from Problems 8 and 14 to discuss qualitatively the scattering of alpha particles by Thomson atoms and by Rutherford atoms.

16

How many times heavier is an alpha particle than an electron?

17

Would you expect tungsten atoms to cause more or less deflection of an alpha particle than aluminum atoms when used in a Rutherford scattering experiment?

18

Suggest why, in a crude mass spectrometer, it is not easy to tell whether a sample contains CO_2 or C_3H_8.

19

The ions produced in a mass spectrometer can

have a mass equal to that of the starting molecule or fragments of it. One compound, known to contain chlorine, produced only ions with masses 154, 35, 37, 119, and 117. Which of these compounds may be in the sample: $SnCl$, $KrCl_2$, $TiCl_3$, CCl_4?

20

Describe the spectrum produced on a photographic plate in a mass spectrograph if a mixture of the isotopes of oxygen (^{16}O, ^{17}O, and ^{18}O) is analyzed. Consider only the record for $1+$ and $2+$ ions.

21

Hydroxylamine, NH_2OH, is subjected to electron bombardment. The products are passed through a mass spectrograph. The two pairs of lines formed indicate charge/mass ratios of 0.0625, 0.0588 and 0.1250, 0.1176. How can this be interpreted?

22

Which of the following statements is FALSE? The atoms of oxygen differ from the atoms of every other element in the following ways:

(a) the nuclei of oxygen atoms have a different number of protons than the nuclei of any other element;

(b) atoms of oxygen have a higher ratio of neutrons to protons than the atoms of any other element;

(c) neutral atoms of oxygen have a different number of electrons than neutral atoms of any other element;

(d) atoms of oxygen have different chemical behavior than do atoms of any other element.

23

List the number and kind of fundamental particles found in a neutral lithium atom that has a nucleus with a nuclear charge three times that of a hydrogen nucleus and with approximately seven times the mass.

24

Helium, as found in nature, consists of two isotopes. Most of the atoms have a mass number 4, but a few have a mass number 3. For each isotope indicate the:

(a) atomic number;   (d) mass number;
(b) number of protons;   (e) nuclear charge.
(c) number of neutrons;

25

How do isotopes of one element differ from each other? How are they the same?

26

Use the exact masses and the percent abundance in Table 8-3 for ^{35}Cl and ^{37}Cl to calculate the average molar mass for atomic chlorine.

27

On a separate sheet of paper copy and complete the following table. Do not write in this book.

	Atomic Number	Particles per Atom			Mass Number
		Protons	Electrons	Neutrons	
Al	13				27
Be			4		9
Bi	83				209
Ca			20	20	
C.		6		6	
F			9		19
P	15			16	
I			53		127

28

Copper occurs naturally in two isotopes $^{63}_{29}Cu$ (69%), and $^{65}_{29}Cu$ (31%). Show how this accounts for the molar mass listed for copper.

29

It is desired to use radioactive sulfur as a tracer. Two beta-emitting isotopes are available: $^{35}_{16}S$ ($t_{1/2} = 87$ days) and $^{37}_{16}S$ ($t_{1/2} = 5$ minutes). Which would you choose and why?

30

Titanium 51 decays with a half life of 6 minutes. What fraction of the radioactive material present at time zero would still be available after 1 hour?

31

Write equations for the following reactions:

(a) beta decay of $^{253}_{98}Cf$.
(b) alpha decay of $^{253}_{100}Fm$.
(c) the formation of $^{120}_{50}Sn$ by positron emission from an antimony isotope.

32

The half-life of $^{253}_{100}Fm$ is 4.5 days. What fraction of a mole of fermium would remain after 13.5 days (three half-lives)?

33

The half-life of $^{125}_{53}I$ is 60 days. What percent of original radioactivity would be present after 360 days?

34

The $^{14}_{6}C$ nucleus undergoes beta decay.

(a) What stable nucleus is formed?
(b) Demonstrate the electron balance in the equation.

35

Fission of uranium gives a variety of fission products, including praseodymium, Pr. If the process by which praseodymium is formed gives $^{147}_{59}Pr$ and three neutrons, what is the other nuclear product?

$$^{235}_{92}U + {}^{1}_{0}n \longrightarrow {}^{147}_{59}Pr + ? + 3\,{}^{1}_{0}n$$

36

A piece of wood recently obtained from a living plant will give carbon having 15.2 ± 0.1 beta particles/minute/gram. What age is a sample that gives 3.8 beta particles/minute/gram?

37

Niobium 93 combines with an alpha particle to produce a neutron and a radioactive isotope. Write an equation to show this reaction and identify the isotope.

38

When chlorine, Cl_2, is examined in a mass spectrograph, Cl_2^+, Cl^+, and Cl^{2+} ions are formed. Remembering that there are two isotopes of chlorine, $^{35}_{17}Cl$ (75%) and $^{37}_{17}Cl$ (25%), describe qualitatively the appearance of the mass spectrum. Which ion will produce lines at the largest radius? Which at the smallest radius? How many lines will each type of ion produce?

39

Suppose a mass spectrograph is used to measure the charge/mass ratio for fluorine ions. Fluorine has only one stable isotope, and its molar mass is 19.0 grams/mole. From the measured charge/mass ratio, 5.08×10^3 coulombs/gram, and the assumption that the ion has one electron charge, calculate the mass of one ion. Use $e = 1.6 \times 10^{-19}$ coulomb. Repeat the calculation, assuming the ion has two electron charges. Now calculate Avogadro's number from the mass of a mole of fluorine ions, using each of your two calculations. Which assumption about ion charge do you prefer? Could the other be correct as well?

40

In addition to undergoing fission, ^{235}U is also radioactive. It is an alpha emitter with a half-life of 7×10^8 years. Write the equation for this decomposition.

Electrons in Atoms

The experiments discussed in Chapter 8 presented exciting new ideas to scientists early in this century. Step by step these discoveries led from one model for the atom to another as scientists searched for explanations of their experiments. The model we use today had its origin in a proposal by Niels Bohr in 1913. We will explore the growth of this atomic model.

Let us see why Rutherford's model of the atom had to be changed. There were two sets of experimental facts that contradicted each other. First, the nuclear atom proposed by Rutherford provided an explanation for the experiments on the scattering of alpha particles. Rutherford suggested that the atom had negative charges surrounding a very small positive nucleus. Second, many experiments had shown that objects with unlike electric charges attract each other. If there is no force holding them back, the objects move toward each other. If the unlike charges are equal, they will neutralize each other when the objects touch. According to all experiments dealing with electric charge, the electrons should be pulled into the nucleus in a very short time. A strange puzzle indeed! The best model for the atom suggested an unstable structure. And yet, atoms are stable. They do not collapse. Evidently something was wrong with the model.

The time was ripe for someone of great vision and imagination to provide an explanation for these facts. The Danish physicist Niels Bohr was such a person. He proposed a new model that stretched the minds of scientists. He proposed that subatomic particles behaved differently from the objects ordinarily observed in the world around us. This huge break with prevailing beliefs enabled Bohr to create a model for atoms that explained many facts no other model could. For example, his model accounted for the light emitted by hydrogen atoms in a discharge tube. Furthermore, like Mendeleev, he was able to predict things that were as yet undiscovered. His model predicted the existence of other kinds of light from hydrogen. To help you understand the importance of this model for atomic structure, we will first discuss the nature of light.

9-1 Light

Many of you have used a small lens to focus sunlight on a piece of paper. With patience you can increase the temperature of the paper until it finally bursts into flame. A solar furnace develops a temperature of several thousand degrees by focusing sunlight. Almost any substance can be melted in such a furnace. The temperature rise means that energy has been absorbed. This energy must be carried by light. A study of the energy carried by light will help us understand additional experiments with gas discharge tubes and will lead us to the model for atomic structure that scientists use today.

Light is often described by means of a wave model. These waves are in some ways similar to water waves. Let us look at such waves first; then we will come back to light waves. As you know, water waves carry energy too. You can drop a stone in a pool at your feet, and the wave formed will cause a piece of wood floating some distance away to bounce up and down. But you might notice that the *water* did not move from your feet to the wood; the *wave* did. Had there been a leaf on the water between your feet and the wood, the leaf would have bobbed up and down. It would not have moved toward the wood. The wave was transmitting energy, not water. A light wave is similar in that it transmits energy.

Two words are often used to describe waves: *wavelength* and *frequency*. The wavelength is the distance between similar points in a set of waves, such as from crest to crest or trough to trough. The Greek letter lambda, λ, is used to represent wavelength. The frequency of a wave is the number of wave crests passing a point every second. In water it is the number of times the piece of wood bobs up every second. The Greek letter nu, ν, is used for frequency.

For water waves on an ocean, λ might be 15 meters (50 feet), whereas ν might be one wave every 20 seconds, or $\frac{1}{20}$ wave per second. For light, wavelengths are much shorter and frequencies

Imagine a person standing on the equator facing east with a super flashlight. A pulse of light is sent out, which for the sake of illustration we will assume travels in a circular path around the Earth. The person can turn around to face west in about one second. While the person turns, the light will have circled the Earth seven times.

Mathematicians make many contributions to science—from abstruse theory to computer operation.

are much greater than for water. Table 9-1 gives some examples. Figure 9-1 illustrates λ and ν with a familiar example. Note that red and violet light have different wavelengths and frequencies. Each color of light can be described accurately by giving its frequency or its wavelength.

TABLE 9-1
Frequency and Wavelength for Different Kinds of Waves

Kind of Wave	Frequency (number per second, or hertz)	Wavelength (centimeters)
Water	5×10^{-2}	1.5×10^{3}
Red light	4.3×10^{14}	7.0×10^{-5}
Violet light	7.5×10^{14}	4.0×10^{-5}

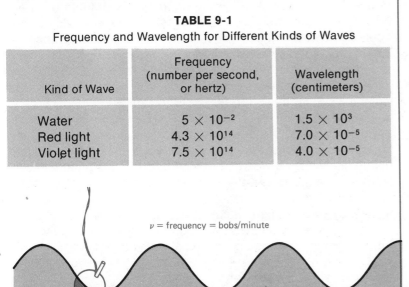

ν = frequency = bobs/minute

λ = wavelength

Figure 9-1
Fishing float.

Astronomers are finding molecules in space by analyzing their spectra.

A spectrograph is an instrument that helps us learn more about light. A simple one is shown in Figure 9-2 and in color Plate I.

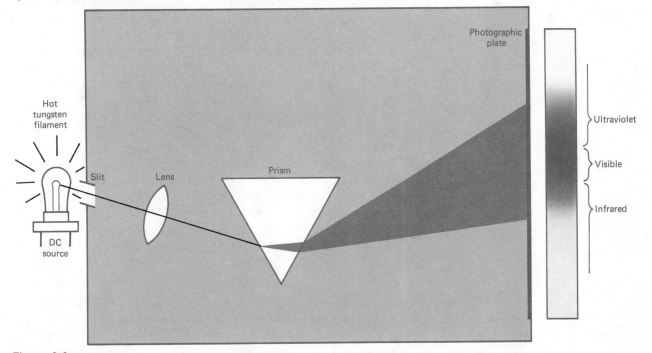

Figure 9-2
The continuous spectrum of light emitted by a hot tungsten wire. (See page 152).

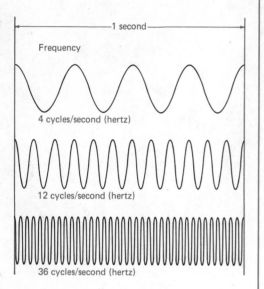

1 second

Frequency

4 cycles/second (hertz)

12 cycles/second (hertz)

36 cycles/second (hertz)

$$h = 9.52 \times 10^{-14} \frac{\text{kcal} \cdot \text{s}}{\text{mol}}$$

Printers may match ink color by obtaining a spectral analysis of the pigments.

Light is provided by a hot tungsten wire in a special light bulb. At about 1000 °C the wire glows with a bright white light. Some of this light enters a narrow slit and is focused onto the prism by the lens. The light beam passing through the prism is bent, or refracted. The different frequencies that make up white light are bent through different angles, and a rainbow of colors can be seen. Each color corresponds to waves of light with a particular frequency and wavelength. After passing through the prism, the light strikes a photographic film. When the film is developed, it shows a broad, multicolored region. The pattern recorded on the film is called the **spectrum**. A continuous color change from red to violet is seen in the light from hot tungsten. Such a spectrum is called a continuous spectrum. There are no gaps in it.

The darkening of the photographic film extends outside the familiar rainbow of colors. There are frequencies of light emitted by the hot tungsten wire that cannot be seen by the human eye. Light with frequencies just lower than the frequency of red light is called **infrared light**. Light with frequencies just higher than the frequency of violet light is called **ultraviolet light**.

It is important to know how much energy is carried by light. The answer is simple in mathematical form but not simple in concept. A German scientist, Max Planck, in 1900 proposed the equation relating energy and frequency:

$$E = h\nu$$

The quantity h is called Planck's constant. It is a conversion factor for changing frequency units into energy units. We have already seen that matter occurs in packages called atoms. Electric charge, you know, also comes in packages. Planck assumed that energy comes in packages too. The word **photon** is used for this package of energy. Each photon carries an amount of energy determined by the frequency of light. The experimental evidence that led to this equation is a fascinating story. However, we will not discuss these experiments in this book. Perhaps you will hear about them in a physics class one day.

Let us look at another experiment with the spectrograph, shown in Figure 9-3. We have changed the light source. The tungsten wire is replaced by a discharge tube containing hydrogen gas at low pressure. When electric current flows in the hydrogen tube, red light is emitted. Once again the spectrum can be recorded on photographic film. This spectrum consists of a series of sharp lines. Each line corresponds to a particular frequency of light emitted by hydrogen atoms. Between these lines the film has not been affected. We see that hydrogen emits light of certain frequencies only. This kind of spectrum is shown in color Plate II and is called a **line spectrum**. All elements in the gas phase emit

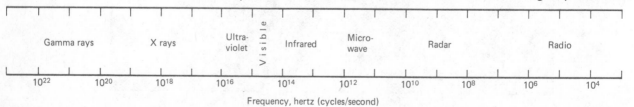

Gamma rays		X rays		Ultra-violet		Visible	Infrared		Micro-wave		Radar			Radio	
10^{22}		10^{20}		10^{18}		10^{16}		10^{14}		10^{12}		10^{10}		10^{8}	10^{6}	10^{4}

Frequency, hertz (cycles/second)

The electromagnetic energy spectrum. All these waves have the same wave character. They differ in wavelength and frequency.

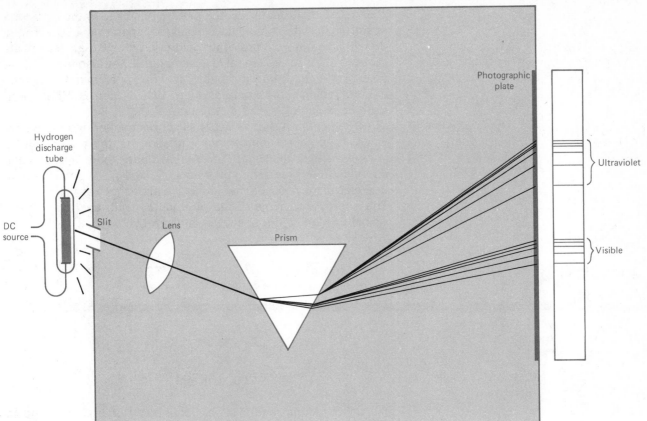

Figure 9-3
The line spectrum of light emitted by a hydrogen discharge tube (See page 152).

characteristic line spectra when they are heated to a high temperature or when an electric discharge passes through them. Most line spectra of the elements are complex, containing many separate lines.

The lines in the hydrogen spectrum can be described by the wavelength, by the frequency, or by the energy of the photons forming them. Chemists are interested in how light affects chemical reactions, for example, as in photosynthesis or the fading of dyes. It is the energy of light that is important. Therefore, we will use the energy description for the different lines in the hydrogen spectrum. Figure 9-4 shows the hydrogen spectrum with these descriptions.

1 angstrom $= 1 \times 10^{-8}$ cm $= 0.1$ nm
Named after A. J. Ångström, a Swedish scientist, it is used to express very small distances, as between atoms. The nanometer will eventually replace the angstrom.

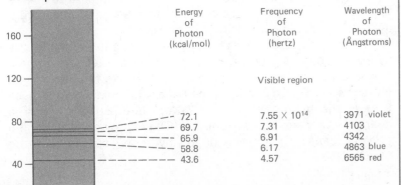

	Energy of Photon (kcal/mol)	Frequency of Photon (hertz)	Wavelength of Photon (Ångstroms)	
			Visible region	
	72.1	7.55×10^{14}	3971	violet
	69.7	7.31	4103	
	65.9	6.91	4342	
	58.8	6.17	4863	blue
	43.6	4.57	6565	red

Figure 9-4
The line spectrum of the hydrogen atom in the visible region.

Power engineers studying solar energy try to use the heat content of sunlight efficiently.

Because of its simplicity, the pattern exhibited in the hydrogen spectrum intrigued scientists. Did the spectrum of hydrogen depend on the structure of the hydrogen atom? Many scientists thought this was a reasonable assumption. They also thought that an explanation for the line spectrum of hydrogen might lead to an understanding of the atomic structure of hydrogen. But the search for this explanation was a long one.

In 1885 Johann Balmer, a Swiss schoolteacher and mathematician, proposed a mathematical relation for the energy of the lines in the hydrogen spectrum. At first glance there is no obvious connection between the numbers 43.6, 58.8, . . . shown as the energies of the lines. Balmer found a relation that was fairly simple. The energy of a mole of the photons causing each line in the visible portion of the spectrum is given by:

$$E_n = 313.6 \left(\frac{1}{2^2} - \frac{1}{n^2} \right) \qquad n = 3, 4, 5, \ldots .$$

The energy of the first line is given by letting $n = 3$:

$$E_n = 313.6 \left(\frac{1}{4} - \frac{1}{9} \right) = 313.6 \left(\frac{5}{36} \right)$$

$$= 43.6 \text{ kcal/mol}$$

The energy of the second line is obtained by letting $n = 4$, and so on.

EXERCISE 9-1

Draw a line 8 cm long on a piece of paper and mark off 2 cm divisions. Label each of these divisions from 40 to 80 kcal/mol. Use the Balmer formula to calculate E when $n = 4, 5, 6, 7$, and 8. Draw a mark for each of these energies on your scale. Also include the value for $n = 3$ worked out above. Compare this with the spectrum in Figure 9-4.

The agreement between the energies calculated from this formula and from the spectral lines was amazing. Scientists were convinced that some simple model for the hydrogen atom would provide an explanation for the spectrum and for the Balmer formula. However, it was almost 30 years later, after many more trials, that a suitable model was proposed.

A helpful development was the discovery of another part of the hydrogen spectrum by an American scientist, Theodore Lyman. This one was in the ultraviolet region, not visible to human eyes. It is shown in Figure 9-5. Does the Balmer formula work for these lines in the hydrogen spectrum? Not quite. But the required change is very small: 2^2 becomes 1^2. The energy of a mole of the photons causing each line of the hydrogen spectrum in the ultraviolet is:

$$E_n = 313.6 \left(\frac{1}{1^2} - \frac{1}{n^2} \right) \qquad n = 2, 3, 4, \ldots .$$

An amazing situation indeed! But how can this be used to build a model? A few more details are needed.

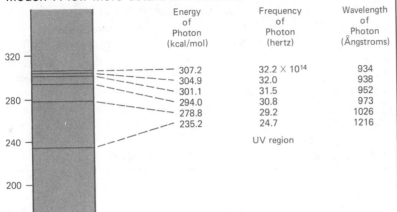

	Energy of Photon (kcal/mol)	Frequency of Photon (hertz)	Wavelength of Photon (Ångstroms)
	307.2	32.2×10^{14}	934
	304.9	32.0	938
	301.1	31.5	952
	294.0	30.8	973
	278.8	29.2	1026
	235.2	24.7	1216
		UV region	

Figure 9-5
The line spectrum of the hydrogen atom in the ultraviolet region.

Lack of contrast makes it very difficult to see white polar bears against the snow. However, pictures taken on film that is sensitive to ultraviolet light reveal polar bears very distinctly. Their fur absorbs much more UV than does the snow, so they appear black on a white background.

9-2 Ionization Energy and the Hydrogen Spectrum

There are two important features of the hydrogen spectrum. First, hydrogen atoms emit light of only certain energies. Second, the lines on the photographic film are spaced systematically. A definite frequency and energy of light can be associated with each of these lines. Let us look at these spectral lines to see if they can be related to the energy of the atom. The hydrogen atom just before emission of light has a certain energy, E_2. Light of frequency, ν, is emitted, carrying away an amount of energy, $h\nu$. The hydrogen atom now must have a smaller amount of energy, E_1.

$$h\nu = E_2 - E_1 = \Delta E$$

All values for $h\nu$ observed in the spectrum are smaller than the ionization energy for hydrogen, 313.6 kcal/mol. This fact suggests that less energy is involved in producing the lines of the spectrum than is needed to remove an electron completely from the hydrogen atom.

A diagram will help us describe some energy changes that the hydrogen atom undergoes. The energy of the hydrogen atom is represented as the lower line in Figure 9-6. The process of ionization is shown by the vertical arrow.

$$H(g) + 313.6 \text{ kcal} \longrightarrow H^+(g) + e^-$$

The products, $H^+(g)$ and e^-, have considerably more energy than the original hydrogen atom. The horizontal line representing the energy for these particles is the higher line in the figure. Energy is absorbed during the ionization of an atom. The hydrogen ion and the electron can recombine to form a neutral hydrogen atom. When this occurs, energy is emitted as shown in Figure 9-7.

$$H^+(g) + e^- \longrightarrow H(g) + 313.6 \text{ kcal}$$

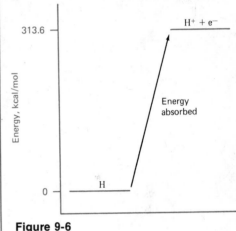

Figure 9-6
Ionization of the hydrogen atom.

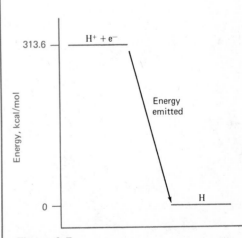

Figure 9-7
Recombination of H^+ and e^- to form the hydrogen atom.

We have already pointed out that there are many lines in the hydrogen spectrum. More important, we saw that the energy of these spectral lines never exceeded the ionization energy, 313.6 kcal/mol. There is an important idea here. Perhaps the line spectrum for hydrogen means the atom can have intermediate energies between two states—for example, between the hydrogen atom, H, and the ionized state, H^+ plus e^-. Maybe the line spectrum is a coded message written in energy instead of words. How can we deduce from the spectrum what energy states a hydrogen atom can have?

9-3 A Model That Explains the Hydrogen Spectrum

If there are certain energy states for a hydrogen atom, perhaps we can use a staircase as a model. Each level on the staircase will represent a different energy state. Imagine many children going up and down this staircase. As the children go higher on the staircase, their potential energy increases. The work that is necessary to move up a staircase is transformed into energy of position. Occasionally one of the children jumps down the staircase. Potential energy is converted into energy of motion. When the child lands on a stair, the energy is converted to different forms, primarily heat and sound. Suppose that we cannot see the staircase. We can hear the children calling out the change they make going up or down the staircase. We never learn which stair they are on. They only announce the change they are making. We hear numbers like "one, one, one, three, four, two, one, two, three, one, four. . . ." Suppose that these are the only numbers heard. They form the energy spectrum for this staircase. We can easily construct the staircase the children are playing on, even though we cannot see it. It would look like the diagram in Figure 9-8. We can be fairly sure that the staircase has only five levels, because the children never announce a jump or change larger than four. We assume that the children could jump more than four steps if the staircase were longer.

There are two points we want to emphasize in this model. First, the children always change position by an integral number of levels. There is no way for them to move up or down by a half or a third of a level. Second, a change from level 5 to level 3 would be called out in the same way as a change from level 2 to level 4. The signal we receive is "2" for each of these changes.

EXERCISE 9-2

List all changes in level possible on this staircase. List them systematically. For example, for the changes that begin on level 1, write $1 \longrightarrow 2$, $1 \longrightarrow 3$, $1 \longrightarrow 4$, and $1 \longrightarrow 5$. For changes that end on level 1, write $5 \longrightarrow 1$, $4 \longrightarrow 1$, $3 \longrightarrow 1$, and $2 \longrightarrow 1$. Next to these indicate the size of each change. Repeat for levels 2, 3, and 4.

9-4 The Hydrogen Atom

The example in Section 9-3 outlined the way to draw a hidden staircase from its observed spectrum. It might be useful to follow

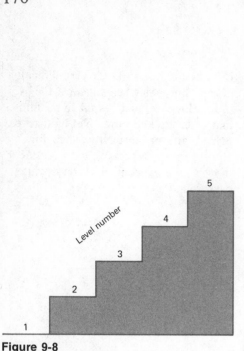

Figure 9-8
Deduced shape of the hidden staircase.

the same procedure for the hydrogen atom. The observed spectral lines for hydrogen might tell us the energy changes made by the hydrogen atom. The hydrogen spectrum in the ultraviolet region is given in Table 9-2. The energy listed for each spectral line is the size of the energy change that the hydrogen atom signals to us. We can draw a diagram of the hydrogen staircase from the energies listed in Table 9-2.

TABLE 9-2
The Ultraviolet Spectrum for
Atomic Hydrogen (Lyman Spectrum)

Level Change	Photon Energy, $h\nu$ (kcal/mol)
$2 \longrightarrow 1$	235.2
$3 \longrightarrow 1$	278.8
$4 \longrightarrow 1$	294.0
$5 \longrightarrow 1$	301.1
$\vdots$	$\vdots$
$\infty \longrightarrow 1$	313.6

We will assign the number 1 to the lowest energy level in the hydrogen atom. The next level, number 2, is drawn 235.2 kcal/mol higher. And so on. The top level of the staircase is assigned the number ∞. This level corresponds to the ionized state of a hydrogen atom, H^+ and e^-. We can build our staircase by indicating a level for each of the energy values in Table 9-2. The result, shown in Figure 9-9, is a staircase all right. But a peculiar one! Not all the steps are the same height. The first step is quite large; then they get smaller and smaller the higher we go. Between level 5 and level ∞ there are many energy levels so close together that it is difficult to draw them on this scale.

Now suppose the hydrogen atom in one of the higher energy levels can change to a lower energy level. Energy in the form of light will be released. As with the children jumping down the staircase, the atom must change by an integral number of levels. There are no halfway resting points in either case. We explain the ultraviolet spectrum by saying the observed energies result when hydrogen atoms change from various higher energy levels to level one. Complete Exercise 9-3 before reading further.

EXERCISE 9-3

Suppose that atoms change from the higher energy states to the one designated No. 2. Use the energy values in Table 9-2 or Figure 9-9 to make a list of the energy changes that occur. Compare your list with the Balmer series in Exercise 9-1. What would you expect for changes to energy state No. 3? Where would you expect the lines for these transitions to appear in the light spectrum?

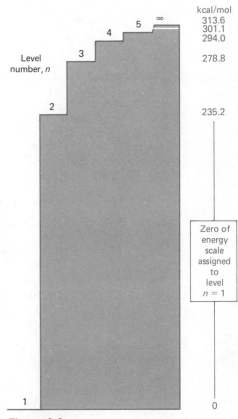

Figure 9-9
The hidden staircase in the hydrogen atom.

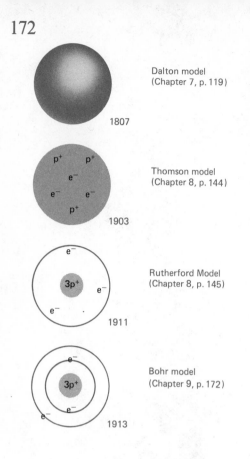

Dalton model
(Chapter 7, p. 119)

1807

Thomson model
(Chapter 8, p. 144)

1903

Rutherford Model
(Chapter 8, p. 145)

1911

Bohr model
(Chapter 9, p. 172)

1913

Atomic models of Li (historical).

These ideas develop into the Quantum Theory.

9-5 Bohr's Model for the Hydrogen Atom

We are now ready to look at the model for the hydrogen atom that explains the hydrogen spectrum. Bohr adopted Rutherford's nuclear atom and proposed that the electron arrangement in an atom is fixed by the energy of the atom. In general, the more energy the atom has, the farther the electron is from the nucleus. He also proposed that only certain energy levels are possible. These levels are called **stationary states**. As long as the atom is in one of the stationary states, no energy is given off. When an atom changes from a higher to a lower stationary state, energy in the form of light is emitted. The spectral line we see is caused by the emitted light. Finally, Bohr *assumed* that the atom could stay in the lowest energy state indefinitely. Negatively charged electrons would not fall into the positively charged nucleus. Bohr saved the atom from catastrophe! We accept this surprising assumption because Bohr's model was so successful in predicting the line spectra for the hydrogen atom.

These ideas were quite revolutionary. They were accepted only because Bohr was able to calculate the hydrogen atom energy levels exactly. Knowing the energy levels, Bohr could calculate the spectrum from the hydrogen atom. The spectral lines in the ultraviolet part of the hydrogen spectrum correspond to the atom changing from the higher energy levels to level 1 in Figure 9-9. You have just calculated another set of spectral lines in Exercise 9-3. They are found in the visible portion of the hydrogen spectrum. These spectral lines are called the Balmer series and appear when atoms change from higher energy levels to level 2. Another set of lines in the hydrogen spectrum is in the infrared region. As you may have guessed, they arise when atoms in higher energy states change to level 3. Bohr predicted these lines, and their discovery was a triumph for his theory.

From 1913 to 1927 there was great turmoil in scientific circles as Bohr's ideas were discussed. During this time our modern concept of atoms was created by combining Bohr's assumption on the behavior of very small particles and Planck's idea on energy packages. The equation in this theory, part of quantum mechanics, requires advanced mathematics. We will just give the results.

Each different energy level has a unique value of n. These n values correspond to the imaginary hydrogen staircase. They are called the principal quantum numbers. For each of the energy levels there are n^2 different arrangements in space of the electron and proton in the hydrogen atom. The electron occupies the space around the proton in a somewhat different manner for each arrangement. The n^2 arrangements for each level all have the same energy but fill the space differently.

There is no experimental evidence that the electron has a path around the nucleus. Therefore, the notion of an orbit or path for an electron was discarded. Instead, we consider the probability of finding the electron at various points around the nucleus. The word **orbital** has been chosen to describe a region of space around the atomic nucleus in which an electron is most likely to be found. In the next section we will discuss orbitals in some detail. Before we do that, however, there is one other important point to consider.

In Chapter 7 the discussion of the noble gas family brought out the fact that these elements show almost no chemical reactivity. We also saw that the first ionization energy for each of these elements is very high. The atomic structure for the noble gases must be particularly stable. Table 9-3 compares the number of orbitals in this model of the hydrogen atom with the number of electrons in each noble gas.

TABLE 9-3

Stable Electron Populations of Noble Gases
Compared to the Hydrogen Atom Orbitals

The Noble Gases			The Hydrogen Atom		
Element	Number of Electrons	Differences	n	Number of Orbitals, n^2	$2 \times n^2$
Helium	2	2	1	1	2
Neon	10	$10 - 2 = 8$	2	4	8
Argon	18	$18 - 10 = 8$			
Krypton	36	$36 - 18 = 18$	3	9	18
Xenon	54	$54 - 36 = 18$			
Radon	86	$86 - 54 = 32$	4	16	32

Notice the last column in each section of this table. The same numbers, 2, 8, 18, and 32, appear in each column. In the left-hand section the numbers come from experimental measurement of atomic number. In the right-hand section the numbers are obtained by doubling the number of orbitals. We can interpret the doubling to mean that each orbital can contain a maximum of two electrons. We will see how this assumption provides an explanation for the periodic table.

9-6 The Meaning of Orbitals

Orbitals are regions of space around a nucleus in which electrons are likely to be found. Is there more chance of finding an electron in one region of an orbital than in another? Yes. The orbital description for the electrons in an atom can be compared with the pattern of holes in a dartboard. After a dartboard has been used for a long time, there are many holes near the bull's-eye. As one looks away from the bull's-eye in any direction, there is a regular decrease in the number of holes per square centimeter of the dartboard. The number of holes per square centimeter at any distance from the bull's-eye is a measure of the probability that the next dart will land there. The holes in the dartboard do not tell us anything about the order in which the holes were made or where the next dart will land. The situation in the atom is similar. The orbital describes the probability that an electron will be at a particular distance and direction from the nucleus. The orbital does not tell us where the electron was, is now, or will be next.

One of the errors in Bohr's model for the atom was the assignment of an exact orbit for the electron. Such an orbit has meaning only if there is some way to measure the orbit. Think for a moment

The word *orbital* was invented by Robert S. Mulliken, an American professor of chemistry at the University of Chicago, who won a Nobel prize in 1966.

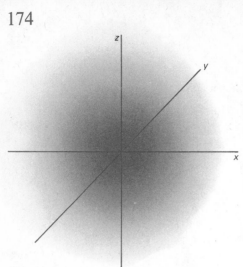

Figure 9-10
The 1s orbital for the hydrogen atom. An electron would be found in the shaded region about 95 percent of the time.

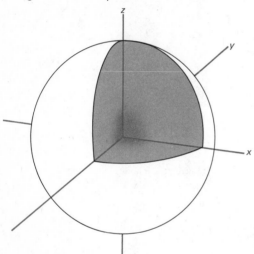

Figure 9-11
A cutaway view of the spherical 1s orbital.

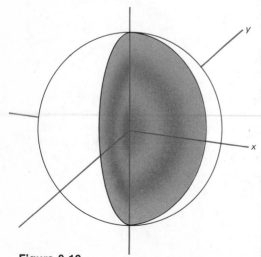

Figure 9-12
The 2s orbital for the hydrogen atom.

how the air-traffic controller locates an airplane. Radar waves reflected from an airplane let him follow the airplane's path. On the atomic scale any device we might use to measure the electron path brings so much energy into the system that the electron path is changed! We must be happy with a fuzzy picture of where the electron might be in an atom instead of the sharply defined orbits proposed by Bohr.

9-7 The Orbitals for the Hydrogen Atom

For the lowest energy level n equals 1. There is only one orbital for this energy level, since $n^2 = 1$. This orbital is called the 1s (one s) orbital. It is drawn in Figures 9-10 and 9-11. Use the letter s to remember that s orbitals have spherical symmetry.

Spherical symmetry is not such a difficult idea. Imagine a hot stove in the middle of a room on a cold day. The probability of finding heat energy would fall off in a spherical way. There would be plenty of heat near the stove and less and less heat as you moved away in any direction. In an s orbital the chance of finding an electron diminishes as you go away from the nucleus in any direction. The shading in drawings of orbitals is to represent the chance of finding the electron. In all our drawings of orbitals the shaded regions indicate the volume where we would find the electron 90–95 percent of the time. Remember, there is always a small chance that the electron will be found farther from the nucleus than our drawings show.

The next energy level has the number $n = 2$. There are $n^2 = 4$ different orbitals. For the hydrogen atom these four orbitals have the same energy. One of the four is called the 2s orbital (two s). It has spherical symmetry. The 2s orbital, shown in Figure 9-12, is larger than the 1s orbital. The larger size seems reasonable because an electron in the 2s orbital has more energy than an electron in the 1s orbital. The electron with higher energy is more likely to be found at a greater distance from the nucleus. For every value of n there is one orbital with spherical symmetry. These orbitals are referred to as s orbitals. As n increases, these spherical orbitals become larger in size.

Now let us describe the other three orbitals for which $n = 2$. They are called 2p (two p) orbitals. These orbitals are not spherically symmetrical. For an electron in a p orbital we are most likely to find the electron in two regions on opposite sides of the nucleus. The three 2p orbitals are shown in Figure 9-13. These orbitals lie along the x, y, and z axes. They are sometimes called $2p_x$, $2p_y$, and $2p_z$ orbitals to emphasize their directional character. Perhaps you can associate the letter p with the word "perpendicular" to help remember the directional properties of p orbitals. We will see later that p orbitals are useful in explaining shapes of molecules. Every energy level with n greater than 1 has three p orbitals. As n increases, these p orbitals become larger in size. This means that on the average the electron has more energy and is farther from the nucleus in a 3p orbital than in a 2p orbital.

When $n = 3$, there are $n^2 = 9$ orbitals, including one 3s orbital, three 3p orbitals, and five 3d orbitals. In the hydrogen atom the

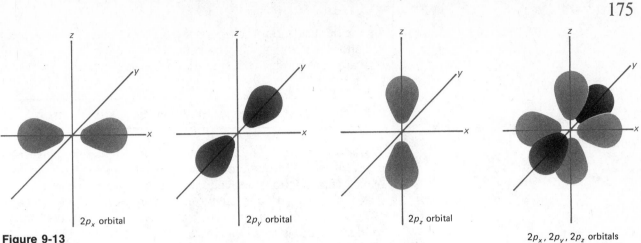

Figure 9-13
The 2p orbitals for the hydrogen atom.

nine orbitals have the same energy. When $n = 4$, there are $n^2 = 16$ orbitals, including one 4s orbital, three 4p orbitals, five 4d orbitals, and seven 4f orbitals. In this course we will not discuss d and f orbitals in any detail. Like the p orbitals, the d and f orbitals are not spherically symmetrical.

The energy level diagram for hydrogen is drawn in Figure 9-14.

Artists and illustrators produce better work when they understand what they are drawing.

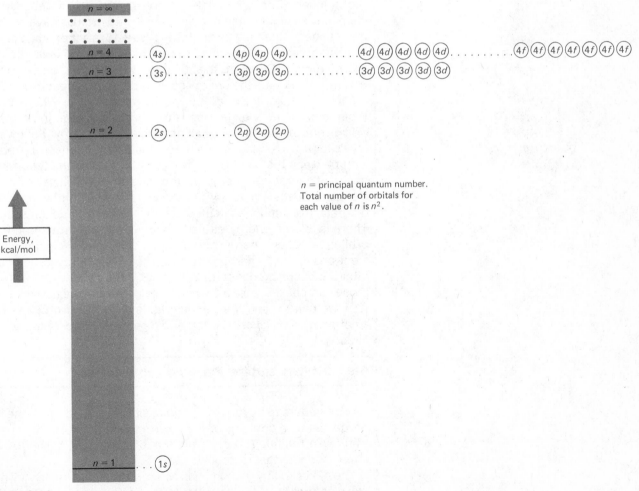

Figure 9-14
The energy level diagram for the hydrogen atom.

On the right side of this diagram the orbitals for each energy level are shown as circles, $\bigcirc$. This representation reminds us that an orbital corresponds to the space in which electrons are most likely to be found.

9-8 Orbitals for Atoms with More than One Electron

The line spectrum for hydrogen is the clue to the energy level diagram for the hydrogen atom. Gaseous samples of every element exhibit line spectra. However, most spectra are much more complex than the hydrogen spectrum shown in the figure on page 167. When these spectra are deciphered, we find that these regularities apply to all elements.

Atoms can have only certain amounts of energy.

The observed spectral lines correspond to the energy differences between these amounts.

The energy level diagrams for elements with more than one electron are quite similar to the diagram for hydrogen. However, there are several important differences. For a particular value of the number n the n^2 orbitals do not have the same energy. In elements with more than one electron the $2p$ orbitals have slightly higher energy than the $2s$ orbital. Figure 9-15, a schematic energy level diagram for all elements except hydrogen, will help you see what happens. Compare this diagram with the one for hydrogen on page 175. Since the energy scale is different for each element, numerical values for energy have been omitted in Figure 9-15. When more than one electron is present in an atom, the orbitals of a given value of n do not all have the same energy. Follow the levels for $n = 3$ or 4 in Figure 9-15. This effect is caused by repulsion between the electrons. The result is to place the $3d$ orbitals at about the same energy as the $4s$ and $4p$ orbitals. Another consequence is shown by the numbers at the right side of this diagram. Remember, we can place two electrons in each orbital. There is a large energy gap after we put two electrons in the $1s$ orbital. Another energy gap occurs after placing eight more electrons in the $2s$ and $2p$ orbitals. The large energy gaps occur after the accommodation of 2, 8, 8, 18, 18, 32 electrons. We saw those numbers in Table 9-3 when we talked about the noble gases. Now we can explain the periodic table in terms of orbitals. The electron configurations for the noble gases provide an important clue.

9-9 Orbitals and the Periodic Table

The procedure to be followed is quite simple. We start with the hydrogen atom. It contains one proton in the nucleus and one electron in an orbital. The electron is accommodated in the lowest energy orbital, the $1s$ orbital.

The next element, helium, has two protons in the nucleus. Then two electrons must be in orbitals to provide electrical neutrality for the atom. Since an orbital can accommodate two electrons, both of the electrons for helium go into the 1s orbital. We say the electron arrangement in the helium atom is $1s^2$ (one s two). This is a shorthand way to show that there are two electrons in the 1s orbital. The notation $1s^2$ represents the arrangement of electrons and is called the **electron configuration** of helium.

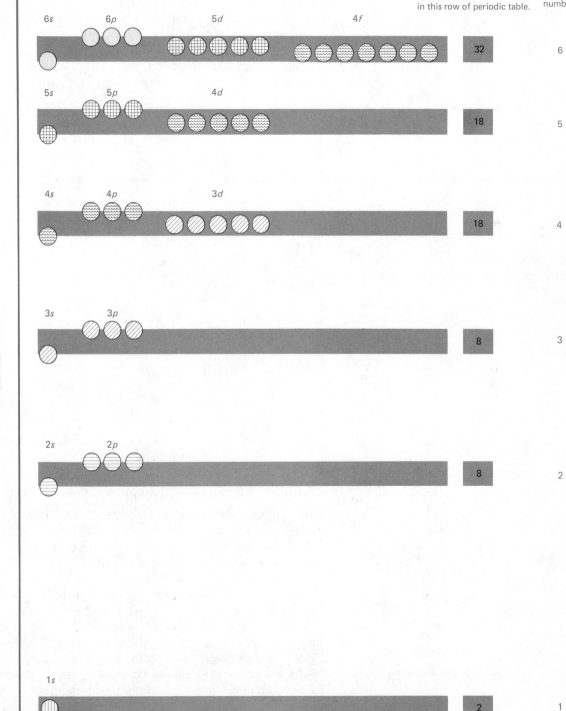

2 times the number of orbitals.

Number of elements (and number of electrons added) in this row of periodic table.

Periodic table row number

Figure 9-15
A schematic energy level diagram for a many-electron atom.

For the next element, lithium, there are three protons in the nucleus. Two electrons occupy the 1s orbital. The third electron cannot enter this orbital because it is filled. The third electron is placed in the next higher energy orbital, the 2s. The lithium atom has the electron configuration 1s²2s (one s two, two s one). The 2s electron in a lithium atom is weakly bound when compared to the 1s electrons.

Some figures will help you to understand what happens. We will use the symbol ◯ to represent any empty orbital. An orbital with one electron is indicated by ⊘ or by ⊗. Such an orbital is half filled. A filled orbital is shown by the symbol ⊗. By this we mean there are two electrons in the orbital. Figure 9-16 shows the electron arrangements for the first three elements, H, He, and Li. The

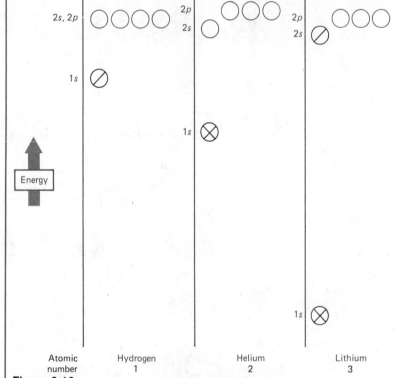

Figure 9-16
Schematic orbital diagrams for hydrogen, helium, and lithium atoms.

2s electron of lithium is much closer to the ionization level than are the electrons of hydrogen and helium. It should be easy to remove the 2s electron to give the lithium ion, Li⁺. In Section 7-4 we pointed out that the alkali metals readily form 1+ ions. The energy diagram provides an explanation for this behavior.

Our schematic diagrams suggest that the electron in the 2s orbital of lithium is much farther away from the nucleus than the electron in the 1s orbital for hydrogen. But this is not true. Its average position is only slightly farther away. To see why, let us look more closely at the electric forces in atoms.

As we construct electron configurations for atoms with high atomic numbers, we must assign electrons to orbitals that have large energy level numbers. This would seem to place them considerably farther from the nucleus. But while adding more electrons, we are also adding more positive charges to the nucleus. The resulting greater attractive force pulls the electrons in closer. These two effects tend to balance each other. The largest atom is only about three times the diameter of the smallest.

The beryllium atom has four protons in the nucleus and four electrons in orbitals. Two electrons can occupy the $1s$ orbital ($1s^2$) and two can enter the $2s$ orbital ($2s^2$). The electron configuration for a beryllium atom is $1s^2 2s^2$ (one s two, two s two). The $2s$ electrons will be most easily removed, forming the ion Be^{2+}.

The fifth electron, which is required for the next element, boron, enters the lowest available orbital, one of the $2p$ orbitals. The electron configuration for boron can be written $1s^2\ 2s^2 2p$ (one s two, two s two, two p one). The pattern for regularity begins to develop. Let us skip a few elements and discuss fluorine, the element with atomic number nine. Nine electrons must be placed in orbitals for the neutral atom of fluorine. The electron configuration is $1s^2\ 2s^2 2p^5$. A quick check to be sure you have the correct number of electrons in a configuration is to add all the exponents of s and p. The total should equal the atomic number of the element. A diagram of this configuration is in Figure 9-17.

EXERCISE 9-4

State in words what the notation $1s^2 2s^2 2p^5$ means.

The next element, neon, has ten electrons. The last space in the $2p$ orbitals is filled with the Ne atom. This configuration is also shown in Figure 9-17. Table 9-4 summarizes what we have been saying.

TABLE 9-4

Electron Configurations for Atoms
of the First Ten Elements

Element	Atomic Number	Electron Configuration	Number of Electrons*
H	1	$1s$	1
He	2	$1s^2$	2
Li	3	$1s^2\ 2s$	3
Be	4	$1s^2\ 2s^2$	4
B	5	$1s^2\ 2s^2 2p$	5
C	6	$1s^2\ 2s^2 2p^2$	6
N	7	$1s^2\ 2s^2 2p^3$	7
O	8	$1s^2\ 2s^2 2p^4$	8
F	9	$1s^2\ 2s^2 2p^5$	9
Ne	10	$1s^2\ 2s^2 2p^6$	10

*Equals sum of exponents in the configuration.

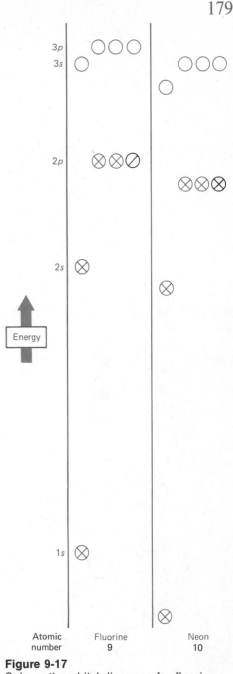

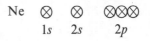

Figure 9-17
Schematic orbital diagrams for fluorine and neon atoms.

When we consider the next element, sodium, we encounter a situation similar to the one found for lithium. The eleventh electron for sodium must be in an orbital of higher energy, the $3s$ orbital. The lower energy orbitals are fully occupied. As we move to the elements chlorine and argon, we find that their electron configurations are very similar to those for fluorine and neon. Figure 9-18 shows the orbital configurations for sodium, chlorine, and argon.

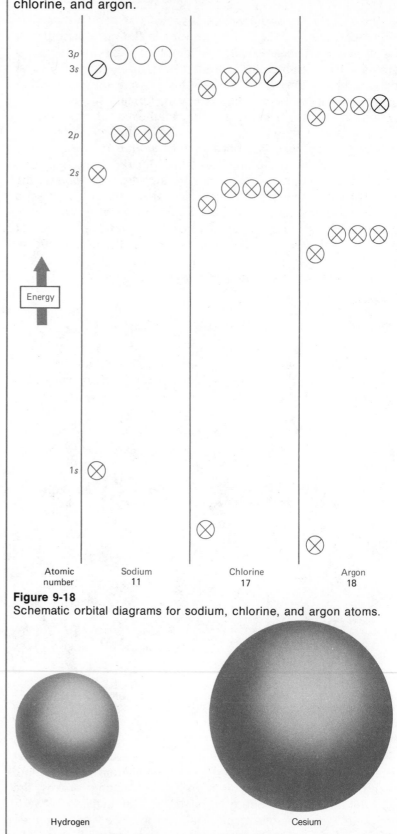

Figure 9-18
Schematic orbital diagrams for sodium, chlorine, and argon atoms.

Representation of the largest and smallest atoms.

9-10   Electron Configuration and the Periodic Table

You have probably recognized that there is an important regularity in the electron arrangements of the elements. This regularity is brought out in Figure 9-19. Each family of elements in the periodic table contains elements which have very similar electron arrangements.

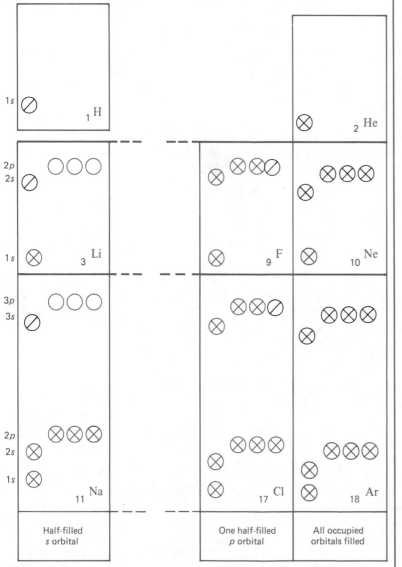

Figure 9-19
Regularity in electron arrangements in the periodic table.

In Chapter 7 we discussed three important families: the noble gases, the alkali metals, and the halogens. We can now look at each of these families in more detail. The noble gases He, Ne, and Ar have electron configurations that completely fill all the orbitals up to a particular energy level. When orbitals are filled in this way, a very stable element is observed. In contrast, the alkali metals and the halogens are elements with high chemical reactivity. Perhaps we can find an explanation for this difference of reactivity by looking at their electron configurations.

The alkali metals have electron configurations that place the electron with highest energy in an s orbital. All other electrons are in levels of considerably lower energy. A relatively small amount of energy is needed to remove the s electron. An ion with charge 1+ forms. This ion has the same electron configuration as the nearest noble gas. We can illustrate what happens with the following equation. The electron configuration is given below each species.

$$\text{Li} + \text{energy} \longrightarrow \text{Li}^+ + e^-$$
$$1s^2 2s \qquad\qquad\qquad 1s^2$$

Li$^+$ has the same electron configuration as He, $1s^2$

$$\text{Na} + \text{energy} \longrightarrow \text{Na}^+ + e^-$$
$$1s^2\, 2s^2 2p^6\, 3s \qquad\qquad 1s^2\, 2s^2 2p^6$$

Na$^+$ has the same electron configuration as Ne, $1s^2\, 2s^2 2p^6$

The chemical properties of the alkali metals result from the stable 1+ ions, which have the same electron configurations as a noble gas.

The halogens, fluorine and chlorine, have configurations with one vacancy in the p orbitals. These elements readily accept one more electron from other elements to fill this vacant position. Ions form with a 1− charge. The ions take on the electron configuration of the nearest noble gas.

$$\text{F} + e^- \longrightarrow \text{F}^- + \text{energy}$$
$$1s^2\, 2s^2 2p^5 \qquad\qquad 1s^2\, 2s^2 2p^6$$

F$^-$ has the same electron configuration as Ne, $1s^2\, 2s^2 2p^6$

$$\text{Cl} + e^- \longrightarrow \text{Cl}^- + \text{energy}$$
$$1s^2\, 2s^2 2p^6\, 3s^2 3p^5 \qquad\qquad 1s^2\, 2s^2 2p^6\, 3s^2 3p^6$$

Cl$^-$ has the same electron configuration as Ar, $1s^2\, 2s^2 2p^6\, 3s^2 3p^6$

The unusual stability of the electron configurations for the noble gases is an important point. The ions Na$^+$ and F$^-$ have the same electron configuration as Ne. We have hinted before that the noble gases provide an important clue to atomic structure. Energy level diagrams show clearly that sodium and fluorine have ions with the same electron arrangement as neon.

Finally, let us look at hydrogen once more. It is placed in an isolated box in the periodic table. The electron configuration for hydrogen resembles those for lithium and sodium. Writing them in a column helps you to see that each has a single s electron in the highest occupied orbital.

Hydrogen		$1s$
Lithium	$1s^2$	$2s$
Sodium	$1s^2\ 2s^22p^6$	$3s$

On the other hand, the electron configuration for hydrogen also resembles those for fluorine and chlorine. Each of these atoms is one electron short of a noble gas structure.

H		$1s$		$1s^2$	He
F	$1s^2$	$2s^22p^5$	$1s^2$	$2s^22p^6$	Ne
Cl	$1s^2\ 2s^22p^6$	$3s^23p^5$	$1s^22s^22p^6$	$3s^23p^6$	Ar

Hydrogen is unusual among all the chemical elements. In some respects it is like an alkali metal. In other ways it is like a halogen. Thus, in most periodic tables hydrogen is shown in a box slightly separated from the other elements.

9-11   Ionization Energy and the Periodic Table

We have referred to ionization energy in Chapter 7 in discussing the three chemical families: the noble gases, the alkali metals, and the halogens. Ionization of a neutral atom can be represented by the equation

$$M(g) + \text{energy} \longrightarrow M^+(g) + e^-$$

Can we relate the size of ionization energy to the orbital from which the electron is removed? The ionization of lithium is shown in Figure 9-20. The ionization energy, 124.3 kcal/mol, is just sufficient to raise the $2s$ electron to the energy level $n = \infty$.

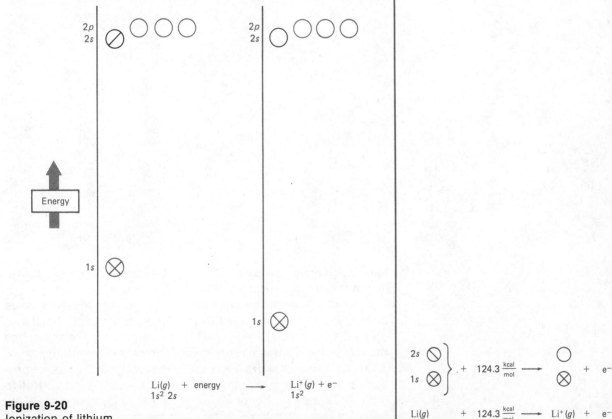

Figure 9-20
Ionization of lithium.

Many systematic determinations of ionization energies were carried out in the decade after Bohr proposed his atomic model. The first measurements were made by bombarding an atomic vapor with high-energy electrons. In this method the energy of the electrons was known very precisely. When the kinetic energy of the bombarding electron is increased slowly, a critical value is reached at which positive ions can be detected. These ions result from interactions between atoms and bombarding electrons that have been given just enough kinetic energy to cause the most weakly bound electron to be ejected from the atom. This critical value is found to be characteristic of the substance being investigated. The ionization energies for the first 20 elements are listed in Table 9-5.

TABLE 9-5
First Ionization Energy for Some Elements

Atomic Number	Element	Ionization Energy (kcal/mol)
1	H	313.6
2	He	566.7
3	Li	124.3
4	Be	214.9
5	B	191.2
6	C	259.5
7	N	335
8	O	313.8
9	F	401.8
10	Ne	497
11	Na	118.4
12	Mg	175.2
13	Al	137.9
14	Si	187.9
15	P	241.7
16	S	238.8
17	Cl	300
18	Ar	363.2
19	K	100
20	Ca	141

Many regularities become apparent when these values are shown in graphical form, Figure 9-21.

First, there is a gradual increase in ionization energy as we move across a row of the periodic table. For instance, notice the jagged upward line from Li to Ne or Na to Ar. The noble gas element has the highest ionization energy of the elements in a particular row. Second, there is a sharp decrease in ionization energy as we proceed from a noble gas to the next element, an alkali metal. Notice the drop from He to Li or Ne to Na. There is a striking similarity between the ionization energies and the periodicity of chemical

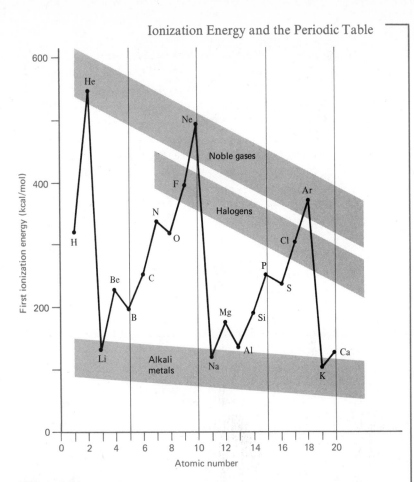

Figure 9-21
First ionization energies for the first 20 elements.

properties. This is not just a coincidence. We will see that many trends in chemical properties can be explained in terms of trends in ionization energies.

It is possible to remove more than one electron from a many-electron atom. Of course more energy is always required to remove the second electron than to remove the first. The second electron has to leave an ion which already has a net positive electric charge. The values of successive ionization energies are important to chemists.

Look at the successive ionization energies of the three elements, helium, lithium, and beryllium, in Table 9-6. These energies correspond to the reactions

$$M(g) + IE_1 \longrightarrow M^+(g) + e^-$$

$$M^+(g) + IE_2 \longrightarrow M^{2+}(g) + e^-$$

$$M^{2+}(g) + IE_3 \longrightarrow M^{3+}(g) + e^-$$

TABLE 9-6
Successive Ionization Energies (kcal/mol)

Element	Electron Configuration of Element	IE_1	IE_2	IE_3
He	$1s^2$	567	1254	—
Li	$1s^2 2s$	124	1744	2823
Be	$1s^2 2s^2$	215	420	3548

Chemists use electron configurations to explain bonding and molecular structure.

We can understand the relative size of the ionization energies by comparing the energy level diagrams for these three elements. A very large amount of energy is necessary to ionize He. We do not expect He⁺ to form readily. A much smaller amount of energy is needed to ionize Li or Be. Figure 9-22 shows that the ions Li⁺ and Be⁺ form readily.

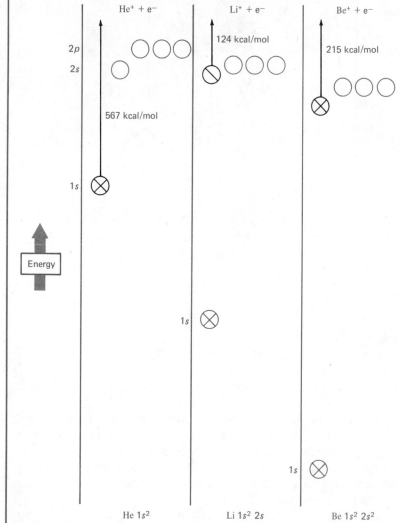

$$\otimes + 567\ \frac{\text{kcal}}{\text{mol}} \longrightarrow \oslash + e^-$$

$$\text{He} + 567\ \frac{\text{kcal}}{\text{mol}} \longrightarrow \text{He}^+ + e^-$$

Figure 9-22
First ionization energy—energy required to remove a single electron from He, Li, and Be atoms.

Let us see what the energy level diagram is like for removing the second electron from each of these ions. This is shown in Figure 9-23. The energy required to form He²⁺ or Li²⁺ is very large. We do not expect these ions to form readily. However, for beryllium, only a comparatively moderate amount of energy is needed to remove the second electron. The formation of Be²⁺ is reasonable. The explanation lies in the fact that formation of Be²⁺ removes electrons from the 2s orbital. For Li²⁺ the second electron comes from the 1s orbital. The 1s orbital is much farther below $n = \infty$ than the 2s orbital.

The electrons that are easily removed from an element establish the chemical properties of that element. Chemists call these the

valence electrons for the element. These electrons are in the highest energy *s* and *p* orbitals used. Lithium has one valence electron. Beryllium has two.

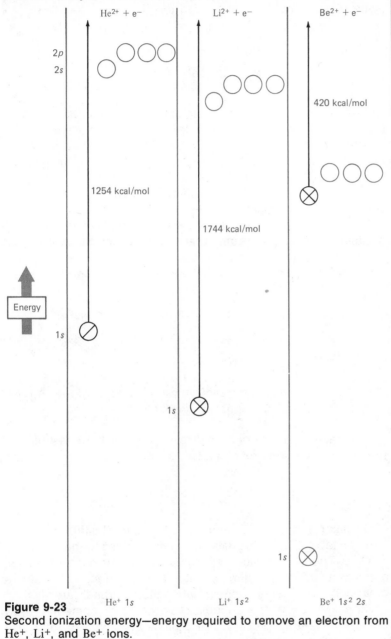

Figure 9-23
Second ionization energy—energy required to remove an electron from He⁺, Li⁺, and Be⁺ ions.

Suntan

Sunlight with wavelengths in the range 2500 to 3200 Å can cause chemical reactions in the skin that lead to sunburn or a tan. The sunlight stimulates certain cells to produce melanin, a dark brown compound that migrates up to the surface layers of the skin—hence the tan. Human evolution has led to predominantly dark-skinned people living in the tropical areas of the Earth. These people have a higher natural amount of melanin in their skin, and as a consequence are protected from the ultraviolet radiation in sunlight, which is more abundant near the equator. Lighter-skinned people are less well adapted to living in regions with large amounts of sunlight.

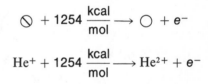

9-12   The Fourth to Sixth Rows of the Periodic Table

We will finish this chapter by discussing the electron configurations for elements beyond argon. Look back at the schematic orbital diagram given in Figure 9-15. The 3*p* orbitals are filled at argon. The next cluster of orbitals must be those with about the same energy as the 4*s* orbital. We see that something new happens. There are nine orbitals with about the same energy: the 4*s* orbital, three 4*p* orbitals, and five 3*d* orbitals. This row in the periodic table is different from the second and third rows. There are 18 elements in the fourth row instead of eight elements.

Potassium and calcium have electron configurations which place them in the families headed by lithium and beryllium.

K	$1s^2$	$2s^2 2p^6$	$3s^2 3p^6$	$4s$
Ca	$1s^2$	$2s^2 2p^6$	$3s^2 3p^6$	$4s^2$

When we consider the next element, scandium, the 21st electron will be placed in the available orbital of lowest energy. The $3d$ orbitals happen to be slightly lower in energy than the $4p$ orbitals. Consequently, the electron configurations for the next ten elements, scandium through zinc, show electrons in $3d$ orbitals. These elements are called **transition elements**. We will discuss some of their chemical properties in Chapter 19.

After the $3d$ orbitals are filled, the next orbitals to fill are the $4p$ orbitals. Let us write the configuration for gallium in a way to stress its direct relation with boron and aluminum. We have moved the $3d^{10}$ configuration ahead of $4s^2$ and $4p$ for convenience.

Ga	$1s^2$	$2s^2 2p^6$	$3s^2 3p^6$	$3d^{10}\ 4s^2 4p$

EXERCISE 9-5

Write the electron configurations of aluminum and boron. In what way are they related to that for gallium?

The remaining elements in this row add $4p$ electrons until the noble gas krypton is reached:

Kr	$1s^2$	$2s^2 2p^6$	$3s^2 3p^6$	$3d^{10} 4s^2 4p^6$

The same pattern of 18 elements is found for the fifth row of the periodic table. The $4d$ orbitals have energy close to the $5s$ and $5p$ orbitals. The ten transition elements, yttrium through cadmium, appear immediately under scandium through zinc. As usual, another noble gas, xenon, appears when the $5p$ orbitals are filled.

The sixth row of the periodic table presents something new once more. Here, four kinds of orbitals are involved that have about the same energy: $6s$, $5d$, $4f$, and $6p$. After two electrons are put in the $6s$ orbital and one is put in the $5d$ orbital, the next 14 electrons go into the seven $4f$ orbitals. This series of 14 elements is called the **rare earth elements**. Their chemical properties are so similar that for many years it was very difficult to separate these elements from each other. In the last 20 years, methods have been developed to achieve separation of the rare earth elements.

We will not pursue this discussion further. The number of elements in each row of the periodic table can be associated with the clustering of orbitals at approximately the same energy level. Table 9-7 summarizes this information.

TABLE 9-7

The Number of Elements in Each Row of the Periodic Table

Row	Number of Elements	Orbitals Being Filled for Each Row
1	2	$1s$
2	8	$2s2p$
3	8	$3s3p$
4	18	$4s3d4p$
5	18	$5s4d5p$
6	32	$6s4f5d6p$
7	(32)	$7s5f(6d7p)$

9-13   Review

Niels Bohr proposed an atomic model in which electron orbits about the nucleus were suggested. This model was the first to offer an explanation for the line spectrum of hydrogen. The Bohr model was based on the idea that the atom can exist only in certain energy states. Changes from one state to another must be accompanied by absorption or emission of energy. *One can think of these transitions in terms of an energy staircase.*

This model was important as a breakthrough. But it was wrong. Bohr's incorrect planetary orbits for the electron have been replaced by **orbitals**. Orbitals are regions of space *in which electrons are most likely to be found.* Orbitals have size and shape, and each orbital can accommodate up to two electrons. Transition from one orbital to another is accompanied by a specific energy change.

The orbital model for the atom offers an explanation for the arrangement of the chemical elements in the periodic table. There is a natural grouping of elements into chemical families on the basis of similar electron configurations.

The number of elements in a row of the periodic table is explained in terms of groupings of orbitals with approximately the same energy. The elements called the **noble gases** occur just as these groups of orbitals are fully occupied. The next set of orbitals is considerably higher in energy. The great chemical stability of the noble gases can be correlated with their electron configuration.

The elements with one electron less than a noble gas are called the **halogens**. The elements with one electron more than a noble gas are called the **alkali metals**. These families have very high chemical activity. They exhibit a great tendency to form ions that have the same electron configuration as a noble gas.

The chemical properties for each family of elements can be related to the electron configuration which is characteristic of that family. The electrons in the highest energy orbitals for any particular element are always the easiest electrons to remove. Chemists call these the **valence electrons** of the element. The valence electrons establish the chemical properties of each element.

Questions and Problems for Chapter 9

1

List an advantage and a disadvantage of the Rutherford model.

2

Use the data about water waves on page 165 to calculate how fast the wave is moving, in kilometers per hour.

3

The electromagnetic waves used in FM broadcasting by radio or television have frequencies of approximately 100 megacycles per second (megahertz). In standard AM radio broadcasting, the frequency is approximately 1 megacycle per second (megahertz). *Mega* means 10^6.

Use the relationship $\lambda = c/\nu$, where c = velocity of light = 3.0×10^{10} cm/s, to calculate the wavelengths used in AM and FM broadcasting. Compare these values with the wavelengths for red and blue light in Table 9-1.

Problems 4 through 8 are something like the problem faced by Balmer. They require you to find a relation between some numbers and to express the relation in terms of *n,* the index of the term. Example: The series 2, 4, 6, 8 is described by the relation; the value of any term = $2n$. For the first term $n = 1$; therefore $2n = 2$. For the second term $n = 2$; therefore $2n = 4$. And so on.

4

Express the relation for these numbers:

$$\tfrac{1}{2}, \ \tfrac{1}{4}, \ \tfrac{1}{8}, \ \tfrac{1}{16}$$

5

Express the relation for these numbers:

$$0, \ 4, \ 18, \ 48$$

6

Express the relation for these numbers:

$$0, \ 3, \ 8, \ 15$$

7

Express the relation for these numbers:

$$0, \ 0, \ 0, \ 6, \ 24$$

8

Express the relation for these numbers:

$$3, \ 6, \ 11, \ 20$$

9

One line in the lithium spectrum has an energy of 46.8 kcal/mol. Determine the frequency for this line. In what part of the spectrum would the line appear? $E = h\nu$, $h = 9.52 \times 10^{-14}$ kcal·s/mol. Refer to the lower figure on page 166.

10

A hidden staircase is known to have energy changes of 1, 3, 4, 5, and 8 units. Draw the staircase. What other change could it have?

11

There are six possible hidden staircases having steps of heights 1, 2, and 4. Draw them and show that there are not six possible sets of energy changes.

12

Explain why the ionization energy for hydrogen atoms is greater than the energy represented by any of the lines in the ultraviolet spectrum.

13

Use the energy level diagram in Figure 9-9 to calculate the energy required to raise the atom from an energy level $n = 1$ to each of the higher energy levels. Compare these energies with the spectral lines shown in the figure on page 169.

14

Repeat Problem 13, using level $n = 2$ for the starting level.

15

Considering the 1s orbital of the hydrogen atom, what relation exists between the surface of a sphere centered about the nucleus and the location of an electron?

16

The modern description of the 1s orbital is similar in some respects to a description of the holes in a much-used dartboard. For example, the "density" of dart holes is constant anywhere on a circle centered about the bull's-eye, and the "density" of dart holes reaches zero only at a very long distance from the bull's-eye. What are the corresponding properties of a 1s orbital?

In the light of your answer, point out erroneous features of the following models of a hydrogen atom:

(a) A ball of uniform density.

(b) A "solar-system" atom with the electron circling the nucleus at a fixed distance.

17

Sometimes a pair of balloons tied together is used to represent a p orbital. List two advantages and two disadvantages of this model.

18

Show in a rough way how electron probability varies in a $1s$ and also in a $2s$ orbital. Plot probability on the y axis and distance from the nucleus along a radius on the x axis.

19

Which of the following statements about orbitals is FALSE?

Orbitals are:

(a) distributed in space around the nucleus.

(b) regions in which electrons are likely to be found.

(c) of different sizes and shapes.

(d) to show the path of the electron.

(e) part of one model for atomic structure.

20

What must be done to an atom to change its $2s$ electron to make it a $3s$ electron? What happens when an atom with a $3s$ electron becomes one with a $2s$ electron?

21

Consider these two electron populations for neutral atoms:

$$\text{A.} \quad 1s^2 \quad 2s^2 2p^6 \quad 3s^1$$
$$\text{B.} \quad 1s^2 \quad 2s^2 2p^6 \quad 6s^1$$

Which of the following is FALSE?

(a) Energy is required to change A to B.

(b) A represents a sodium atom.

(c) A and B represent different elements.

(d) Less energy is required to remove one electron from B than from A.

22

Use a drawing similar to the right-hand one in Figure 9-13 to show the placement of the $2p^4$ electrons in the valence level of oxygen. Indicate the number of electrons in each orbital.

23

Name the elements that correspond to each of the following electron configurations:

(a) $1s^2$

(b) $1s^2 \quad 2s^1$

(c) $1s^2 \quad 2s^2 2p^1$

(d) $1s^2 \quad 2s^2 2p^3$

(e) $1s^2 \quad 2s^2 2p^6 \quad 3s^2 3p^6 \quad 4s^1$

24

Name the atoms whose orbital occupancy corresponds to those listed below. Assume all lower energy orbitals to be full and the atom to be in its lowest energy state.

(a) $2s^1$ (d) $3p^6$ (g) $1s^2$

(b) $3p^4$ (e) $4p^1$ (h) $6s^1$

(c) $3s^1$ (f) $2p^1$ (i) $5p^5$

25

Write the orbital occupancy for the elements indicated. Refer to the orbital diagram, Figure 9-15 on page 177.

(a) element with atomic number 9

(b) element with atomic number 13

(c) element with atomic number 20

(d) element with atomic number 7

26

Write the outer-level electron configuration for Ca, Sc, and Ti.

27

Name elements with the following orbital occupancy. Assume all lower energy levels are filled and the atom is in its lowest energy state.

(a) $3s^2$ (c) $2p^6$ (e) $3d^1$

(b) $5p^4$ (d) $3p^5$ (f) $6s^2$

28

Draw a sketch of the periodic table showing all elements (including elements 57–71 and 89–103) in place.

29

If you are told that the highest half-filled or filled orbital of an element in the ground state is a $3p$ orbital, what could you say about the element?

30

The electron configuration for lithium is $1s^2 2s^1$, and for beryllium it is $1s^2 2s^2$. The first ionization energy for Na is 118 kcal/mol. Estimate the approximate ionization energies to remove first one, then a second, electron from lithium and beryllium. Explain your estimates.

31

Which of the following electron configurations

would you expect to have the lowest second ionization energy? Give reasons for your choice.

(a) $1s^2 2s^2 2p^6$
(b) $1s^2 2s^2 2p^6 3s^1$
(c) $1s^2 2s^2 2p^6 3s^2$

32

The first four ionization energies of boron atoms in kcal/mol are as follows:

$$E_1 = 191 \qquad E_3 = 872$$
$$E_2 = 578 \qquad E_4 = 5962$$

Deduce the number of valence electrons of boron. Explain.

33

How many valence electrons has carbon? Silicon? Phosphorus? Hydrogen? Write the electron configuration for a neutral atom of each element.

34

How many valence electrons has radium? Barium? Bromine? Bismuth? (Count only s and p electrons.) Write the valence electron configuration for a neutral atom of each element.

35

Write the orbital description for the *valence* electrons of each element in the column headed by

(a) lithium   (c) oxygen
(b) beryllium   (d) fluorine

36

Write the valence electron configuration for

(a) the oxygen family,   (b) the carbon family

37

The first three ionization energies for Mg are 176, 346, and 1847 kcal/mol, the first two for Ca are 141 and 274 kcal/mol, and the first for Sr is 131. Predict the third for Ca, the second for Sr, and the first two for Ba and Ra.

38

Would you expect barium to have a high third-ionization energy? Why?

39

The first four ionization energies for thallium are 141, 471, 687, and 1171 kcal/mol. Suggest formulas for thallium bromide salts.

40

Write valence orbital electron configurations for each of the following elements of the 5th row of the periodic table:

(a) Rb (b) Sr (c) Te (d) I (e) Xe

41

State two similarities and two differences between ultraviolet light (black light) and X rays.

42

Consider the bonds within the molecules of your skin, and explain why infrared light makes you feel warm but ultraviolet can destroy some skin.

Chemical Bonding

In the last chapter we saw how the orbital model leads to the electron configurations of the atoms. In this chapter we want to see how the orbital model is useful in understanding molecules.

Some atomic arrangements stay together long enough for us to measure the chemical and physical properties of the molecules. For some molecules we have to act fast if we hope to measure their properties. Molecules such as OH and CH_3 have very high chemical activity. They react in a fraction of a second. Many molecules, however, are like H_2O and CH_4. Their chemical activity is relatively low at room temperature. We do not have to hurry to measure their properties.

Chemists recognize that electric attractions hold atoms together in molecules. When all the electric attractions and repulsions between two atoms are summed up, a molecule can form if the electric attractions are stronger than the electric

Chemists considering reactions in the upper atmosphere must take into account molecules and ions, such as OH, O_2^-, O_3, and Cl.

repulsions. Chemists then say that a **chemical bond** forms between two atoms. An understanding of the nature of a chemical bond is one of the chemist's major goals. After all, think what happens in chemical reactions. The number of atoms does not change. Some chemical bonds disappear. New chemical bonds form. Our ideas of chemical bonding should provide answers to questions like these:

Why are only certain chemical formulas found? Why is hydrogen gas H_2 instead of H_3?

Why do some molecules such as OH show very high chemical activity whereas molecules such as H_2O do not?

Why do molecules have different shapes? BF_3 is a flat, or planar, molecule. NF_3 has the shape of a pyramid.

Why do chemical bonds form at all?

This last question is perhaps the most important, yet in certain ways it is the easiest question to answer. A chemical bond can form between two atoms when electrons are attracted simultaneously to both atomic nuclei. We can represent what we are saying with orbital drawings. If a chemical bond forms between atoms *A* and *B*, then the probability of finding electrons in the region between the two nuclei is very high. If a chemical bond does not form between atoms *X* and *Y*, then the probability of finding electrons in the region between the two nuclei is very low.

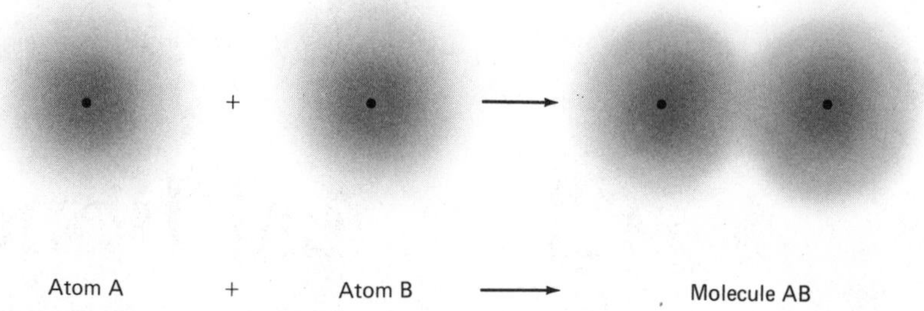

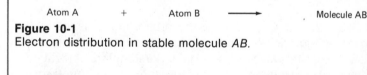

| Atom A | + | Atom B | ⟶ | Molecule AB |

Figure 10-1
Electron distribution in stable molecule *AB*.

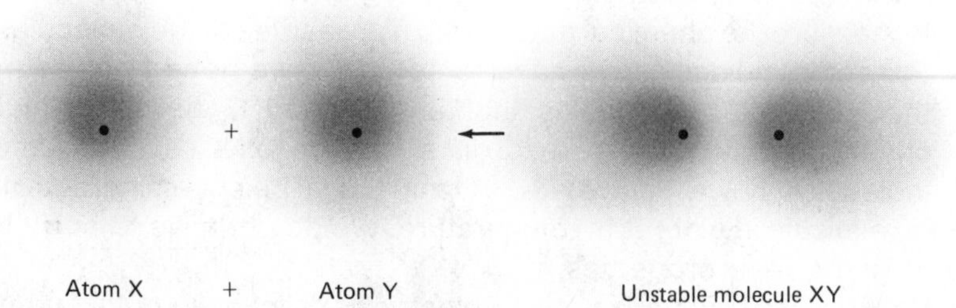

| Atom X | + | Atom Y | | Unstable molecule XY |

Figure 10-2
Electron distribution in unstable molecule *XY*.

Our discussion of chemical bonding will be in two parts. First we will discuss ionic bonding and then covalent bonding. Before we finish this chapter we will see that all chemical bonds have both similarities and differences. The similarities involve the basic nature of bonding: in all cases the bond consists of the attraction between electrons and nuclei of two atoms. The differences are brought out by the several words chemists use to indicate bond type. These are to help recall that a range of properties is produced by the various ways the electrons are attracted to two nuclei.

10-1   Ionic Bonding

We talked about the reaction of metallic sodium with chlorine gas in Section 7-3. The product, sodium chloride, is a white crystalline solid. The crystal is built up of positive ions (Na^+) alternating with negative ions (Cl^-).

$$2\,Na(s) + Cl_2(g) \longrightarrow 2\,Na^+Cl^-(s)$$

Solids such as sodium chloride are called **ionic solids**. We use the words **ionic bonds** to describe the bonding in ionic solids. Table 10-1 lists some of the general properties for substances with ionic bonding.

TABLE 10-1
Some Properties of Ionic Solids

Observed Property	Interpretation
High melting temperatures.	Strong forces hold particles together in the solid.
When molten, good conductors of electricity.	Ions are present in the molten state.
If soluble in water, solutions are good conductors of electricity.	Ions are present in aqueous solutions.

Our model for ionic bonding is a very simple one. When sodium reacts with chlorine, ions with opposite electric charge form during the chemical reaction. The stability of an ionic solid arises primarily because of electrostatic interactions between the ions. Ions with opposite electric charge attract each other.

$$\oplus \; + \; \ominus \; \longrightarrow \; \oplus\ominus \; + \; energy$$

This means the potential energy of the system is smaller when the ions are close together and energy is needed to separate them.
What happens if a third ion enters the system?

$$\oplus\ominus \; + \; \oplus \; \longrightarrow \; \oplus\ominus\oplus \; + \; energy$$

The force required to pull the 2 atoms of a chlorine molecule apart is the force created by fixing one end of the molecule and hanging 3.5×10^{15} chlorine molecules from the other end.

The arrangement of the ions on the right has less potential energy than the one on the left. Let us see why. There are now two attractive forces, one between each positive ion and the negative ion. But there is also one repulsive force between the two positive ions. However, the positive ions are farther apart than either positive-negative pair, and therefore the repulsive force is somewhat smaller. The net effect of the two attractive forces and one (smaller) repulsive force is more attraction than provided by one attractive force.

 has more attraction and less potential energy

than either ⊕⊖ or ⊕⊖ + ⊕.

We can continue to let our "crystal" grow in one dimension. Attractive and repulsive forces come into play as each ion is added. But the new attractive forces are always greater than the new repulsive forces, because opposite charges are closer than like charges. The ionic crystal grows. The potential energy continues to decrease. In one dimension the crystal looks like this:

. . . ⊕⊖⊕⊖⊕⊖⊕⊖⊕ . . .

In two dimensions the crystal can be drawn like this:

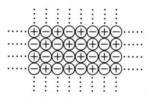

This process continues in the third dimension to form many of our common crystals. Table salt is an example of such a crystal. See Figure 6-9. The larger the crystal, the lower the potential energy of the system. It is easy to understand why ionic crystals grow large enough to be seen.

One important point needs to be emphasized. The energy that is released when ions approach each other must be removed somehow for the bond to form. If this is not done, there will be enough energy to allow the ions to move away from each other again. There are a number of ways that this energy can be taken away. Other ions can take up the energy. Solvent molecules can do the same thing. Or energy can be transferred to the walls of the reaction vessel.

Let us return to the orbital model for the atom. Does an understanding of orbitals help us to understand ionic bonding? Can we predict the electric charge ions have? A look at the example Na^+Cl^- will show how the orbital model guides us. The important clue is the great chemical stability of the noble gases.

Tables 10-2 and 10-3 show electron configurations for some alkali and halogen atoms, their ions, and the nearest noble gases. Note how each alkali atom forms an ion by losing an electron. It then has the same configuration as the nearest noble gas. The halogen atoms do the same by gaining an electron.

TABLE 10-2

Electron Configurations for Some of the
Alkali Atoms, Ions, and the Nearest Noble Gas

Element		Ion		Nearest Noble Gas	
Li	$1s^22s$	Li$^+$	$1s^2$	He	$1s^2$
Na	$1s^22s^22p^63s$	Na$^+$	$1s^22s^22p^6$	Ne	$1s^22s^22p^6$
K	$1s^22s^22p^63s^23p^64s$	K$^+$	$1s^22s^22p^63s^23p^6$	Ar	$1s^22s^22p^63s^23p^6$

TABLE 10-3

Electron Configurations for Some of the
Halogen Atoms, Ions, and the Nearest Noble Gas

Element		Ion		Nearest Noble Gas	
F	$1s^22s^22p^5$	F$^-$	$1s^22s^22p^6$	Ne	$1s^22s^22p^6$
Cl	$1s^22s^22p^63s^23p^5$	Cl$^-$	$1s^22s^22p^63s^23p^6$	Ar	$1s^22s^22p^63s^23p^6$

Two important generalizations are suggested by these examples:

Ionic bonding occurs when elements gain and lose electrons to form ions.

The electron configuration for each ion is the same as that for a noble gas.

We can test this generalization by looking at some other substances. Let us look at the elements in the second and sixth columns of the periodic table. The alkaline earth metals Be through Ra form ions with a 2+ charge. The elements O through Po form negative ions with a 2− charge. These elements form compounds such as BeO and MgS with the general formula MX. Table 10-4 compares electron configurations for some of the elements in these families.

TABLE 10-4

Electron Configurations for Some Atoms of the
Alkaline Earth and Oxygen Families, Their Ions, and the Nearest Noble Gas

Element		Ion		Nearest Noble Gas	
Be	$1s^22s^2$	Be^{2+}	$1s^2$	He	$1s^2$
Mg	$1s^22s^22p^63s^2$	Mg^{2+}	$1s^22s^22p^6$	Ne	$1s^22s^22p^6$
O	$1s^22s^22p^4$	O^{2-}	$1s^22s^22p^6$	Ne	$1s^22s^22p^6$
S	$1s^22s^22p^63s^23p^4$	S^{2-}	$1s^22s^22p^63s^23p^6$	Ar	$1s^22s^22p^63s^23p^6$

We see an immediate explanation for the general formula MX. Electrical neutrality is achieved when one ion with charge 2+ and one with charge 2− combine. Several examples illustrate the ionic nature of these compounds.

$$Be^{2+}O^{2-} \qquad Mg^{2+}O^{2-} \qquad Mg^{2+}S^{2-}$$

Each ion has the electron configuration of a noble gas element.

What chemical formula is expected when beryllium reacts with chlorine or sodium with oxygen? We already know the ions each element forms. The only additional requirement in writing an empirical formula is to achieve electrical neutrality. Write the formulas in expanded form first:

$$Be^{2+} + Cl^- + Cl^- \longrightarrow BeCl_2$$
$$Na^+ + Na^+ + O^{2-} \longrightarrow Na_2O$$

The second generalization under Table 10-3 is helpful. The electron configuration of an element guides us to the type of ion it forms. The requirement of electrical neutrality then guides us in writing the empirical formula of an ionic compound.

EXERCISE 10-1

Write out the electron configuration for Al. If aluminum forms an ion, what would you expect its electric charge to be? What formula would you expect if aluminum and oxygen form an ionic compound?

10-2   Covalent Bonding

In the introduction to this chapter we mentioned that chemists find it convenient to speak of two kinds of chemical bonds, ionic and covalent. The orbital model for the atom seems to provide an explanation for the formation of ionic bonds. **Ionic bonds** arise when there is *electron exchange between two elements*. **Covalent bonds** are the result of two atoms *sharing electrons*. Does the orbital model prove helpful in understanding covalent bonding? Let us check this by inspecting the simplest molecule, H_2.

The orbital model tells us that, for a hydrogen atom in its lowest energy state, the electron is in the 1*s* orbital. In Figure 10-3 a set of drawings shows the energy changes as two hydrogen atoms, H_A and H_B, approach each other. The shading in these drawings shows the electron density averaged over a period of time. At any instant we can imagine the electron at some particular point in the atoms or in the molecule. The protons in these atoms are shown as black dots inside the colored shading that represents the electrons. The energy of the hydrogen atom H_A can be expressed in terms of the average attraction between its electron and its proton. The electrical attraction depends on the average

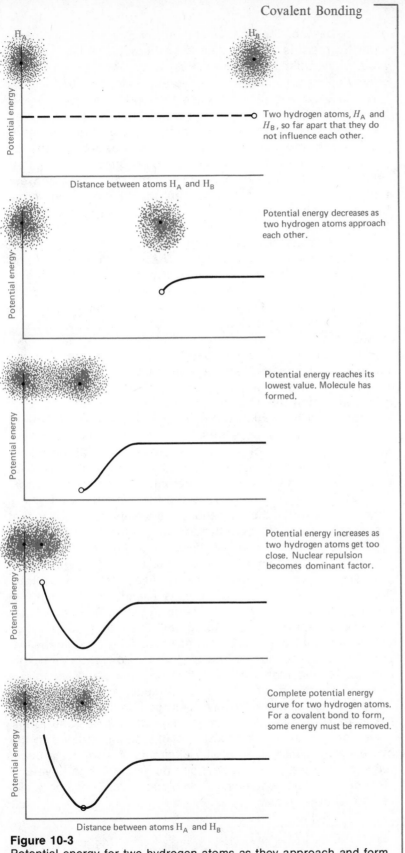

Two hydrogen atoms, H_A and H_B, so far apart that they do not influence each other.

Potential energy decreases as two hydrogen atoms approach each other.

Potential energy reaches its lowest value. Molecule has formed.

Potential energy increases as two hydrogen atoms get too close. Nuclear repulsion becomes dominant factor.

Complete potential energy curve for two hydrogen atoms. For a covalent bond to form, some energy must be removed.

Physicians work with a complex mixture of ionic and covalent bonds. Muscles, fat, and nerve cells are mostly covalently bonded carbon compounds. Bones, blood, and lymph have inorganic, ionic components.

Figure 10-3
Potential energy for two hydrogen atoms as they approach and form a covalent bond.

distance between the electron and proton. Similarly for hydrogen atom H_B there is an attractive force between its electron and proton. We arbitrarily assign the value of zero for the potential energy of the system when the two atoms are far apart.

As the two atoms approach each other, both electrons begin to interact with both protons. The potential energy of the system decreases. Our diagrams show that the orbitals begin to overlap or merge. The probability of finding the electrons between the two protons increases and a chemical bond forms. However, the orbitals cannot merge completely. The repulsive force between the protons becomes more important than the attractive forces between electrons and protons as the distance between H_A and H_B becomes small.

The system has the lowest potential energy when the two atoms are not too close or not too far apart. The minimum in the potential energy graph occurs at a distance which is the bond distance, or bond length, in the hydrogen molecule. At this distance there is a balance between the electric forces in the molecule. Both electrons are now attracted by both protons. There are repulsive forces between the two electrons and between the two protons. For a chemical bond to form between two atoms, the attractive forces must be greater than the repulsive forces. Also remember that some energy must be removed from the system or else the atoms will simply rebound from each other.

What would this look like if hydrogen atoms were the size of ping-pong balls? Suppose these atoms, each with a spherical electric field formed by its electron, were about 25 cm apart. Of course they are moving around rapidly. Suppose they head for each other. As the distance between the atoms decreases from 25 to 20 cm, we find that the electric field on each atom is still spherical. But when they are about 5–8 cm apart, we notice that the electric field is higher in the direction of the other atom. This is what we expect, since we know opposite charges attract. The electron, held to one nucleus by this attraction, begins to be pulled by the nucleus of the other atom. At about 3 cm, the attraction become appreciable. Now there is a much higher probability for electrons to be between the atomic centers. You might ask, "Don't the electrons repel each other?" Yes, they do, but they can be fairly far from each other and yet be fairly close to the two positively charged nuclei. The sketches below show how this can be. As the atoms come still closer, the repulsive forces between the two nuclei increase. Eventually a kind of balance will be achieved when the two hydrogen atoms are about 2.2 cm apart (0.74 Å in the real molecule). A chemical bond forms.

We can simplify our discussion of the chemical bond in the hydrogen molecule using orbital diagrams. We will let a circle represent the orbital. An orbital can be empty, it can have one electron, or it can accommodate two electrons. These possibilities are shown here:

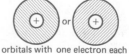

orbital empty   orbitals with one electron each   orbital with two electrons

The drawing below shows what happens when two hydrogen atoms approach each other. The orbitals overlap. The darkest cross-hatched area indicates that the two electrons can be near the two protons much of the time. In this overlap region the electrons are

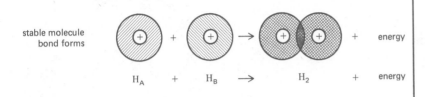

strongly attracted by both protons. Simultaneously, each H atom appears to have two electrons in its $1s$ orbital.

What is the situation for two He atoms? We know from experiments that He_2 is not a stable molecule. Does our orbital model agree with experiment? Helium has two electrons in the $1s$ orbital. As two helium atoms come together, no orbital overlap can take place. The two electrons already in the $1s$ orbital prevent any more electrons from entering that space.

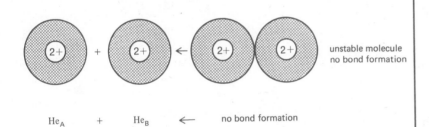

Apparently the electrons in one He atom do not get close enough to the nucleus of the other He atom to be appreciably attracted toward it. The $1s$ orbitals are already filled in the helium atoms. No overlap of filled orbitals takes place.

Let us generalize from these two examples. As long as the generalization agrees with the experiments, it will be useful.

> Covalent chemical bonds form if valence electrons
> are shared by two atoms.

10-3   How Chemists Represent Covalent Bonds

Figure 2-6 presented five ways that the structure of a molecule may be shown. Each has its place, depending on the use and the point being made. It happens that there are also five ways that a covalent bond is represented. They are shown in Table 10-5. The first three specifically show covalent bonds. The last two are often used with the assumption that the reader knows the meaning behind the more compact symbol.

Biochemists need several ways to show bonds in the chemicals from living organisms.

TABLE 10-5
Representation of a Covalent Bond,
HF Used as an Example

Name	Representation
1. Orbital diagram The electron configurations of each atom are shown, with electrons indicated. The overlapping orbitals are highlighted.	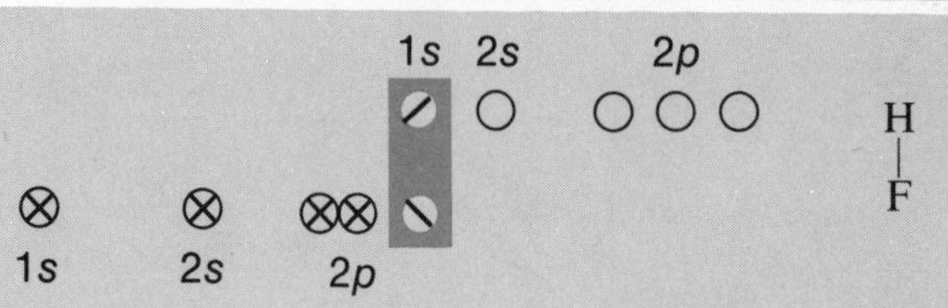 $1s$ $2s$ $2p$ ... H—F
2. 3-D drawing The general shape of valence orbitals is given. The overlap of orbitals can be seen.	H—F  ... $1s$ three $2p$ orbitals
3. Electron dot diagram Chemical symbols represent the nucleus and all electrons except the valence electrons. These are shown as dots, with the bonding electrons as a pair of colored dots between the symbols.	H:F̈:
4. Line The chemical symbols again represent the nucleus and all electrons except the valence electrons. A line shows the shared electron pair. Other valence electrons are omitted.	H—F This is the form most used by experienced chemists.
5. Formula The bond is not shown explicitly.	HF

It is easy to show the formation of a fluorine molecule, F_2, with these diagrams

(1)

bond forms

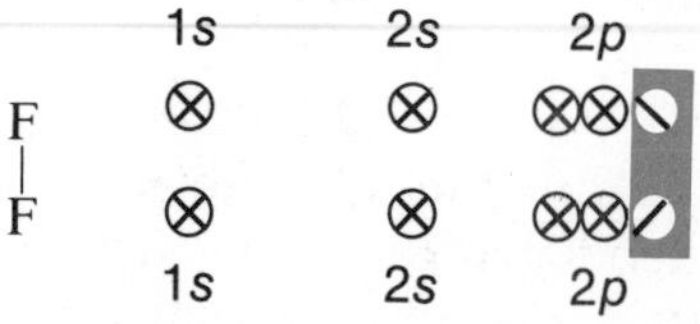

$1s$ $2s$ $2p$

F—F

$1s$ $2s$ $2p$

(2)

$2p$ ... $2p$

(3) :F̈:F̈: (4) F—F (5) F_2

Overlap of the half-filled $2p$ orbitals occurs when two fluorine atoms approach each other. A covalent bond forms.

You may be wondering why the valence electrons for each atom of fluorine in F_2 are indicated by four pairs of dots. Perhaps eight dots equally spaced would be as good. Chemists are suggesting in an electron dot diagram something that is clearly shown in the orbital diagram. Only two electrons can be placed in an orbital. Therefore the four pairs of dots carry the suggestion that the valence electrons are grouped in four orbitals, the $2s$ and the three $2p$ orbitals.

These ideas apply to a large number of molecules. In Section 9-9 electron configurations for the elements were derived. At that time we were dealing with the atoms of these elements in the gas phase. Atoms in molecules do not always have the same electron configurations as they do when isolated. We will let experimentally determined formulas guide us in writing electron configurations for atoms *when they are in molecules.* Table 10-6 contains formulas for the hydrides and fluorides of the first ten elements. These formulas have been determined experimentally by methods similar to the one you used in Experiment 17.

We know hydrogen usually forms one bond per atom. Fluorine does the same. Therefore the number of bonds between H (or F) and another atom suggests the number of unpaired electrons in that other atom. And the number of unpaired electrons suggests an electron configuration for the atom when it is part of a molecule.

We can profit from a closer look at some of these elements. If a hydrogen atom approaches an oxygen atom, the formation of a chemical bond can be represented as follows:

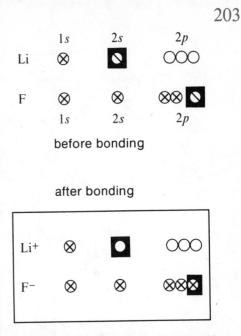

before bonding

after bonding

Ions form via electron transfer. Ionic bond forms because of electrostatic attraction.

(1) 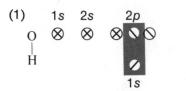   (2) 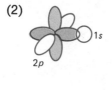   (3) $:\ddot{O}\cdot \ +\ \cdot H \longrightarrow\ :\ddot{O}{:}H$ (4) O—H   (5) OH

The electronic structure for OH is similar to that for the fluorine atom. Each has the electronic structure $1s^2 2s^2 2p^5$. Like the fluorine atom, OH is a very reactive species because it has residual bonding capacity. There is still an unpaired electron. Chemists have been able to detect this molecule in high-temperature flames. Recently astronomers have interpreted radio waves coming from the center of our galaxy to mean that OH molecules may exist in space, between the stars in our galaxy.

There are several ways in which the bonding capacity of the oxygen atom in OH can be satisfied. If another hydrogen atom approached the oxygen atom, the molecule H_2O forms:

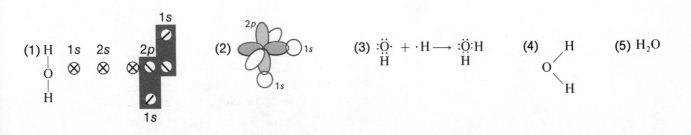

TABLE 10-6
Derived Electron Configurations for the First Ten Elements

Element	Compound with Hydrogen		Compound with Fluorine		Derived Number of Unpaired Electrons per Atom of the Element	Derived Electron Configuration		
	Formula	Number of Bonds	Formula	Number of Bonds		1s	2s	2p
H	H_2	1	HF	1	1	⊘	○	○○○
He	—	0	—	0	0	⊗	○	○○○
Li*	LiH	1	LiF	1	1	⊗	⊘	○○○
Be*	BeH_2	2	BeF_2	2	2	⊗	⊘	⊘○○
B	$(BH_3)**$	3	BF_3	3	3	⊗	⊘	⊘⊘○
C	CH_4	4	CF_4	4	4	⊗	⊘	⊘⊘⊘
N	NH_3	3	NF_3	3	3	⊗	⊗	⊘⊘⊘
O	H_2O	2	OF_2	2	2	⊗	⊗	⊗⊘⊘
F	HF	1	F_2	1	1	⊗	⊗	⊗⊗⊘
Ne	—	0	—	0	0	⊗	⊗	⊗⊗⊗

*The lithium and beryllium compounds have ionic structures at room temperature.
**The molecule BH_3 exists only as a short-lived intermediate in some chemical reactions. The boron hydride, B_2H_6, has the lowest molar mass of the stable compounds of boron and hydrogen. For many years chemists could not account for the bonding in many boron compounds. Now satisfactory explanations have been found.

Another possibility is the formation of hydrogen peroxide when two OH molecules approach each other. Compare this diagram with the one for formation of F_2.

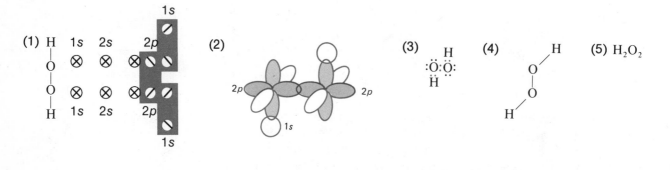

(1) ... (2) ... (3) $:\ddot{O}:\ddot{O}:$ ... (4) ... (5) H_2O_2

The formula for H_2O_2 is somewhat easier to see if the chemical bonds are drawn as lines, not dots. Each line represents a pair of bonding electrons. The valence electrons not involved in bonding are omitted.

The atoms in H_2O and H_2O_2 are deliberately not drawn in a straight line. Instead, a zigzag arrangement is used. We are trying to suggest the shape or geometry for the molecule when writing the formula in this fashion. Look at the orbital diagram for water again. The valence electrons for oxygen can be written

$$2s^2 \qquad 2p^2{}_x \quad 2p_y \quad 2p_z$$

Bond formation with hydrogen atoms can occur if the orbitals of the hydrogen atoms overlap with the $2p_y$ and $2p_z$ orbitals of oxygen. We saw in Figure 9-13 that the $2p$ orbitals do not have spherical symmetry. The electron density is highest along the x or y or z-axis. We expect that the two bonds in H_2O would be perpendicular to each other, one along the y-axis and the other along the z-axis. Although the topic of molecular geometry will not be discussed until Chapter 17, structural formulas are drawn to suggest molecular shapes.

Now look at the carbon atom. Many experiments suggest that the orbital diagram for carbon must contain four unpaired electrons to agree with the formulas CH_4 and CF_4.

$$\begin{array}{cccc} & 1s & 2s & 2p \\ C & \otimes & \oslash & \oslash\oslash\oslash \end{array}$$

Suppose four hydrogen atoms approach a carbon atom. We would expect four bonds to form as the orbitals of the hydrogen atoms overlap with the four orbitals on the carbon atom. Methane, the molecule that forms, can be represented in several ways. These are the three usually used:

Prof. Robert B. Woodward is one of the most successful synthesizers of essential organic chemicals. He has received the Nobel Prize.

EXERCISE 10-2

Draw electron dot formulas for the molecules CH_3, CF_3, CHF_3, CH_2F_2, and CH_3F. Which of these would you expect to be extremely reactive? Why?

There are many simple molecules which are quite similar in many respects. Let us write out their electron dot formulas:

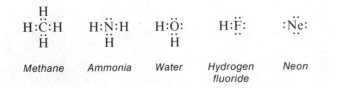

| Methane | Ammonia | Water | Hydrogen fluoride | Neon |

The central atom in each molecule in this set has the same electron configuration as the noble gas neon. We saw something similar when discussing ionic compounds in Section 10-1. Atoms react to form compounds in which the electronic structure for each atom is the same as one of the noble gases. In methane, ammonia, water, and hydrogen fluoride, each H atom has a pair of electrons in the $1s$ orbital (the He structure). The four atoms C, N, O, and F each have eight electrons in the $2s$ and $2p$ orbitals (the Ne structure).

In Section 10-1 we proposed two generalizations that helped us to understand ionic bonding. Let us propose another set of generalizations for covalent bonding.

> Covalent bonding occurs when atoms can share electrons.

> Each atom in the compound acquires an electron configuration like that for one of the noble gases.

EXERCISE 10-3

Draw the electron dot formulas for the ions NH_4^+ and H_3O^+. First draw the electron dot formulas for NH_3 and H_2O. Then add H^+ to each formula. H^+ has no electrons.

EXERCISE 10-4

Draw the electron dot formula for the ionic solid ammonium chloride, NH_4Cl.

10-4   Families of Covalent Compounds

In the last section we pointed out that the molecule OH is similar in electron structure to the fluorine atom, F. The chemical reactivity for these two species is very high. This comparison can be extended to include the very reactive molecules $\cdot NH_2$ and $\cdot CH_3$

$$:\ddot{F}: \qquad :\ddot{O}:H \qquad :\overset{H}{\underset{..}{N}}:H \qquad H:\overset{H}{\underset{..}{C}}:H$$

Propane, one of the simple organic gases, is convenient fuel.

When a hydrogen atom approaches each of these, the molecules HF, H_2O, NH_3, and CH_4 form, with the same electron structure as neon. Also, the two molecules F_2 and H_2O_2 are known to form readily. Table 10-7 lists the molecules that arise when all possible pairs of these four reactive molecules combine:

TABLE 10-7

Compounds with the Same Electron
Configuration as Fluorine Gas

	$\cdot\ddot{F}:$	$\cdot\ddot{O}:H$	H $\cdot\ddot{N}:H$	H $\cdot\ddot{C}:H$ H
H H:$\ddot{C}\cdot$ H	$H_3C{-}F$	$H_3C{-}OH$	$H_3C{-}NH_2$	$H_3C{-}CH_3$
H H:$\ddot{N}\cdot$	$H_2N{-}F$	$H_2N{-}OH$	$H_2N{-}NH_2$	
H:$\ddot{O}\cdot$	$HO{-}F$	$HO{-}OH$	*All these compounds are known.*	
:$\ddot{F}\cdot$	$F{-}F$			

EXERCISE 10-5

Convince yourself that the electron dot formulas for CH_3OH (methanol) and $H_2N{-}NH_2$ (hydrazine) are the same as the electron dot formula for F_2 (fluorine).

   The results in Table 10-7 are important. First, our generalization on covalent bonding has guided us to the correct electron structure of ten more molecules. Second, we can predict some of the chemical and physical properties of these substances. Look at H_2O_2, CH_3OH, and C_2H_6. It seems reasonable to expect hydrogen peroxide, H_2O_2, to have some properties rather similar to water. And ethane, C_2H_6, should have properties like methane, CH_4, but not at all like water. The substance methanol, CH_3OH, should have properties like water in some respects and like methane in others. After all, half of the molecule CH_3OH resembles methane, $CH_3{-}H$, and the other half resembles water, $H{-}OH$.

10-5 Hydrocarbons

In the last section we showed molecules like $H_2N—NH_2$ and $H_3C—CH_3$, involving identical atoms bonding to each other. Of all the elements carbon shows the greatest tendency to form molecules with many atoms of the same kind joined in a chain. Let us start with methane to illustrate what we mean. Although our examples do not correspond to the usual methods of synthesizing these compounds, the structure of each final molecule is known to be correct.

1.
$$CH_4 \longrightarrow \cdot CH_3 + H\cdot$$

Methane dissociates into a methyl molecule, $\cdot CH_3$, and $\cdot H$, a hydrogen atom.
Then two methyl molecules react.

$$\cdot CH_3 + \cdot CH_3 \longrightarrow CH_3—CH_3 \qquad \text{ethane}$$

Using the same procedure, we can get other carbon compounds.

2.
$$CH_3—CH_3 \longrightarrow CH_3—CH_2\cdot + \cdot H$$
$$CH_3—CH_2\cdot + \cdot CH_3 \longrightarrow CH_3—CH_2—CH_3 \qquad \text{propane}$$

3.
$$CH_3—CH_2—CH_3 \longrightarrow CH_3—CH_2—CH_2\cdot + \cdot H$$
$$CH_3—CH_2—CH_2\cdot + \cdot CH_3 \longrightarrow CH_3—CH_2—CH_2—CH_3 \quad \text{normal butane}$$

There is another way for propane to "grow":

4.
$$CH_3—CH_2—CH_3 \longrightarrow CH_3—\overset{\cdot}{C}H—CH_3 + \cdot H$$

$$CH_3—\overset{\cdot}{C}H—CH_3 + \cdot CH_3 \longrightarrow CH_3—\overset{\overset{\textstyle CH_3}{|}}{C}H—CH_3 \qquad \textit{isobutane}$$

Petroleum chemists and geologists need to understand the bonding and arrangement of atoms in hydrocarbons.

The two butanes are given different names—normal or *n*-butane and *iso*butane. They have the same molecular formula (C_4H_{10}) but different **structural formulas**. Normal butane has four carbon atoms linked in a linear fashion; isobutane has four carbon atoms linked in a branched fashion. *Substances that have the same molecular formula but different structural formulas are called* **isomers**.

The molecules named above are examples of carbon-hydrogen compounds called **saturated hydrocarbons**, or **alkanes**. They are the principal components of natural gas and are an important energy source. An extensive network of pipelines in the United States brings natural gas to many cities. Many of our homes are heated with natural gas, which is mostly methane. Some of the properties of these substances are given in Table 10-8.

TABLE 10-8
Properties of Some Hydrocarbons

Name	Molecular Formula	Molar Mass (grams)	Melting Temperature (°C)	Boiling Temperature (°C)
methane	CH_4	16	−182.5	−161.5
ethane	C_2H_6	30	−183.3	−88.6
propane	C_3H_8	44	−187.7	−44.1
n-butane	C_4H_{10}	58	−138.4	−0.5
isobutane	C_4H_{10}	58	−159.6	−11.7

There is a way to express the molecular formula for any hydrocarbon in this family. Perhaps you have noticed in our four examples that each new member adds the unit $-CH_2-$ to the preceding member. The general formula can be written:

$$C_nH_{2n+2}$$

EXERCISE 10-6

The next compound in the saturated hydrocarbon family would have five carbon atoms. The name *pentane* is used for this compound. Show how pentane can "grow" from each of the butane isomers. How many isomers of pentane would you expect? Draw them.

10-6   Molecules with Double Bonds

In Sections 10-3, 10-4, and 10-5 we have discussed a number of molecules which have single bonds. This statement means one orbital of atom *A* overlaps with one orbital of atom *B*. We have represented that situation with electron dot structures or with line structures. For example, the bonding in hydrogen fluoride can be described in several ways. Here are two:

$$H:\ddot{F}: \quad \text{or} \quad H-F$$

There are many molecules that are best described in terms of double bonds. The orbital model provides an explanation for these molecules. The hydrocarbon ethylene is used to illustrate double bonds. Ethylene, C_2H_4, has two fewer hydrogen atoms than ethane, C_2H_6. Suppose we try to write an electron dot formula for ethylene, using only single bonds. The result is

Alkanes C_nH_{2n+2}	
Number of	
C Atoms	Isomers
1, 2, or 3	1
4	2
5	3
6	5
7	9
8	18
9	35
10	75
20	366 319

Polymer chemists work extensively with the theory of double bonds.

$$H:\overset{\displaystyle H}{\underset{\displaystyle \cdot}{C}}:\overset{\displaystyle H}{\underset{\displaystyle \cdot}{C}}:H \quad \text{or} \quad H-\overset{\displaystyle H}{\underset{\displaystyle |}{C}}-\overset{\displaystyle H}{\underset{\displaystyle |}{C}}-H$$

These formulas show two unpaired electrons. From earlier examples, ·OH and ·CH$_3$, this unused bonding capacity would suggest very high reactivity for ethylene. But ethylene does not have the activity of a compound with unpaired electrons. There is a way to use up the bonding capacity in ethylene within the molecule. The two electrons can be paired:

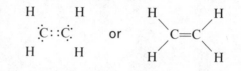

C—C in ethane	1.54 Å (0.154 nm)
C=C in ethylene	1.34 Å (0.134 nm)

The carbon atoms are said to be joined by a **double bond**. Eight valence electrons are placed around each carbon atom (the neon structure) and two electrons are placed near each hydrogen atom (the helium structure). The only new idea that appears in the ethylene structure is the placement of four electrons between the two carbon atoms.

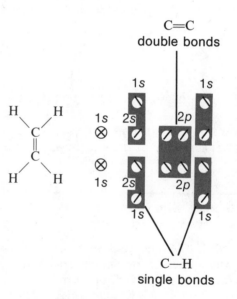

Double bonds appear in molecules when two orbitals of atom *A* overlap with two orbitals of atom *B*. These molecules have the same electron configuration as ethylene:

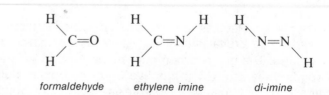

formaldehyde   *ethylene imine*   *di-imine*

Oxygen, O$_2$, has the same electron configuration as ethylene, and it seems straightforward to predict that O$_2$ would have a double bond.

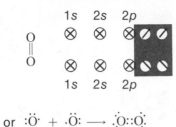

or $:\ddot{O}\cdot + \cdot\ddot{O}: \longrightarrow \cdot\ddot{O}::\ddot{O}:$

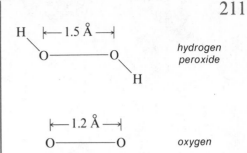

hydrogen
peroxide

oxygen

The structure of oxygen has proved to be a challenge to chemists. Many of the properties of oxygen are consistent with this double-bonded structure of O_2. The bond in the oxygen molecule is stronger than the bond between oxygen atoms in hydrogen peroxide (Page 204). More energy is required to break the bond in O_2 than is required to break the O—O bond in H_2O_2. In addition, the bond length in the O_2 molecule is shorter than the oxygen-oxygen bond in H_2O_2. The short bond length in the O_2 molecule shows that the two oxygen atoms are drawn together more effectively than in H_2O_2. These experimental facts suggest that there are extra bonding electrons between the two oxygen atoms in O_2.

However, other experimental measurements are not in agreement with the double-bond description for O_2. These measurements indicate that there are two unpaired electrons in O_2. Our simple model for chemical bonding is only partially correct for one of the most common molecules. However, this model does give satisfactory explanations for a very large number of compounds. We will not discuss the more complex model, which gives an adequate treatment of O_2.

10-7 Molecules with Triple Bonds

The hydrocarbon acetylene is a good example of a molecule with a triple bond. Acetylene has the molecular formula C_2H_2. The neon and helium configurations are achieved when we assign these structures for acetylene:

C≡C in acetylene   1.20 Å

$$H:C:::C:H \quad \text{or} \quad H—C≡C—H$$

The orbital representation looks like this:

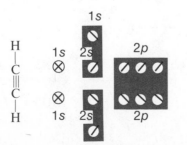

Nitrogen and hydrogen cyanide have the same electron configuration as acetylene:

$$N\equiv N \qquad H—C\equiv N \qquad H—C\equiv C—H$$

EXERCISE 10-7

Why are double and triple bonds progressively shorter than single bonds?

How We Taste

Most of us can recall some pleasant tastes, the very thought of which makes our mouth water—a roast beef sandwich, a luscious mango, or a chocolate éclair. But not all tastes are pleasing. What is the chemistry of these sensations?

Sour tastes are produced by acids. In fact, the word *acid* is almost directly from the Latin "to be sour." The receptors for sour are at the sides of the tongue. Apparently, they are activated by H^+, although the mechanism is not known. As with ionic reactions in laboratory beakers, the source of H^+ is not important as far as producing sourness is concerned.

Sweetness is detected mostly at the tip of the tongue. There is one theory relating sweetness to structure. Many sweet chemicals have two hydrogen-bonding groups that are 3 Å apart. These two groups must be separated so that they cannot bond to each other. The tongue has matching sites so that a pair of hydrogen bonds can form as below:

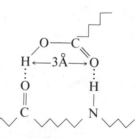

Part of sweet compound.

Sweet site on tongue.

Once the sweet substance bonds to the matching site, the specialized nerve cells of the tongue send a series of message impulses and the sensation of "sweetness" is registered.

This theory works fairly well for selecting possible sweet substances but does not give a clue to how sweet they will be. Some sweet substances, with their "sweet group" highlighted, are shown. The numbers give the sweetness relative to sucrose.

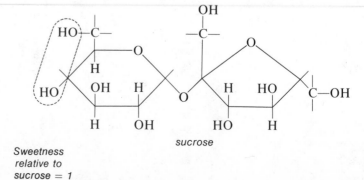

sucrose

Sweetness relative to sucrose = 1

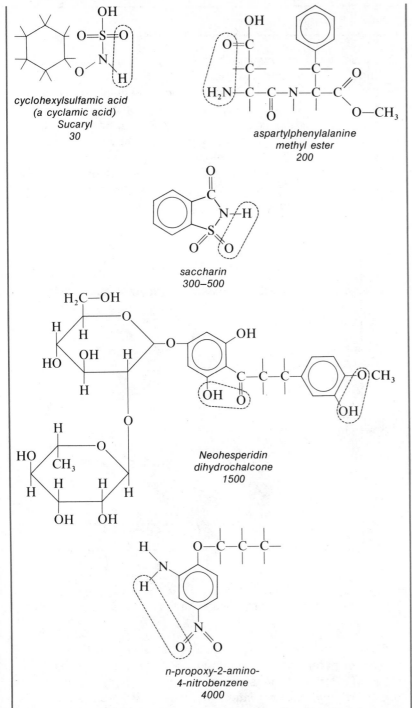

cyclohexylsulfamic acid
(a cyclamic acid)
Sucaryl
30

aspartylphenylalanine
methyl ester
200

saccharin
300–500

Neohesperidin
dihydrochalcone
1500

n-propoxy-2-amino-
4-nitrobenzene
4000

It is of some interest that one group of workers has developed a very similar idea to explain bitter substances. According to their research on one kind of plant chemicals, bitterness was usually found in substances that had the same two hydrogen bond donor and acceptor groups as described above. But the groups had to be about 1.5 Å apart and able to form the H bond between themselves.

There is still much to learn about how we detect subtle taste differences and why a substance seems delicious to one person and distasteful to another person.

10-8 Hydrogen Bonding

Our discussion of covalent bonding has been limited to compounds of the second-row elements, C, N, O, and F. From our earlier discussion of the periodic table we would expect to find that our explanations of covalent bonding would be applicable to all elements in the same periodic family. Similar orbital representations would explain the bonding in Cl_2, Br_2, and I_2; in H_2S, H_2Se, and H_2Te; and in CCl_4, CBr_4, and CI_4.

Figures 10-4 and 10-5 show the increase in melting and boiling temperatures for the noble gases, the halogens, and the carbon compounds with general formula CX_4.

Medical researchers encounter hydrogen bonds throughout the human body. Their understanding of protein structure, gene replication, and enzyme action depends on knowledge of hydrogen bonds.

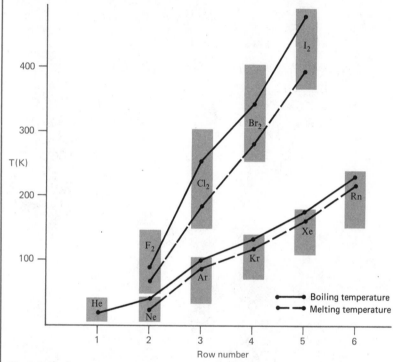

Figure 10-4
The melting and boiling temperatures of the noble gases and of the halogens.

Figures 10-6 and 10-7 show plots of melting and boiling behavior for hydrides of elements in the families headed by C, N, O, and F. Periodic trends are evident *if we ignore the first compound in each series.* Water, ammonia, and hydrogen fluoride seem to have abnormally high melting and boiling temperatures. Perhaps, instead of isolated molecules in the liquids and solids of these three substances, clusters of molecules form, leading to the higher melting and boiling temperatures. Does the orbital model give support to this explanation of the experimental facts? If hydrogen atoms serve as a bridge to join several molecules together, this bridge would provide the clusters that we need. This type of bonding is given the name **hydrogen bonding** and is represented by a dashed line in these drawings at the left.

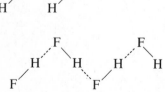

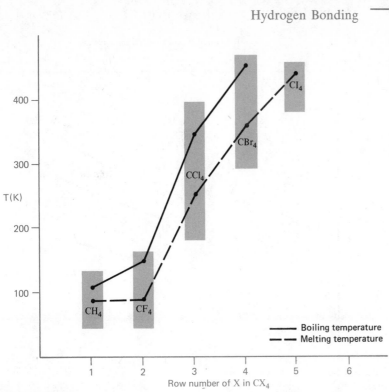

Figure 10-5
The melting and boiling temperatures of carbon compounds with formula CX_4.

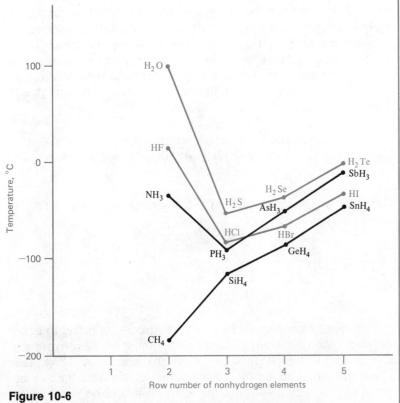

Figure 10-6
Trends in boiling temperatures of hydrides of four families.

Chemical Bonding

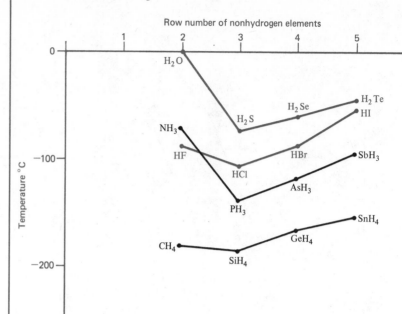

Figure 10-7
Trends in the melting temperatures of hydrides of four families.

Ice

We are not ready to provide a complete explanation of hydrogen bonding at this time. However, we can offer a simplified view that will be discussed more completely in Chapter 17. The clue lies in the fact that the hydrogen atom, with only a $1s$ orbital for bond formation, cannot form two covalent bonds. And yet our suggestion above implies that hydrogen is involved in more than one bond.

At various times we have emphasized that all chemical bonds arise for the same reason: an electron is simultaneously attracted to two nuclei. The same situation holds in hydrogen bonding, with a slight change:

> Hydrogen bonding occurs when the hydrogen nucleus is simultaneously attracted to two electron pairs.

Consider two oxygen atoms in two adjacent water molecules, as in these diagrams:

Two requirements must be met for hydrogen bonding to occur between two molecules. One molecule must contain hydrogen. One molecule must have easily accessible electrons. Often these electrons are supplied by a small atom which has valence electrons not already involved in bonding. The second requirement explains why hydrogen bonding is most common for compounds containing the atoms F, O, and N (and to a lesser extent Cl). Sometimes hydrogen bonding occurs within one molecule; more often hydrogen bonding occurs between two molecules, which do not have to be identical.

Hydrogen bonding is important in a number of chemical systems. It is particularly important in many biological systems. We will refer to hydrogen bonding in the succeeding chapters of this book.

10-9 Review

In this chapter we have used the words **ionic bond** and **covalent bond** in discussing chemical bonding. In either case the nature of the chemical bond is the same: *bonding electrons are simultaneously attracted by two nuclei.*

The orbital model for the atom helps us to understand chemical bonds. In ionic bonding, electrons are **transferred** from one element to another element. Positive and negative ions form, each ion having acquired the electron configuration of a noble gas. The electrical attraction between these ions leads to the formation of an ionic solid. Positive ions alternate with negative ions in such a manner that electrical neutrality is achieved.

In covalent bonding, electrons are **shared** by two elements. Sharing can occur when each element has a partially filled orbital. A number of different diagrams are used by chemists to indicate the formation of a covalent chemical bond. The orbital representation of covalent bonding shows most clearly what happens:

Bond forms; the 1s orbitals of two H atoms overlap.

Much simpler but less detailed is the electron dot method of showing the formation of a covalent bond:

$$H\cdot \; + \; \cdot \ddot{\underset{\cdot\cdot}{F}} : \; \longrightarrow \; H : \ddot{\underset{\cdot\cdot}{F}} :$$

We say that the H atom has acquired the He electron configuration in this molecule. At the same time the F atom has acquired the Ne electron configuration. Still simpler and very convenient is the use of a line to represent the bonding electron pair:

$$H\!-\!F$$

A **single bond** arises when an orbital of one atom overlaps an orbital of a second atom to share one pair of electrons. If two orbitals of an atom overlap two orbitals of a second atom sharing two pairs of electrons, we say that a **double bond** exists between the atoms. The bonding in the three hydrocarbons ethane, ethylene, and acetylene illustrates single, double, and triple bonds:

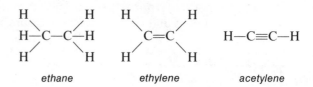

The chapter concludes with a brief discussion of **hydrogen bonding**. Under certain circumstances the H atom acts as a bridge between molecules, giving rise to a pair or larger cluster of molecules. One consequence of this phenomenon is the unusually high melting and boiling temperatures for water. Hydrogen bonding is particularly important in many biological systems.

Questions and Problems for Chapter 10

1

Which of the properties listed are characteristic of an ionic solid?

(a) low melting temperature.
(b) conducts electricity as a solid.
(c) dissolves in water to form a solution containing mostly ions.
(d) dissolves to form a solution containing mostly molecules.
(e) when fused, the melt conducts electricity.

2

Which families of elements tend to form ionic solids?

3

Describe the electron configuration for atoms of lithium and fluorine after they have reacted to form an ionic solid.

4

How many atoms of fluorine are needed per atom of calcium to form the ionic compound calcium fluoride?

5

Write the empirical formulas, assuming that these elements react to form ionic compounds. The atomic number is given to help you locate the element in the periodic table.

(a) Al(13) and S(16)
(b) Mg(12) and N(7)
(c) Ba(56) and At(85)
(d) Fr(87) and O(8)
(e) Ra(88) and I(53)

6

Add the energy term E to the equations

(a) $K \longrightarrow K^+ + e^-$
(b) $K^+ + I^- \longrightarrow KI$

7

What type of bonding would you expect to find in MgO? Explain.

8

Lithium atoms with many empty valence orbitals do not attract electrons to become Li^- ions. However, fluorine with one vacancy in a valence orbital forms a negative ion. Suggest reasons for this behavior.

9

In general, what conditions cause two atoms to combine to form

(a) a bond that is mainly covalent?
(b) a bond that is mainly ionic?

10

What energy condition must exist if a chemical bond is to form between two approaching atoms?

11

What valence orbital and valence electron conditions must exist if a chemical bond is to form between two approaching atoms?

12

Draw the orbital representations of

(a) H, H$^+$, and H$^-$

(b) sodium fluoride, NaF

(c) beryllium fluoride, BeF$_2$

13

Show that NaF and MgO have the same electron configuration. How would you expect their melting temperatures to compare?

14

Give the orbital and also the electron dot representations for the bonding in these molecules: Cl$_2$, HCl, Cl$_2$O.

15

Using the electron dot representation, show a neutral, a negatively charged, and a positively charged OH group.

16

Draw the orbital representation of the molecule N$_2$H$_4$, hydrazine.

17

Draw electron dot formulas of compounds that have the same electron configuration as Cl$_2$. Use the periodic table and the examples in Table 10-7 as guides.

18

Knowing the orbitals carbon uses for bonding, use the periodic table to predict the formula of the chloride of silicon. What orbitals does silicon use for bonding?

19

The borohydride ion, BH$_4^-$, can be thought of as a combination of BH$_3$ and H$^-$ ion. Give the orbital and also the electron dot representation for the borohydride ion.

20

Make use of your answer to Problem 19 to describe the bonding in the compounds sodium borohydride and lithium aluminum hydride.

21

Draw four representations of carbon dioxide (see Table 10-5). Do not do a 3-D drawing.

22

Draw five representations of the nitrogen gas molecule (see Table 10-5).

23

Write an electron dot formula for boric acid, H$_3$BO$_3$. The B(OH)$_3$ molecule contains three —OH groups.

24

Indicate why each of these bonding arrangements is WRONG:

(a) O≡C—S

(b) H : : Na :

(c)  NH$_4$

(d)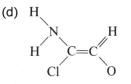

25

Here is a part of a DNA double helix. Find any bonding arrangements not explained in Chapter 10.

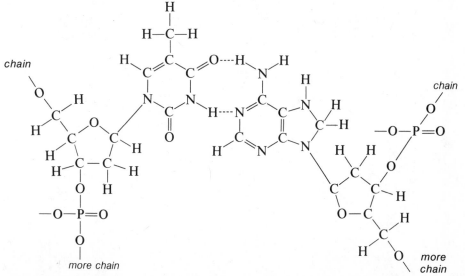

26

Look at Figure 3-1 (page 51). Now that you know the electronic structure of hydrogen, oxygen, and water, what does taking spheres apart and re-assembling them mean in terms of electrons and bonds? Show by a diagram.

27

H_2O_2 is a well-known chemical. Use its structure to help you draw bonding arrangements for H_2S_3, H_2S_4, and S_8.

28

Draw electron dot formulas for the molecules CH_3Cl, CH_2Cl_2, $CHCl_3$, and CCl_4.

29

In Section 10-5 we showed how the hydrocarbon family, C_nH_{2n+2}, can be derived from methane. Similar families of compounds can be derived from methyl alcohol.

(a) Show how ethyl and propyl alcohols, C_2H_5OH and C_3H_7OH, can be derived from methyl alcohol, CH_3OH.
(b) How many isomers would you expect for propyl alcohol? Draw the structure of each. Use a dash for each bond.

30

Show a possible bonding arrangement for cyclo-butane, C_4H_8, in which the four carbon atoms are in a ring. Use a dash for each bond. Is your arrangement consistent with the electron con-figuration in Table 10-6?

31

Ethylene is the first of a family of hydrocarbons called *alkenes*. Each alkene has one double bond in the structure. Use line drawings to show bonding in the compounds ethylene, C_2H_4, and propylene, C_3H_6.

32

Acetylene is the first of a family of hydrocarbons called *alkynes*. Each alkyne has one triple bond in

the structure. Use line drawings to show bonding in the compounds acetylene, C_2H_2, and propyne, C_3H_4.

33

The cyanide ion contains one carbon and one nitrogen atom. Draw an orbital diagram of it. What kind of bond occurs between the C and N? Write formulas for sodium cyanide and barium cyanide.

34

Which of these molecules would you expect to be hydrogen-bonded in the liquid or solid state?

(a) H_3COH (d) H_3CNH_2
(b) H_3CH (e) $H_2N-C-NH_2$
(c) Cl_3CH $\overset{\|}{O}$

35

Is liquid ammonia hydrogen-bonded? What evidence do you have for your answer?

36

Use Figures 10-6 and 10-7 to predict the melting and boiling temperatures H_2O and HF would have if they were not hydrogen-bonded.

37

Use hydrogen bonding to suggest why ethanol (CH_3CH_2OH) is soluble in any proportion in H_2O, acetone

$$(CH_3\overset{\overset{O}{\|}}{C}-CH_3),$$

and dimethyl ether (CH_3-O-CH_3) but is hardly soluble in octane (C_8H_{18}).

38

Use bonding orbital diagrams to show why water molecules are not linear.

39

Describe the properties molecules must have for hydrogen bonding to occur.

Energy in Chemical and Nuclear Reactions

11

Now that we have some understanding of molecular structure, let us see what happens when molecules react with one another. We will discover that chemical reactions form the heart of chemistry. In the next four chapters chemical reactions are considered from several viewpoints. Of course, as before, we will be searching for regularities to help simplify and organize our observations.

When a chemical reaction occurs, some bonds in molecules are broken and new bonds form. Energy is required to break a chemical bond. However, energy is released when new chemical bonds form. The energy effects in a chemical reaction are the results of bond-breaking and bond-forming events.

For many years man has depended on chemical fuels to satisfy most of his energy requirements. At first wood was the important fuel. During the last 150 years we have used coal, petroleum, and, more recently, natural gas to supply the major energy requirements for our rapidly expanding technology. The rate at which these resources are consumed, however, increases each year.

All citizens should be interested in stored energy. Petroleum and natural gas are desirable energy sources because they store much energy in a form convenient for handling.

Since there is a limited reserve of chemical fuels, many scientists and engineers are exploring ways to develop nuclear, solar, geothermal, tidal, and wind energy as economical energy sources.

Why do some reactions release energy? How is energy stored in molecules? What is the source of this energy? How can it be measured? And how can this energy be released when needed? We will look at some chemical reactions in search of answers to these questions.

The large coal-burning power plant in Madison, Wisconsin.

11-1 Heat Energy and Chemical Reactions

Large amounts of soft coal are heated out of contact with air to produce a number of very important chemical compounds. These substances are used to make fertilizers, dyes, drugs, and plastics. After these compounds are distilled off, the material left behind is almost pure carbon. It is called coke, a hard, brittle substance that burns with an intense heat without smoke. It is an important industrial fuel, widely used in blast furnaces for the production of iron. Coke is also used to make a gaseous fuel called "water gas." This reaction is fairly simple and involves simple molecules. It provides a good reaction for study.

The water-gas reaction is used in brick-making to get good color. During firing, organic matter in some clays produces carbon, which darkens the brick. Steaming removes carbon via the water-gas reaction.

At temperatures near 600 °C steam passed over hot coke reacts to give carbon monoxide and hydrogen:

$$H_2O(g) + C(s) \longrightarrow CO(g) + H_2(g)$$

The mixture of gases produced is called water gas. It is an excellent industrial fuel. In the preparation of water gas a chemical engineer finds by experiment that heat energy is absorbed during the reaction. Periodically the steam must be turned off and the coke reheated to keep the reaction going. It is possible to measure the amount of heat energy absorbed by the system and write it as part of the chemical reaction. Such a measurement shows that 31.4 kcal of heat energy is absorbed whenever one mole of carbon reacts to produce a mole of CO plus a mole of H_2. Since heat energy needs to be supplied, it is placed on the left side of the equation with the reactants.

$$H_2O(g) + C(s) + 31.4\,kcal \longrightarrow CO(g) + H_2(g)$$

Suppose a mechanical engineer wants to design a boiler which is to be heated by burning water gas as the fuel. When water gas is burned in air, two main reactions occur:

$$CO(g) + \frac{1}{2}O_2(g) \longrightarrow CO_2(g) + energy$$

and

$$H_2(g) + \frac{1}{2}O_2(g) \longrightarrow H_2O(g) + energy$$

The mechanical engineer would like to know how much heat energy these reactions provide. He can determine the heat energy produced for each reaction. It is placed on the right side of the equation with the products. Experiments give these values:

$$CO(g) + \frac{1}{2}O_2(g) \longrightarrow CO_2(g) + 67.6\,kcal$$

$$H_2(g) + \frac{1}{2}O_2(g) \longrightarrow H_2O(g) + 57.8\,kcal$$

The total heat energy released is 125.4 kcal when one mole of $CO(g)$ and one mole of $H_2(g)$ are burned.

Suppose an accountant decides to look into the cost of using water gas as a fuel. He thinks in terms of gains and losses. He observes that the consumption of coke and water to generate water gas is followed by the burning of water gas to form carbon dioxide and water. He can see that the overall reaction is the combustion of coke to form carbon dioxide. The overall equation can be obtained by adding the individual equations:

$$\cancel{H_2O(g)} + \quad C(s) \longrightarrow \cancel{CO(g)} + \cancel{H_2(g)}$$

$$\cancel{CO(g)} + \frac{1}{2}O_2(g) \longrightarrow CO_2(g)$$

$$\cancel{H_2(g)} + \frac{1}{2}O_2(g) \longrightarrow \cancel{H_2O(g)}$$

$$\overline{\quad C(s) + \quad O_2(g) \longrightarrow CO_2(g) \quad}$$ net reaction

The accountant might ask, "Why not burn the coke directly and save the cost of manufacturing the water gas?"

The mechanical engineer wants to know, "How much heat energy will the boiler receive if I use coke instead of water gas?"

The chemical engineer must go to the laboratory for answers to these questions. He measures the heat energy released when one mole of carbon is burned. The experiment shows that 94.0 kcal/mol is released.

$$C(s) + O_2(g) \longrightarrow CO_2(g) + 94.0\,kcal$$

10 kcal of energy can be obtained by either of the following methods:

—burn 1 gram of wax
—drop 312 pounds (38 gallons) of water 100 feet

The amount of carbon monoxide in the rural atmosphere varies between 0.1 and 0.9 parts per million. Of this about 93% comes from the decay of organic matter and about 7% is man-made.

To produce 0.45 kg (1 lb) of aluminum, 5200 kcal are needed.

The chemical engineer now can answer the accountant's questions. If one mole of carbon is burned directly, 94.0 kcal of heat energy is released. If one mole of carbon is converted to water gas that is burned, 125.4 kcal can be obtained. The mechanical engineer has a better fuel.

The accountant might ask the chemical engineer, "Where did this extra heat energy come from? Did we get something for nothing?" The answer to this last question is "No." Water gas releases more heat energy per mole of carbon because energy was stored in the system when hot coke reacted with steam. The accountant can balance his books this way:

1. $H_2O(g) + C(s) + 31.4$ kcal $\longrightarrow CO(g) + H_2(g)$

2. $CO(g) + \frac{1}{2}O_2(g) \longrightarrow CO_2(g) \qquad + 67.6$ kcal

3. $H_2(g) + \frac{1}{2}O_2(g) \longrightarrow H_2O(g) \qquad + 57.8$ kcal

Now these chemical equations can be added to give an overall equation. At the same time the heats can be added too.

4. $C(s) + O_2(g) + 31.4$ kcal $\longrightarrow CO_2(g) \qquad + 125.4$ kcal

or

By subtracting 31.4 kcal from both sides of the equation,

$C(s) + O_2(g) \longrightarrow CO_2(g) \qquad + 94.0$ kcal

The experimental value of the heat of this reaction has been measured directly. It is in agreement with the value of 94.0 kcal found by combining the heat terms from the three equations. Figure 11-1 summarizes what we have been saying in graphical form.

Our example shows that 31.4 more kcal were stored in the water gas than in the starting materials, coke and steam. We can get that energy back any time we want it, by burning the water gas. The energy is stored as potential energy in the H_2 and CO molecules. The bonds in these molecules have more stored energy than those in C and H_2O.

The energy in the sunlight received by the southwestern United States is equivalent to 1 barrel of petroleum per square meter per year.

11-2   Heat Content of a Substance

When sunlight falls on the leaves of a tree, chlorophyll molecules receive some of the radiant energy. An amazing chemical factory is set into operation. Molecules of water and carbon dioxide are converted into sugar molecules and oxygen molecules:

$$6 \; H_2O + 6 \; CO_2 + energy \longrightarrow C_6H_{12}O_6 + 6 \; O_2$$

During photosynthesis, bonds in H_2O and CO_2 are broken and new bonds are formed to give sugar and O_2. The energy needed comes from sunlight and is stored as potential energy in the new arrange-

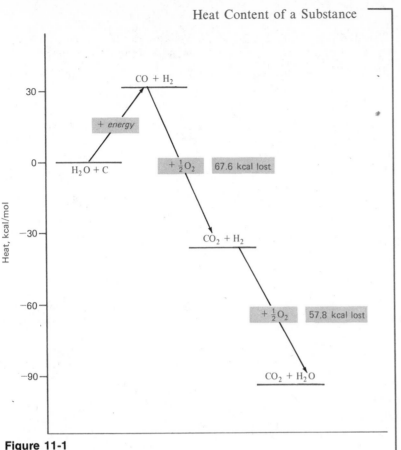

Heat, kcal/mol

30 — CO + H₂

+ energy

0 — H₂O + C   +½O₂   67.6 kcal lost

−30 — CO₂ + H₂

−60 — +½O₂   57.8 kcal lost

−90 — CO₂ + H₂O

Figure 11-1
Heat effects in the manufacture and use of water gas.

ment of atoms. The energy is stored in sugar molecules and in oxygen molecules. Chemists have a special name for this type of potential energy. The potential energy stored in a substance during its formation is called the **heat content** of the substance. A mole of each substance has a characteristic heat content just as it has a characteristic mass. The heat effect in a chemical reaction is the difference between the heat contents of the products and the heat contents of the reactants. Remember, *the energy effects in a chemical reaction are the result of bond-breaking and bond-forming events.*

The water gas example will help us to understand heat content better. Here are equations for the two reactions:

$$H_2O(g) + C(s) + 31.4 \text{ kcal} \longrightarrow H_2(g) + CO(g)$$

$$CO(g) + \frac{1}{2}O_2(g) \longrightarrow CO_2(g) + 67.6 \text{ kcal}$$

The first reaction absorbs heat energy. It is an *endothermic* reaction. The second reaction gives off heat energy. It is an *exothermic* reaction. If you can imagine yourself standing inside the reaction chamber for each of these reactions, you would be able to say:
"Heat energy is being added to the first system. The heat content of the products must be greater than the heat content of the reactants."

The *Calorie* used by nutritionists to describe the fuel value of food is a kilocalorie (4.2 kilojoules).

Accountants for public utilities use the heat content of gas instead of its volume to set the price.

"Heat energy is being given off by the second system. The heat content of the products must be less than the heat content of the reactants."

Endothermic Reaction	Exothermic Reaction
$H_2O(g) + C(s) + 31.4\ kcal \longrightarrow CO(g) + H_2(g)$	$CO(g) + \frac{1}{2}O_2(g) \longrightarrow CO_2(g) + 67.6\ kcal$
Energy is absorbed.	Energy is produced.
The product molecules contain more potential energy than the reactant molecules.	The product molecules contain less potential energy than the reactant molecules.

These ideas are presented graphically in Figures 11-2 and 11-3.

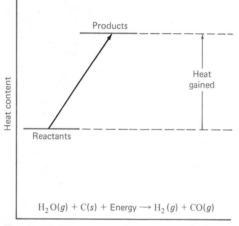

Figure 11-2
Change in heat content during an endothermic reaction. The system gains energy.

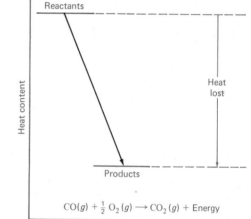

Figure 11-3
Change in heat content during an exothermic reaction. The system loses energy.

11-3   Determination of Heats of Reaction

You have calculated heat effects for a number of chemical reactions in your own laboratory work. You found, for example, that the reaction between aluminum metal and a solution of copper chloride generated a large amount of heat. In the more careful work of Experiment 26 you determined the heat of reaction when one mole of acid reacted with one mole of base.

The heat of a chemical reaction is measured with a calorimeter. Several kinds of calorimeters are illustrated in Figure 11-4. You used the kind on the left. A more elaborate calorimeter is shown in schematic form in part B of the figure. The chemical reaction between known masses of substances is allowed to take place in the reaction chamber. The heat effect of this reaction changes the temperature of the water in the insulated reservoir. If we know the mass of water and the temperature change, we can calculate

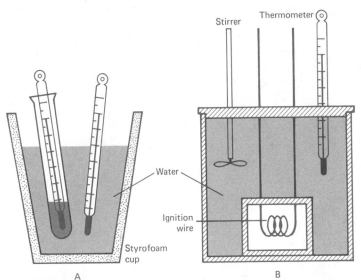

Figure 11-4
A. A simple calorimeter to measure heat of reaction in aqueous solutions.
B. Schematic drawing of a calorimeter.
C. Actual calorimeter used in research.

the heat energy, in calories, for the chemical reaction. This is the same method you employed in Experiment 26, using a plastic cup as the calorimeter. Chemists have used these and other devices to measure the heats of a large number of reactions.

Clearly the amount of heat produced is related to how much material reacts. It is customary to report heats of reaction per mole as in Table 11-1.

11-4   Additivity of Reaction Heats

In Section 11-1 we saw that a series of chemical equations were added to give a net chemical equation. At the same time the heat terms were combined to give the heat term for the net equation. You did this for a different set of equations in Experiment 27. Chemists have made many similar combinations, and they all give the same conclusion. This leads to an important regularity:

> You can add equations for chemical reactions
> algebraically. The result is a net equation
> which includes the heat of the reaction.

This principle can be used to calculate the heat of many reactions. For example, let us find the heat of combustion for nitric oxide (NO) in this reaction:

$$NO(g) + \frac{1}{2} O_2(g) \longrightarrow NO_2(g) \quad \text{heat of reaction} = ?$$

TABLE 11-1

Heat of Reaction Between Elements
in Kilocalories per Mole of Product
$t = 25\,°C \qquad P = 1$ atmosphere

Reactants	Products
$C(s) + \frac{1}{2}O_2(g)$	$\longrightarrow CO(g) + 26.4$ kcal
$C(s) + O_2(g)$	$\longrightarrow CO_2(g) + 94.0$ kcal
$C(s) + 2\,H_2(g)$	$\longrightarrow CH_4(g) + 17.9$ kcal
$2\,C(s) + 3\,H_2(g)$	$\longrightarrow C_2H_6(g) + 20.2$ kcal
$3\,C(s) + 4\,H_2(g)$	$\longrightarrow C_3H_8(g) + 24.8$ kcal
$H_2(g) + \frac{1}{2}O_2(g)$	$\longrightarrow H_2O(g) + 57.8$ kcal
$H_2(g) + \frac{1}{2}O_2(g)$	$\longrightarrow H_2O(l) + 68.3$ kcal
$\frac{1}{2}H_2(g) + \frac{1}{2}I_2(s) + 6.2$ kcal	$\longrightarrow HI(g)$
$\frac{1}{2}H_2(g) + \frac{1}{2}I_2(g)$	$\longrightarrow HI(g) + 1.2$ kcal
$\frac{1}{2}N_2(g) + \frac{1}{2}O_2(g) + 21.6$ kcal	$\longrightarrow NO(g)$
$\frac{1}{2}N_2(g) + O_2(g) + 8.1$ kcal	$\longrightarrow NO_2(g)$
$\frac{1}{2}N_2(g) + \frac{3}{2}H_2(g)$	$\longrightarrow NH_3(g) + 11.0$ kcal
$\frac{1}{8}S_8(s) + O_2(g)$	$\longrightarrow SO_2(g) + 71.0$ kcal
$\frac{1}{8}S_8(g) + H_2(g) + 2\,O_2(g)$	$\longrightarrow H_2SO_4(l) + 194$ kcal

We look for equations in Table 11-1 that include the compounds
NO and NO_2:

$$\frac{1}{2}N_2(g) + \frac{1}{2}O_2(g) + 21.6 \text{ kcal} \longrightarrow NO(g)$$

$$\frac{1}{2}N_2(g) + O_2(g) + 8.1 \text{ kcal} \longrightarrow NO_2(g)$$

We want to combine these equations so that NO is the reactant and NO_2 is the product. To do this, reverse the first of these two equations:

$$NO(g) \longrightarrow \frac{1}{2} N_2(g) + \frac{1}{2} O_2(g) + 21.6 \text{ kcal}$$

If 21.6 kcal of heat energy is absorbed when one mole of NO is formed, then 21.6 kcal of heat energy is released when one mole of NO is decomposed. Now let us rewrite the two equations and add algebraically both the chemical substances and the heat values:

$$\frac{1}{2} \cancel{N_2(g)} + O_2(g) + 8.1 \text{ kcal} \longrightarrow NO_2(g)$$

$$NO(g) \longrightarrow \frac{1}{2} \cancel{N_2(g)} + \frac{1}{2} O_2(g) + 21.6 \text{ kcal}$$

$$NO(g) + \frac{1}{2} O_2(g) \longrightarrow NO_2(g) + (21.6 - 8.1) \text{ kcal}$$

The net heat of reaction is 13.5 kcal. The reaction is exothermic. Heat energy is given off when nitric oxide reacts with oxygen.

Here is another example, the combustion of methane, CH_4:

$$CH_4(g) + 2 O_2(g) \longrightarrow CO_2(g) + 2 H_2O(g) \qquad \text{heat of reaction} = ?$$

Since there are three compounds in this reaction, we must look for the equations in Table 11-1 that include these molecules. We write the equations so that CH_4 is on the left as a reactant while CO_2 and $H_2O(g)$ appear on the right as products:

$$CH_4(g) + 17.9 \text{ kcal} \longrightarrow C(s) + 2 H_2(g)$$

$$C(s) + O_2(g) \longrightarrow CO_2(g) + 94.0 \text{ kcal}$$

$$2 H_2(g) + O_2(g) \longrightarrow 2 H_2O(g) + 115.6 \text{ kcal}$$

The amount of reactants and products and the heat of reaction shown in the last equation have been multiplied by 2 because two moles of H_2O are needed.

Add the chemical formulas and the heats of reaction:

$$CH_4(g) + 2 O_2(g) \longrightarrow$$
$$CO_2(g) + 2 H_2O(g) + (94.0 + 115.6 - 17.9) \text{ kcal}$$
$$\text{heat of reaction} = 191.7 \text{ kcal}$$

This is also an exothermic reaction. Methane is a very good fuel. A large amount of heat energy is given off when methane burns. The gas used in most school laboratories and stoves at home is about 80 percent methane.

EXERCISE 11-1

Use the equation $C(s) + O_2(g) \longrightarrow CO_2(g) + 94.0$ kcal to convince yourself that the heat of reaction will double when two moles of carbon are burned.

EXERCISE 11-2

Use values in Table 11-1 to calculate the heat of this reaction:

$$CO(g) + \frac{1}{2}O_2(g) \longrightarrow CO_2(g)$$

Compare your result with the heat given for this reaction in Section 11-1.

EXERCISE 11-3

a. Calculate the heat of reaction for one mole of NH_3 reacting with O_2. Use

$$4\ NH_3(g) + 3\ O_2(g) \longrightarrow 2\ N_2(g) + 6\ H_2O(g)$$

b. Is this reaction exothermic or endothermic?

EXERCISE 11-4

Use values in Table 11-1 to calculate how much heat energy is required to vaporize one mole of H_2O at 25 °C.

$$H_2O(l) \longrightarrow H_2O(g)$$

Insect Defenses

A look at chemical defense methods leads into some interesting happenings in the insect kingdom. The beetle *Brachinus* provides one of the most spectacular. This bright orange and blue insect seems dressed for the clown's part. But if you're an ant, don't be deceived into attacking him. He will quickly rotate the end of his abdomen and fire off a spray of hot, pungent-smelling liquid right at you. Most attackers are glad to retreat and find a friendlier tidbit for lunch. It's easy to see why *Brachinus* is called the bombardier beetle. But how does he do it?

The beetle has two compartments in the spray gland. One holds a mixture of hydroquinone plus hydrogen peroxide. The other has enzymes that catalyze this reaction:

$$HO-\bigcirc-OH + 3H_2O_2 \longrightarrow O=\bigcirc=O + O_2 + 4H_2O + \text{heat}$$

hydroquinone   *quinone*

The heat boils the water, and the pressure of steam and hot O_2 sprays the 100 °C stinging quinone at the enemy.

In a very similar mechanism a millipede (*Apheloria*) also has a double gland arrangement. In this case

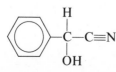 reacts with enzymes to give

$$\bigcirc\!\!-\!\!\overset{\displaystyle H-C=O}{} + HCN\ (g)$$

The HCN gas is extremely poisonous, and in the enclosed spaces under logs where *Apheloria* live it is an effective repellent.

Another beetle in the family *Meloidae* is called a blister beetle. When molested he "bleeds" at the leg joints. This "blood" is a solution, about 0.01 *M* of cantharidin.

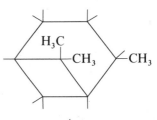

pinene

cantharidin

It is actually quite poisonous and will raise a blister if it gets on your skin. The insect is not deadly to humans because there is little chance anyone would eat it and ingest the "blood."

Sawfly larvae (*Neodiprion sertifer*) are pests that do a great deal of damage to pine forests. They turn the tree's defense into their own. Pine needles are not too tasty to many animals or insects because of the resin containing pinene. The larva eats the needles but doesn't swallow the resin. Somehow it separates and stores the resin in two sacs near its "throat." There the resin is used to manufacture several acids, such as at the right.

Ants, spiders, and even birds find being spit on with this stuff just too much.

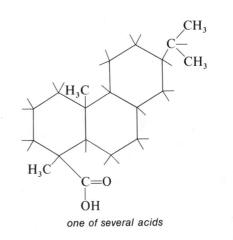

one of several acids

One of the hydroelectric plants of the Tennessee Valley Authority (Norris Dam).

Energy Value of Foods and Fuels

Food	Energy Value (kcal/g)
Cheese: cheddar	4.73
Eggs	1.59
Fish: salmon	1.32
Meat: round steak	1.84
bacon	6.46
Milk	0.72
Bread: wheat	2.6
Cereals: corn flakes	3.83
oatmeal	3.96
wheat flour	3.69
Fruit: apples, raw	0.64
oranges	0.53
Nuts: peanuts	5.64
Vegetables: lima beans	1.31
navy beans	3.54
fresh corn	1.04
Candy: butterscotch	7.89
Fats: butter	7.95
oleomargarine	7.77

Fuel	
Coal	6.7
Gasoline	11.4
Propane	12.0
Wood, oak	4.0
pine	4.4

11-5 Conservation of Energy

How often in the morning do you feel full of energy? You feel ready to accomplish something that day, whether it is schoolwork or playing football or going to a dance. We all know what the word *energy* means in these expressions. In this section we will see another characteristic of energy. Some examples will help.

When gasoline is burned in an automobile engine, part of the potential energy in this fuel is converted into heat energy. The expansion of hot gases moves the engine pistons. A gear system transfers this motion to the wheels and the car moves. The car gains in kinetic energy. The amount and kind of fuel used in an automobile engine determine how far and how fast it moves.

Water flowing over a dam can drive a paddle wheel. The potential energy of water is transformed into mechanical energy of a rotating wheel. The wheel may be part of a system which generates electricity. Mechanical energy is transformed by a generator into electrical energy.

These examples show that energy can be converted from one form to another. Many careful experiments have led scientists to the view that although energy can be changed from one form to another, it is never destroyed, only transformed. This regularity is called the **law of conservation of energy**. It says that in every experiment so far performed, energy is conserved provided all the different forms of energy are taken into account. For example, when electrical energy is used to light a bulb, some is changed into heat (98 percent) and some into light (2 percent). If electrical energy drives a motor, about 98 percent appears as kinetic energy of the rotating shaft and 2 percent as heat. The sum is always 100 percent.

11-6 Comparison of Energy Changes

What kinds of energy changes take place at the molecular level? In Section 4-4 we related the absolute temperature of a gas directly to the translational motion of molecules. There are other important forms of molecular motion. Let us imagine a molecule as a group of balls hooked together by springs. The balls represent atoms and the springs represent the bonds between atoms. The total kinetic energy for a molecule is a result of all the kinds of molecular motion shown in Figure 11-5.

Translational motion is the movement of the whole molecule from place to place. This type of motion is directly related to the absolute temperature of a substance.

Rotational motion is the movement of a molecule around its center of mass.

Vibrational movement is the movement of the atoms in a molecule toward and away from its center of mass.

Now let us follow what happens at the molecular level as we add thermal energy to a cold crystalline solid. The low temperature means that the translational motion about the regular crystal

| Translational motion | Rotational motion | Vibrational motion |

Figure 11-5
The three kinds of motion that a molecule has.

positions is not very large. As energy is added, the temperature of the solid rises. The translational motion of the molecules increases. At some temperature the kinetic energy of the molecules causes so much random movement that the crystal is no longer stable; the solid melts. A phase change takes place.

Source of energy	Absolute temperature	Observed behavior	State of atoms and molecules	Molecular process
Supernova explosions	100 000 000			
Center of stars	10 000 000	Nuclear reactions	$4^1_1\text{H} \longrightarrow {}^4_2\text{He} + 2^0_{+1}\text{e}$	Kinetic energy exceeds nuclear energy.
Plasma	1 000 000	Ionization of atoms	$\text{H} \longrightarrow \text{H}^+ + \text{e}^-$	Kinetic energy exceeds ionization energy.
	100 000			
Surface of sun	10 000	Dissociation of molecules	$\text{H}-\text{H} \longrightarrow \text{H} + \text{H}$	Vibrational energy exceeds chemical bond energies.
Bunsen burner	1 000	Iron melts		Molecules move freely and rotate.
	100	Water boils Ice melts Nitrogen boils		Molecules move back and forth around their equilibrium positions in crystal.
	10	Hydrogen boils Hydrogen melts		
	1	Helium boils		
	0.1			Almost no motion of molecules in perfect crystals.

Figure 11-6
Comparison of energy changes.

The kinetic energy of the molecules in a liquid is primarily in the form of translation and rotation. Warming the liquid increases the molecular motion. Molecules tend to move about in a random fashion in the liquid. On further heating, collisions become so energetic that molecules bounce far apart. Bubbles form. As boiling occurs, another phase change takes place. The liquid vaporizes and gas molecules move throughout the container.

As more energy is added to the gas, vibration within molecules begins to be a major factor. Ultimately a temperature is reached when the kinetic energy of translation, vibration, and rotation in the molecule becomes comparable to chemical bond energies. Molecules begin to dissociate. Only the simplest molecules are stable at temperatures above several thousand degrees.

If we continue to add thermal energy to our system, a temperature will be reached when the kinetic energy approaches the ionization energies for the atoms. The atoms ionize. This state of matter is called **plasma**, a gas made up of electrons and positive ions. The behavior of plasma is an important research topic today. In the future it may provide a new way to make electricity.

Finally, at a temperature of several million degrees, the kinetic energy is so great that collisions cause nuclear reactions. The particles collide with such tremendous force that nuclear reactions begin. There is good reason to think that many nuclear reactions take place in stars. These reactions are believed to be the source of a star's energy.

Researchers at the forefront of new kinds of energy production study plasmas. Astronomers need to know the behavior of plasmas to understand the stars.

11-7 The Energy Involved in Nuclear Reactions

Nuclear reactions can be either endothermic or exothermic, just as chemical reactions are. However, the amount of energy in a nuclear reaction is about a million times greater than the energy in chemical reactions. This is a consequence of the relatively large change in mass in a nuclear reaction. For chemical reactions the change in mass between reactants and products is so small that it is not measurable. This is not true in nuclear reactions.

Let us take the example of the β-decay of ^{14}C.

$$^{14}_{6}C \longrightarrow {}^{14}_{7}N + {}_{-1}^{0}e^- + \text{energy}$$

Precise measurements with a mass spectrometer provide the mass values for ^{14}C and ^{14}N:

Mass of ^{14}C =	14.003 242 g/mol
Mass of ^{14}N =	14.003 074 g/mol
Mass difference =	0.000 168 g/mol

There is a decrease of 0.000 168 gram per mole when ^{14}C decays. An equivalent amount of energy is released. The Einstein mass-energy relation is given by the equation $E = mc^2$, where m is the mass and c is the velocity of light.

In the formation of one mole of ^{14}N from one mole of ^{14}C, the energy released would be

One of the geothermal power plants at The Geysers in California.

$$E = mc^2 = \left(0.000\ 168\ \frac{g}{mol}\right) \times \left(3 \times 10^{10}\frac{cm}{s}\right)^2$$

$$= 1.51 \times 10^{17}\ \frac{g \times cm^2}{mol \times s^2}$$

This number can be converted to units of kilocalories:

$$E = \left(1.51 \times 10^{17}\frac{g \times cm^2}{mol \times s^2}\right) \times \left(2.4 \times 10^{-11}\ \frac{kcal \times s^2}{g \times cm^2}\right)$$

$$= 3.6 \times 10^6\ \frac{kcal}{mol}$$

In this example 3.6 million kilocalories of energy is released and corresponds to the maximum energy the beta particles from ^{14}C can have.

   The stability of a nucleus depends on its neutron/proton ratio. Even among those nuclei that are considered stable, however, there is a variation in the forces which hold the nucleus together. In order to study this variation in the energy needed to break a nucleus apart, consider the process of building a nucleus from protons and neutrons. For example, let us look at the hypothetical reaction

$$2\ {}_{1}^{1}H + 2\ {}_{0}^{1}n \longrightarrow {}_{2}^{4}He$$

First compare the masses of the reactants with those of the products:

Mass of 2 moles of protons	$= 2 \times 1.007\ 82 = 2.015\ 64$ grams
Mass of 2 moles of neutrons	$= 2 \times 1.008\ 67 = 2.017\ 34$ grams
Total mass of reactants	$= 4.032\ 98$ grams
Mass of 1 mole of ${}_{2}^{4}He$ produced	$= 4.002\ 60$ grams
Mass difference between products and reactants	$= 0.030\ 38$ gram

There is a decrease of 0.030 38 gram per mole of helium nuclei formed in this reaction. An equivalent amount of energy is released. Using the Einstein mass-energy relationship allows us to calculate the energy released when a mole of He atoms forms from two moles of protons and two moles of neutrons:

$$E = mc^2 = 0.03 \frac{g}{mol} \times \left(3 \times 10^{10} \frac{cm}{sec} \right)^2$$

$$= 2.7 \times 10^{19} \frac{g \times cm^2}{mol \times s^2}$$

$$E = \left(2.7 \times 10^{19} \frac{g \times cm^2}{mol \times s^2} \right) \times \left(2.4 \times 10^{-11} \frac{kcal \times s^2}{g \times cm^2} \right)$$

$$= 6.4 \times 10^8 \frac{kcal}{mol}$$

This means that 640 million kilocalories of energy are released. This much energy must be supplied to dissociate a mole of $_2^4$He nuclei into two moles each of protons and neutrons. Dividing this by four gives 160 million kilocalories per mole of nuclear particles in ^{4}He. This amount of energy is called the **nuclear binding energy**. It takes millions of times more energy to separate the particles in a nucleus than to separate atoms in molecules.

Similar calculations can be made for other nuclei. The binding energy per mole of particles varies in a systematic way when the mass number of the nucleus increases, as shown in Figure 11-7.

The nuclei that have a mass number of approximately 60 have the highest binding energy per nuclear particle and are therefore the most stable nuclei. The graph helps us to understand the processes of nuclear fission and nuclear fusion. If a nucleus of a heavier element such as uranium is split into two smaller fragments, the binding energy per nuclear particle is greater in the lighter nuclei. As a consequence, energy is released in nuclear fission. Generally this fission reaction is induced by the bombardment of a particular uranium nucleus with neutrons.

When more than one neutron is released, the fission reaction is a self-propagating reaction, or **chain reaction**. Neutrons released by one fission event may induce other fissions. When fission reactions are run under controlled conditions in a nuclear reactor, the energy released eventually appears as heat. The energy released by the fission of *1 kilogram* of $_{92}^{235}$U is equivalent to that obtained from more than *2 million kilograms* of coal. Fission reactions will be discussed in Section 11-8.

Figure 11-7 shows that when very light nuclei, such as $_1^1$H or $_1^2$H, are brought together to form heavier elements, the binding energy per mole of nuclear particles again increases. As in every other reaction in which the products are more stable than the reactants,

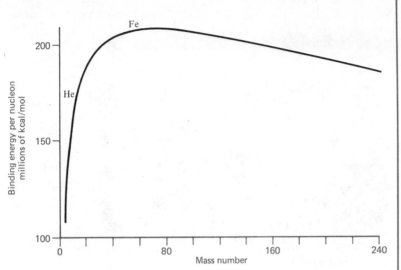

Figure 11-7
The binding energy per mole of nuclear particles in the nucleus.

energy is given off in nuclear fusion. The graph also shows that the energy released is considerably greater in the fusion process than in the fission reaction. By use of a set of reactions in which four protons are converted into a helium nucleus and two positrons, *1 kilogram* of hydrogen could produce energy equivalent to that obtained from *20 million kilograms* of coal. For this reason, and because of the great abundance of hydrogen, fusion reactions are potential sources of enormous amounts of energy. Fusion reactions are discussed in Section 11-9.

11-8   Nuclear Fission

In 1939 the discovery was announced that neutrons could cause the fission of an isotope of uranium, ^{235}U. Soon after that it was found that neutrons were produced as products of the fission reaction. The following is a typical fission reaction:

$$^{235}_{92}U + ^{1}_{0}n \longrightarrow ^{137}_{56}Ba + ^{96}_{36}Kr + 3\ ^{1}_{0}n + 1.7 \times 10^5\ \text{kcal}$$

Atomic bombs are based on many nuclear fission reactions occurring in a very short time. This develops explosions of high energy. Fortunately it is possible to control the reaction. First a moderator like carbon or beryllium or deuterium slows the neutrons down. The probability of fission increases as the energy of the neutron decreases. Second, a substance like cadmium, which is a good absorber of neutrons, is used to control the rate of the

A nuclear power plant.

^{252}Cf, a man-made isotope of element 98, emits a large number of neutrons during spontaneous fission. The half-life is 2.65 years. One millionth of a gram emits 10^6 neutrons per second. The Energy Research and Development Agency (ERDA) hopes to have enough ^{252}Cf to sell in 1980 for $1 per microgram.

fission reaction. Cadmium rods are placed between the rods containing ^{235}U in the nuclear reactor. As the cadmium rods are raised, neutrons are able to react with ^{235}U. In this way the reaction is controlled so that an explosion does not take place. The energy released in fission then is used to produce steam to drive turbines which generate electricity. A number of nuclear reactors have been built in the United States and other countries to provide power.

The first nuclear reactors built to produce electricity were based on the fission of ^{235}U. The abundance of this isotope in natural uranium is only 0.71 percent. The rest is ^{238}U, an isotope which does not undergo fission with slow neutrons. However, a type of reactor that uses ^{238}U is being developed. It is called a breeder reactor, because it produces more fissionable material than it consumes. This is possible because ^{239}Pu is produced by the reactions

$$^{238}_{92}\text{U} + ^{1}_{0}n \longrightarrow ^{239}_{92}\text{U}$$

$$^{239}_{92}\text{U} \longrightarrow ^{239}_{93}\text{Np} + ^{0}_{-1}e$$

$$^{239}_{93}\text{Np} \longrightarrow ^{239}_{94}\text{Pu} + ^{0}_{-1}e$$

Like ^{235}U, the isotope ^{239}Pu undergoes fission with slow neutrons. In the example given above for the fission of ^{235}U, three neutrons are produced. One of these is used to keep the chain reaction going, but the other two can form ^{239}Pu from ^{238}U. So in a breeder reactor *two* atoms of ^{239}Pu can be made each time *one* ^{235}U undergoes fission.

Fossil fuel power plants that burn coal or petroleum may pollute the environment with gases like SO_2, with dust particles, or with waste heat. Nuclear reactors also give rise to waste heat. In addition, since the products of nuclear fission are radioactive, it is essential to prevent their escape into the environment. Moreover, it is necessary to store them for many years in a safe manner until their radioactivity has reached a safe level. This is particularly true for ^{239}Pu, which is formed in breeder reactors, since plutonium is one of the most toxic substances known. No completely satis-

Safety inspectors and union leaders have to understand the radioactivity, flammability, and toxicity of chemicals in order to protect workers.

factory solution for storage of the radioactive products of nuclear fission has been found so far, although many proposals have been made. This problem must be resolved if nuclear reactors are to replace fossil fuel plants for energy production.

11-9   Nuclear Fusion

The energy production in stars is based on the fusion of nuclei of small mass. In most stars hydrogen, the most abundant element in the universe, is converted into helium. A temperature of about 100 million degrees is required for these reactions to occur. During the last 25 years scientists in the United States and Russia have attempted to produce a controlled fusion reaction. If this can be achieved, there would be an almost inexhaustible energy source. Moreover, the pollution problems would be much less than with fossil fuel or nuclear fission plants.

Unfortunately, nuclear fusion has been controlled in the laboratory for only a few hundredths of a second. (Hydrogen bomb explosions are based on fusion reactions, but these devices cannot be used to produce electrical power.) There are two requirements. The first is raising the temperature of the gas to several hundred million degrees, and several methods have been developed to do this. The second is to find a "container" to keep the reactants together. Strong magnetic fields can confine the high-temperature gas for short periods of time, but so far no one has been able to achieve a stable system.

11-10   Review

Every chemical compound has a characteristic mass. Every chemical compound has a characteristic heat content. The heat content of a substance is a measure of the potential energy stored in the substance during its formation. Energy is stored in the bonds, and it changes when the number and kind are altered in a chemical reaction. The heat effects in a chemical reaction measure the difference between the heat contents of the products and the heat contents of the reactants.

If there is an increase in heat content during a chemical reaction, the reaction is **endothermic**. Such a reaction absorbs heat energy from its surroundings. If there is a decrease in heat content during a chemical reaction, the reaction is **exothermic**. The reaction gives up heat energy to its surroundings.

Chemists have measured the heats of many reactions. Just as several chemical equations can be added to give an overall equation, so can heat values be combined to give the heat of reaction for the overall chemical reaction. This important regularity has been found to apply in every system that chemists have studied.

Energy can be transformed from one type to another. The sum of all types is constant for a fixed system. On a molecular basis potential energy is present in the bonding arrangement and kinetic energy is present in the motions of the atoms and molecules.

The energy in nuclear reactions is about a million times greater

Of the oil used for freight transportation on land, 60 percent is used by trucks, but they carry only 19 percent of our freight. Trucks require 600 kcal and trains 200 kcal to carry one ton one mile.

Energy in Chemical and Nuclear Reactions

than in a chemical reaction, on a molar basis. The energy of a nuclear reaction can be calculated using the Einstein mass-energy relation $E = mc^2$. Both nuclear fission and nuclear fusion are possible ways to produce large amounts of energy. Nuclear fission reactors at the present time are being used as a source of electrical energy.

Questions and Problems for Chapter 11

1

In the process of making water gas, the coke cools. Propose a method of heating this coke.

2

Consider both solid and gaseous fuels. Contrast advantages of using each.

3

Which contains more stored energy (potential energy)?

(a) A burned or an unburned match head
(b) A potato or the chemicals a plant needs to make the potato
(c) A used or unused photographer's flashbulb
(d) Freshly cut grass or grass that has been through a compost pile

4

A 1 M H_2SO_4 solution is made by adding concentrated acid to water. The temperature of the final solution is about 18 °C higher than the starting temperature. The equation for the reaction is

$$H_2SO_4(l) + H_2O \longrightarrow H_2SO_4(1.0\ M)$$

Determine the molar heat for this reaction.

5

The energy to heat 1.0 gram of metal one degree Celsius varies. For Cu and Al the values are 0.11 and 0.22 cal/g · °C respectively. Five hundred grams of Cu at 400 °C is placed in contact with 500 g of Al at 0 °C. Calculate the final temperature. Assume no heat loss to the surroundings.

6

The amount of solar radiation received in Arizona is about 2 000 000 kcal/m^2/year. How much coke (C) must be burned to CO_2 to produce this amount of heat energy?

7

On which side of the equation is the heat term for an endothermic reaction?

8

On which side of the equation is the heat term for an exothermic reaction?

9

The formation of one mole of $TiBr_3$ from the elements liberates 132 kcal. Find the heat produced in making 55.6 grams.

10

What is the minimum energy required to produce one mole of nitric oxide, NO, from the elements?

11

How much energy is liberated when 0.100 mole of H_2 at 25 °C and 1 atmosphere is combined with enough $O_2(g)$ to make liquid water at the same conditions?

12

How much energy is consumed in the decomposition of 5.0 grams of $H_2O(l)$ at 25 °C and 1 atmosphere into its gaseous elements at the same conditions?

13

Use this balanced chemical equation to help identify the FALSE statement:

$$H_2(g) + 103\ kcal \longrightarrow 2\ H(g)$$

(a) The reaction is endothermic.
(b) Two grams of H(g) contain more energy than 2 grams of $H_2(g)$.
(c) Burning one gram H(g) will produce more heat than one gram $H_2(g)$.
(d) Energy is released when 2 hydrogen atoms form a hydrogen molecule.

14

To change the temperature of a particular calorimeter and the water it contains by one degree Celsius requires 1550 calories. The complete combustion of 1.40 grams of ethylene gas, $C_2H_4(g)$, in the calorimeter causes a temperature rise of

10.7 degrees. Find the heat of combustion per mole of ethylene.

15

Using Table 11-1, calculate the heat of burning ethane in oxygen to give CO_2 and water vapor.

16

Given:

$$C(\text{diamond}) + O_2(g) \longrightarrow CO_2(g) + 94.50 \text{ kcal}$$

$$C(\text{graphite}) + O_2(g) \longrightarrow CO_2(g) + 94.05 \text{ kcal}$$

Find the heat of reaction for the manufacture of diamond from graphite.

$$C(\text{graphite}) \longrightarrow C(\text{diamond})$$

Is heat absorbed or evolved as graphite is converted to diamond?

17

The thermite reaction is spectacular and highly exothermic. It involves the reaction between Fe_2O_3, ferric oxide, and metallic aluminum. The reaction produces white-hot, molten iron in a few seconds. Given:

$$2 \text{ Al} + \frac{3}{2}O_2 \longrightarrow Al_2O_3 + 400 \text{ kcal}$$

$$2 \text{ Fe} + \frac{3}{2}O_2 \longrightarrow Fe_2O_3 + 200 \text{ kcal}$$

Determine the amount of heat liberated in the reaction of 1 mole of Fe_2O_3 with Al.

18

How much energy is released in the manufacture of 1.00 kg of iron by the thermite reaction mentioned in Problem 17?

19

How many grams of water could be heated from $0\,°C$ to $100\,°C$ by the heat liberated per mole of aluminum oxide formed in the thermite reaction of Problem 17?

20

Which would be the better fuel on the basis of the heat released per mole burned, nitric oxide, NO, or ammonia, NH_3? Assume the products are $NO_2(g)$ and $H_2O(g)$.

21

What is the minimum energy required to produce one mole of sulfur dioxide from sulfuric acid?

$$H_2SO_4(l) \longrightarrow SO_2(g) + H_2O(g) + \frac{1}{2}O_2(g)$$

22

The heat released during the formation of $MgO(s)$ from the elements is 144 kcal/mol of $MgO(s)$. How much heat is liberated when magnesium reduces the carbon in CO_2 to free carbon? See Table 11-1.

23

SO_2 can be combined with oxygen to give SO_3. The heat released in this reaction is 23.0 kcal/mol SO_2. Calculate the heat of reaction to form one mole of SO_3 from S_8 and O_2.

24

The formation of liquid methanol, CH_3OH, from the elements releases 152.6 kcal/mol CH_3OH. Calculate the heat for combustion of one mole of methanol to CO_2 and H_2O.

25

How much water can be boiled by using the heat from completely burning one mole of carbon?

(a) If the water is at $100\,°C$
(b) If it is at $0\,°C$ and must be warmed to $100\,°C$ first

26

Combustion of acetylene, C_2H_2, is represented by

$$C_2H_2(g) + \frac{5}{2}O_2(g) \longrightarrow$$
$$2\ CO_2(g) + H_2O(l) + 308 \text{ kcal}$$

What is the heat of formation for one mole of acetylene from carbon and hydrogen?

27

Which gives more heat on burning, a mole of acetylene or a mole of ethane? See Problem 26 and Table 11-1 for data.

28

Note these reactions:

$$W + 2 \text{ Br}_2 \longrightarrow WBr_4 + 35 \text{ kcal}$$

$$W + 3 \text{ Br}_2 \longrightarrow WBr_6 + 44 \text{ kcal}$$

$$WBr_4 + Br_2 \longrightarrow WBr_6$$

What is the energy term for the third equation?

29

The heats of formation for LiCl and some lithium chloride hydrates from their elements are listed:

Forming 1 mole of	Liberates (kcal)
LiCl	53
LiCl · H_2O	170
LiCl · 2 H_2O	242
LiCl · 3 H_2O	314

Find the heat liberated by each additional mole of water and comment on the meaning of the values.

30

Find the heat of this reaction:

$$H_2S(g) + O_2(g) \longrightarrow H_2O(g) + SO_2(g)$$

Given: $H_2(g) + \dfrac{1}{8}S_8(s) \longrightarrow H_2S(g) + 4.8 \text{ kcal}$

31

Suppose the reaction described by the equation

$$H_2(g) + I_2(?) \longrightarrow 2\,HI(g)$$

was carried out in a sealed metal calorimeter. The experimenter observes a temperature change. How can the direction of this change and Table 11-1 be used to decide whether the I_2 was gaseous or solid?

32

In Chapter 10, the family of saturated hydrocarbons was represented by the formula C_nH_{2n+2}. Each successive member of this family adds a —CH_2— unit. Use the values in Table 11-1 and the equation

$$4\,C(s) + 5\,H_2(g) \longrightarrow C_4H_{10}(g) + 29.8 \text{ kcal}$$

to estimate the heat of formation for one mole of pentane, C_5H_{12}, from the elements. (Hint: Calculate the change in energy for each additional CH_2 unit.)

33

Why is the law of conservation of energy considered to be valid?

34

What do you think would happen in scientific circles if a clear-cut, well-verified exception was found to the law of conservation of energy as stated in the text?

35

Is energy conserved when a ball of mud is dropped from your hand to the ground? Explain your answer.

36

List several things that can be done to a steel spring that will increase the energy stored in it.

37

What becomes of the energy supplied to water molecules as they are heated in a closed container from 25 °C to 35 °C?

38

Outline the events and associated energy changes that occur on the molecular level when steam at 150 °C and 1 atmosphere pressure loses energy continually until it finally becomes ice at −10 °C.

39

For $^{16}_{8}O$, the mass difference between products and reactants in the equation

$$8\,^{1}_{1}H + 8\,^{1}_{0}n \longrightarrow\ ^{16}_{8}O$$

is 0.137 g/mol. Calculate the binding energy per nuclear particle in $^{16}_{8}O$ as kcal per mol.

40

Which of the following reactions is most likely to

(a) liberate 505 kcal of energy?
(b) liberate 3.6×10^6 kcal of energy?
(c) require 7.2 kcal of energy?
   (i) $UF_6(l) \longrightarrow UF_6(g)$
   (ii) $U(s) + 3\,F_2(g) \longrightarrow UF_6(l)$
   (iii) $^{14}_{6}C \longrightarrow\ ^{14}_{7}N +\ ^{0}_{-1}e$

41

A typical fission process occurs after $^{235}_{92}U$ absorbs a neutron and becomes the unstable isotope $^{236}_{92}U$. This isotope can break apart, producing a $^{137}_{52}Te$ nucleus, a $^{97}_{40}Zr$ nucleus, and 2 neutrons. Write an equation for this nuclear reaction.

42

In a nuclear fusion reaction two nuclei come together to form a larger nucleus. For example, deuterium nuclei, $^{2}_{1}H$, and tritium nuclei, $^{3}_{1}H$, can "fuse" to form helium nuclei, $^{4}_{2}He$, and a neutron:

$$^{2}_{1}H + \ ^{3}_{1}H \longrightarrow\ ^{4}_{2}He + \ ^{1}_{0}n + 4.05 \times 10^7 \text{ kcal}$$

How many grams of hydrogen would have to be burned (to gaseous water) to liberate the same amount of heat as liberated by fusion of one mole of $^{2}_{1}H$ nuclei? Express the answer in metric tons (1 metric ton = 1×10^6 g).

The Rates of Chemical Reactions

12

An iron nail reacts slowly in air as it rusts. White phosphorus bursts into flame when exposed to air. Candle wax burns after we light the wick of the candle. These reactions with oxygen in air take place at different rates. When we know the factors that influence the rate of a chemical reaction, we can control the reaction. In this chapter we will study the rates of chemical reactions by finding what factors influence them.

What do we mean by the rate of reaction? An example will help you to understand. When hydrogen iodide gas is heated to 400 °C, hydrogen and iodine are the products of the reaction:

$$2 \, HI(g) \longrightarrow H_2(g) + I_2(g)$$

243

Metallurgists do a great deal of research to slow down or prevent corrosion reactions.

The purple color of iodine vapor gradually intensifies as the reaction proceeds. We can calculate the rate of the reaction by determining the color change during a certain time interval. Since H_2 and HI are colorless, the color change indicates the change in iodine concentration. The rate of the reaction is given by the equation

$$rate = \frac{change\ in\ iodine\ concentration}{time\ interval}$$

12-1 The Nature of the Reactants

You can draw on your experience in the laboratory to compare rates of different chemical reactions. In Experiment 23 you made qualitative comparisons of the rates of these reactions:

$$5\,Fe^{2+} + MnO_4^- + 8\,H^+ \longrightarrow 5\,Fe^{3+} + Mn^{2+} + 4\,H_2O \qquad fast$$

$$5\,C_2O_4^{2-} + 2\,MnO_4^- + 16\,H^+ \longrightarrow 10\,CO_2 + 2\,Mn^{2+} + 8\,H_2O \quad slow$$

Both ferrous ion, Fe^{2+}, and oxalate ion, $C_2O_4^{2-}$, react with permanganate ion, MnO_4^-, at room temperature.* Yet there is a large difference in the rates of these reactions. The purple color of the permanganate ion disappeared much more rapidly in the first reaction. The concentrations of permanganate and hydrogen ions were the same at the start of your experiments. In addition, the temperature was approximately the same. Therefore, the difference in the rates must be associated with specific properties of Fe^{2+} and $C_2O_4^{2-}$.

When colorless nitric oxide escapes from a test tube into the air, the reddish-brown color of nitrogen dioxide gas appears very rapidly. When carbon monoxide in the exhaust fumes of an automobile mixes with air, the reaction to form carbon dioxide is very slow:

$$2\,NO + O_2 \longrightarrow 2\,NO_2 \qquad fast\ at\ 25\,°C$$

$$2\,CO + O_2 \longrightarrow 2\,CO_2 \qquad very\ slow\ at\ 25\,°C$$

The form of these balanced equations is identical. Clearly the difference in reaction rates must depend on the nature of NO and CO. The determination of the molecular properties which affect rate behavior is an important frontier of chemistry.

12-2 Effect of Concentration: Collision Theory

In Experiment 28 you studied the rate of the reaction between peroxydisulfate ion, $S_2O_8^{2-}$, and iodide ion, I^-. You found that the reaction rate increased when you increased the concentration of either reactant. According to the molecular view of matter, chemical reactions depend on collisions between the reacting

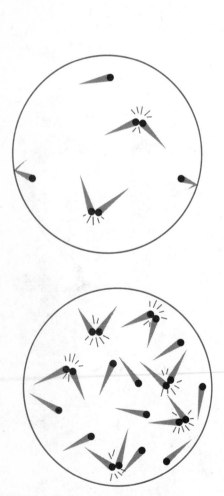

Figure 12-1
Number of collisions depends on concentration.

*To simplify equations, we will often omit the symbol (*aq*), although all ions are aquated in water solutions.

molecules. This model, used to explain reaction rates, is called the **collision theory**. It helps us understand the effect of concentration on reaction rate. When the concentration of a reactant increases, the number of molecules or ions in a given volume increases. The number of collisions per second increases. We would expect the reaction rate to increase.

EXERCISE 12-1

Assume that you have 1 mole of HI gas in a 1-liter flask at 400 °C.

(a) What is the concentration of HI in moles per liter?
(b) What would the concentration be if the same amount of HI were put in a 500 ml flask?
(c) Will the concentration of HI in (a) or (b) give a faster reaction?

$$2 \text{ HI}(g) \longrightarrow \text{H}_2(g) + \text{I}_2(g)$$

EXERCISE 12-2

Reactions between gases and solids are very important, particularly in many industrial processes. Consider the same mass of a solid divided into cubes of different sizes: cubes 1 cm, 10^{-1} cm, and 10^{-3} cm on edge.

When a gas reacts with each of these solids, in which case is the reaction fastest?

Some reactions are fast—some, like rusting, are slow.

12-3　Effect of Temperature: Collision Theory

In the laboratory you observed that raising the temperature speeds up the reaction between $\text{S}_2\text{O}_8{}^{2-}$ and I^-. The same effect is observed in the reaction between air and methane in your laboratory burner. A match "lights" the methane by raising its temperature. The combustion reaction releases enough heat to keep the temperature high. The reaction continues at a reasonable rate. Raising the temperature speeds up the reaction.

Two questions come to mind:

"Why does a temperature rise increase the rate of a reaction?"
"Why does a temperature rise have such a large effect?"

Perhaps the collision theory model can lead to answers to these questions.

Cooks use different temperatures to get different cooking "effects." Automobile repairmen use heat lamps to speed paint drying.

We can calculate for a mixture of carbon monoxide and air under normal conditions that a particular CO molecule collides with an O_2 molecule about once in 10^{-9} second. Every second a CO molecule collides with 10^9 O_2 molecules. Yet virtually no reaction occurs at room temperature. Most collisions between molecules are not effective. Chemists have learned that chemical reactions occur only when collisions have sufficient energy to cause a rearrangement of atoms. We can understand this if we think of collisions between cars. Frequently, in slowly moving traffic, there are gentle bumps from the car behind. No damage is done to either car. Occasionally a high-speed collision occurs. High-energy collisions cause auto damage. High-energy molecular collisions cause the "molecular damage" called a chemical reaction.

In Section 4-6 we described an experiment to measure the kinetic energies for molecules. That experiment showed that there is a distribution of molecular energies. A few molecules traveled at very high speeds. They had high kinetic energy. If one of these molecules collided with another molecule, we would expect "molecular damage" to take place. Most molecules in the sample had much lower speed and energy. The distribution curve at temperature T_1, showing the fraction of collisions having a particular energy, is drawn in Figure 12-2. This curve will be useful in discussing the effect temperature has on the rate of a chemical reaction. Let us propose that chemical reactions take place only if the *two colliding molecules bring enough energy to the collision* so that rearrangement of atoms to form new molecules occurs. The minimum amount of energy is called the "threshold energy," E. A vertical line is drawn in Figure 12-2 to indicate this energy. The shaded area to the right of this line shows us the fraction of collisions with energy greater than E. Remember that it is not necessary for each reacting molecule to have energy greater than the threshold energy. If a low-energy molecule collides with a very high energy molecule, a reaction may occur.

At the temperature T_1 not many molecules have high energies. Not many collisions involve energies greater than the threshold energy. Very few of the collisions lead to chemical reaction. What happens when the temperature is increased to T_2? The distribution curve changes shape. It flattens and spreads out as shown in Figure 12-2. The average speed of the molecules is greater at the higher temperature. There are many more molecules now that have high kinetic energy. Many more of the collisions involve energy greater than E. Therefore, the reaction rate is much greater at a higher temperature.

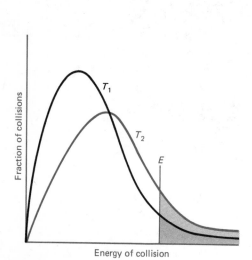

Figure 12-2
Collision energy distributions at two temperatures. Number of collisions with energy greater than E is much larger at the higher temperature, T_2.

12-4   Reaction Mechanisms

Molecules or ions must collide for a chemical reaction to occur. The equation for the reaction between Fe^{2+} and MnO_4^- indicates that 14 ions react with each other:

$$5\ Fe^{2+} + MnO_4^- + 8\ H^+ \longrightarrow 5\ Fe^{3+} + Mn^{2+} + 4\ H_2O$$

The balanced equation seems to suggest that all these ions would have to collide at the same time. The probability of that happening is very small. You can see why from the fact just given that CO and O_2 collide 10^9 times per second. Each contact must be very short. The chance of a third molecule striking while the first two are colliding is low. For 14 molecules to come together at the same instant the chances would be essentially zero. The rate of a chemical reaction which depends on so many particles coming together at one time would be very small. And yet you have seen in the laboratory that this reaction is fast. It must proceed by a series of reactions or steps each of which involves more probable collisions. Chemists call such a series of reactions the **reaction mechanism**.

Consider another, less complicated reaction than the ferrous-permanganate reaction. You have studied the reaction between peroxydisulfate ion and iodide ion in some detail:

$$S_2O_8^{2-} + 2\,I^- \longrightarrow 2\,SO_4^{2-} + I_2$$

Quantitative studies of the rate for this reaction show that doubling the concentration of the peroxydisulfate ion doubles the rate of the reaction. Doubling the concentration of the iodide ion also doubles the rate of the reaction. Yet, in the balanced equation, two iodide ions are needed for one peroxydisulfate ion. Why does a change in iodide concentration have the same effect as an equal change in peroxydisulfate concentration?

An explanation can be given by proposing that this reaction takes place in two steps:

$$S_2O_8^{2-} + I^- \longrightarrow SO_4^{2-} + SO_4I^- \qquad \text{slow}$$
$$SO_4I^- + I^- \longrightarrow SO_4^{2-} + I_2 \qquad \text{fast}$$

First, notice that adding these equations gives the overall equation

$$S_2O_8^{2-} + 2\,I^- \longrightarrow 2\,SO_4^{2-} + I_2$$

For any proposed reaction mechanism we must always be able to add up all the separate steps to give the balanced equation for the observed reaction.

Second, observe that each reaction requires a collision of only two ions. We can see that the first step is the "bottleneck" in the reaction between peroxydisulfate and iodide ions. Almost as soon as the ion SO_4I^- forms, it disappears in the second, fast reaction. The rate of I_2 formation is determined by the rate of the slow reaction in the sequence. The slow reaction in a reaction mechanism is called the **rate-determining step**. Now we can understand why peroxydisulfate and iodide are equally effective in increasing the reaction rate. One peroxydisulfate ion collides with one iodide ion in the slow, rate-determining reaction. Doubling the concentration of one reactant is just as effective as doubling the concentration of the other.

Civil engineers are concerned with reaction rates—setting of concrete, rusting, and deterioration of all kinds.

Efficiency experts search operations for the rate-determining reaction. They may then improve conditions to speed that "reaction" so the whole process goes faster.

Flower Power

All plants need energy to grow, and most get it from the sun. Plants in the far north or far south have a special problem. For example, at Ellesmere Island, which is 600 miles from the North Pole, the warm-weather growing season is very short, only about six weeks. Flowers must grow rapidly, so some have developed interesting ways of capturing more sunlight. Capturing more sunlight means more energy and higher temperature, leading to increased rates of reaction.

Many flowers and leaves on plants throughout the world turn to face the sun as it moves across the sky each day. Some arctic flowers have evolved a shape that acts as a miniature solar furnace. Their petals form a bowl that tends to focus the sun's radiant energy onto the central group of pistils and stamens. By this means the temperature at the reproducing area of the plant is increased 6–8 °C for up to 50% of the time. In effect, the growing season is lengthened by about 25%.

Insects have discovered the warm, cozy resting place inside the flower. So they bask there and in the process fertilize the flower. Flower power increases the temperature and the rate of growth. The plant can survive a bit farther north.

EXERCISE 12-3

Imagine five people working together to wash dishes. The first two clear the table and hand the dishes to the third person. He washes them and hands them on. The last two people dry and stack them. Which step is likely to be the rate-determining step? Discuss how the rate of the overall process would be affected if a sixth person joined the group (a) as a table clearer; (b) as a second dishwasher; (c) as a dish dryer.

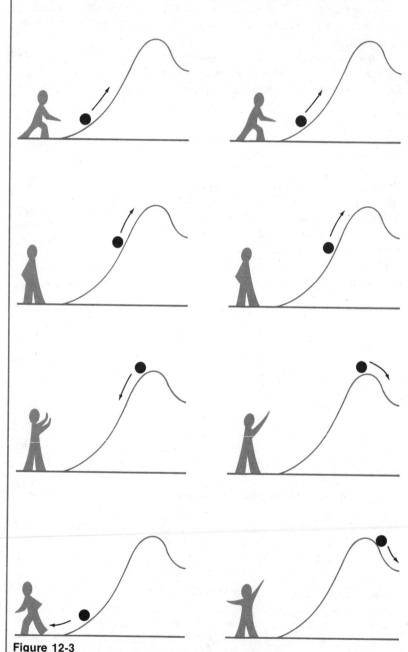

Figure 12-3
Insufficient energy; ball returns to original level.

Figure 12-4
Sufficient energy; ball goes over to a new level.

12-5   Activation Energy

Why is there a threshold energy for chemical reaction? Why don't all collisions cause new atomic arrangements? Imagine someone trying to roll a bowling ball up a very steep hill. On most tries the bowling ball slows down and stops before it gets to the top of the hill. The kinetic energy of the bowling ball is converted to potential energy as the ball slows down. Then it rolls back down on the same side of the hill. The hill acts as a barrier. Look at Figure 12-3 to see what happens. Only occasionally does the bowler give the ball enough kinetic energy so that it gets to the top of the hill and rolls down the other side. A successful try is shown in Figure 12-4.

We can picture a similar situation for molecules in a chemical reaction. During molecular collisions atoms can take up new bonding arrangements that have more potential energy than either the reactants or the products. These atomic arrangements have high potential energy like the bowling ball at the top of the hill. In our model the collision theory suggests there is a minimum potential energy that must be achieved by colliding reactants before they can convert to some other form. In Figure 12-5 we show the distribution curve for the kinetic energy of molecular collisions placed next to the potential energy hill for a chemical reaction. (Remember, however, there is no actual "hill" between reactants and products. It is only an energy barrier.) To react, molecules must collide with enough energy to assume the high-energy configuration of atoms represented by the top of the hill. With less energetic collisions the molecules do not react. Several values are marked on the energy distribution curve with circles. If molecular collisions having those energies occurred, the system could reach

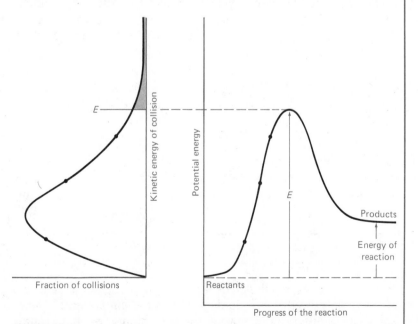

Figure 12-5
Comparison of kinetic energy distribution curve with activation energy diagram. Only a small fraction of collisions have sufficient kinetic energy to reach the top of the potential energy hill.

Operators of manufacturing plants are much concerned with heat effects—getting enough in at some places, out at others.

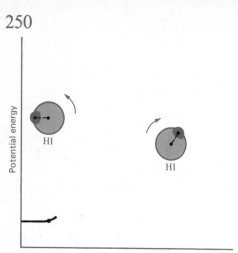

Figure 12-6
The two HI molecules are so far apart they do not have any appreciable interactions. The potential energy of the system is constant and is represented by the dot on the horizontal line on the left. The HI molecules have kinetic energy of translation and rotation.

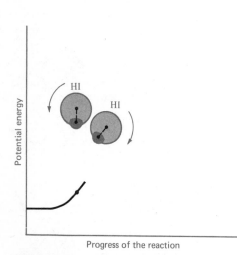

Figure 12-7
As the molecules get closer to each other, they interact and the four atoms begin to take on a new arrangement. The potential energy of the system increases. This increase in potential energy must be compensated by a decrease in kinetic energy of the HI molecules. The molecules slow down. If the two molecules are not approaching each other with sufficient combined energy, they rebound and separate. The system goes back to the one shown in Figure 12-6. However, if the molecules approach with a large amount of kinetic energy, the situation develops as shown in Figure 12-8.

the corresponding circles on the potential energy diagram. Quite obviously these collisions are not successful ones.

The energy barrier shows the minimum threshold energy, E. Chemists have given E the name **activation energy**. The atomic configuration at the top of the energy barrier is a "molecule" called the **activated complex**. At first, this molecule may seem unusual to you. It has a very short lifetime and gets rid of its high potential energy by breaking apart, forming either the reactants or the products. Either of these atomic arrangements has less potential energy than the activated complex.

Figures 12-6 to 12-10 will help you visualize what happens when two hydrogen iodide molecules react to form hydrogen and iodine. Potential energy is plotted vertically, and the horizontal direction shows the progress of the reaction. The position of the circle in each of these figures represents the potential energy for the entire system. The most favorable geometry for these collisions is shown. This geometry corresponds to the smallest possible value for E in the reaction.

12-6   The Heat of Reaction

The reaction between HI molecules is endothermic. The potential energy or heat content of the products, H_2 and I_2, is greater than the heat content of the reactants. Figure 12-10 shows that the energy change for this reaction is 2.4 kcal per mol of hydrogen formed. The heat of reaction depends only on the energy difference between the reactants and the products of a reaction. The heat of the reaction does not depend on the height of the activation barrier.

Let us reverse our series of pictures. We can trace the reaction between H_2 and I_2 by starting with Figure 12-10 and working back to Figure 12-6. All the ideas we have been discussing would be applicable to this reaction.

$$I_2 \rightleftharpoons 2\,I$$
$$H_2 + 2\,I \rightleftharpoons H_2I_2 \qquad \text{(activated complex)}$$
$$H_2I_2 \rightleftharpoons HI + HI$$

Iodine molecules dissociate, giving iodine atoms. The activated complex forms if the hydrogen molecule and the two iodine atoms collide with enough energy to reach the top of the potential energy barrier.

12-7   Action of Catalysts

Many reactions that take place slowly can be made to take place more rapidly by the introduction of special substances. These substances are called **catalysts**. Unlike ordinary reactants, catalysts are not used up in the reaction. You have seen several examples of catalysts in your laboratory work. The reaction of $C_2O_4^{2-}$ with MnO_4^- is faster after the addition of the catalyst,

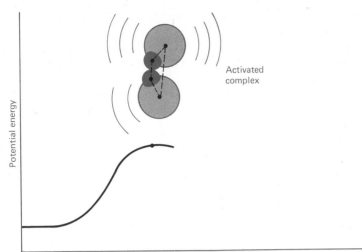

Figure 12-8
The molecular collision involves enough energy to bring the four atoms close enough to form a new molecule, H_2I_2. Chemists call this molecule the activated complex. It is an unusual molecule in that it does not exist for very long. This arrangement of the four atoms has a large amount of potential energy. A large fraction of the kinetic energy that the HI molecules started with has been transformed into potential energy of the H_2I_2 molecule. This molecule can either re-form the reactants, HI and HI, Figure 12-6, or it can form the product molecules, H_2 and 2 I. Go on to Figure 12-9 to see this.

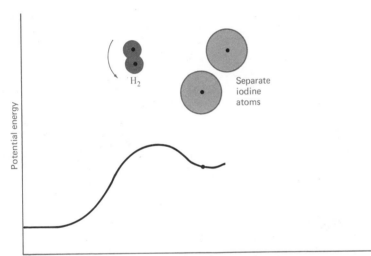

Figure 12-9
If the reaction proceeds, one H_2 molecule and two I atoms form. Some of the high potential energy of the activated complex, H_2I_2, appears as kinetic energy of translation and rotation in H_2 and in 2 I. As the products move apart, they interact less and less. The potential energy level on the right is characteristic of two hydrogen atoms and two iodine atoms arranged as H_2 and 2 I. The potential energy of the system is still very high because of the energy of the two iodine atoms.

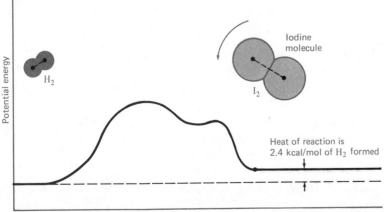

Figure 12-10
The iodine atoms have combined to form an iodine molecule. The potential energy level on the right is characteristic of two hydrogen atoms and two iodine atoms arranged as one H_2 molecule and one I_2 molecule. This level is higher than the initial potential energy level for the system. Almost all the kinetic energy brought into the collision is now in the form of the translation and rotation of the products.

A modern catalytic refinery.

Biocatalysts

Enzymes are excellent examples of catalysts. Although their structure is complex, we can learn the general features of their action without it. The different enzymes that help digest the protein in our food have the same main features. They are large molecules (molar mass 25 000 to 40 000 g), they fold up into a more or less spherical shape, and they have a special slot or pocket on one side that holds the protein. Each enzyme is structured to work on one or a few specific amino acids in the protein chain. Thus several digestive enzymes are needed. We will show an enzyme and a protein by a schematic method. The zigzag line represents the protein chain without showing the atoms specifically. The action goes something like this:

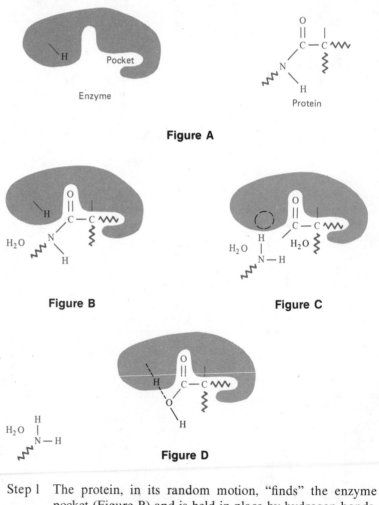

Step 1   The protein, in its random motion, "finds" the enzyme pocket (Figure B) and is held in place by hydrogen bonds.

Step 2   A covalent C—N bond in the main chain is broken and part of the protein is released (Figure C).

Step 3   A water molecule approaches and binds between the protein and the enzyme (Figure D).

Step 4   The H—O bonds are broken to release H^+ and add H to the enzyme.

Step 5   The enzyme-protein complex comes apart. The enzyme is back in its original condition and free to repeat the cycle.

Although there is only a small amount of catalyst present, a new reaction path is provided, the activation energy is lowered, and the reaction rate is increased. A qualitative activation energy diagram looks like this:

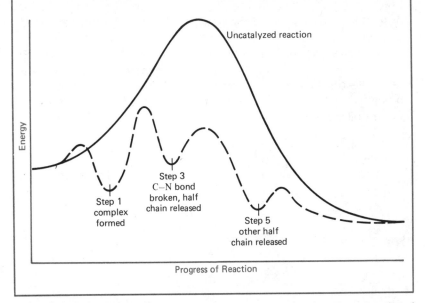

Mn^{2+}. The cupric ion, Cu^{2+}, acts as a catalyst for the reaction between S$_2$O$_8{}^{2-}$ and I$^-$ ions.

Let us go back to the fellow trying to roll bowling balls over a hill. Suppose rain washed away part of the hilltop and somehow made a smooth path at a lower level. The bowler would have an easier time. He would not have to work so hard rolling the bowling ball to the other side of the hill. The newly made path offers a low-energy route. More bowling balls would get to the other side of the hill in a certain period of time. Fewer bowling balls would roll back down the hill. Of course, the bowler may occasionally want to see if he is still strong enough to roll the bowling ball by the first path, over the top of the hill. Both routes are possible. The two routes make it possible for more bowling balls to get to the other side of the hill per unit of time.

We can imagine a similar situation when thinking about catalysts. We add to our model the idea that the catalyst provides a low-energy path from the reactants to the products. More particles can get over the new lower-energy barrier per unit of time. The reaction proceeds at a greater rate. The effect of the catalyst on the activation energy is shown in Figure 12-11. The catalyzed route has a lower activation energy, E_{cat}, than the original, non-catalyzed path. The new reaction path corresponds to a new reaction mechanism. The molecules combine with the catalyst to form a different activated complex. Notice that the activation energy for the reverse reaction is lowered exactly the same amount as for the forward reaction. A catalyst speeds up the reverse reaction just as much as it speeds up the forward reaction. On the other hand, the value for the heat of the reaction does not change when a catalyst is present. This fact is illustrated in Figure 12-11. The energy levels for reactants and products are not changed by the catalyst. The reaction mechanism and the activation energy do change.

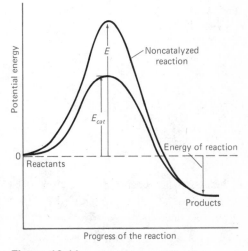

Figure 12-11
Activation energy diagram for catalyzed and noncatalyzed reactions.

Before discussing some important chemical reactions, let us look at the arrangement of energy diagrams shown in Figure 12-12. The curve showing distribution of collision energy and the potential energy diagram are placed next to each other. The two horizontal lines represent the activation energy for the catalyzed and noncatalyzed reactions. The shaded areas indicate the number of collisions having kinetic energy greater than E_{cat} and E. There are many collisions having energy greater than E_{cat}. Only a few collisions have energy greater than E. The catalyzed reaction has a higher reaction rate than the noncatalyzed reaction, since more collisions have the required energy.

It is useful to compare an activation energy diagram to a road map. A map might show several roads over a mountain range. All will let you pass from one side to the other, but only one requires minimum energy. An activation energy diagram could show many paths (many types of collisions) that lead from reactants to products. However, in practice only the one requiring minimum energy is shown.

If the mountain has a tunnel drilled through it, even less energy will be required to get from one side to the other. With a chemical reaction a catalyst can provide a path requiring less energy than is normally required.

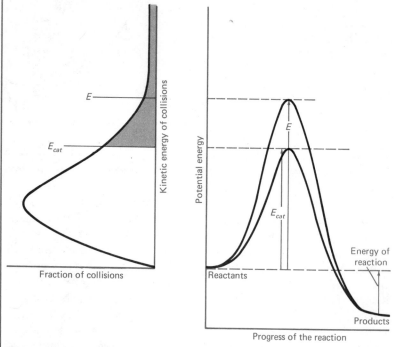

Figure 12-12
Comparison of energy curves for a catalyzed and noncatalyzed reaction path. A larger fraction of collisions have sufficient kinetic energy to reach the top of the lower potential energy hill. *However,* the energy of reaction does not change.

12-8   Some Reaction Mechanisms

A. Molecular Inversion

The reaction between methyl bromide and hydroxide ion is moderately slow at 25 °C.

$$CH_3Br + OH^- \longrightarrow CH_3OH + Br^-$$

An increase in either hydroxide or methyl bromide concentration has the same effect in speeding up the reaction. A collision between one hydroxide ion and one methyl bromide molecule is the rate-determining step in the reaction. The molecular models in

Chemists who specialize in making new compounds are vitally interested in the path of reactions.

Figure 12-13 help us follow the reaction.

Several points are worth mentioning:

   (a) The hydroxide ion approaches one side of the CH_3Br molecule (left side of Figure 12-13). The bromide ion leaves from the opposite side of the CH_3Br molecule (right side of Figure 12-13).

   (b) The potential energy of the activated complex is very high. The atoms have taken up unstable positions during the short lifetime of the activated complex. (Middle of Figure 12-13.)

   (c) The methyl group has been turned inside out in this reaction, like an umbrella in a strong wind. This is the reason the reaction is called an **inversion**. (Compare the drawing of the methyl group on the left with that on the right.)

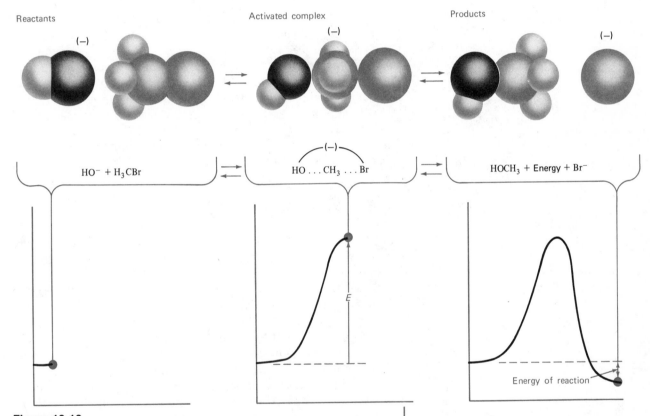

Figure 12-13
The mechanism and potential energy diagram for the reaction $CH_3Br + OH^- \rightleftharpoons CH_3OH + Br^-$.

   This mechanism applies to many reactions. One vibrational motion of the NH_3 molecule is an inversion. The number of times an NH_3 molecule turns inside out is known with great precision, $2.387\ 701\ 293\ 00 \times 10^{10}$ times each second. This vibration is the basis for some very precise measurements of time.

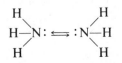

Polymer scientists use chain reactions to make many useful products.

B. Chain Reactions

The reaction between H_2 and I_2 is slow. Rate measurements lead to a reaction mechanism based on one H_2 molecule colliding with two I atoms. You might expect the $H_2 + Cl_2$ reaction to be similar. However, we find the reactions are very different. The hydrogen and chlorine reaction is very fast, almost an explosion. The reaction can be triggered at room temperature by shining light on a mixture of H_2 and Cl_2. The mechanism for this reaction appears to be this set of steps:

$$Cl_2 + light \rightleftharpoons 2\ Cl$$
$$Cl + H_2 \longrightarrow HCl + H$$
$$H + Cl_2 \longrightarrow HCl + Cl$$
$$Cl + H_2 \longrightarrow HCl + H$$
$$H + Cl_2 \longrightarrow HCl + Cl$$

$$many\ H_2 + many\ Cl_2 \longrightarrow many\ HCl$$

As soon as one Cl atom is formed, it sets off a chain reaction. A large number of H_2 and Cl_2 molecules react almost instantaneously. A large amount of energy is liberated in a very short time. The temperature and pressure of the system increase rapidly.

There are many important examples of chain reactions in which very large molecules can be built in a controlled fashion. We will discuss some of these in Chapter 16.

C. Acid Catalysis

In all cases of catalysis the catalyst acts by providing a lower energy path for a reaction. Without the catalyst these paths would not be available. Some step in the new reaction mechanism regenerates the catalyst. One of the most important catalysts is the hydrogen ion, H^+.

Consider now the decomposition of formic acid, HCOOH. This substance decomposes by two reaction paths. We will discuss the noncatalyzed path first. Figure 12-14 shows how this molecule might decompose. If the hydrogen atom attached to carbon migrates over to the OH group, one carbon-oxygen bond can break to give a molecule of water and a molecule of carbon monoxide. This migration, shown in the center drawing, requires a large amount of energy. The activation energy is high. The reaction occurs very slowly.

$$HCOOH \longrightarrow CO + H_2O$$

If sulfuric acid, H_2SO_4, or any other good source of H^+ is added to an aqueous solution of formic acid, bubbles of carbon monoxide form rapidly.

Chemists have a rather clear picture of how H^+ catalyzes the decomposition of HCOOH. The H^+ in the solution makes a new reaction path available. The new reaction mechanism begins with the addition of hydrogen ion to formic acid, as shown in Figure 12-15. The catalyst is consumed first, forming the new species, $HCOOH_2^+$. In this species one of the carbon-oxygen bonds is

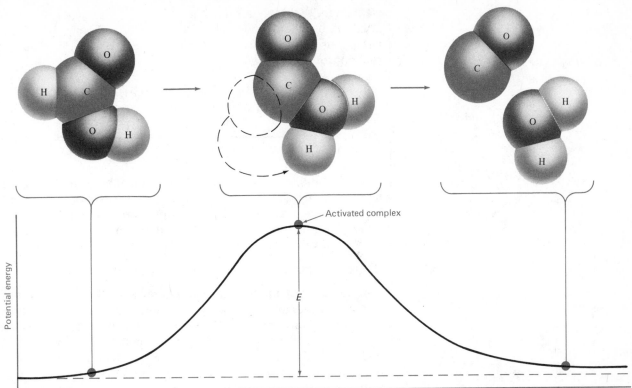

Figure 12-14
Mechanism and activation energy diagram for noncatalyzed decomposition of formic acid.

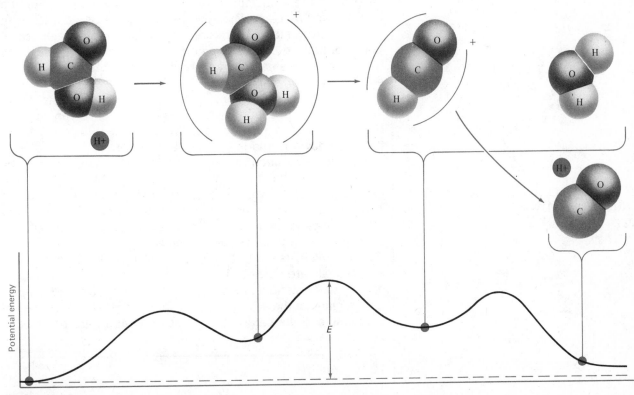

Figure 12-15
Mechanism and activation energy diagram for catalyzed decomposition of formic acid.

weakened. With only a small expenditure of energy, the next reaction can occur, producing HCO^+ and H_2O. Finally, HCO^+ decomposes to produce carbon monoxide (CO) and H^+. This last reaction of the sequence regenerates the catalyst H^+.

$$HCOOH + H^+ \longrightarrow HCOOH_2^+$$
$$HCOOH_2^+ \longrightarrow HCO^+ + H_2O$$
$$HCO^+ \longrightarrow CO + H^+$$
$$\overline{}$$
$$HCOOH \longrightarrow CO + H_2O$$

Each of the steps in this new reaction mechanism is in agreement with the principles that apply to a simple reaction. Each reaction has an activation energy. The overall reaction has a potential energy diagram that is merely a composite of the energy curves for the individual reactions.

D. Other Catalysts

In some reactions the catalyst is a solid substance on whose surface a reactant molecule can be held in a favorable position. The word **adsorption** is used to describe the interaction between the solid and the molecule. When a molecule of another reactant having enough energy reaches the same area on the solid, products form. Metals such as iron, nickel, and platinum act as catalysts for many reactions involving gases. Experimental evidence suggests that the bonds within adsorbed, reactant molecules are weakened or actually broken. The bonds formed between the catalyst and the reactant release enough energy to weaken the bonds in the reactant. The adsorbed molecule or atom exists in a high energy state. Therefore, the second reactant molecule does not have to bring to the collision as much energy as in the noncatalyzed system. Many more collisions would have the energy needed for reaction.

The substances called *enzymes* are important catalysts. There are many enzymes found in living tissue that have very specific catalytic functions. For example, ptyalin in saliva is important for the breakdown of the large starch molecules in our food. This process leads to much smaller molecules which can be utilized by body cells. Pepsin is another important enzyme. It serves as a catalyst for the conversion of proteins to simpler molecules. In 1965 chemists first determined the molecular structure of an enzyme. It appears that the catalytic activity may reside in a rather small portion of the enzyme molecule.

Biochemistry is the branch of chemistry in which living plants and animals are studied. The application of chemical principles and an understanding of molecular structure have been important in many of the advances made in biochemistry. The rates of reactions and the catalysts that speed them up are particularly important.

Catalytic chemists have improved gasolines, drugs, polymers, and many other products by finding better catalysts.

12-9 Review

A simple and effective way of understanding the rates of chemical reactions is provided by the **collision theory**. To change reactants into products, a certain minimum amount of energy is required. This is called the **activation energy**. Colliding molecules must bring enough kinetic energy into a collision to achieve this energy. The molecular grouping temporarily formed is called the **activated complex**.

The collision theory shows that the rate of a reaction can be increased in three ways:

(a) by increasing the number of collisions per unit time by raising the concentration or by raising the temperature.

(b) by increasing the average kinetic energy brought into the collision by raising the temperature.

(c) by providing a different reaction mechanism with lower activation energy by adding a catalyst.

Catalysts provide an alternative reaction mechanism with a second, lower energy path from reactants to products. Catalysts are regenerated at some point in the reaction mechanism. The search for catalysts for chemical reactions is an important area of chemical research. The mechanism of catalysis is not yet understood in most reactions.

A chemical reaction may proceed in a single step, or it may occur in several successive steps. The detailed set of reactions is called the **reaction mechanism**. The rate of a chemical reaction is determined by the slowest, or **rate-determining**, step in the reaction mechanism.

Questions and Problems for Chapter 12

1

The rate of movement of an automobile can be expressed in the units kilometers per hour. In what units would you discuss the rate of

(a) movement of movie film through a projector?
(b) rotation of a motor shaft?
(c) gain of altitude?
(d) consumption of milk by a family?
(e) production of automobiles by an auto assembly plant.

2

Pick the member of each pair having the greater reaction rate. Assume similar conditions within each pair.

(a) Evaporation of gasoline or evaporation of water.
(b) Fresh apples or bananas ripening in a grocery store.
(c) Iron rusting or copper tarnishing.
(d) Solid wax or paper burning

3

Explain (at the molecular level) why an increase in concentration of a reactant may cause an increase in rate of reaction.

4

The rate of a gaseous reaction may increase if the total pressure is increased. State three methods by which the pressure of a gaseous system might be increased.

5

Give two factors that would increase the rate of a reaction and explain why these do increase the rate.

6

Consider two gases, A and B, in a container at room temperature. What effect will the following changes have on the rate of the reaction between these gases?

(a) The pressure is doubled (volume halved).
(b) The number of molecules of gas A is doubled.
(c) The temperature is decreased at constant volume.

7

In an important industrial process for producing ammonia (the Haber process), the overall reaction is

$$N_2(g) + 3 H_2(g) \longrightarrow 2 NH_3(g) + 24,000 \text{ calories}$$

A yield of approximately 98% can be obtained at 200 °C and 1000 atmospheres of pressure. The process makes use of a catalyst which is usually finely divided iron oxides containing small amounts of potassium oxide, K_2O, and aluminum oxide, Al_2O_3.

(a) Is this reaction exothermic or endothermic?
(b) Suggest a reason for the fact that this reaction is generally carried out at a temperature of 500 °C and 350 atmospheres in spite of the fact that the yield under these conditions is only about 30%.
(c) What is the heat of reaction in kilocalories per mole of $NH_3(g)$?
(d) How many grams of hydrogen must react to form 1.60 moles of ammonia?

8

Do you think the equation

$$C_2H_4(g) + 3\,O_2(g) \longrightarrow 2\,CO_2(g) + 2\,H_2O(g)$$

represents the mechanism by which ethylene, C_2H_4, burns? Why?

9

A group of students is preparing a ten-page directory. The pages have been printed and are stacked in ten piles, page by page. The pages must be (1) assembled in order, (2) straightened, and (3) stapled in sets. If three students work together, each performing a different operation, which might be the rate-controlling step? What would be the effect on the overall rate if the first step were changed by ten helpers joining the individual assembling the sheets? What if these ten helpers joined the student working on the second step? The third step?

10

Hydrogen peroxide reacts with hydrogen ion and iodide ion according to this equation:

$$H^+ + I^- + H_2O_2 \longrightarrow H_2O + HOI$$

The mechanism often suggested for this reaction is

$$H^+ + H_2O_2 \longrightarrow H_3O_2^+ \qquad \text{fast}$$

$$H_3O_2^+ + I^- \longrightarrow H_2O + HOI \qquad \text{slow}$$

(a) Satisfy yourself that the addition of these two equations gives the overall equation.
(b) How would you expect the rate to be affected if the I^- concentration is doubled?

11

Describe the life and death of an ordinary, empty water glass. Utilize the concept "threshold energy."

12

Describe three situations at home or at school in which a minimum (or threshold) energy must be supplied before a "reaction" can take place.

13

Explain why food kept in a refrigerator does not spoil as rapidly as the same type of food left on the kitchen counter.

14

An increase in temperature of 10 °C rarely doubles the kinetic energy of particles, and hence the number of collisions is not doubled. Yet, this temperature increase may be enough to double the rate of a slow reaction. How can this be explained?

15

In a collision of particles what is the primary factor that determines whether a reaction will occur?

16

In Figure 12-11 why is kinetic energy decreasing as two HI go up the left side of the barrier and why is kinetic energy increasing as H_2 and I_2 go down the right side? Explain in terms of conservation of energy and also in terms of what is occurring to the various particles in relation to each other.

17

Phosphorus, P_4, exposed to air burns spontaneously to give P_4O_{10}; the heat for this exothermic reaction is 712 kcal per mol of P_4.

(a) Draw an energy diagram for the net reaction, explaining the critical parts of the curve.
(b) How much heat is produced when 12.4 grams of phosphorus burn?

18

Considering that so little energy is required to convert graphite to diamond (see Problem 16, Chapter 11), how do you account for the great difficulty found in the industrial process for accomplishing this?

19

Why does a burning match light a candle?

20

Why is it difficult to "hard-boil" an egg at the top of

Pikes Peak? Is it also difficult to cook scrambled eggs there? Explain.

21

For the reaction $CO + NO_2 \longrightarrow CO_2 + NO$, the activation energy for the forward reaction is known to be 32 kcal/mol.

(a) Calculate the heat of reaction, using values from Table 11-1.
(b) Using the forward activation energy and the heat of reaction, calculate the activation energy for the reverse reaction.
(c) Draw the potential energy diagram for this system, indicating all three energy values.

22

Sketch a potential energy diagram which might represent an endothermic reaction. Label the parts of the curve representing activated complex, activation energy, and net energy absorbed.

23

Draw potential energy diagrams for two reactions that have the same heat of reaction, except that one reaction is fast and the other is slow.

24

Explain why a catalyst increases the rates of chemical reactions the same amount for both the forward and reverse reactions.

25

The reaction of $S_2O_8^{2-}$ with I^- is catalyzed by Cu^{2+} ions. A suggested mechanism involves these steps:

$$2\,Cu^{2+} + 2\,I^- \xrightarrow{fast} 2\,Cu^+ + I_2$$

$$Cu^+ + S_2O_8^{2-} \xrightarrow{slow} CuSO_4^+ + SO_4^{2-}$$

$$Cu^+ + CuSO_4^+ \xrightarrow{fast} 2\,Cu^{2+} + SO_4^{2-}$$

Add these equations to show that Cu^{2+} is not consumed in the overall reaction.

26

Explain why there is danger of explosion where a large amount of dry, powdered, combustible material is allowed to mix with air.

27

For the reaction of marble, $CaCO_3(s)$, with acid,

$$CaCO_3(s) + 2\,H^+ \longrightarrow Ca^{2+} + CO_2(g) + H_2O,$$

compare the rate of reaction when $CaCO_3(s)$ is in the form of large marble chips or in the form of a fine dust.

28

^{226}Ra is a radioactive isotope of radium with a half-life of 1600 years.

(a) Construct a graph of the amount of ^{226}Ra as a function of time. Start with 1.0 gram of ^{226}Ra and show the amount after 1600, 3200, 4800, and 6400 years.
(b) Use your graph to estimate how much ^{226}Ra is present after one year, after ten years, and after 2400 years.

29

One gram of ^{226}Ra emits 3.7×10^{10} alpha particles per second. The nuclear reaction can be written

$$^{226}_{88}Ra \longrightarrow {}^{222}_{86}Rn + {}^{4}_{2}He$$

Calculate an approximate value for Avogadro's number. Compare the number of moles of ^{226}Ra with the total number of alpha particles given off in 1600 years.

30

How many moles of solute are contained in 100 ml of a 2.0 M solution? How many millimoles?

31

What will be the molarity of a solution made by dissolving 80 g of $NaOH$ in enough water to make 1.0 liter of solution?

32

How many moles of solute are needed to make 2.0 liters of a 3.0 M solution?

33

How many moles of common table salt could be obtained by evaporating 100 liters of a 0.00100 M solution of salt?

34

How many moles of $KSCN$ (potassium thiocyanate) are in 5.0 ml of a 0.0020 M solution of this salt?

35

If a solution contains 0.010 mole of solute in 100 ml of solution, what is its concentration?

36

What will be the molarity of a solution made by diluting 100 ml of 3 M $NaCl$ to 600 ml?

37

What will be the molarity of a solution made by diluting 10.0 ml of 0.200 M $Fe(NO_3)_3$ to a final volume of 25 ml?

13

Chemical Equilibrium

In the last chapter the rate of the reaction $2\,HI \longrightarrow H_2 + I_2$ was discussed. Then later in the chapter the rate of the reverse reaction $H_2 + I_2 \longrightarrow 2\,HI$ was considered. The rate of these gas phase reactions can be determined easily because iodine is the only colored substance present. In the first reaction the purple color of iodine vapor becomes more intense as the reaction proceeds; in the second reaction the color decreases in intensity as the I_2 changes to HI. As a reaction takes place, reactants are consumed and their concentrations decrease. Consequently, the rate of the reaction decreases. At the same time concentrations of products increase, and so does the rate of the reverse reaction.

The $2\,HI \longrightarrow H_2 + I_2$ reaction can be followed by direct observation of the color of iodine vapor. The I_2 concentration changes rapidly at first, but soon the color no longer changes. Figures 13-1 and 13-2 represent schematically what happens in each reaction. When observable changes no longer occur in the reacting chemical system, the system is in a **state of equilibrium**. The equilibrium situation raises many interesting questions. How is equilibrium recognized? What is the molecular behavior when a state of equilibrium is reached? What factors change the state of equilibrium? How can an understanding of equilibrium help us control chemical reactions? In this chapter we will seek answers to these questions.

13-1 Recognizing Equilibrium

We have encountered equilibrium earlier in this course. When phase changes were discussed in Chapter 5, the liquid-gas equilibrium that fixes the vapor pressure of a liquid was considered. In Chapter 6 the solubility of a solid in a liquid was interpreted as an equilibrium situation. How is equilibrium recognized? Several experiments will help answer this question.

Experiment 1

When liquid water is placed in an evacuated flask at 25 °C a manometer can be used to follow the changes in gas pressure as some of the water evaporates. At first the pressure increases; but when it reaches 23.8 mmHg, the pressure remains constant as long as the temperature is constant. Since no further change in the system is observed, *the system is said to be at equilibrium.*

Experiment 2

If solid iodine is added to a water-alcohol mixture, a reddish color appears very quickly in the solution near the crystals. Iodine is dissolving. After the solution is stirred for a short time, no further change can be observed. The color of the solution stays constant, and the mass of the iodine crystals no longer changes as long as the temperature is constant. *The system has reached a state of equilibrium.* This experiment is shown in Figure 13-3.

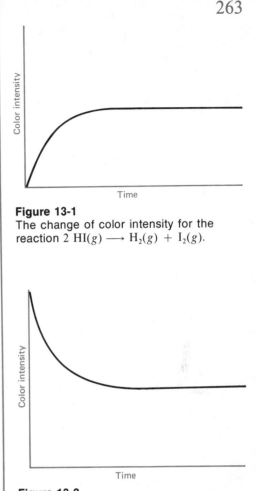

Figure 13-1
The change of color intensity for the reaction $2\ HI(g) \longrightarrow H_2(g)\ +\ I_2(g)$.

Figure 13-2
The change of color intensity for the reaction $H_2(g)\ +\ I_2(g) \longrightarrow 2\ HI(g)$.

Upon addition, solid I_2 begins to dissolve.

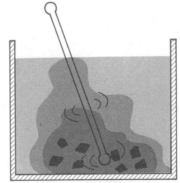

For a time it continues to dissolve.

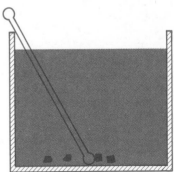

Eventually, no observable changes occur. Equilibrium exists.

Figure 13-3
Iodine dissolving in a stirred mixture of H_2O—alcohol. Equilibrium is recognized by constant color of the solution.

Chemical Equilibrium

Experiment 3

Imagine two glass bulbs, at the same pressure, containing nitrogen dioxide gas. Place the first bulb in an ice bath and the
second in boiling water. Figure 13-4 shows what is observed when
equilibrium is established in each bulb. The gas in the bulb at
0 °C is almost colorless. The gas in the second bulb, at 100 °C, is
reddish-brown. Other experiments show that most of the molecules in the colder bulb have the formula N_2O_4. Since the gas is
almost colorless, N_2O_4 must not absorb visible light. On the other
hand, experiments show that most of the molecules in the warmer
bulb have the formula NO_2. Since the gas is reddish-brown in
color, NO_2 must absorb some visible light. When these bulbs
are moved to a water bath at 25 °C, the color of each sample
changes. Figure 13-5 illustrates what happens. The color in bulb
1 deepens. A chemical change is occurring.

$$\text{bulb 1} \qquad \underset{\text{colorless}}{N_2O_4} \quad \longrightarrow \quad \underset{\text{reddish-brown}}{2\,NO_2}$$

During the same time interval the color in bulb 2 fades. A chemical
change is taking place in this bulb also.

$$\text{bulb 2} \qquad \underset{\text{colorless}}{N_2O_4} \quad \longleftarrow \quad \underset{\text{reddish-brown}}{2\,NO_2}$$

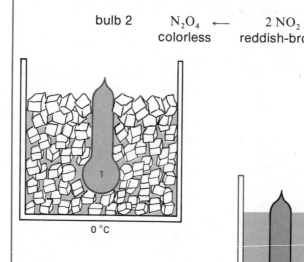

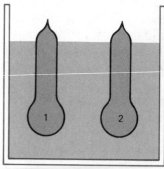

Figure 13-4
The equilibrium reaction $N_2O_4 \rightleftharpoons 2\,NO_2$ at 0 °C and 100 °C.
Figure 13-5
The equilibrium reaction $N_2O_4 \rightleftharpoons 2\,NO_2$ at 25 °C.

The gas color in the two bulbs becomes identical when they reach the same temperature. No further color changes occur. *A new state of equilibrium has been established in each bulb.*

What factors do these three experiments have in common? Are there similarities that help us recognize equilibrium? Yes; here is a list:

(a) Equilibrium occurs only when a constant temperature is maintained.

(b) After the experiment is started, no substances are added to or taken from the system. Such a system is called a **closed system**.

(c) In each experiment some easily measured property, such as pressure or color, changes with time and then reaches a constant value. There are no further changes in the properties of the system.

We can put these observations together in one generalization. *For a closed system at a constant temperature, equilibrium is reached when all properties of the system stay constant.*

13-2 The Dynamic Nature of Equilibrium

The kinetic theory led us to think of the evaporation of a liquid in terms of molecular behavior. Figure 13-6 shows schematically how

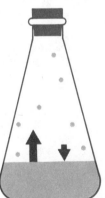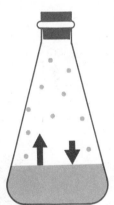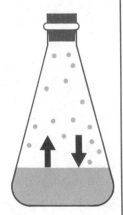

Figure 13-6
Equilibrium vapor pressure is a dynamic balance between evaporation and condensation.

equilibrium is established when water evaporates in a closed system. The size of each arrow indicates the rate at which molecules leave or return to the liquid. At first the gas pressure increases as the number of molecules in the gas phase increases. Soon the pressure reaches a constant value. The number of molecules entering the gas phase each second is the same as the number returning to the liquid. *Equilibrium is reached when there is a dynamic balance between evaporation and condensation.* At equilibrium, molecules continue to move back and forth between the two phases. Evaporation and condensation occur *at the same rate.*

The same explanation helps us understand how equilibrium is established when a crystal of iodine dissolves. Molecular vibration

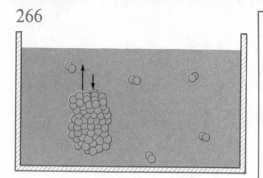

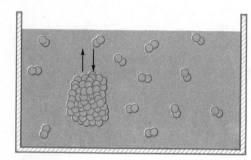

Figure 13-7
Equilibrium solubility is a dynamic balance between dissolving and crystallizing.

and interaction with the solvent tend to dislodge a molecule from the surface of the crystal. The molecule is now free to move throughout the solvent. At first the rate at which molecules leave the crystal is much greater than the rate of their return. As more molecules enter the solution the rate at which they return to the crystal increases. Soon a balance between these rates is reached. Solubility equilibrium is established. Molecules leave the crystal and return to it *at the same rate*. Figure 13-7 shows schematically what takes place in solubility equilibrium.

Now look at the $N_2O_4 - NO_2$ system again. In Figure 13-8 a molecular view of the $N_2O_4 - NO_2$ equilibrium is presented in schematic form. Each molecule of NO_2 is represented by a single circle, and each molecule of N_2O_4 is shown by two circles joined together. The color of the system at equilibrium is suggested by the drawing. The relative concentration for each gas is shown in the right-hand drawings where the labeled pieces are proportional to the number of molecules in the figure.

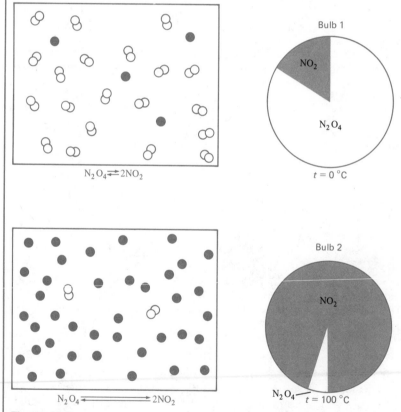

Figure 13-8
The molecular view of the $N_2O_4 \rightleftharpoons 2\,NO_2$ equilibrium at 0 °C and 100 °C.

In the equations arrows of equal length indicate that the system has reached a state of equilibrium. Throughout this discussion the rate of a reaction will be indicated by the length of the arrow. At 0 °C short arrows emphasize that both rates of reaction are low. At 100 °C long arrows indicate that the rates of reaction are high. If both bulbs are transferred to a 25 °C water bath, the faint reddish-brown color in bulb 1 becomes more intense. A chemical reaction is occurring which produces a higher concentration of NO_2. On the other hand, the color in bulb 2 fades rapidly. A chemical reaction takes place which produces a lower concentration of reddish-brown NO_2. How can these results be explained?

Raising the temperature increases the rate of a chemical reaction. The forward and the reverse reactions are faster in bulb 1 when the temperature is changed from 0 °C to 25 °C. The fact that the color becomes more intense means that, initially, the rate of the forward reaction is *increased more* by the temperature change than is the rate of the reverse reaction.

$$N_2O_4 \rightleftharpoons 2\ NO_2$$
colorless   reddish-brown

The net concentration of NO_2 increases. Now there will be more collisions between NO_2 molecules. This causes the rate of the reverse reaction to increase. Soon forward and reverse reaction rates are equal once more, but the rates are greater than they were at 0 °C. Equilibrium is established again.

What happens in bulb 2 when the temperature is lowered from 100 °C to 25 °C? The forward and the reverse reactions in bulb 2 slow down. The fact that the color becomes less intense must mean that the rate of the forward reaction *is decreased more* by the temperature change than is the rate of the reverse reaction.

$$N_2O_4 \rightleftharpoons 2\ NO_2$$
colorless   reddish-brown

The net concentration of NO_2 decreases. As before, the rates of forward and reverse reactions soon become equal and a new state of equilibrium is reached. Figure 13-9 shows the situation in either bulb in the 25 °C water bath.

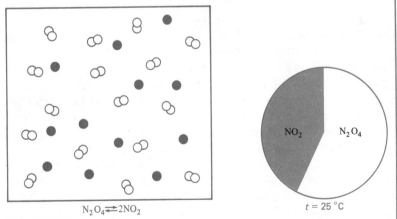

$N_2O_4 \rightleftharpoons 2NO_2$ $t = 25\ °C$

Figure 13-9
The molecular view of the $N_2O_4 \rightleftharpoons 2\ NO_2$ equilibrium at 25 °C.

These examples demonstrate that at the molecular level equilibrium systems are dynamic, not static. Molecules interact continually, changing back and forth from one species to another. *The equality between the rates of the forward and reverse reactions gives the constant properties which we can observe and measure at equilibrium.*

Physicians can determine the effects of some drugs by watching changes in equilibrium concentrations. An example is the treatment of sickle-cell anemia and its effect on oxygen transport.

13-3 Effect of Concentration Changes

The concentration of NO_2 at equilibrium can be changed easily. Raising the temperature increases the NO_2 concentration. Lowering the temperature decreases the NO_2 concentration. What other factors might alter the relative concentrations of reactants and products at equilibrium? In the experiments discussed in Section 13-2 a state of equilibrium is reached when the rates of opposing reactions become equal. Therefore, any factor that changes the rate of one of the reactions involved in the equilibrium may affect the relative concentrations of reactants and products.

In Chapter 12 we saw that concentration, temperature, pressure, and the presence of a catalyst are factors that affect the rate of a reaction. Do these also affect the state of equilibrium? Additional examples will help us decide if there is a regularity.

In Experiment 29 you studied the reaction between ferric ion and thiocyanate ion. The product of the reaction is an ion which has a deep red color. The equilibrium reaction is represented by the equation

$$Fe^{3+} \quad + \quad SCN^- \quad \rightleftharpoons \quad FeSCN^{2+}$$

light yellow   colorless   deep red

Since the $FeSCN^{2+}$ ion is the only highly colored species in the system, the red color of the solution is a direct measure of its concentration. The color of the solution allows us to follow changes in the equilibrium state. What happens when crystals of NH_4SCN are added to the equilibrium system? The SCN^- concentration increases as the crystals dissolve. Moreover, the red color of the solution deepens. The $FeSCN^{2+}$ concentration has increased too. *A new state of equilibrium is attained.* The SCN^- concentration becomes greater, but the chemical reaction uses some, and the final concentration of SCN^- is less than we would calculate.

In the original equilibrium the rate of the reaction between Fe^{3+} and SCN^- is equal to the rate of dissociation of $FeSCN^{2+}$. When NH_4SCN crystals are added, the concentration of SCN^- increases. Because of this the number of collisions between Fe^{3+} and SCN^- goes up. The rate of the forward reaction increases. Then, as more $FeSCN^{2+}$ ions form, the rate of the reverse reaction increases too. A new state of equilibrium is achieved, with SCN^- and $FeSCN^{2+}$ concentrations higher than in the first equilibrium. These changes can occur only if the Fe^{3+} concentration decreases. The schematic diagram in Figure 13-10 illustrates what happens. The arrows are longer in the second diagram, indicating that the rates of the reactions are larger than those represented in the first diagram. However, for each system *the rates of forward and reverse reactions are equal. Each system is at equilibrium.*

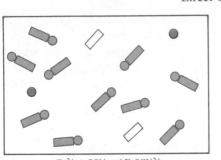

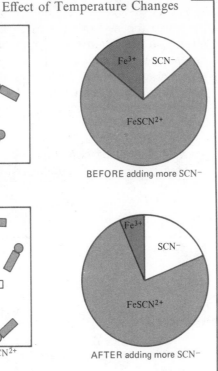

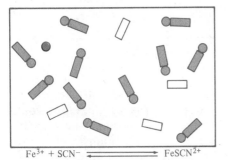

Fe³⁺ + SCN⁻ ⇌ FeSCN²⁺

$Fe^{3+} + SCN^- \rightleftharpoons FeSCN^{2+}$

Figure 13-10
The molecular view of the $Fe^{3+} + SCN^- \rightleftharpoons FeSCN^{2+}$ equilibrium.

EXERCISE 13-1

Sodium chromate, Na_2CrO_4, dissolves in water to give a yellow solution. Sodium dichromate, $Na_2Cr_2O_7$, dissolves in water to give an orange solution. In either reaction the equilibrium equation is

$$2\ CrO_4^{2-} + 2\ H^+ \rightleftharpoons Cr_2O_7^{2-} + H_2O$$

(a) What would happen if you added hydrochloric acid to a solution of sodium chromate?
(b) What would happen if you added $Cr_2O_7^{2-}$ to the solution in part (a)?

13-4 Effect of Temperature Changes

It was shown in Section 13-2 that the concentrations of N_2O_4 and NO_2 at equilibrium are affected by temperature changes. Calorimetric measurements show that the decomposition of N_2O_4 is endothermic. We can include the heat energy in the equilibrium equation:

$$N_2O_4 + 14.1\ kcal \rightleftharpoons 2\ NO_2$$

When energy is added, the equilibrium system is subjected to a change. We observe that the reddish-brown color deepens. This color change means more NO_2 molecules form. Not all the energy added to the system causes a temperature rise. Some of the energy is absorbed by N_2O_4 molecules and is used to break chemical bonds instead of raising the temperature. We added heat energy to raise the temperature, but a chemical reaction occurred in the system, absorbing some of the heat energy. The temperature rises less than expected.

EXERCISE 13-2

How would the addition of more energy affect the amount of NH_3 at equilibrium in this reaction?

$$N_2(g) + 3\ H_2(g) \rightleftharpoons 2\ NH_3(g) + 22\ \text{kcal}$$

13-5 Effect of Pressure Changes

In Section 13-3 the effect of changing the concentration of one component in an equilibrium system was discussed. What would happen if the concentrations of all components were altered? This can most easily be done with a gas phase equilibrium by changing the volume of the system. The N_2O_4—NO_2 equilibrium can be our example.

$$N_2O_4(g) \rightleftharpoons 2\ NO_2(g)$$

A sudden decrease in volume by a factor of two doubles the partial pressure of each gas. We might expect the color to deepen because the molecules are crowded closer together. When this experiment is carried out, the gas becomes darker but not twice as dark. This means that the concentration of NO_2 has increased but not doubled. Some NO_2 molecules have reacted to form N_2O_4. The balanced equation shows that two moles of NO_2 react to form one of N_2O_4. This means there are fewer molecules per liter, producing less gas pressure. The total pressure in the system decreases as N_2O_4 forms. We tried to raise the pressure by decreasing the volume. Chemical reaction occurred in the system, so that the total number of molecules decreased. At equilibrium the pressure is then not quite as large as the volume change alone would have made it.

A change in pressure does not always affect an equilibrium state. Look at the H_2—I_2—HI equilibrium once more:

$$H_2(g) + I_2(g) \rightleftharpoons 2\ HI(g)$$

Decreasing the volume increases the partial pressure of each gas. However, any chemical change in this system does not alter the partial pressure of the gases, because two moles of reactants form two moles of products. The stress caused by decreasing the volume cannot be relieved by a chemical reaction, in either the forward or reverse direction. Consequently, in any equilibrium system where the total number of molecules stays the same during chemical reaction, any volume change we make causes the expected pressure change.

EXERCISE 13-3

What happens in these gas phase equilibria if the volume of each system is increased by a factor of two?

$$PCl_3(g) + Cl_2(g) \rightleftharpoons PCl_5(g)$$
$$2\ NO(g) \rightleftharpoons N_2(g) + O_2(g)$$
$$4\ NH_3(g) + 5\ O_2(g) \rightleftharpoons 4\ NO(g) + 6\ H_2O(g)$$

13-6   Effect of a Catalyst on Equilibrium

You have seen in your laboratory work that Cu^{2+} functions as a catalyst, increasing the rate of reaction between I^- and $S_2O_8{}^{2-}$. In Section 12-8 other examples of catalysis were discussed. Chemists have found in many different experiments that addition of a catalyst has no effect on the equilibrium concentrations of reactants or products. At first this may be surprising. However, if you had determined product concentrations in the I^-—$S_2O_8{}^{2-}$ reaction, with and without a catalyst, you would have found the equilibrium states were the same. Why is this? Look back at Figure 12-12, which shows the activation energy diagram for a catalyzed reaction. A catalyst speeds up a reaction by providing a low-energy reaction path from reactants to products. At the same time this low-energy path becomes available for the reverse reaction. Both the forward and the reverse reaction rates increase by the same amount. Because of this situation, *a catalyst produces no net change in the equilibrium system.* The system reaches equilibrium much more rapidly when a catalyst is present, but the equilibrium concentrations of reactants and products are not changed.

13-7   Le Châtelier's Principle: A Regularity

We have seen that equilibrium is attained in a chemical system when the rates of opposing reactions become equal. Anything that changes the rate of either reaction in the equilibrium system may affect the equilibrium concentrations. A regularity first proposed by a French chemist, Henry Louis Le Châtelier, helps us to predict whether the concentrations of reactants or products are favored by some change.

Le Châtelier studied the effects in a large number of chemical equilibria when temperature, pressure, or concentration was altered. The regularity that he proposed can be stated this way:

If a closed system at equilibrium is subjected to a change, processes occur that tend to counteract that change.

This generalization has been found to be applicable to such a large number of systems that it is now called **Le Châtelier's prin-**

Chemical engineers use Le Châtelier's principle to maximize production of the desired substance or reduce an unwanted material.

Chemical Equilibrium

ciple. Table 13-1 summarizes the different systems we have discussed.

TABLE 13-1

An Important Regularity, Le Châtelier's Principle

Reaction	Change	Reaction Behavior	Final Result at New Equilibrium
$Fe^{3+} + SCN^- \rightleftharpoons FeSCN^{2+}$	Add SCN^-.	The concentration of $FeSCN^{2+}$ increases, using up some Fe^{3+} and some SCN^-.	The concentration of SCN^- is lower than the sum of original plus added concentration.
$N_2O_4 + 14.1 \text{ kcal} \rightleftharpoons 2 NO_2$	Add heat energy.	Color of gas darkens. Some N_2O_4 decomposes to NO_2, absorbing energy.	The temperature is lower than expected.
$N_2O_4(g) \rightleftharpoons 2 NO_2(g)$	Increase pressure by reducing volume.	Color darkens but some N_2O_4 decomposes to NO_2, absorbing energy.	Pressure is lower than expected from the volume change. Color less dark.
$H_2(g) + I_2(g) \rightleftharpoons 2 HI(g)$	Increase pressure by reducing volume.	Both rates increase equally. Total number of molecules is constant.	Pressure is the pressure expected for the volume change.
Any reaction at equilibrium	Add catalyst.	Equilibrium state remains the same but is reached more rapidly.	A catalyst does not affect equilibrium concentrations.

13-8 The Synthesis of Ammonia by the Haber Process

The principles we have been discussing can be applied to some large-scale industrial processes. For example, nitrogen compounds are needed for fertilizers, explosives, dyes, and plastics. There is an almost inexhaustible supply of nitrogen in the atmosphere, but most plants and animals cannot use nitrogen gas directly. It must be converted from the element N_2, **free nitrogen**, to some chemical compound, in which it is called **fixed nitrogen**. The two most important industrial forms of fixed nitrogen are ammonia gas and nitric acid. From these a wide range of nitrogen compounds can be made.

In the early years of this century nearly two thirds of the world's supply of fixed nitrogen came from nitrate deposits in Chile. Huge as the Chilean nitrate deposits were, scientists predicted that the world's requirement of nitrogen compounds for fertilizers and for explosives would soon exceed the supply. It was essential that an economical method be developed to convert atmospheric nitrogen into a compound such as NH_3 or NO_2. Fritz Haber, a German scientist, successfully developed a process by which atmospheric nitrogen is converted into ammonia:

$$N_2 + 3\ H_2 \rightleftharpoons 2\ NH_3 + 22\ \text{kcal}$$

The formation of NH_3 represents a decrease in total moles of gas from 4 moles to 2 moles. Therefore, we know from Le Châtelier's principle that high pressure would increase the relative amount of NH_3 at equilibrium. The reaction to form NH_3 is exothermic. From Le Châtelier's principle we can readily see that a high temperature favors the decomposition of NH_3. Low temperature favors formation of NH_3.

But are these conditions practical? Reaction rates are low at low temperatures. A compromise is needed. Low temperature favors NH_3 formation. High temperature is necessary for a satisfactory reaction rate. The compromise used for the industrial process involves an intermediate temperature near 500 °C. Even then the success of the process depends upon the presence of a suitable catalyst to achieve a reasonable reaction rate.

Another compromise is needed in deciding on the pressure conditions. It is expensive to build high-pressure equipment. A pressure of about 350 atmospheres is used. Yet with these conditions, 350 atmospheres and 500 °C, only about 30 percent of the reactants are converted to NH_3. Ammonia is removed from the mixture by liquefying it under conditions at which N_2 and H_2 remain gases. The unreacted N_2 and H_2 are then recycled until the conversion to NH_3 is very high.

Almost all the nitrogen compounds that are used today are derived from NH_3, which is made by the Haber process.

13-9 Production of Diamonds from Graphite

Chemists have recognized since 1880 one set of conditions needed to convert graphite to diamond. In 1955 this conversion was accomplished. Now synthetic diamonds are made for industrial use. The equilibrium that we must consider can be written

$$C\ (\text{graphite}) + 0.45\ \text{kcal} \rightleftharpoons C\ (\text{diamond})$$

The density of diamond is greater than the density of graphite. This means the molar volume of diamond is less than the molar volume of graphite. Therefore, high pressure would favor formation of diamond. Since the reaction is endothermic, adding heat would increase the amount of diamond produced. At the present stage of development the commercial production of diamond requires temperatures near 2000 °C and pressures in the range of 50 000 to 100 000 atmospheres. Even under these conditions catalysts are needed to obtain a useful rate. Metals such as chromium, iron, and platinum serve as catalysts. Although most diamonds formed by this process are not gemlike in appearance, they are very valuable for cutting and grinding operations. One-carat gem stones have been produced, but as of 1975 they were more expensive than natural diamonds of like quality.

World diamond production, 1973
9 metric tons mined
9 metric tons man-made

1 inch

Synthetic diamonds
about 1 carat

13-10   The Equilibrium Constant

In the laboratory you studied the reaction

$$Fe^{3+} + SCN^- \rightleftharpoons FeSCN^{2+}$$

From the red color of the solution you estimated the concentration of $FeSCN^{2+}$. We will use square brackets to mean concentration. For example, **[FeSCN^{2+}]** is the chemist's shorthand way of saying "the concentration of $FeSCN^{2+}$ in moles per liter." After calculating values for [Fe^{3+}] and [SCN$^-$], you combined these three concentration terms in various ways and found that the ratio

$$\frac{[FeSCN^{2+}]}{[Fe^{3+}] \times [SCN^-]}$$

was approximately constant. Look back at the equilibrium reaction. You can see that the concentration of the *product*, $FeSCN^{2+}$, appears in the numerator. The concentrations of the *reactants* are multiplied, [Fe^{3+}] × [SCN$^-$], and are placed in the denominator. Arranging the concentrations this way gives a constant. Even though the concentrations of these species may vary a great deal, this ratio does not vary appreciably as long as the temperature is held constant. You may have wondered why the reciprocal of the ratio was not used. It too gives a constant. The decision was a matter of choice. Chemists have agreed to use the ratio with concentrations of products in the numerator and with concentrations of reactants in the denominator.

Accurate data on the H_2—I_2—HI system at equilibrium are shown in Table 13-2. Concentration units are moles per liter. These data can be used to calculate values for various combinations of concentrations found at equilibrium in the system

$$2\ HI(g) \rightleftharpoons H_2(g) + I_2(g)$$

The results are shown in Table 13-3. Two of the combinations of terms do not give constant values. The other set gives very good results.

TABLE 13-2

Equilibrium Concentrations for
HI, H_2, and I_2 at 423 °C

Experiment Number	[HI]	[H$_2$]	[I$_2$]
1	17.7 × 10^{-3}	1.83 × 10^{-3}	3.13 × 10^{-3}
2	16.5 × 10^{-3}	2.91 × 10^{-3}	1.71 × 10^{-3}
3	13.5 × 10^{-3}	4.56 × 10^{-3}	0.74 × 10^{-3}
4	3.53 × 10^{-3}	0.48 × 10^{-3}	0.48 × 10^{-3}
5	8.41 × 10^{-3}	1.14 × 10^{-3}	1.14 × 10^{-3}

Values in experiments 1, 2, and 3 were obtained by heating H_2 and I_2. Values in experiments 4 and 5 were obtained by heating HI.

TABLE 13-3
Values for Various Ratios from
Data in Table 13-2

Experiment Number	$\dfrac{[H_2][I_2]}{[HI]}$	$\dfrac{[H_2][I_2]}{[HI]^2}$	$\dfrac{[H_2][I_2]}{2[HI]}$
1	3.24×10^{-4}	1.83×10^{-2}	1.62×10^{-4}
2	3.02×10^{-4}	1.83×10^{-2}	1.51×10^{-4}
3	2.50×10^{-4}	1.85×10^{-2}	1.25×10^{-4}
4	0.65×10^{-4}	1.85×10^{-2}	0.32×10^{-4}
5	1.55×10^{-4}	1.84×10^{-2}	0.77×10^{-4}
	ratio not constant	ratio constant	ratio not constant

We can write

$$\frac{[H_2][I_2]}{[HI]^2} = \text{a constant} = 1.84 \times 10^{-2} \text{ (at 423 °C)}$$

This ratio is the product of the equilibrium concentrations of hydrogen and iodine, the substances produced in the reaction

$$[H_2] \times [I_2]$$

divided by the square of the concentration of the reacting substance

$$[HI]^2$$

In this ratio the power to which we raise the concentration of each substance is equal to its coefficient in the balanced chemical equation. Perhaps this may be clearer to you if we write the chemical equation in a slightly different way.

$$HI + HI \rightleftharpoons H_2 + I_2$$

Then our constant ratio has the form

$$\frac{[H_2][I_2]}{[HI][HI]} = \frac{[H_2][I_2]}{[HI]^2}$$

13-11 The Law of Chemical Equilibrium

These observations and many others like them lead to the generalization known as the **law of chemical equilibrium**. Consider the general reaction

$$aA + bB \rightleftharpoons eE + fF$$

Technicians help determine equilibrium constants so that engineers can calculate the maximum yield under a given set of conditions.

Chemical Equilibrium

When equilibrium is established, a simple relation always exists between the concentrations of products, [E] and [F], and the concentrations of reactants, [A] and [B]:

$$\frac{[E]^e\,[F]^f}{[A]^a\,[B]^b} = K \text{ (a constant at a given temperature)}$$

Some more examples may help. Table 13-4 lists some chemical reactions. The equilibrium law expression is given for each reaction.

TABLE 13-4
Some Equilibrium Constants

Reaction	Equilibrium Law Expression	K, at Stated Temperature	
$Ag^+ + 2\,NH_3 \rightleftharpoons Ag(NH_3)_2^+$	$K = \dfrac{[Ag(NH_3)_2^+]}{[Ag^+][NH_3]^2}$	1.7×10^7	25 °C
$N_2O_4(g) \rightleftharpoons 2\,NO_2(g)$	$K = \dfrac{[NO_2]^2}{[N_2O_4]}$	8.3×10^{-1}	55 °C
$2\,HI(g) \rightleftharpoons H_2(g) + I_2(g)$	$K = \dfrac{[H_2]\,[I_2]}{[HI]^2}$	1.84×10^{-2}	423 °C
$HSO_4^- \rightleftharpoons H^+ + SO_4^{2-}$	$K = \dfrac{[H^+][SO_4^{2-}]}{[HSO_4^-]}$	1.3×10^{-2}	25 °C
$CH_3COOH \rightleftharpoons H^+ + CH_3COO^-$	$K = \dfrac{[H^+][CH_3COO^-]}{[CH_3COOH]}$	1.8×10^{-5}	25 °C

There are several points in this table that should be emphasized. First, K may be a large number. It may be a small number. Only through experiments can we know the numerical value for K. Second, each substance must be present at equilibrium. If this condition were not satisfied, one of the concentration terms in the expression for the equilibrium constant would be equal to zero. K may be small, but it is never equal to zero.

What does the numerical value for K tell us? If K is large, either the numerator in the equilibrium expression must be large or the denominator must be small. Either way, at equilibrium there is a high concentration of products relative to reactants. A small value for K means the opposite. At equilibrium there is a high concentration of reactants relative to products. Whenever you see a numerical value for an equilibrium constant, K, think of it this way:

A large value for K means products are favored at equilibrium.
A small value for K means reactants are favored at equilibrium.

13-12 Special Cases of Equilibrium Constants

For the reaction

$$H_2O \rightleftharpoons H^+ + OH^-$$

the equilibrium expression would be written

$$K = \frac{[H^+][OH^-]}{[H_2O]}$$

The very low conductivity of water provides evidence that only a small fraction of the water molecules form ions. Thus the concentration of water has essentially a constant value fixed by its density and molar mass. It is convenient to combine K and $[H_2O]$ to define a new constant, K_w.

$$K_w = [H^+][OH^-] = K \times [H_2O]$$

Convince yourself that the concentration of water is approximately constant by completing Exercise 13-4.

EXERCISE 13-4

a) Water has a density of one gram per milliliter. Calculate the concentration of water in moles per liter in pure water.
b) Now calculate the concentration of water in 0.10 M aqueous solution of acetic acid, CH_3COOH, assuming each molecule of CH_3COOH occupies the same volume as one molecule of H_2O.

The same kind of argument applies to the reaction

$$Cu(s) + 2\ Ag^+ \rightleftharpoons 2\ Ag(s) + Cu^{2+}$$

Chemists have found it convenient to write the equilibrium law expression this way

$$K = \frac{[Cu^{2+}]}{[Ag^+]^2}$$

You might have expected the expression

$$K' = \frac{[Cu^{2+}]\ [Ag]^2}{[Cu]\ [Ag^+]^2}$$

The concentration terms for solid Cu and solid Ag are combined with the equilibrium constant K' somewhat as the concentration of H_2O "disappeared" in the previous example. The concentration of a solid is fixed by its density. As long as the temperature and pressure are kept constant, the concentration of a solid does not change.

Whenever an equilibrium system includes water as the solvent or a solid like Cu or Ag, concentration terms for these substances do not appear in the equilibrium law expression. Some additional examples are given in Table 13-5.

TABLE 13-5
More Special Cases of Equilibrium Constants

Reaction	Equilibrium Expression	K at 25 °C
$Cu(s) + 2\ Ag^+ \rightleftharpoons 2\ Ag(s) + Cu^{2+}$	$K = \dfrac{[Cu^{2+}]}{[Ag^+]^2}$	2×10^{15}
$Cu(s) + Cu^{2+} \rightleftharpoons 2\ Cu^+$	$K = \dfrac{[Cu^+]^2}{[Cu^{2+}]}$	1×10^{-6}
$AgCl(s) \rightleftharpoons Ag^+ + Cl^-$	$K_{sp} = [Ag^+][Cl^-]$	1.7×10^{-10}
$H_2O \rightleftharpoons H^+ + OH^-$	$K_w = [H^+][OH^-]$	1.0×10^{-14}
$AgI(s) \rightleftharpoons Ag^+ + I^-$	$K_{sp} = [Ag^+][I^-]$	8.5×10^{-17}

When silver chloride dissolves in water, silver ions, Ag^+, and chloride ions, Cl^-, are found in the solution in equilibrium with the solid AgCl. The concentrations of these species, Ag^+ and Cl^-, are the ones which fix the equilibrium solubility. The equilibrium equation which represents AgCl dissolving in water is

$$AgCl(s) \rightleftharpoons Ag^+ + Cl^-$$

The equilibrium expression has the form

$$K = \frac{[Ag^+][Cl^-]}{[AgCl]}$$

Since AgCl is a solid, we can change this equation to the form

$$K \times [AgCl] = K_{sp} = [Ag^+][Cl^-]$$

Similarly, for $PbCl_2$ we write

$$PbCl_2(s) \rightleftharpoons Pb^{2+} + 2\ Cl^-$$
$$K_{sp} = [Pb^{2+}][Cl^-]^2$$

Solubility equilibrium expressions are given a special name, the **solubility product**. The symbol K_{sp} is used. A low value of K_{sp} means the concentrations of ions are low at equilibrium. Consequently, a low value for K_{sp} must mean that the solubility is very low. Some K_{sp} values are given in Table 13-6.

TABLE 13-6
Some Solubility Products at 25 °C

Compound	K_{sp}	Compound	K_{sp}
AgCl	1.7×10^{-10}	$SrCrO_4$	3.6×10^{-5}
AgBr	5.0×10^{-13}	$BaCrO_4$	8.5×10^{-11}
AgI	8.5×10^{-17}	$PbCrO_4$	2×10^{-16}
$AgBrO_3$	5.4×10^{-5}		
$AgIO_3$	3.1×10^{-8}	$CaSO_4$	2.4×10^{-5}
		$SrSO_4$	7.6×10^{-7}
		$PbSO_4$	1.3×10^{-8}
		$BaSO_4$	1.5×10^{-9}
		$RaSO_4$	4×10^{-11}

EXERCISE 13-5

Write the equation for the dissolving of calcium sulfate, $CaSO_4$. Write the solubility product expression.

EXERCISE 13-6

Write the equation for the dissolving of silver chromate, Ag_2CrO_4. Write the solubility product expression. Silver chromate dissolves to give Ag^+ and CrO_4^{2-} ions.

EXERCISE 13-7

Compare the K_{sp} values for AgCl, AgBr, and AgI. Which of these compounds is most soluble in water? Which is least soluble?

13-13 Calculation of the Solubility of Silver Chloride in Water

Suppose we wish to know how much AgCl will dissolve in one liter of water at 25 °C. Find the numerical value of K_{sp} in Table 13-6.

$$K_{sp} = [Ag^+][Cl^-] = 1.7 \times 10^{-10}$$

Silver chloride dissolves until the concentrations of silver ions and chloride ions increase enough to make their product equal to 1.7×10^{-10}.

We can designate the solubility of AgCl in water by the symbol s. This symbol, s, equals the number of moles of solid AgCl that dissolve to make one liter of saturated solution. If s moles of AgCl dissolve, s moles of Ag^+ and s moles of Cl^- are produced in one liter.

$$[Ag^+] = [Cl^-] = s \text{ moles/liter}$$

Substituting into the K_{sp} expression, we can calculate the value for s, the solubility of AgCl.

$$K_{sp} = [Ag^+][Cl^-] = s \times s$$
$$K_{sp} = s^2 = 1.7 \times 10^{-10}$$
$$s = \sqrt{1.7 \times 10^{-10}} = 1.3 \times 10^{-5} \text{ mole/liter}$$

AgCl is not very soluble. Only 0.000 013 mole of AgCl dissolves in one liter of water at 25 °C.

EXERCISE 13-8

Calculate the solubility, in moles per liter, of calcium sulfate in water, using the solubility product given in Table 13-6.

13-14   The Factors Which Determine Equilibrium

Why does one reaction favor reactants and another reaction favor products? What factors cause sodium chloride to have a large solubility in water and silver chloride to have a low solubility? Why does equilibrium favor the reaction of oxygen with iron to form Fe_2O_3 but not the reaction of oxygen with gold? As scientists, we cannot help wondering what factors determine the conditions at equilibrium.

This is the activity of science we called "wondering why." Perhaps looking at a familiar situation will help us find an explanation. Figure 13-11 shows a station wagon being driven down a

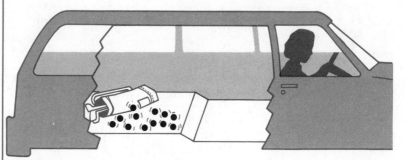

Figure 13-11
Golf balls rolling on the floor of a station wagon.

smooth road. A golf bag has been thrown into the rear of the station wagon. Unfortunately, the ball pocket is open. All the golf balls have spilled out onto the floor. Because the floor has a step in it, the golf balls tend to roll to the lower level spontaneously. As each golf ball does this, its potential energy becomes kinetic energy. Finally, the kinetic energy is dissipated as heat energy on the floor of the station wagon. Now the golf balls lie at rest at the lower floor level.

This situation is similar to the chemical change in a spontaneous, exothermic reaction. The reactants, with high heat content, react spontaneously to form products with lower heat content. As each molecular reaction occurs, the excess heat content becomes kinetic energy. As the product molecules collide with other molecules, this energy is dissipated in the form of heat energy. The comparison of a chemical reaction to golf balls rolling downhill is illustrated in Figure 13-12.

Let us list the similarities.

(a) There are two states of each system.

	Initial State		Final State
Golf balls:	on upper level	$\longrightarrow$	on lower level
Reaction:	reactants	$\longrightarrow$	Reaction products

(b) The potential energy of the initial state is higher than the potential energy of the final state.

	Initial State	*Final State*
Golf balls:	high potential energy	⟶ low potential energy
Reaction:	high heat content	⟶ low heat content

(c) As the change from initial state to final state proceeds, the form of the energy changes.

	Initial State	*Final State*
Golf balls:	potential energy	⟶ kinetic energy, and then heat
Reaction:	heat content	⟶ molecular kinetic energy, and then heat

(d) The changes from initial to final state proceed spontaneously toward lowest potential energy. Both systems "roll down" an energy hill.

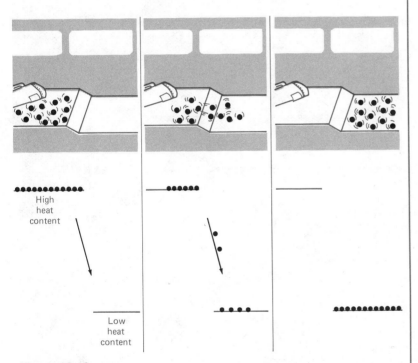

High heat content

Low heat content

Figure 13-12
Comparison of a chemical reaction *to golf balls rolling downhill.*

Is there a useful "regularity" that we can see here? Golf balls always roll downhill spontaneously. Perhaps chemical reactions always move spontaneously in the direction of minimum energy.

This proposal leads us to expect that a reaction will take place if the products have lower heat content than the reactants. We usually find this to be true, especially for reactions which release a large amount of heat.

There are two serious difficulties with our explanation. (Remember, "cylindrical objects burn.") Some endothermic reactions proceed spontaneously. For example, water absorbs heat energy when evaporation occurs. When ammonium chloride dissolves in water, the solution becomes cooler. Again, heat energy is absorbed. In both examples reactions spontaneously "move up an energy hill."

An even more serious difficulty faces us. Spontaneous chemical reactions do not go to completion. Even if a reaction is exothermic, it proceeds only to the equilibrium state.

In our golf-ball analogy "equilibrium" is reached when all the golf balls are on the lower level. This suggests *all* reactant molecules would be converted to products. But such is not the case.

We need to alter our proposed explanation. A new analogy that agrees with the behavior of chemical reactions is needed. How should the golf-ball analogy be changed to bring it into better accord with the experimental facts? Here is a possible view.

Suppose the station wagon is driven down a bumpy road. The situation is shown in Figure 13-13.

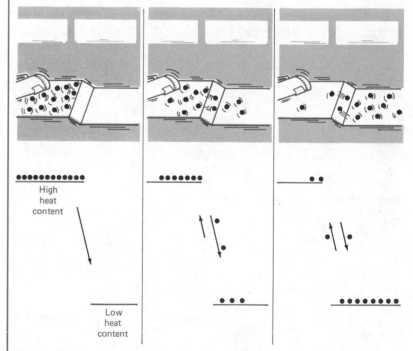

Figure 13-13
Golf balls rolling on the floor of a station wagon *driving on a bumpy road*. The thermal energy drives some molecules "uphill."

Now the golf balls are shaken and jostled about. They roll around and collide with each other. Every now and then one of the golf balls accumulates enough energy to return to the upper level of the station wagon floor. Of course, any golf ball that is bounced up tends to roll back down to the lower level a little later. As this bumpy ride continues, a state is reached in which golf balls are being jostled up to the higher level at the same rate they are falling down to the lower level. Then "equilibrium" exists. Some of the golf balls are on the lower level and some on the upper level. Since the rate of rolling up equals the rate of rolling down, a dynamic balance exists.

The new analogy solves the problem of the simpler "golf balls roll downhill" picture. The bumpy road model contains a new feature that gives a basis for explaining the spontaneity of some endothermic reactions. What happens if the road becomes smoother? The "jostling up" reaction is less favored. The equilibrium conditions change to favor golf balls on the lower level.

Think of a chemical reaction again. What feature in a reacting chemical system corresponds to the jostling of the bumpy road in our analogy? It is the *temperature*. At any temperature except absolute zero there is a constant random jostling of the molecules. Some molecules have low kinetic energies. Some have high kinetic energies. Occasionally some molecules will get enough energy to "roll uphill" to less stable molecular forms. We encountered a number of examples in the preceding chapter in our discussion of reaction rates. At low temperature very few collisions involved enough energy to reach the top of the activation energy barrier. Increasing the temperature increased the random jostling. The rate of chemical reaction increased.

Now we have an analogy that aids us in understanding chemical reactions and equilibrium. Consider the following features of chemical reactions:

(a) *Chemical reactions proceed spontaneously to approach the equilibrium state.*

(b) *One factor that fixes the equilibrium state is the energy. Equilibrium tends to favor the state of lowest energy.*

(c) *The other factor that fixes the equilibrium state is the randomness implied by the temperature. Equilibrium tends to favor the state of greatest randomness.*

(d) *The equilibrium state is a compromise between these two factors: minimum energy and maximum randomness. At very low temperatures, energy tends to be the more important factor. Then equilibrium favors the molecular substances with the lowest heat content. At very high temperatures randomness becomes more important. Then equilibrium favors a random distribution among reactants and products without regard for potential energy differences.*

13-15   Review

For a closed system at a uniform temperature chemical equilibrium is recognized by the constant properties of the system. Chemical equilibrium is a dynamic state in which the rates of the forward and reverse reactions are equal.

Any condition that changes the rates of the reactions involved in the equilibrium system may affect the concentrations of the reactants or products. An important regularity, *Le Châtelier's principle,* serves as a qualitative guide in predicting how the state of equilibrium is affected when one of the equilibrium conditions is altered:

If a closed system at equilibrium is subjected to a change, processes occur that tend to counteract that change.

The quantitative aspects of chemical equilibrium are expressed in the *law of chemical equilibrium.* The equilibrium law expression has the form

$$K = \frac{[E]^e\ [F]^f}{[A]^a\ [B]^b}$$

for the chemical reaction

$$aA + bB \rightleftharpoons eE + fF$$

A special form of the equilibrium expression, K_{sp}, is useful for solubility calculations.

There are two factors that determine the state of equilibrium. One factor is the energy. *Equilibrium tends to favor the state of lowest energy.* The other factor is the randomness implied by the temperature. *Equilibrium tends to favor the state of greatest randomness.*

The equilibrium state results from a *balance* between these two factors: *minimum energy* and *maximum randomness.*

Questions and Problems for Chapter 13

1

Sugar is added to a cup of coffee until no more sugar will dissolve. Does the addition of another spoonful of sugar increase the rate at which the sugar molecules leave the crystal phase and enter the liquid phase? Will the sweetness of the liquid be increased by this addition? Explain.

2

Is equilibrium established in a fire burning in a fireplace? Explain.

3

What, specifically, is "equal" in a chemical reaction that has attained a state of equilibrium?

4

One drop of water may or may not establish a state of vapor pressure equilibrium when placed in a closed bottle. Explain.

5

Why are chemical equilibria referred to as "dynamic"?

6

The following chemical equation represents the reaction between hydrogen and chlorine to form hydrogen chloride:

$$H_2(g) + Cl_2(g) \rightleftharpoons 2\ HCl(g) + 44.0\ kcal$$

(a) List four important pieces of information conveyed by this equation.

(b) What are three important areas of interest concerning this reaction for which no information is indicated?

7

Each of the following systems has come to equilibrium:

(a) What will be the effect of an increase in pressure on each of the systems? (Increase in pressure is caused by a volume reduction.)

(b) What will be the effect on the equilibrium concentration of each substance in the system (increase, decrease, or no change) when the listed reagent is added?

Reaction
(1) $C_2H_6(g) \rightleftharpoons H_2(g) + C_2H_4(g)$
(2) $CO(g) + \frac{1}{2}O_2(g) \rightleftharpoons CO_2(g) + \text{heat}$
(3) $Cu^{2+}(aq) + 4\ NH_3(aq) \rightleftharpoons Cu(NH_3)_4{}^{2+}(aq)$
(4) $PbSO_4(s) + H^+(aq) \rightleftharpoons Pb^{2+}(aq) + HSO_4{}^-(aq)$
(5) $Ag^+(aq) + Cl^-(aq) \rightleftharpoons AgCl(s)$

Added Reagent
(1) $H_2(g)$
(2) heat
(3) $CuSO_4(s)$
(4) $Pb(NO_3)_2(s)$
(5) $AgCl(s)$

8

Given the equation for the reaction

$$CO(g) + NO_2(g) \rightleftharpoons CO_2(g) + NO(g) + 54.1 \, kcal$$

What happens in this system at equilibrium if

(a) the temperature is increased?
(b) the volume is decreased by a factor of ten?

9

The following equation represents one method for making methanol (methyl alcohol):

$$CO(g) + 2 \, H_2(g) \rightleftharpoons CH_3OH(g) + heat$$

Predict the effect on equilibrium concentrations if

(a) the temperature is increased with pressure and the amount held constant.
(b) the pressure is increased with temperature and the amount held constant.

10

If the phase change represented by

$$heat + H_2O(l) \rightleftharpoons H_2O(g)$$

has reached equilibrium in a closed system:

(a) What will be the effect of a reduction of volume by increasing the pressure?
(b) What will be the effect of an increase in temperature?
(c) What will be the effect of injecting some steam into the closed system, thus raising the pressure? Assume no temperature change.

11

Consider two separate closed systems, each at equilibrium:

(a) HI and the elements from which it is formed.
(b) H_2S and the elements from which it is formed.

What would happen in each system if the total pressure were increased? Assume that conditions are such that all reactants and products are gases.

12

Given:

$$SO_2(g) + \frac{1}{2}O_2(g) \rightleftharpoons SO_3(g) + 23 \, kcal$$

(a) Discuss the conditions that favor a high equilibrium concentration of SO_3.
(b) How many grams of oxygen gas are needed to form 1.00 gram of SO_3?

13

How does a catalyst affect the equilibrium conditions of a chemical system?

14

In any discussion of chemical equilibrium why are concentrations expressed in moles per unit volume rather than in grams per unit volume?

15

Consider the reaction:

$$4 \, HCl(g) + O_2(g) \rightleftharpoons 2 \, H_2O(g) + 2 \, Cl_2(g) + 27 \, kcal$$

What effect would the following changes have on the equilibrium concentration of $Cl_2(g)$? Give reasons for each answer.

(a) Increasing the temperature of the reaction vessel.
(b) Decreasing the total pressure.
(c) Increasing the concentration of O_2.
(d) Increasing the volume of the reaction chamber.
(e) Adding a catalyst.

16

Suggest four ways to increase the concentration of SO_3 in the following equilibrium reaction:

$$SO_2(g) + \frac{1}{2}O_2(g) \rightleftharpoons SO_3(g) + 23 \, kcal$$

17

When heated, solid HgO decomposes into $Hg(g)$ and $O_2(g)$. At a temperature of 740 K the equilibrium pressure is 1.5 atm. Write a balanced equation using 1 mole of O_2. Calculate the partial pressures of the gases and find the equilibrium constant using these pressures.

18

Nitric oxide, NO, releases 13.5 kcal/mol when it reacts with oxygen to give nitrogen dioxide.

(a) Write an equation for this reaction.
(b) Predict the effect that raising the temperature will have on
    (1) the equilibrium concentrations,
    (2) the numerical value of the equilibrium constant,
    (3) the speed of formation of NO_2.
(c) Also, predict how increasing the NO concentration will affect (1), (2), and (3).

19

Given:

$$H_2(g) + I_2(g) \rightleftharpoons 2 \, HI(g)$$

At 450 °C, $K = 50.0$ for this reaction. Calculate

the equilibrium constant at 450 °C if the reaction is written:

$$2\,HI(g) \rightleftharpoons H_2(g) + I_2(g).$$

20

Write the equilibrium law expression for the following reactions:

(a) $N_2(g) + 3\,H_2(g) \rightleftharpoons 2\,NH_3(g)$
(b) $CO(g) + NO_2(g) \rightleftharpoons CO_2(g) + NO(g)$
(c) $Zn(s) + 2\,Ag^+(aq) \rightleftharpoons Zn^{2+}(aq) + 2\,Ag(s)$
(d) $PbI_2(s) \rightleftharpoons Pb^{2+}(aq) + 2\,I^-(aq)$
(e) $CN^-(aq) + H_2O(l) \rightleftharpoons HCN(aq) + OH^-(aq)$

21

This equation:

$$CO_2(g) + H_2(g) \rightleftharpoons CO(g) + H_2O(g)$$

describes a reaction that was carried out at 900 °C with the following results:

Trial Number	Partial Pressure (atm) at Equilibrium			
	CO	H₂O	CO₂	H₂
1	0.352	0.352	0.648	0.148
2	0.266	0.266	0.234	0.234
3	0.186	0.686	0.314	0.314

(a) Write the equilibrium law expression.
(b) Verify that the expression in (a) is a constant, using the data given.

22

In the reaction:

$$2\,HI(g) \rightleftharpoons H_2(g) + I_2(g)$$

at 448 °C the partial pressures of the gases at equilibrium are as follows:

partial pressure of $HI = 4.0 \times 10^{-3}$ atm
partial pressure of $H_2 = 7.5 \times 10^{-3}$ atm
partial pressure of $I_2 \ = 4.3 \times 10^{-5}$ atm

When pressures are properly used in the equilibrium expression, a constant is obtained. What is that constant for this reaction?

23

Reactants A and B are mixed, each at a concentration of 0.80 mole/liter. They react slowly, producing C and $D{:}A + B \rightleftharpoons C + D$. When equilibrium is reached, the concentration of C is measured and found to be 0.60 mole/liter. Calculate the value of the equilibrium constant.

24

Given:

$$CaCO_3(s) \rightleftharpoons CaO(s) + CO_2(g)$$

At a fixed temperature, what effect would adding more $CaCO_3$ have on the concentration of CO_2 in the region above the solid phase? Explain.

25

Equilibrium constants (K) are given below for several systems. In which case does the reaction as written occur to the greatest extent?

Reaction
(a) $CH_3COOH(aq) \rightleftharpoons H^+(aq) + CH_3COO^-(aq)$
(b) $CdS(s) \rightleftharpoons Cd^{2+}(aq) + S^{2-}(aq)$
(c) $H^+(aq) + HS^-(aq) \rightleftharpoons H_2S(aq)$

K
(a) 1.8×10^{-5}
(b) 7.1×10^{-28}
(c) $1 \ \times 10^7$

26

One of the steps in the production of nitric acid is the reaction between ammonia gas and oxygen gas to form nitric oxide, NO, and water.

(a) Write a balanced chemical equation for this reaction, using 4 moles of ammonia.
(b) Write the equilibrium law expression for the reaction.

27

In the upper atmosphere some oxygen gas, O_2, is converted into ozone, O_3, by ultraviolet light.

(a) Write a balanced equation for this reaction.
(b) Write the equilibrium law expression for this reaction.

28

Write the equilibrium law expression for the following reactions:

(a) $C_2H_6(g) \rightleftharpoons H_2(g) + C_2H_4(g)$
(b) $Cu^{2+}(aq) + 4\,NH_3(aq) \rightleftharpoons Cu(NH_3)_4^{2+}(aq)$
(c) $Ag^+(aq) + Cl^-(aq) \rightleftharpoons AgCl(s)$
(d) $PbSO_4(s) + H^+(aq) \rightleftharpoons Pb^{2+}(aq) + HSO_4^-(aq)$
(e) $CO(g) + \frac{1}{2}O_2(g) \rightleftharpoons CO_2(g) + \text{heat}$

29

Isomerization is a commercial process of great importance. One example is the change of normal butane to isobutane. At 25 °C the equilibrium constant is 2.5 for the reaction described by the equation

$$CH_3{-}CH_2{-}CH_2{-}CH_3(g) \rightleftharpoons CH_3{-}CH{-}CH_3(g) \atop \qquad\qquad\qquad\qquad\qquad\qquad\quad | \atop \qquad\qquad\qquad\qquad\qquad\qquad\quad CH_3$$

If the total pressure is 35 atmospheres, what is the partial pressure of each gas?

30

Use the data table given below to find the equilibrium constant when one mole of alcohol is added to one mole of acid to produce ethyl acetate, as in the equation:

$$C_2H_5OH + CH_3COOH \rightleftharpoons C_2H_5CH_3COO + H_2O$$

Moles of Alcohol Added to 1 Mole of Acid	Moles of Ethyl Acetate Produced
0.50	0.42
1.00	0.66
1.50	0.78
2.00	0.84

31

$AgNO_3(s)$ is added to an extremely dilute solution of NaI until the $Ag^+(aq)$ concentration is 0.001 M. No precipitate forms. What is the maximum $I^-(aq)$ ion concentration possible? (See Table 13-6.)

32

The solubility product of $CaCO_3$ is 0.99×10^{-8} at 18°C and 0.87×10^{-8} at 25°C. Does the solubility of $CaCO_3$ increase or decrease as temperature is increased?

33

Cadmium, cobalt, and cupric chlorides are dissolved together in one container of water. What will happen if you slowly add a very dilute solution containing S^{2-} ions?

34

A saturated solution of silver acetate, $AgCH_3COO$, is about 0.06 M.

(a) What is the Ag^+ ion concentration in this solution?
(b) What is the K_{sp} for silver acetate?

35

Consider the effect of each of the following factors on both the solubility and the rate of dissolving of sodium chloride:

(a) Decrease in particle size.
(b) Increase in temperature.
(c) Stirring the solution.
(d) Addition of more solid NaCl.

36

Write the solubility product expression for each of the following equations:

(a) $BaSO_4(s) \rightleftharpoons Ba^{2+}(aq) + SO_4^{2-}(aq)$
(b) $Zn(OH)_2(s) \rightleftharpoons Zn^{2+}(aq) + 2\,OH^-(aq)$
(c) $Ca_3(PO_4)_2(s) \rightleftharpoons 3\,Ca^{2+}(aq) + 2\,PO_4^{3-}(aq)$

37

Write the solubility product expression for each of the following substances in water:

(a) calcium carbonate.
(b) silver sulfide.
(c) aluminum hydroxide.

38

Experiments show that only 0.0059 gram of $SrCO_3$ will dissolve in 1.0 liter of water at 25°C. What is K_{sp} for $SrCO_3$?

39

The solubility product of AgCl is 1.4×10^{-4} at 100°C. Calculate the solubility of silver chloride in boiling water.

40

For each of the following reactions, state: (1) whether the tendency toward minimum energy favors reactants or products, (2) whether the tendency toward maximum randomness favors reactants or products.

(a) $H_2O(l) \rightleftharpoons H_2O(s) + 1.4\,kcal$
(b) $H_2O(l) + 10\,kcal \rightleftharpoons H_2O(g)$
(c) $CaCO_3(s) + 43\,kcal \rightleftharpoons CaO(s) + CO_2(g)$
(d) $I_2(s) + 1.6\,kcal \rightleftharpoons I_2$ (in alcohol)
(e) $4\,Fe(s) + 3\,O_2(g) \rightleftharpoons 2\,Fe_2O_3(s) + 400\,kcal$

41

When a solid evaporates directly (without melting), the process is called **sublimation**. Evaporation of solid CO_2 is a familiar example. Two other substances that sublime are FCN and ICN:

$$FCN(s) + 5.7\,kcal \rightleftharpoons FCN(g)$$
$$ICN(s) + 14.2\,kcal \rightleftharpoons ICN(g)$$

(a) In sublimation, does the tendency toward maximum randomness favor solid or gas?
(b) In sublimation, does the tendency toward minimum energy favor the solid or the gas?
(c) In view of part (b) would you expect solid ICN to have a lower or higher vapor pressure than solid FCN at the same temperature?

14

Aqueous Acids and Bases

You have encountered the words *acid* and *base* a number of times in this course, both in the early chapters of this book and in your laboratory program. In Experiment 10 you dissolved metallic silver in nitric acid; in Experiment 12 you measured the volume of hydrogen gas when a known mass of magnesium metal reacted with hydrochloric acid; and in Experiment 26 you determined the heat of reaction when an acid and a base react. Acids and bases are among the most common and most important chemicals that are found in the laboratory. In addition, a number of acids and bases are often found in our homes: lemon juice owes its sour taste to citric acid, vinegar contains acetic acid, baking soda contains sodium hydrogen carbonate, and household ammonia contains ammonium hydroxide.

In this chapter we will explore how the definitions of acids and bases have changed as chemists searched for regularities and explanations of their experimental results. We will see how the concept of chemical equilibrium provides a way to organize a great deal of information about acids and bases. Most important of all, we will find a way to predict the extent to which an acid-base reaction will occur.

14-1 Operational Definitions of Acids and Bases

Definitions of acids and bases were presented in Section 6-9, page 111, when we discussed electrolytes. **Electrolytes** are substances that dissolve in water to give solutions that conduct electricity. The classification of electrolytes as acids, bases, and salts is based directly on the observed properties of the solutions. These properties provide the simplest definition for each class of compounds. *When we classify or define something in terms of "what happens," we are using an* **operational definition**. Suppose we encounter a new compound. We can decide whether to call it

Sulfur is found as an impurity in fossil fuels. Heretofore much of it was wasted by being dumped into the air as SO_2, which was formed as the fuel burned. Interest in preserving the environment has accelerated the development of methods to recover this sulfur. In 1974, for the first time, recovered sulfur exceeded the amount mined directly.

Most sulfur is used to make sulfuric acid, which in turn is used to make fertilizers, pickle steel, and leach copper ore. Some new uses include putting sulfur in asphalt for roads, foaming sulfur under Arctic highways for insulation, and adding it to concrete to increase strength and resistance to acids.

Figure 14-1
Some familiar acids.

Figure 14-2
Some familiar bases.

an acid or a base by carrying out some of the experiments indicated in the definition.

The experimentally observed properties of aqueous acids and bases are summarized below. These lists form the operational definitions of an acid and of a base.

An **acid** is a compound that dissolves in water to give a solution that does all the following:

conducts electricity;

reacts with metals such as Zn or Mg, liberating H_2;

changes the color of the dye litmus from blue to red;

tastes sour.

A **base** is a compound that dissolves in water to give a solution that does all the following:

conducts electricity;

reacts with an acid to destroy or neutralize its properties;

changes the color of the dye litmus from red to blue;

tastes bitter and feels slippery.

During the 19th century chemists tried to find explanations for the behavior of acids and bases. They began to replace operational definitions (what happens?) with conceptual ones (why does it happen?). A **conceptual definition** *seeks to identify the causes of observed behavior.* The concept underlying the definition often contains ideas of composition and structure.

For many years chemists believed that all acids contain oxygen. When experiments showed that one of the most important acids, hydrochloric acid, contained only hydrogen and chlorine, this belief was abandoned. The generalization that all acids contain hydrogen was then proposed. This change has led to a more valid concept of acids and bases. The Swedish chemist Svante Arrhenius provided one of the first definitions of acids and bases that went beyond a cataloguing of experimental observations.

14-2   The Arrhenius Definitions of Acids and Bases

One of the most intriguing questions that challenged Arrhenius and other chemists was "Why do some substances exhibit acidic or basic properties to a greater degree than other substances?" When 1 M HCl and 1 M acetic acids are compared, we find that the conductivity of the HCl solution is much greater than the conductivity of acetic acid solutions. The rate of reaction of each acid with magnesium or zinc can also be measured. The rate with 1 M HCl is much greater than with 1 M acetic acid.

As part of his theory of ionic dissociation Arrhenius proposed conceptual definitions for acids and bases. He suggested that an ionic substance like $NaCl(s)$ dissolved in water to furnish the ions Na^+ and Cl^-. He also explained the high conductivity of electrolyte solutions in terms of ionic movement toward the electrodes.

Along with these ideas Arrhenius postulated that *an acid is a substance that dissolves in water to furnish the hydrogen ion, H^+.* Similarly, he called a substance *a base if it could furnish the hydroxide ion, OH^-.* The chemical activity and the electrical conductivity of acidic and basic solutions could be directly related to

The color of some flowers is determined by the [H^+] of the soil. For example, hydrangeas produce pink blossoms in basic soil and blue blossoms in acidic soil.

the degree to which these ions formed when substances dissolved in water.

When an acid such as HCl dissolves in water, almost all of it ionizes. Arrhenius called acids that behaved this way **strong acids**. He represented the chemical reaction with the equilibrium

$$HCl \rightleftharpoons H^+ + Cl^- \qquad (K \text{ is a large number.})$$

When acetic acid dissolves in water, only a small fraction of the molecules ionize. Such an acid is called **a weak acid**. The equilibrium reaction can be written

$$CH_3COOH \rightleftharpoons H^+ + CH_3COO^- \qquad (K \text{ is a small number.})$$

The words *strong* and *weak,* used in this manner, are sometimes confusing. They do *not* refer to the initial concentration of the electrolytes. Instead these words refer to the *degree of ionization*. It is possible to have either a dilute or a concentrated solution of a strong or a weak electrolyte.

The information presented in Table 14-1 will help you to see the difference between strong acids and weak acids. Note that each solution is made by dissolving 1.0 mole of the acid in enough water to make 1.0 liter of solution.

Carbon dioxide from the air dissolves in rainwater to give an $[H^+]$ of about 10^{-6}. Pollution caused by SO_2 from burning low-grade fuels and NO_2 from internal-combustion engines can increase $[H^+]$ in rainwater to 10^{-4}—an increase of 100 times.

TABLE 14-1

Comparison of Strong and Weak Acids
(1 *M* concentration)

Strong Acid	Weak Acid	Approximate $[H^+]$	Electrical Conductivity	Rate of Reaction with Mg
1.0 *M* HCl		1 *M*	High	Fast
1.0 *M* H_2SO_4		1 *M*	High	Fast
	1.0 *M* H_3PO_4	0.1 *M*	Intermediate	Intermediate
	1.0 *M* CH_3COOH	0.004 *M*	Low	Slow

Arrhenius proposed that *strong electrolytes* dissociated almost 100% when dissolved in water. The dissociation of *weak electrolytes* such as CH_3COOH is very small. Very few ions form when CH_3COOH dissolves in water. Arrhenius compared the strengths of acids and bases by measuring the conductivity of solutions. We will discuss acid-base strength in Section 14-8. But first let us consider the reaction between an acid and a base, one of the most important reactions in chemistry. It is given a special name, **neutralization**.

14-3   The Neutralization Reaction

We can write the equation for the reaction of hydrochloric acid and sodium hydroxide solutions in several ways. One of them is

$$H^+(aq) + Cl^-(aq) + Na^+(aq) + OH^-(aq) \longrightarrow$$
$$H_2O + Cl^-(aq) + Na^+(aq)$$

Products used to clear clogged drains are obtainable in most grocery stores. They commonly contain about 50 percent NaOH (very corrosive, keep well away from small children) and about 4 percent metallic aluminum. The heat of solution of NaOH raises the temperature enough to melt grease and cause it to saponify. The soap produced is more soluble than the grease. The aluminum reacts with NaOH solution to generate hydrogen gas. This stirs the solution, speeds the reaction, and helps loosen the material clogging the drain.

Doctors treat some stomach ulcers by neutralizing the digestive acids with bland food and basic compounds.

The sodium and chloride ions appear as reactants and products. They do not enter into the neutralization reaction. *Ions that are present but do not participate in the reaction are called* **spectator ions**. Frequently chemists do not include them in the equation. This procedure simplifies the equation and emphasizes the reaction that is taking place. The result is called a **net ionic equation**, such as

$$H^+(aq) + OH^-(aq) \longrightarrow H_2O$$

Remember, however, that you cannot find a bottle in the chemical stockroom that contains only $H^+(aq)$ or $OH^-(aq)$ ions!

This reaction must be written as an equilibrium system. Even though the electrical conductivity of pure water is very low, precise measurements show that water is a weak electrolyte. The conductivity measurement indicates that the ions $H^+(aq)$ and $OH^-(aq)$ are present at very low concentrations in pure water.

$$H_2O \rightleftharpoons H^+(aq) + OH^-(aq)$$

On page 277 we saw that the equilibrium expression for this system can be written

$$K_w = [H^+][OH^-]$$

The constant K_w is often called the *ion product* for water. The value for K_w at 25 °C is 1.00×10^{-14}.

In pure water, every time an $H^+(aq)$ ion forms, an $OH^-(aq)$ ion must form too. Therefore, we know that

$$[H^+] = [OH^-] \qquad \text{(in pure water)}$$

This relationship allows us to write

$$K_w = [H^+][OH^-] = [H^+]^2$$
$$[H^+] = \sqrt{K_w} = \sqrt{1.0 \times 10^{-14}}$$
$$[H^+] = 1.0 \times 10^{-7} \ M \quad \text{(in pure water at 25 °C)}$$

In addition we can see that

$$[OH^-] = 1.0 \times 10^{-7} \ M \qquad \text{(in pure water at 25 °C)}$$

At equilibrium the ion concentrations are only 10^{-7} M. *Water is a weak electrolyte.*

EXERCISE 14-1

Show that the concentration of H_2O in a liter of pure water is 55.5 M. Assume that the mass of one liter of water is 1.00×10^3 grams.

EXERCISE 14-2

What is the concentration of H_2O in 1.00×10^2 ml of water? In 1.00 ml?

14-4   The Special Relation of H$^+$(aq) to OH$^-$(aq)

In pure water the concentrations of H$^+$(aq) and OH$^-$(aq) are equal. But what happens if HCl(g) is added? HCl(g) acts as a strong electrolyte when it dissolves in water, forming the hydrated ions H$^+$(aq) and Cl$^-$(aq). All acids increase the [H$^+$] but not the [OH$^-$] in the system. The [H$^+$] and [OH$^-$] are no longer equal. However, experiments show that the equilibrium relation is still valid for every aqueous solution containing H$^+$(aq) and OH$^-$(aq) ions.

$$K_w = [\text{H}^+][\text{OH}^-]$$

We can rearrange this equation to show

$$[\text{OH}^-] = \frac{K_w}{[\text{H}^+]}$$

If [H$^+$] increases, then [OH$^-$] must decrease. We represent the relation schematically in Figure 14-3.

Suppose, on the other hand, we add the strong electrolyte NaOH to pure water. The [H$^+$] and [OH$^-$] are no longer equal because the base NaOH increases the hydroxide ion concentration without adding to the hydrogen ion concentration. The concentration of H$^+$(aq) would decrease and be given by the relation:

$$[\text{H}^+] = \frac{K_w}{[\text{OH}^-]}$$

Some examples will give you practice with this concept. Suppose we start with 1.0 liter of pure water. We have just seen that [H$^+$] = [OH$^-$] = 10^{-7} M in water. Now add 0.1 mole of hydrogen chloride to the water. Since HCl is a strong electrolyte, 0.1 mole will furnish 0.1 mole of H$^+$(aq) and 0.1 mole of Cl$^-$(aq). The maximum concentration for H$^+$(aq) would initially be the sum of [H$^+$] from water and from HCl.

$$[\text{H}^+]_{\text{total}} = [\text{H}^+]_{\text{water}} + [\text{H}^+]_{\text{HCl}} = 10^{-7}\ M + 10^{-1}\ M$$

The very small amount of H$^+$(aq) coming from water becomes even smaller when the effect predicted by Le Châtelier's principle is considered. The contribution of H$^+$ from water is so small it can be neglected. The concentration of hydroxide ion can be calculated easily.

$$[\text{OH}^-] = \frac{K_w}{[\text{H}^+]} = \frac{10^{-14}}{10^{-1}} = 10^{-13}\ M$$

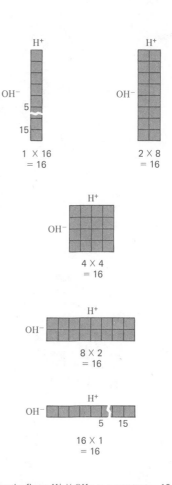

for the figure H$^+$ $\times$ OH$^-$ = a constant = 16
in real terms [H$^+$][OH$^-$] = 10^{-14}

Figure 14-3
The constant product H$^+$ $\times$ OH$^-$.

Food technicians measure the fatty acid content of fats by neutralization. Technicians in automotive and petroleum laboratories study oil oxidation by the same technique.

An addition of 0.1 mole of HCl to a liter of water reduces the hydroxide concentration by a factor of a million! Review this example, using Le Châtelier's principle as a guide. If HCl is added to water, a stress is placed on a closed system at equilibrium. The concentration of $H^+(aq)$ is increased. Reaction between $OH^-(aq)$ and $H^+(aq)$ takes place to relieve the stress. The "box score" can be seen in Table 14-2.

TABLE 14-2
The Concentrations of $H^+(aq)$ and $OH^-(aq)$
When 0.1 Mole of HCl is Added to 1.0 Liter of Water

Concentrations Before Adding HCl (System at Equilibrium)		Hypothetical Situation Immediately After Adding HCl (System Not at Equilibrium)	Final Concentrations (System at New Equilibrium)
$[H^+]$	$10^{-7} M$	$10^{-1} M + 10^{-7} M$	$10^{-1} M$
$[OH^-]$	$10^{-7} M$	$10^{-7} M$	$10^{-13} M$
$[H^+][OH^-]$	$(10^{-7}) \times (10^{-7}) = 10^{-14}$	not applicable	$(10^{-1}) \times (10^{-13}) = 10^{-14}$

EXERCISE 14-3

Show that the addition of 0.010 mole of solid NaOH to 1.0 liter of water reduces the concentration of $H^+(aq)$ to $1.0 \times 10^{-12} M$.

EXERCISE 14.4

Suppose that 3.65 grams of HCl are dissolved in 10.0 liters of water. What is the value of $[H^+]$? Show that $[OH^-] = 1.00 \times 10^{-12} M$.

EXERCISE 14-5

How many hydrogen and hydroxide ions would there be in 1 liter of H_2O?
How many hydrogen and hydroxide ions would there be in 1 liter of 0.1 M HCl?

The concentrations of $H^+(aq)$ and $OH^-(aq)$ always are related through the equilibrium relation $K_w = [H^+][OH^-]$.

In acidic solutions $\quad [H^+] > [OH^-]$ ⎫
In neutral solutions $\quad [H^+] = [OH^-]$ ⎬ but $[H^+][OH^-] = 10^{-14}$ in all cases at 25°C.
In basic solutions $\quad [H^+] < [OH^-]$ ⎭

The ease with which we can control and vary the concentrations of $H^+(aq)$ and $OH^-(aq)$ is important. These ions take part in many reactions that occur in aqueous solutions. If $H^+(aq)$ is a reactant or a product in a reaction, the variation of the hydrogen ion concentration may have an enormous effect on the reaction. Such variations cause changes in the concentrations of all the reactants and products so that the numerical value of the equilibrium law expression continues to equal the equilibrium constant. Furthermore, there are many reactions for which either the hydrogen ion or the hydroxide ion is a catalyst. An example was discussed in Section 12-8, the decomposition of formic acid catalyzed by H^+ from sulfuric acid. Formic acid is reasonably stable until the hydrogen ion concentration is raised. Then the rate of decomposition becomes very rapid.

14-5   Acid-Base Titrations

In making quantitative measurements chemists frequently must determine the concentrations of a solution. There are several methods of doing this. One of the most important is called *titration*. The following discussion illustrates what happens in a titration using the reaction between a strong acid and a strong base as the example.

If 0.1 mole of HCl is dissolved in 100 ml of H_2O, the concentration of hydrogen ion is 1.0 M. Addition of small amounts of solid NaOH decreases the concentration of hydrogen ion because of the neutralization reaction:

$$H^+(aq) + OH^-(aq) \rightleftharpoons H_2O$$

Initially the solution is acidic. As more and more NaOH is added, the solution becomes less acidic. When 0.10 mole of NaOH has been added, the solution is neutral. The concentrations of $H^+(aq)$ and $OH^-(aq)$ would then be equal to each other. When equimolar amounts of HCl and NaOH have been mixed in a titration, we say that the **equivalence point** is reached. Now more NaOH makes the solution basic. Numerical values for the hydrogen and hydroxide concentrations at different points in the titration are summarized in Table 14-3.

Analysts in all fields use the technique of titration.

TABLE 14-3
The Changes in [H^+] and [OH^-] During the Titration of 100 ml of 1.00 M HCl

Initial Number of Moles of HCl	Number of Moles of NaOH(s) Added	Excess Moles of HCl or NaOH	Equilibrium	
			[H^+]	[OH^-]
0.100	0.000	0.100	1.00	1.00×10^{-14}
0.100	0.090	0.010	1.0×10^{-1}	1.0×10^{-13}
0.100	0.099	0.001	1×10^{-2}	1×10^{-12}
0.100	0.100	none	1.0×10^{-7}	1.00×10^{-7}
0.100	0.101	0.001	1×10^{-12}	1×10^{-2}
0.100	0.110	0.010	1.0×10^{-13}	1.0×10^{-1}
0.100	0.200	0.100	1.00×10^{-14}	1.00

If we plot the concentration of hydrogen ion as NaOH(s) is added to the solution, the changes during a titration are shown clearly. Figure 14-4 indicates that the change in [H^+] is quite gradual until close to the equivalence point. In the early stages of the titration notice that the [H^+] changes by a factor of 100 when 0.099 mole of NaOH(s) is added. But near the equivalence point, 0.002 mole of NaOH(s) changes the [H^+] from 10^{-2} M to 10^{-12} M, a factor of 10^{10}.

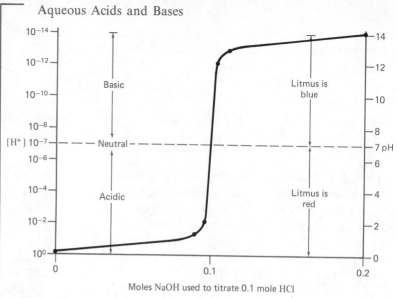

Figure 14-4
Titration curve for the reaction of HCl with NaOH.

Swimming pool maintenance men use indicators to analyze the water. Television admen show *p*H-balanced shampoo with an indicator paper.

Nurses and biochemical technicians must consider *p*H in working with animal tissues.

Microbiologists working for penicillin manufacturers add both acidic and basic substances to maintain *p*H in the range 6.8–7.4 for maximum yield from the mold.

EXERCISE 14-6

Calculate the [H⁺] and [OH⁻] for the titration just discussed when 0.0999 mole of NaOH(s) has been added.

The conditions that exist at the equivalence point make it possible for us to determine an unknown concentration of an acid. At the equivalence point,

$$(\text{number of moles})_{\text{acid}} = (\text{number of moles})_{\text{base}}$$

Now if both the acid and the base are supplied by solutions, we can use the relation

$$\text{molarity} = \frac{\text{number of moles}}{\text{number of liters}}$$

to change the first equation to

$$(\text{molarity} \times \text{liters})_{\text{acid}} = (\text{molarity} \times \text{liters})_{\text{base}}$$

Since we usually titrate small volumes of acids and bases, we can change this equation to

$$(\text{molarity} \times \text{milliliters})_{\text{acid}} = (\text{molarity} \times \text{milliliters})_{\text{base}}$$

If we know any three of these quantities, we can calculate the fourth. For example, we can determine the concentration of an acid solution. We need to know how many milliliters of it have to be added to a known volume of a base (whose concentration is known) to reach the equivalence point. Our problem now is how to know when the equivalence point is reached.

One way is with special chemicals called **indicators** which change color at or near the equivalence point. Litmus dye is such an indicator. Indicators are weak acids and bases which have one color in acid solution and another color in basic solution. We can represent how they function by this equilibrium equation:

$$H(Ind) \rightleftharpoons \qquad Ind^- \qquad + H^+(aq)$$

color 1	color 2
Addition of acid increases the amount of H(Ind).	Addition of base removes H^+ and increases the concentration of Ind^-.

Litmus is red in acidic solutions: $H(Ind)$ is red. It is blue in basic solutions: Ind^- is blue. A small amount of litmus added to an acidic solution makes the solution red. (The original H^+ concentration is not changed appreciably by this small amount of litmus.) Now we are ready to titrate. As base is added, the H^+ concentration decreases gradually until the equivalence point is almost reached. See Figure 14-4. Then a drop or two of base causes the H^+ concentration to decrease rapidly and the red color of litmus changes to blue. This color change tells us that we have just passed the equivalence point. At that point

$$[H^+] = [OH^-]$$

Now let us see how this works using actual data. Suppose 18.00 ml of an HCl solution requires 24.00 ml of a 0.300 M NaOH solution to produce the red-to-blue color change with litmus. What is the concentration of the HCl solution?

From the relation

$$(M \times ml)_{acid} = (M \times ml)_{base}$$

we can write

$$M_{acid} = \frac{ml_{base}}{ml_{acid}} \times M_{base}$$

$$= \frac{24.00 \ ml}{18.00 \ ml} \times 0.300 \ M$$

$$= 0.400 \ M$$

Perhaps you noticed the symbol pH in the label on the right side of Figure 14-4. When very large or very small numbers are encountered, it is often convenient to refer only to the exponent of the number. For example, 10^{-13} could be referred to as 13. The term pH is defined as the exponent for the hydrogen ion concentration with the sign changed.

$$pH = x \qquad when \ [H^+] = 10^{-x}$$

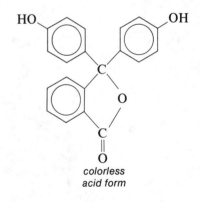

colorless
acid form

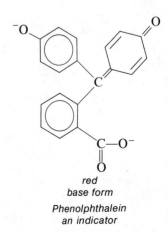

red
base form

Phenolphthalein
an indicator

Using the pH system we see that

$$pH < 7 \quad \text{for acidic solutions}$$
$$pH = 7 \quad \text{for neutral solutions}$$
$$pH > 7 \quad \text{for basic solutions}$$

EXERCISE 14-7

You have 100 ml of an HCl solution whose concentration you do not know. Titration with 0.10 M NaOH solution requires 50 ml of the base to reach the equivalence point. What was the original concentration of the HCl solution?

pH

0 1 M HCl
1 Gastric (stomach) juice
2 Lemon juice
3 Grapefruit
   Soft drink
4 Tomato
5 Black coffee
6 Human saliva
   Drinking water
   Cow's milk
7 Pure water
   Blood plasma
   Human urine
8 Seawater
9
10 Soap solution
11
12 Ca(OH)$_2$, saturated solution
13
14 1 M NaOH

14-6 The Brønsted-Lowry Definitions of Acids and Bases

The Arrhenius view of acids and bases was a great advance. However, difficulties began to occur when new questions were asked. Why should H$^+$ leave a compound in which it was close to a pair of electrons? The separation of H$^+$ from such a compound can be compared with the removal of an e$^-$ from a hydrogen atom. In both cases H$^+$ is produced. Ionization of hydrogen atoms requires 313.6 kcal/mol, so one would expect that dissolving an acid in water would be endothermic. However, the opposite is almost always true. Acids dissolve in water and heat is liberated. What could be the source of this heat? Perhaps the H$^+$ forms bonds to the solvent, liberating energy.

The very nature of H$^+$, which was unknown to Arrhenius, now makes this seem reasonable. Since the hydrogen atom has only one electron, the ion H$^+$ must correspond to the nucleus of the atom, a proton. Such a small positive ion would interact strongly with electrons on other molecules or ions. Look at the orbital diagram for water. Note the electrons in the filled valence orbitals that attract H$^+$. When a positive ion interacts with water in this fashion, it is said to be *hydrated*. A number of different experiments support the idea that the hydrogen ion is hydrated when water is the solvent. Some experiments suggest that the hydrogen ion should be represented by the formula H$_3$O$^+$. Other experiments indicate that there are more water molecules, corresponding to the formula H$_9$O$_4^+$. All experiments agree that the unhydrated hydrogen ion does not exist to any appreciable extent in water. Some chemists indicate hydration of ions by writing equations in this manner:

$$\text{HCl} + \text{water} \rightleftharpoons \text{H}^+(aq) + \text{Cl}^-(aq)$$

$$\text{CH}_3\text{COOH} + \text{water} \rightleftharpoons \text{H}^+(aq) + \text{CH}_3\text{COO}^-(aq)$$

Other chemists prefer to represent these same reactions another way, but in either method the hydration of the proton is clearly shown:

$$HCl(aq) + H_2O \rightleftharpoons H_3O^+(aq) + Cl^-(aq)$$
$$CH_3COOH(aq) + H_2O \rightleftharpoons H_3O^+(aq) + CH_3COO^-(aq)$$

Recognition that the solvent plays a direct role in acid-base systems removes another difficulty of the Arrhenius definition. There are other substances, like NH_3 and Na_2CO_3, which do not contain hydroxide ion. However, they dissolve in water to form solutions that have the properties of bases. The explanation for these observations appears when we write equations which include the solvent.

$$NH_3(g) + H_2O \rightleftharpoons NH_4^+(aq) + OH^-(aq)$$
$$Na_2CO_3(s) + H_2O \rightleftharpoons HCO_3^-(aq) + OH^-(aq) + 2\,Na^+(aq)$$

Ammonia and carbonate ions react with the solvent to produce $OH^-(aq)$. The properties of these solutions are similar to the solutions of other bases. These reactions clearly emphasize the important role played by the solvent. Recognition of the importance of the solvent led chemists to propose more general definitions of acids and bases.

In 1923 the Danish chemist J. N. Brønsted and the English chemist T. M. Lowry independently proposed new conceptual definitions for acids and bases. They proposed that

>**an acid** is a substance that can *donate a proton.*
>**a base** is a substance that can *accept a proton.*

We can write some equations which will show the meaning of these definitions. The acid will be written as the first reactant in each equation. For convenience the notation *(aq)* after each ion is again omitted.

$$HCl(g) + H_2O \rightleftharpoons H_3O^+ + Cl^-$$
$$CH_3COOH + H_2O \rightleftharpoons H_3O^+ + CH_3COO^-$$
$$H_2O + NH_3(g) \rightleftharpoons NH_4^+ + OH^-$$
$$H_2O + CO_3^{2-} \rightleftharpoons HCO_3^- + OH^-$$

Four important generalizations can be derived from the ideas we have been discussing:

(1) Water as a solvent plays an important role in the Brønsted-Lowry system. In the first two equations water acts as a base; water accepts protons. In the last two equations water acts as an acid; water donates protons.

(2) These definitions are not limited to reactions taking place in aqueous solutions. The proton transfer in the reaction

$$HCl(g) + NH_3(g) \rightleftharpoons NH_4^+ + Cl^-$$

shows that $HCl(g)$ is an acid and $NH_3(g)$ is a base.

3. Close inspection of these equations helps us realize that the products in these reactions are acids and bases too.

$$CH_3COOH + H_2O \rightleftharpoons H_3O^+ + CH_3COO^-$$
$$H_2O + NH_3 \rightleftharpoons NH_4^+ + OH^-$$
$$HB_1 + B_2 \rightleftharpoons HB_2^+ + B_1^-$$
$$Acid_1 + Base_2 \rightleftharpoons Acid_2 + Base_1$$

Each reaction is reversible. Acetic acid can donate a proton to the base, water. The acid H_3O^+ can donate a proton to the acetate ion, CH_3COO^-, a base. The members of each pair, CH_3COOH—CH_3COO^- or H_3O^+—H_2O, differ only by a proton. They are **acid-base pairs**.

A strong acid would have a large tendency to donate a proton. *The base paired with a strong acid would be a weak base. The base paired with a weak acid would be a strong base.* A strong base has a large tendency to keep a proton.

4. In acid-base reactions a proton is transferred from one electron pair to another. A look at the electronic structure of acids and bases will help us visualize what is happening. When a collision occurs, we expect an activated complex to form:

This mechanism suggests that hydrogen bond formation provides the route for proton transfer.

14-7 Experimental Determination of K_A

How have chemists determined values for equilibrium constants involving acids? There are several different methods. Perhaps the easiest method makes use of an indicator like litmus. Indicators change color as the hydrogen ion concentration changes. The method we will outline is based on matching the indicator color in two solutions. If the color is the same in both solutions, we assume the hydrogen ion concentration is the same.

The procedure to be followed is illustrated in Figure 14-5. A set of standard solutions is prepared by dilution of an HCl solution whose concentration is known. The same amount of indicator is added to each of these solutions. The color varies from one test tube to another because the hydrogen ion concentration is different in each solution. HF is a weak acid whose equilibrium constant, K, we want to determine. The solution on the right is 0.100 M HF. The same amount of indicator has been added to this test tube as was added to the HCl solutions. The color of the HF solution seems to match the second HCl test tube, where

$[H_3O^+] = 8 \times 10^{-3}$ M. Now the constant for HF can be found. First write the equation and equilibrium expression.

$$HF + H_2O \rightleftharpoons H_3O^+ + F^-$$
$$K = \frac{[H_3O^+][F^-]}{[H_2O][HF]}$$

Since the concentration of H_2O is constant, it is combined with K (see Section 13-12) to give K_A:

$$K_A = K[H_2O] = \frac{[H_3O^+][F^-]}{[HF]}$$

The balanced equation indicates that the concentration of F^- must be equal to the concentration of H_3O^+. The only source of ions in this example is from the dissociation of HF. Table 14-4 summarizes these results to yield the concentration values.

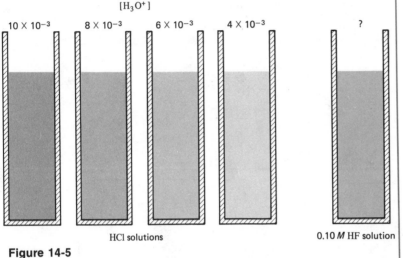

$[H_3O^+]$

10×10^{-3} 8×10^{-3} 6×10^{-3} 4×10^{-3} ?

HCl solutions   0.10 M HF solution

Figure 14-5
Using an acid-base indicator to estimate $[H_3O^+]$ in a weak acid solution.

Table 14-4
Concentrations in a 0.100 M HF Solution

Species	Initial Concentration	Equilibrium Concentration	Method Used to Find Concentration
HF	0.100 M	$[HF] - [H_3O^+] =$ $0.100 - 0.008 = 0.092$ M	Initial concentration from titration with NaOH solution of known concentration. Equilibrium concentration by noting that each H_3O^+ formed uses one HF
H_3O^+	—	8×10^{-3} M	Color matching with HCl solutions of known concentration
F^-	—	8×10^{-3} M	$[H_3O^+] = [F^-]$

The calculation is then straightforward:

$$K_A = \frac{[H_3O^+][F^-]}{[HF]} = \frac{8 \times 10^{-3} \times 8 \times 10^{-3}}{9 \times 10^{-2}}$$
$$= 7 \times 10^{-4}$$

14-8   The Strengths of Acids and Bases

The equilibria prevailing in acidic and basic solutions can be used to determine the relative strengths of acids and bases. For example, consider the behavior of two weak acids, acetic acid and hydrofluoric acid:

$$CH_3COOH + H_2O \rightleftharpoons H_3O^+ + CH_3COO^-$$

$$HF + H_2O \rightleftharpoons H_3O^+ + F^-$$

Measurements of the electrical conductivities of 0.10 M solutions of these two acids show that the conductivity of the HF solution is higher than the conductivity of the acetic acid solution. This must mean that there are more ions in the 0.10 M HF solution than in the 0.10 M acetic acid solution. Acetic acid shows less tendency to donate a proton to the base, water, than hydrofluoric acid does. We can express this tendency quantitatively in equilibrium law expressions for the reactions. For acetic acid,

$$K = \frac{[H_3O^+][CH_3COO^-]}{[H_2O][CH_3COOH]}$$

$$K_A = \frac{[H_3O^+][CH_3COO^-]}{[CH_3COOH]} = 1.8 \times 10^{-5}$$

In a similar way we find for HF,

$$K_A = \frac{[H_3O^+][F^-]}{[HF]} = 6.7 \times 10^{-4}$$

It is customary to refer to values of K_A as the equilibrium constant in acid-base systems. The larger value for the equilibrium constant for HF means that the reaction products are more favored in the HF system than in the acetic acid system. A larger fraction is ionized. A 0.1 M HF solution will produce a higher $[H^+]$ than will a 0.1 M acetic acid solution. HF is a stronger acid than acetic acid. A larger fraction of the HF molecules have formed ions. These ideas can be summarized in terms of a general acid, HB. The acidic nature of HB is related to its ability to donate protons to H_2O:

$$HB + H_2O \rightleftharpoons H_3O^+ + B^-$$

The equilibrium constant for this reaction has the form

$$K_A = \frac{[H_3O^+][B^-]}{[HB]}$$

It is important to recognize that in each of these examples, CH_3COOH, HF, and HB, we are measuring the tendency for the acid to donate a proton to the *same base*, H_2O. This procedure allows us to rank acids in order of their tendency to donate protons. Table 14-5 is a list of some of the more common acid-base pairs. The larger the value for K_A, the stronger is the acid. The larger the value for K_A, the higher the concentration of H_3O^+.

TABLE 14-5

Equilibrium Constants for Acids in Aqueous Solution

$$HB + H_2O \rightleftharpoons H_3O^+ + B^-$$

Acid-Base Pairs		Relative Strength of Acid	Relative Strength of Base	$K_A = \dfrac{[H_3O^+]\,[B^-]}{[HB]}$
HCl	Cl$^-$			Very large
		Very strong		
HNO$_3$	NO$_3^-$		Very weak	Very large
H$_2$SO$_4$	HSO$_4^-$			Large
		Strong		
HSO$_4^-$	SO$_4^{2-}$			1.3×10^{-2}
HF	F$^-$	Weak		6.7×10^{-4}
CH$_3$COOH	CH$_3$COO$^-$			1.8×10^{-5}
H$_2$CO$_3$	HCO$_3^-$			4.4×10^{-7}
H$_2$S	HS$^-$			1.0×10^{-7}
NH$_4^+$	NH$_3$			5.7×10^{-10}
HCO$_3^-$	CO$_3^{2-}$		Weak	4.7×10^{-11}
HS$^-$	S^{2-}	Very weak		1.3×10^{-13}
H$_2$O	OH$^-$		Strong	1.8×10^{-16}
OH$^-$	O^{2-}		Very strong	$< 10^{-36}$

A larger table is given in Appendix 3, p. 447.

EXERCISE 14-8

Which of the following acids is the strongest and which is the weakest? Use Appendix 3 to verify your answer.

nitrous acid	HNO$_2$	$K_A = 5.1 \times 10^{-4}$
sulfurous acid	H$_2$SO$_3$	$K_A = 1.7 \times 10^{-2}$
phosphoric acid	H$_3$PO$_4$	$K_A = 7.1 \times 10^{-3}$

Another important aspect of the Brønsted-Lowry definitions for acids and bases is the role of the solvent. The acidic form of the solvent (H_3O^+) and the basic form of the solvent (OH^-) are the strongest acid and base that can exist at any appreciable concentration in the solvent (H_2O). This means that very strong acids like HCl and HNO_3 do not exist as undissociated molecules in water. They react 100 percent with the solvent to form H_3O^+.

$$HCl(g) + H_2O \longrightarrow H_3O^+ + Cl^-$$

Similarly, an oxide like Na_2O dissolves in water to form OH^- rather than the very strong base oxide ion, O^{2-}.

$$Na_2O(s) + H_2O \longrightarrow 2\,Na^+ + 2\,OH^-$$

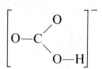

Hydrogen Carbonate ion
(bicarbonate)

In Table 14-5 acids are not only ranked in order of their tendency to donate protons to the base water, but the acids are also ranked in terms of their tendency to donate protons to any base in aqueous solution. This interpretation guides us in answering a question like this: Are reactants or products favored when $Na_2CO_3(s)$ is added to an aqueous solution of HF? First, decide what the reactants are. Since Na_2CO_3 is a soluble salt, it provides CO_3^{2-}. HF is a weak acid and will provide HF molecules. With these reactants the products would be HCO_3^- and F^-. Therefore,

$$HF + CO_3^{2-} \rightleftharpoons HCO_3^- + F^-$$

To decide whether reactants or products are favored, we must know which is the stronger acid. Looking at Table 14-5, we find equilibrium constants for the two acids:

$$HF + H_2O \rightleftharpoons H_3O^+ + F^- \qquad K_A = 6.7 \times 10^{-4}$$
$$HCO_3^- + H_2O \rightleftharpoons H_3O^+ + CO_3^{2-} \qquad K_A = 4.7 \times 10^{-11}$$

The K_A values show us that HF has a much greater tendency to donate a proton. Since HF is a stronger acid than HCO_3^-, proton donation from HF to the base CO_3^{2-} is more likely than proton donation from HCO_3^- to F^-. This must mean that the products of the reaction between Na_2CO_3 and HF are favored.

Other examples of this kind suggest a useful regularity:

> *Products will be favored when an acid reacts with the base of any acid-base pair below it* in Table 14-5.

EXERCISE 14-9

Convince yourself that the equilibrium constant for the reaction

$$CO_3^{2-} + H_3O^+ \rightleftharpoons HCO_3^- + H_2O$$

is $1/K_A$ where K_A is the equilibrium constant for the reaction

$$HCO_3^- + H_2O \rightleftharpoons H_3O^+ + CO_3^{2-}$$

EXERCISE 14-10

Are reactants or products favored in the reaction between CH_3COOH and NH_3? Use the qualitative guide just discussed to answer this question.

The numerical value for the equilibrium constant for the reaction

$$HF + CO_3^{2-} \rightleftharpoons HCO_3^- + F^-$$

can be determined by a simple mathematical technique. The equilibrium law expression for the reaction is:

$$K = \frac{[F^-]\,[HCO_3^-]}{[HF]\,[CO_3^{2-}]}$$

If we multiply both numerator and denominator by $[H_3O^+]$, the value of K does not change.

$$K = \frac{[F^-]}{[HF]} \times \frac{[HCO_3^-]}{[CO_3^{2-}]}$$

$$= \frac{[F^-][H_3O^+]}{[HF]} \times \frac{[HCO_3^-]}{[H_3O^+][CO_3^{2-}]}$$

The first factor is K_A for HF. The second factor is $1/K_A$ for HCO_3^-. The equilibrium constant for the reaction is:

$$K = \frac{K_A(\text{for HF})}{K_A(\text{for } HCO_3^-)} = \frac{6.7 \times 10^{-4}}{4.7 \times 10^{-11}} = 1.4 \times 10^7$$

14-9   Calculations of $[H_3O^+]$

If a value of K_A for an acid has been determined, we can use it in equilibrium calculations. Here are two examples.

Suppose that a chemist wants to know the hydrogen ion concentration in a solution that was made by dissolving 0.02 mole of acetic acid in enough water to make one liter of solution. Of course, he could go to the laboratory and compare the color of an indicator in his solution with colors of the same indicator in solutions of known hydrogen ion concentration. Or he can calculate the value of $[H_3O^+]$ using the K_A. The equilibrium constant K_A can be found in Table 14-5.

$$K_A = \frac{[H_3O^+][CH_3COO^-]}{[CH_3COOH]} = 1.8 \times 10^{-5}$$

The numerical value for K_A is small. This fact tells us that the numerator in the equilibrium expression must be much smaller than the denominator. The chemical reaction is

$$CH_3COOH + H_2O \rightleftharpoons H_3O^+ + CH_3COO^-$$

Every time a hydrogen ion forms, an acetate ion forms. Also every time a hydrogen ion forms, an acetic acid molecule must dissociate. We can write:

$$[H_3O^+] = [CH_3COO^-]$$

$$[CH_3COOH] = 0.02 - [H_3O^+]$$

Since the hydrogen ion concentration is very low, we can assume that

$$[CH_3COOH] = 0.02\ M$$

Substituting in the equilibrium expression gives

$$K_A = \frac{[H_3O^+][CH_3COO^-]}{[CH_3COOH]} = \frac{[H_3O^+][H_3O^+]}{0.02} = 1.8 \times 10^{-5}$$

$$[H_3O^+]^2 = 0.02 \times 1.8 \times 10^{-5} = 36 \times 10^{-8}$$

$$[H_3O^+] = 6 \times 10^{-4} \; M$$

The concentration of H_3O^+ is very low. Our assumption that $[CH_3COOH] = 0.02 \; M$ is a reasonable one.

As another example, suppose a solution is made by adding 0.10 mole of CH_3COOH and also 0.10 mole of $NaCH_3COO$, sodium acetate, to enough water to make one liter of solution. Sodium acetate is a strong electrolyte, so it ionizes completely when it dissolves in water:

$$NaCH_3COO(s) \longrightarrow CH_3COO^- + Na^+$$

The concentration of the acetate ion from this source would be 0.10 M. Notice that the acetate ion comes from two sources, $NaCH_3COO$ and CH_3COOH. Therefore, we must add the contribution from each to give the total acetate concentration. The acetate ion from acetic acid equals the H_3O^+ concentration. On the other hand, the concentration of CH_3COOH decreases by ionization, so we must subtract the $[H_3O^+]$. The reaction we must consider is

$$CH_3COOH + H_2O \rightleftharpoons H_3O^+ + CH_3COO^-$$

$$[CH_3COO^-] = 0.10 + [H_3O^+]$$

$$[CH_3COOH] = 0.10 - [H_3O^+]$$

As in our first example, for every H_3O^+ there will be one CH_3COO^- formed. We anticipate that $[H_3O^+]$ is quite small and we will assume that

$$[CH_3COO^-] = 0.10 \; M$$

$$[CH_3COOH] = 0.10 \; M$$

Using the equilibrium expression, we find that

$$K_A = \frac{[H_3O^+][CH_3COO^-]}{[CH_3COOH]} = \frac{[H_3O^+] \times 0.10}{0.10} = 1.8 \times 10^{-5}$$

$$[H_3O^+] = 1.8 \times 10^{-5} \; M$$

Our assumption is quite reasonable. The hydrogen ion concentration is very small.

14-10   Review

In this chapter we have seen how equilibrium principles can be applied to acid-base systems. We began by defining acids and bases in terms of the properties of their aqueous solutions. This **operational** approach is very useful. It tells what experiments to carry out to decide whether a substance should be classed as an acid or as a base.

Arrhenius was the first chemist to offer an explanation for the behavior of acids and bases. According to Arrhenius an acid was a substance that released H^+ and a base a substance that released OH^-. Later Brønsted and Lowry proposed a broader definition in which they explained the behavior of acids and bases in terms of proton transfer.

An acid *is a substance that can donate a proton.*
A base *is a substance that can accept a proton.*

Not only does this point of view develop the important role of the solvent, but it also leads to an ordering of acids in terms of their tendency to donate protons to the reference base, H_2O. The equilibrium constants for these reactions offer a method for dealing with acids and bases on a quantitative basis.

The equilibrium expression for water

$$K_w = [H^+]\,[OH^-]$$

emphasizes the importance of water in acid-base systems. In addition, the concentrations of H^+ and OH^- can be controlled easily. These ions take part in many important reactions that occur in aqueous solutions, often influencing the state of equilibrium or the rate of a reaction.

There are still other definitions that chemists have proposed for acids and bases. We have not discussed them in this chapter. It is important for you to realize that these definitions complement each other. A chemist finds it convenient to use one set of definitions in some of his work but another set when he deals with other systems. It is easy for us to forget that much of the chemistry on this planet is tied intimately to the solvent H_2O. If you met a chemist from another planet, his definitions for acids and bases might be linked to a different solvent.

Questions and Problems for Chapter 14

1

Vinegar, lemon juice, and curdled milk all taste sour. What other properties would you expect them to have in common?

2

Give the names and formulas of three hydrogen-containing compounds that are not classified as acids. State for each compound one or more properties common to acids that it does not possess.

3

Devise an operational and also a conceptual definition of a gas.

4

At 20 °C, 0.0090 g of $Mg(OH)_2$ will dissolve to make a liter of saturated solution. The magnesium hydroxide that dissolves also ionizes. Is $Mg(OH)_2$ a strong or weak electrolyte? Determine $[OH^-]$.

5

As a solution of barium hydroxide is mixed with a solution of sulfuric acid, a white precipitate forms and the electrical conductivity decreases markedly. Write equations for the reactions that occur, and account for the conductivity change.

6

What is the concentration of $H^+(aq)$ in an aqueous solution in which $[OH^-] = 1.0 \times 10^{-3}$ *M*?

7

The 100 ml of the HCl solution described in Exercise 14-7 is diluted with water to 1.00 liter.

What is the concentration of $H^+(aq)$? What is $[OH^-]$ in this solution?

8

Is the reaction $H^+(aq) + OH^-(aq) \rightleftharpoons H_2O$ exothermic or endothermic? Use your answer and Le Châtelier's principle to decide whether K_W increases or decreases with increasing temperature.

9

What will happen to the equilibrium

$$CH_3COOH \rightleftharpoons H^+ + CH_3COO^-$$

as OH^- ions are added? Even though CH_3COOH is a weak acid, one mole of it will require how many moles of OH^- for neutralization?

10

An eyedropper was calibrated by counting the number of drops required to deliver 1.0 ml. Twenty drops were required.

(a) What is the volume of one drop?
(b) Suppose one such drop of 0.20 M HCl is added to 100 ml of water. What is $[H^+]$?
(c) By what factor does $[H^+]$ change when the one drop is added?

11

Suppose drops of 10 M NaOH are added, one at a time, to 100 ml of 0.020 M HCl. See Problem 10 for a description of the dropper.

(a) What will be $[H^+]$ after one drop is added?
(b) What will be $[H^+]$ after four drops are added?
(c) What will be $[H^+]$ after six drops are added?

12

Calculate $[H^+]$ and $[OH^-]$ in a solution made by mixing 50.0 ml 0.200 M HCl and 49.0 ml 0.200 M NaOH.

13

Calculate $[H^+]$ and $[OH^-]$ in a solution made by mixing 50.0 ml 0.200 M HCl and 49.9 ml 0.200 M NaOH.

14

How much more 0.200 M NaOH solution must be added to the solution in Problem 13 to change $[H^+]$ to 10^{-7} M?

15

If the pH of a solution is 5, what is $[H^+]$? Is the solution acidic or basic?

16

What is $[H^+]$ in a solution whose $pH = 8$? Is the solution acidic or basic? What is $[OH^-]$ in the same solution?

17

How many grams of $NaHCO_3$ are needed to neutralize 100 ml of tomato juice ($pH = 4$)?

18

If rainwater ($pH = 6$) and seawater ($pH = 8$) are mixed in equal volumes, what will the final pH be?

19

In what ratio must lemon juice ($pH = 2$) and household ammonia ($pH = 11$) be mixed to yield a neutral solution?

20

How many H^+ ions are present in 1 ml of a solution at $pH = 5$?

21

An acid was titrated to the equivalence point with 0.0100 M KOH. It required 52.0 ml of KOH for 26.0 ml of acid. What was the acid molarity?

22

Three samples of a base were titrated to the equivalence point with 0.0500 M HCl. The volumes used were:

Acid (ml)	Base (ml)
23.2	18.3
36.5	31.4
17.6	14.8

Find the concentration of the base to the proper number of significant figures.

23

A beginning technician was told to standardize an NaOH solution. He carried out the titration and reported that 1.65 ml of base required 27 ml of 0.050 00 M acid. He therefore concluded that the NaOH was 0.818 18 M. Assume you are his supervisor. Check the results and criticize the work.

24

A mixture of solid benzoic acid and a neutral material weighing 0.100 g was titrated with 40.0 ml of 0.002 50 M NaOH. Benzoic acid has a molar mass of 122 g and one hydrogen that reacts with a base. What is the percent by weight of benzoic acid in the mixture?

25

An acid is a substance H*B* that can form $H^+(aq)$ in the equilibrium:

$$HB(aq) \rightleftharpoons H^+(aq) + B^-(aq)$$

(a) Does equilibrium favor reactants or products for a strong acid?
(b) Does equilibrium favor reactants or products for a very weak acid?
(c) If acid HB_1 is a stronger acid than acid HB_2, is K_1 a larger or smaller number than K_2?

$$K_1 = \frac{[H^+][B_1^-]}{[HB_1]} \qquad K_2 = \frac{[H^+][B_2^-]}{[HB_2]}$$

26

(a) Which of the following acids is the strongest and which is the weakest?
Ammonium ion, NH_4^+ (in an NH_4Cl solution)
hydrogen sulfate ion, HSO_4^- (in a $KHSO_4$ solution)
Hydrogen sulfide, H_2S
(b) If 0.1 *M* solutions are made of NH_4Cl, $KHSO_4$, and H_2S, in which will $[H^+]$ be highest and in which will it be lowest?

27

From a study of Appendix 3, what generalization can you make concerning acids which contain more than one atom of hydrogen in their molecules or ions?

28

When sodium acetate, $NaCH_3COO$, is added to an aqueous solution of hydrogen fluoride, HF, a reaction occurs in which the weak acid HF loses H^+.

(a) Write the equation for the reaction.
(b) What base is competing with F^- for H^+?

29

(a) Write the equation for the reaction that shows the acid-base reaction between hydrogen sulfide, H_2S, and carbonate ion, CO_3^{2-}.
(b) What are the two bases competing for H^+?
(c) From the values of K_A for these two acids, predict whether the equilibrium favors reactants or products.

30

Write the equation for the reaction in each of the following examples. For each reaction, predict whether reactants or products are favored (using values of K_A given in Appendix 3).

(a) $HNO_2(aq) + NH_3(aq) \rightleftharpoons$
(b) $NH_4^+(aq) + F^-(aq) \rightleftharpoons$
(c) $C_6H_5COOH(aq) + CH_3COO^-(aq) \rightleftharpoons$

31

Write the equations for the reactions between each of the following acids and bases. For each reaction, predict whether reactants or products are favored.

(a) $H_2SO_3(aq) + HCO_3^-(aq) \rightleftharpoons$
(b) $H_2CO_3(aq) + SO_3^{2-}(aq) \rightleftharpoons$
(c) $H_2SO_3(aq) + SO_3^{2-}(aq) \rightleftharpoons$

32

A 0.25 *M* solution of benzoic acid (symbolize it H*B*) is found to have $[H^+] = 4 \times 10^{-3}$ *M*. Assuming the simple reaction:

$$HB(aq) \rightleftharpoons H^+(aq) + B^-(aq)$$

calculate K_A for benzoic acid.

33

If 23 grams of formic acid, HCOOH, are dissolved in 10.0 liters of water at 20 °C, the $[H^+]$ is found to be 3.0×10^{-3} *M*. Calculate K_A.

34

A chemist dissolved 30 grams of CH_3COOH in enough water to make one liter of solution. What is the concentration of this acetic acid solution? What is the concentration of $H^+(aq)$? Assume a negligible change in $[CH_3COOH]$ because of dissociation.

35

The HF in a 0.100 *M* aqueous solution is 8% dissociated. What is the value of its K_A?

36

A hot solution of 1 *M* acetic acid is a better conductor of electricity than is a cold solution of the same concentration. Explain.

37

The K_A value for HCN is 4.8×10^{-10}. What is the equilibrium constant for the following reaction? Are products favored?

$$H_2CO_3 + CN^- \rightleftharpoons HCO_3^- + HCN$$

38

K_A for H_2O_2 producing H^+ is 2.4×10^{-12}. Write the equation for the reaction with water to produce H_3O^+ and the base OOH^-. Is pure H_2O_2 a stronger or weaker acid than water?

Oxidation and Reduction

Chemists use the words *oxidation* and *reduction* to describe certain kinds of chemical reactions. There is a very close comparison between acid-base reactions, discussed in Chapter 14, and oxidation-reduction reactions, which are the subject of this chapter. There are many familiar examples of this type of chemical reaction. Here are a few:

Wood burning in a campfire
Reactions in batteries
Gasoline reacting with oxygen in an automobile engine.
Destruction of harmful bacteria by chlorine in drinking-water supplies
The corrosion of metals.
Bleaching hair with hydrogen peroxide.

Lead storage batteries in cars and dry cells in a flashlight are examples of oxidation and reduction. They are called electro-chemical cells. When you changed the dry cells in a flashlight because the old ones were dead, did you wonder what had happened inside the cell? Why does electric current flow from a new dry cell but not from one that has been used many hours? These are important questions in chemistry. By studying the chemical reactions that occur in an electrochemical cell, we will see what chemists mean by the terms *oxidation* and *reduction*. More important, we will find a basis for predicting whether reactants or products are favored in an oxidation-reduction system.

15-1   The Chemistry of Electrochemical Cells

A good way to investigate what happens in an electrochemical cell is to build one. To do this, put a dilute solution of copper sulfate in one beaker. To another beaker add a dilute solution of silver nitrate. Put a strip of copper metal in the $CuSO_4$ solution and a rod of silver metal in the $AgNO_3$ solution. Connect the silver rod to one terminal of an ammeter, which measures electric current. Connect the other terminal of the ammeter to the copper strip. To complete the electric circuit, a connection between the two solutions must be made. One way of doing this is shown in Figures 15-1 and 15-2. A glass U-tube is filled with a solution of a strong electrolyte, usually KNO_3. Cotton plugs or porous plates keep the solutions from mixing too freely. This tube is called a salt bridge. When the salt bridge is put in place, the ammeter needle moves. Electric current is moving through the circuit. Gradually, the copper strip gets smaller and the silver rod becomes larger. Silver is being deposited on it. Apparently a chemical reaction takes place. As time goes by, the ammeter shows less and less current flowing until finally, when the copper strip has disappeared or the silver ions are all plated out, there is no current.

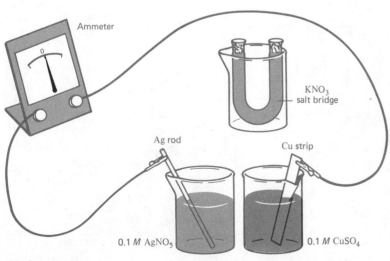

Figure 15-1
Apparatus for an electrochemical experiment. The circuit is incomplete because the solutions are not connected.

So far we have just looked at these cells in a qualitative manner; no measurements were made. Useful information is usually obtained from quantitative observations. Let us try to answer these questions. How much did the silver rod increase in mass? How much did the copper rod decrease? Let us repeat the experiment, recording the mass of the metal pieces before and after the experiment. One set of data indicates the mass of the copper strip has decreased 0.635 gram, and the mass of the silver rod has increased 2.16 grams. This information is more useful when expressed in moles:

$$\text{moles of Cu reacting} = 0.635 \text{ gram Cu} \times \frac{1 \text{ mole Cu}}{63.5 \text{ grams}}$$

$$= 0.0100 \text{ mole Cu}$$

$$\text{moles of Ag reacting} = 2.16 \text{ grams Ag} \times \frac{1 \text{ mole Ag}}{108 \text{ grams}}$$

$$= 0.0200 \text{ mole Ag}$$

A simple relation exists between the amounts of copper and silver involved in the reaction. One mole of copper goes into solution for every two moles of silver deposited on the silver rod. This value agrees with the molar ratios studied in Chapter 2 and Experiment 9.

Here is a proposal that may explain these results. Copper atoms release electrons to the wire. The cupric ions formed, Cu^{2+}, go into solution. The electrons move through the external circuit and the ammeter to the silver rod in the other beaker. The positively charged silver ions in solution draw electrons from the silver rod and become neutral silver metal atoms. These processes can be summarized:

In the beaker on the right, $Cu(s) \longrightarrow Cu^{2+} + 2 \ e^-$

In the beaker on the left, $2 \ Ag^+ + 2 \ e^- \longrightarrow 2 \ Ag(s)$

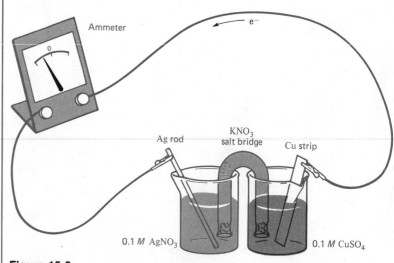

Figure 15-2
An electrochemical experiment in progress. The salt bridge connects the solutions and completes the circuit.

Adding gives the overall equation

$$Cu(s) + 2\ Ag^+ \longrightarrow Cu^{2+} + 2\ Ag(s)$$

This equation describes what goes on in the electrochemical cell. In half of the cell, copper metal dissolves to form Cu^{2+} ions. In the other half of the cell, metallic silver is deposited from a solution of Ag^+ ions. Each of these reactions is called a *half-cell reaction,* or more simply, a *half-reaction.*

There are several important ideas presented in this description.

(1) In the electrochemical cell *two* reactions occur in separate beakers. The changes can be considered as two separate reactions. *Equations for the two half-reactions can be written separately, but the half-reactions do not occur alone.*

(2) *Electrons are written as part of the equation for each half-reaction.* The ammeter shows that electrons move through the circuit. They flow when the reaction starts and do not flow when the reaction stops. Noting that the copper strip loses mass and becomes Cu^{2+} while Ag^+ ion is converted to Ag metal gives us a means of deducing the direction of electron flow through the external circuit.

(3) *Chemical changes take place in each half of the cell.* The copper strip is converted to copper ions (the strip loses mass and the solution becomes bluer). Silver ions are changed to metal (the silver rod gains mass). The new species can be explained in terms of electron gain by silver ions and electron loss by copper atoms.

(4) *The two equations, when combined, express the overall, or net equation.*

$$Cu(s) + 2\ Ag^+ \longrightarrow Cu^{2+} + 2\ Ag(s)$$

The net equation shows that the number of moles of electrons lost by copper atoms equals the number of moles of electrons gained by silver ions.

You may be wondering why there are no electrons shown in the net equation. Electrical measurements indicate both solutions remain electrically neutral. *The number of electrons lost by one solution must equal the number of electrons gained by the other.* This is another aspect of conservation of mass. If electrons were either made or destroyed, the total mass would change. Such a chemical reaction has never been observed. The reaction that occurs in an electrochemical cell is conveniently described using two equations, one for each half-reaction. In one, electrons are lost; in the other, electrons are gained. To distinguish these half-reactions, two identifying names are helpful.

Oxidation occurs in the half-reaction in which electrons are lost. Copper is oxidized to cupric ions:

$$Cu(s) \longrightarrow Cu^{2+} + 2\ e^-$$

Workers in many industries deal with oxidation-reduction—metallurgy, fuel cells, sulfuric acid manufacture, battery production, corrosion prevention, and fermentation.

Are Negative Ions

Reduction occurs in the half-reaction in which electrons are gained. Silver ions are reduced to metal:

$$2 \text{ Ag}^+ + 2 \text{ e}^- \longrightarrow 2 \text{ Ag}(s)$$

The overall reaction is called an *oxidation-reduction,* or *redox, reaction:*

$$\text{Cu}(s) + 2 \text{ Ag}^+ \longrightarrow \text{Cu}^{2+} + 2 \text{ Ag}(s)$$

It may seem strange that an electron gain can be called reduction! The name for this type of chemical reaction was invented many years ago, long before anyone knew about electrons. Early metallurgists introduced the word *reduction* for the process of changing ores to metals. They reduced large piles of ore to small amounts of metal. Reduction was a very apt name for the process. Centuries later, after the electron was discovered (1897) and the existence of ions was established, chemists realized the word *reduction* had been applied to a process in which electrons were being added to the positive metallic ions in ores.

In an electrochemical cell electrons enter and leave through electrical conductors called *electrodes.* In our example oxidation takes place at the copper electrode. *The electrode where oxidation occurs is called the* **anode**. Negative charge leaves this electrode as electrons move through the external circuit. Positive charge, in the form of Cu^{2+} ions, is produced in this half of the cell. These actions make this half-cell positive. How is electrical neutrality of the solution maintained? Movement of ions through

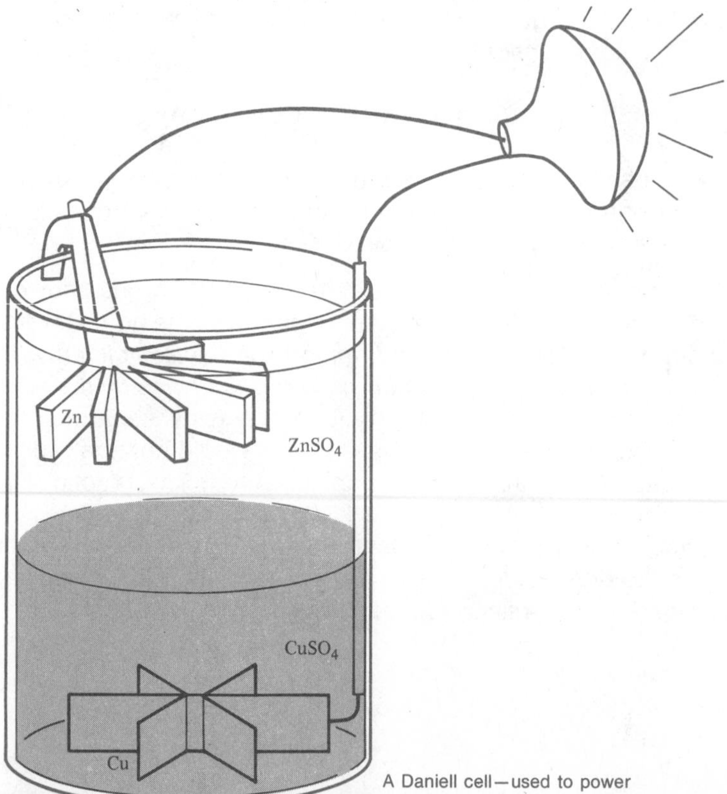

A Daniell cell—used to power early telegraph systems

Zn

ZnSO₄

CuSO₄

Cu

the solution provides an explanation. All negative ions, SO_4^{2-} and NO_3^-, drift toward the anode, balancing the positive charge being created there by the formation of Cu^{2+}. Positive ions, Ag^+, K^+, and Cu^{2+}, move away from the anode. Negative ions are called *anions,* because they move towards the anode.

The other half-cell consists of a silver electrode in a solution of silver nitrate. Negative charge arrives at this electrode as electrons move through the external circuit. At the surface of this electrode electrons encounter Ag^+ ions in the solution. There is a chemical reaction. Silver metal is formed. Reduction takes place at the silver electrode. *The electrode where reduction takes place is called the* **cathode**. The reaction $Ag^+ + e^- \longrightarrow Ag$ removes positive charge from the solution, making this half-cell negative. Electrical neutrality is achieved as negative ions (NO_3^-) drift out of this half-cell and positive ions (K^+, Cu^{2+}) move into it. Positive ions are called *cations,* because they move towards the cathode.

The importance of the salt bridge becomes apparent. As the cell begins to operate, positively charged Cu^{2+} ions form at the surface of the copper anode. The negative anions in solution and in the salt bridge start to drift towards the anode and balance the positive charge. At the same time positive charge decreases near the silver cathode. The positive cations in solution and in the salt bridge start to move towards the cathode to replace the positive charge. Negative electric charge is carried away from the copper anode through the external circuit to the silver electrode. *Anions carry negative electric charge through the solutions and the salt bridge back to the copper anode.* The circuit is complete and an electric current flows. Figure 15-3 shows the same operating cell as Figure 15-2 but in the schematic fashion we will use throughout this chapter.

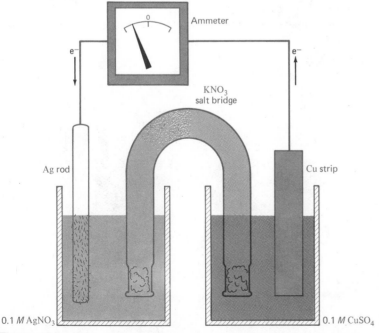

Figure 15-3
Schematic diagram of Cu-Ag electrochemical cell.

15-2   Redox Reactions in a Beaker

It is not necessary to set up an electrochemical cell in order to study an oxidation-reduction reaction. A series of figures explains this point. Figure 15-4 shows the first experiment. The ammeter has been removed and the electrodes have been directly connected. Chemical reactions take place as before. Copper dissolves at the anode. Silver is deposited at the cathode.

In Figure 15-5 the salt bridge has been removed. A porous clay wall separates the two half-cells. Once again copper dissolves at the anode and silver is deposited at the cathode. What happens if we take the clay wall away and mix the solutions? Chemical reactions still occur.

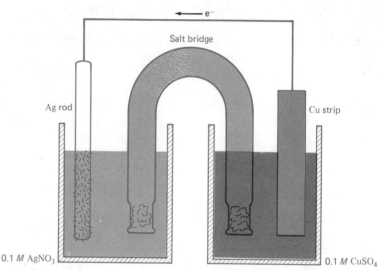

Figure 15-4
An electrochemical cell in which the electrodes are joined by a good conductor.

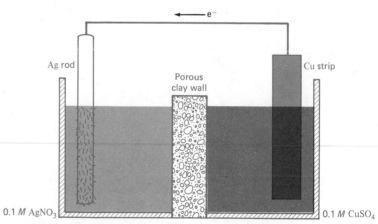

Figure 15-5
A cell with a porous clay wall connecting the solutions.

Two additional experiments come to mind. Does any chemical reaction take place if a silver rod is placed in a copper sulfate solution? Does any reaction occur if a copper strip is placed in a silver nitrate solution? Experiments provide answers to these questions. Figures 15-6 and 15-7 show what happens. There is no visible reaction when a silver rod is placed in a copper sulfate solution.

$$Ag(s) + Cu^{2+} \longrightarrow \text{no reaction}$$

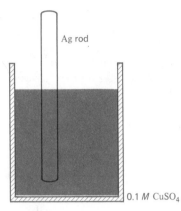

Figure 15-6
Does a chemical reaction occur? No.
$Ag(s) + Cu^{2+}(aq) \longrightarrow$ No visible reaction.

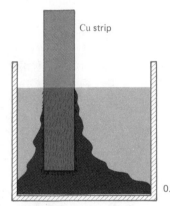

Figure 15-7
Does a chemical reaction occur? Yes.
$Cu(s) + 2\,Ag^+(aq) \longrightarrow 2\,Ag(s) + Cu^{2+}(aq)$.

However, when metallic copper is placed in a silver nitrate solution, we see evidence of reaction. Silvery crystals form and the solution turns blue.

$$Cu(s) + 2\,Ag^+ \longrightarrow Cu^{2+} + 2Ag$$

Electron transfer occurs as silver ions collide with the copper rod. Electrons leave the copper and react with the Ag^+ ions. Because of the presence of Cu, silver ions are reduced. Chemists say that Cu acts as a *reducing agent*. At the same time Cu is oxidized because of the presence of Ag^+. Chemists refer to Ag^+ as the *oxidizing agent*.

$$Cu^{2+} \longleftarrow 2\,e^- \longrightarrow 2\,Ag^+$$

$$Cu(s) + 2\,Ag^+ \rightleftharpoons Cu^{2+} + 2\,Ag(s)$$

$$\text{metal}_1 + \text{ion}_2 \qquad \rightleftharpoons \qquad \text{ion}_1 + \text{metal}_2$$

Many other oxidation-reduction reactions take place in aqueous solutions. One of these was mentioned in Section 14-1 when acids were discussed. Zinc metal reacts with an acid to form H_2 gas and Zn^{2+} ions.

$$Zn(s) + 2\,H^+ \longrightarrow Zn^{2+} + H_2(g)$$

Each Zn atom loses two electrons. Two H^+ ions gain electrons. Molecular hydrogen forms as Zn metal dissolves. Zinc atoms are oxidized. Hydrogen ions are reduced. The equation for this reaction can be obtained by combining the two half-reactions:

$2\,H^+ + 2\,e^- \longrightarrow H_2(g)$	reduction
$Zn(s) \longrightarrow Zn^{2+} + 2\,e^-$	oxidation
$2\,H^+ + Zn(s) \longrightarrow Zn^{2+} + H_2(g)$	net equation

Not all metals react with acids. Among the more common metals, magnesium, aluminum, zinc, iron, and nickel react with HCl solutions to form H_2. Other metals—such as copper, mercury, silver, and gold—do not react with HCl solutions. Apparently some metals release electrons to H^+ and others do not.

As a third oxidation-reduction example, place a strip of metallic zinc in a solution of copper nitrate. The zinc is soon coated with metallic copper and the blue color of Cu^{+2} in the solution disappears. Chemical tests show that the zinc ion, Zn^{2+}, forms and the concentration of Cu^{2+} decreases.. The net equation

$$Zn(s) + Cu^{2+} \longrightarrow Zn^{2+} + Cu(s)$$

can be separated into two equations.

$Cu^{2+} + 2\,e^- \longrightarrow Cu(s)$	reduction
$Zn(s) \longrightarrow Zn^{2+} + 2\,e^-$	oxidation

Zinc atoms are oxidized and copper ions are reduced. Here, copper ions *gain* electrons from zinc atoms. In Experiment 9 and in the reaction shown in Figure 15-7 copper atoms lose electrons to silver ions.

15-3   Competition for Electrons

The reactions that have been discussed can be viewed as competition for electrons. A state of equilibrium will be reached when this competition reaches a balance between opposing reactions. For the reaction of metallic copper with silver nitrate solution, Ag^+ accepted electrons from Cu. At equilibrium the products Cu^{2+} and $Ag(s)$ are greatly favored.

The same sort of competition for electrons is involved in the reaction between $Zn(s)$ and Cu^{2+}. In this system equilibrium greatly favors the products, Zn^{2+} and $Cu(s)$.

Competition for electrons in redox reactions is very similar to the competition for protons in acid-base reactions. Using the Brønsted-Lowry concept for acids and bases, we saw that the stronger base gains a proton. In redox reactions the stronger oxidizing agent gains the electron:

$$HB_1 + B_2^- \longrightarrow (B_1^- \longleftarrow H^+ \longrightarrow B_2^-) \longrightarrow B_1^- + HB_2$$

$$\text{acid}_1 + \text{base}_2 \quad \rightleftharpoons \quad \text{base}_1 + \text{acid}_2$$

$$M_1 + M_2^+ \longrightarrow (M_1^+ \longleftarrow e^- \longrightarrow M_2^+) \longrightarrow M_1^+ + M_2$$

$$\text{metal}_1 + \text{ion}_2 \quad \rightleftharpoons \quad \text{ion}_1 + \text{metal}_2$$

The similarity suggests that a table might be developed in which metallic ions are listed by their tendency to gain electrons. We can start with the half-reactions encountered in this chapter. The equations will be written to show gain of electrons and then arranged in order of their tendency to do so.

In the reaction between metallic copper and silver ions, copper ions and silver atoms form. This experimental evidence leads us to believe Ag^+ accepts electrons from Cu. We can arrange the equations for the two half-reactions with silver first. Silver ions accept electrons more readily than copper ions do:

$$Ag^+ + e^- \longrightarrow Ag(s)$$

$$Cu^{2+} + 2\,e^- \longrightarrow Cu(s)$$

Another reaction discussed in Section 15-2 led us to believe that copper ions gain electrons more readily than zinc ions. Therefore, the Zn^{2+}–Zn half-reaction would be placed below the Cu^{2+}–Cu half-reaction:

$$Ag^+ + \quad e^- \longrightarrow Ag(s)$$

$$Cu^{2+} + 2\,e^- \longrightarrow Cu(s)$$

$$Zn^{2+} + 2\,e^- \longrightarrow Zn(s)$$

This order suggests that Ag^+ will gain electrons from Zn, forming Ag metal and Zn^{2+} ions. Now let us try to add the H^+–H_2 half-reaction to the list. The fact that Zn metal dissolves in HCl but Cu metal does not tells us that the H^+–H_2 half-reaction equation should be placed above Zn^{2+}–Zn but below Cu^{2+}–Cu. Hydrogen ions accept electrons more readily than Zn^{2+} ions. Both Cu^{2+} and Ag^+ ions gain electrons more readily than H^+:

$$Ag^+ + \quad e^- \longrightarrow Ag(s)$$

$$Cu^{2+} + 2\,e^- \longrightarrow Cu(s)$$

$$2\,H^+ + 2\,e^- \longrightarrow H_2(g)$$

$$Zn^{2+} + 2\,e^- \longrightarrow Zn(s)$$

EXERCISE 15-1

From the statement that nickel reacts with H^+ to give H_2 and the additional information that zinc metal reacts readily with Ni^{2+}, decide where to place the Ni^{2+}–Ni equation in our list.

In Chapter 14 we were able to make the discussion of acids and bases quantitative by using equilibrium constants. Is there a similar way to make quantitative statements for oxidation-reduction reactions? The voltages of electrochemical cells provide such quantitative measures.

15-4 Volts, Amperes, and Coulombs

Some of the words used in describing electrochemical cells may seem quite strange to you. Perhaps their meaning will be clear if the flow of electric current through a wire is compared to the flow of water through a pipe. Suppose that you were a fireman trying to put out a fire and that you had just hooked your hose to a fire hydrant. You would be interested in three things:

Is there enough water available to put out the fire? You know it won't do you much good to put out half the fire. The total amount of water available is important.

How fast can water flow through the pipeline to the fire hydrant? You won't be able to fight the fire very effectively if there is a large reservoir of water but such a narrow pipeline that you get only a very thin trickle of water.

Finally, *how high will you be able to reach* with the water coming out of your hose? How much water pressure is there in the system? If the stream of water only reaches to the third floor of a building when the fire is on the fourth floor, you will have trouble putting the fire out.

The amount of water, its flow rate, and its pressure are important to a fireman. The same kinds of things are important when working with electrochemical cells. We need *enough* electricity, moving with adequate *rate* at sufficiently high *pressure* to do the job at hand. Table 15-1 and Figure 15-8 compare the names of important quantities in the fireman's water system with those in a chemist's electrochemical cell.

TABLE 15-1

A Comparison of Terminology

Quantity Measured	Units Used with Water	Units Used with Electricity
amount of flow	gallons	coulombs
rate of flow	gallons/minute	coulombs/second (also called amperes)
tendency to flow (pressure)	pounds/inch²	volts

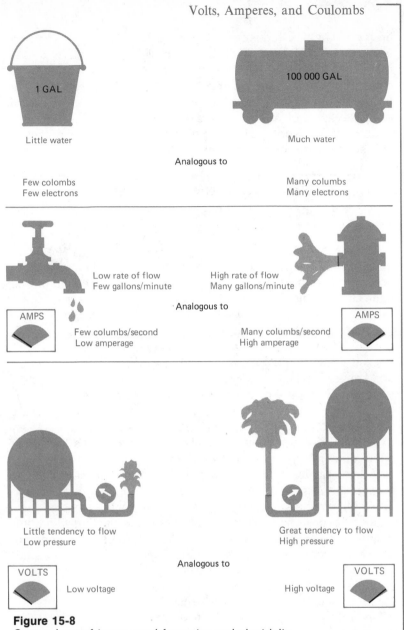

Figure 15-8
Comparison of terms used for water and electricity.

The amount of water can be expressed as the number of molecules, but a more common unit is the gallon. The amount of electricity can be expressed as a number of electrons, but a more common unit is the coulomb. A coulomb is 1.04×10^{-5} mole of electrons.

The rate of flow is the amount divided by time. Gallons per minute for water and coulombs per second for electricity are often used to indicate rate of flow. One coulomb per second is also called an *ampere*. A circuit through which one coulomb is passing per second is said to be carrying a current of one ampere. In Section 15-10 the amount and rate of flow will be discussed further.

Electrical pressure is expressed in volts. Voltage is just one of the many ways to talk about potential energy. The electrical voltage corresponds directly to the water pressure in our story of the fireman. A high voltage means that electrons are in a high energy state. When the switch is closed in an electric circuit, electrons move through the circuit. They may operate a motor or perhaps light a light bulb. Like water flowing downhill, electrons spontaneously move from a position of high potential energy to one of low potential energy. The voltage of a cell measures its tendency to do electrical work. Cells using different combinations of metals and solutions produce different voltages.

15-5   The Voltage of an Electrochemical Cell and the Tendency to Accept Electrons

We would like to measure the contribution each half-reaction makes to the cell voltage. The voltage for a particular cell may be considered as having two parts; the first is characteristic of one half-reaction and the second is characteristic of the other half-reaction. Chemists call these two contributions to the cell voltage "half-cell potentials," a term that emphasizes the relation between voltage and potential energy. Half-cell potentials are symbolized E. Since the voltage of a cell depends on concentration and temperature, chemists have agreed to use 25 °C as the reference temperature. For ionic solutions the reference concentration is 1 M. For gases a pressure of one atmosphere is chosen as the standard pressure. The symbol $E°$ (called "E zero") is used to indicate that measurements have been carried out at the reference temperature, pressure, and concentration.

There is a close parallel between the half-reaction view of redox reactions and the Brønsted-Lowry concept of acids and bases. The table of acid strengths was established on the basis of competition for protons. In redox reactions we are dealing with competition for electrons. Chemists have agreed to use the tendency of H^+ to accept electrons in the H^+–$H_2(g)$ half-reaction as the reference system. The value of 0.00 volt for this half-reaction is an arbitrary assignment; it is convenient to measure the tendency for an ion M^+ to gain electrons from $H_2(g)$.

Electrochemical cells can be constructed in which one half-cell is the reference system H^+–$H_2(g)$. The other half-cell can then be chosen to compare with the reference system. Figure 15-9 shows two examples. Notice that both cells are constructed so that electrons flow from left to right through the external circuit. The first drawing (A) represents the cell made from the Zn^{2+}–Zn and H^+–$H_2(g)$ half-cells. Experiments show that zinc metal dissolves and hydrogen gas forms when this cell operates. The equation for the reaction is

$$Zn(s) + 2 H^+ \longrightarrow Zn^{2+} + H_2(g)$$

Zinc metal gives up electrons. Hydrogen ions accept them. The voltmeter shows a reading of 0.76 volt for this combination of half-cells. Since the voltage of the H^+–$H_2(g)$ half-reaction is 0.00 volt, then the voltage of the entire cell can be assigned to the Zn–Zn^{2+} half-reaction:

$$Zn(s) \longrightarrow Zn^{2+} + 2\,e \qquad E° = 0.76 \text{ volt}$$

This reaction represents oxidation of zinc. However, chemists have agreed to compare reduction reactions. Therefore, the equation must be reversed and the sign of $E°$ changed to

$$Zn^{2+} + 2\,e^- \longrightarrow Zn(s) \qquad E° = -0.76 \text{ volt}$$

The negative sign for $E°$ indicates that Zn^{2+} has less tendency to accept electrons than H^+ does. Therefore Zn^{2+}–Zn is below H^+–$H_2(g)$ in the table of electron-gaining ability.

The second electrochemical cell (B) in Figure 15-9 is made from the two half-cells, Cu^{2+}–Cu and H^+–$H_2(g)$. Experiments show that the reaction for this system is

$$Cu^{2+} + H_2(g) \longrightarrow Cu(s) + 2\,H^+$$

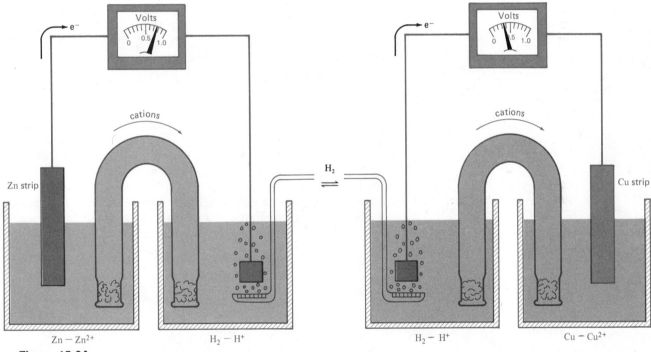

Figure 15-9A
The Zn–Zn^{2+} half-cell compared to the hydrogen reference half-cell.

Figure 15-9B
The Cu–Cu^{2+} half-cell compared to the hydrogen reference half-cell.

Hydrogen gas molecules give up electrons. Copper ions accept them. The voltmeter indicates a value of 0.34 volt. As before, this voltage can be assigned to the Cu^{2+}–Cu half-reaction:

$$Cu^{2+} + 2\,e^- \longrightarrow Cu(s) \qquad E° = 0.34 \text{ volt}$$

Notice that this reaction is already written as a reduction process so that it does not have to be reversed. Now we can write the three half-reactions in order of their tendency to accept electrons:

$$Cu^{2+} + 2\,e^- \longrightarrow Cu(s) \qquad E° = +0.34 \text{ volt}$$

$$2\,H^+ + 2\,e^- \longrightarrow H_2(g) \qquad E° = 0.00 \text{ volt}$$

$$Zn^{2+} + 2\,e^- \longrightarrow Zn(s) \qquad E° = -0.76 \text{ volt}$$

Chemists have determined a large number of half-cell voltages. The magnitude of the voltage is a numerical measure of the tendency for the oxidized species in the half-reaction to accept electrons in comparison with H^+ ions.

> If the sign of the voltage is *positive*, the oxidized species has a *greater* tendency to accept electrons than do H^+ ions.

> If the sign is *negative*, the oxidized species has *less* tendency to accept electrons than do H^+ ions.

In Table 14-5 acids are arranged in order of their tendency to donate protons to the reference base, H_2O. Table 15-2 is an arrangement for oxidized species showing their tendency to accept electrons from the reference reducing agent, H_2. A more complete list is given in Appendix 4.

15-6   Predicting Redox Reactions

Chemists use half-cell potentials to predict whether an oxidation-reduction reaction can occur. Let us see how to do this with some examples.

Will iron dissolve in a solution that is 1 M in Ni^{2+}? We perform an experiment and find that it does. How can this result be related to the electron-accepting tendency and the sign of $E°$ for the net reaction? We find the two half-reactions which must be considered in Table 15-2:

$$Ni^{2+} + 2\,e^- \longrightarrow Ni(s) \qquad E° = -0.25 \text{ volt}$$

$$Fe^{2+} + 2\,e^- \longrightarrow Fe(s) \qquad E° = -0.44 \text{ volt}$$

Remember, $E°$ values show the tendency for oxidized species to accept electrons; they show the tendency for reduction to take place. From these particular $E°$ values it can be concluded that Ni^{2+} has a greater tendency to accept electrons than does Fe^{2+}. This suggests that Ni^{2+} will gain electrons. To fit the experiment, we need Fe as a reactant. So we reverse the second equation. This changes the sign of $E°$ from minus to plus:

$$Fe(s) \longrightarrow Fe^{2+} + 2\,e^- \qquad E° = +0.44 \text{ volt}$$

Now adding the equations for the two half-reactions, we obtain an equation that agrees with the experiment. Iron dissolves in Ni^{2+} solution. Note the positive sign for $E°$:

When E° is

POSITIVE
RODUCTS
REDOMINATE
AT EQUILIBRIUM

$$Ni^{2+} + 2\,e^- \longrightarrow \quad Ni(s) \qquad E° = -0.25 \text{ volt}$$

$$\underline{Fe(s) \longrightarrow \quad Fe^{2+} + 2\,e^- \qquad E° = \quad 0.44 \text{ volt}}$$

$$Ni^{2+} + Fe(s) \longrightarrow Fe^{2+} + Ni(s) \qquad E° = +0.19 \text{ volt}$$

A calculated positive $E°$ allows us to predict that products predominate when the reaction reaches equilibrium.

TABLE 15-2

Standard Reduction Potentials for Some Half-Reactions

Oxidized Species	$+ e^-$	$\longrightarrow$ Reduced Species	$E°$ Volts
F_2	$+ 2\,e^-$	$\longrightarrow$ $2\,F^-$	$+2.87$
$PbO_2 + SO_4^{2-} + 4\,H^+$	$+ 2\,e^-$	$\longrightarrow$ $PbSO_4 + 2\,H_2O$	$+1.68$
$MnO_4^- + 8\,H^+$	$+ 5\,e^-$	$\longrightarrow$ $Mn^{2+} + 4\,H_2O$	$+1.52$
Cl_2	$+ 2\,e^-$	$\longrightarrow$ $2\,Cl^-$	$+1.36$
$4\,H^+ + O_2$	$+ 4\,e^-$	$\longrightarrow$ $2\,H_2O$	$+1.23$
Br_2	$+ 2\,e^-$	$\longrightarrow$ $2\,Br^-$	$+1.06$
$NO_3^- + 4\,H^+$	$+ 3\,e^-$	$\longrightarrow$ $NO + 2\,H_2O$	$+0.96$
Ag^+	$+ e^-$	$\longrightarrow$ Ag	$+0.80$
Fe^{3+}	$+ e^-$	$\longrightarrow$ Fe^{2+}	$+0.77$
I_2	$+ 2\,e^-$	$\longrightarrow$ $2\,I^-$	$+0.53$
Cu^{2+}	$+ 2\,e^-$	$\longrightarrow$ Cu	$+0.34$
$2\,H^+$	$+ 2\,e^-$	$\longrightarrow$ H_2	0.00
Ni^{2+}	$+ 2\,e^-$	$\longrightarrow$ Ni	-0.25
Co^{2+}	$+ 2\,e^-$	$\longrightarrow$ Co	-0.28
$PbSO_4$	$+ 2\,e^-$	$\longrightarrow$ $Pb + SO_4^{2-}$	-0.36
Fe^{2+}	$+ 2\,e^-$	$\longrightarrow$ Fe	-0.44
Zn^{2+}	$+ 2\,e^-$	$\longrightarrow$ Zn	-0.76
Al^{3+}	$+ 3\,e^-$	$\longrightarrow$ Al	-1.66

Here is another example. Metals such as Al, Mg, and Zn are oxidized by 1 M HCl to produce hydrogen gas. However, when Ag metal is placed in 1 M HCl, there is no appreciable reaction. The half-reactions from Table 15-2 are

Geochemists use tables of reduction potentials to help decide what conditions were probably present in past geological eras.

$$2\,Ag^+ + 2\,e^- \longrightarrow 2\,Ag \qquad\qquad E^\circ = +0.80 \text{ volt}$$

$$2\,H^+ + 2\,e^- \longrightarrow H_2 \qquad\qquad E^\circ = 0.00 \text{ volt}$$

Again, we want to relate these equations to the experiment we tried. Therefore, these half-reactions must be combined so that Ag and H^+ are reactants. This is achieved by writing the first equation as an oxidation instead of as a reduction:

$$2\,Ag \longrightarrow 2\,Ag^+ + 2\,e^- \qquad E^\circ = -0.80 \text{ volt}$$

$$2\,H^+ + 2\,e^- \longrightarrow H_2 \qquad\qquad E^\circ = 0.00 \text{ volt}$$

$$\overline{2\,Ag + 2\,H^+ \longrightarrow H_2 + 2\,Ag^+ \qquad E^\circ = -0.80 \text{ volt}}$$

Our experiment showed that H^+ does not react with Ag. At equilibrium, reactants predominate.

A calculated negative E° allows us to predict that reactants predominate when the reaction reaches equilibrium.

Notice that the E° value for the Ag^+–Ag half-reaction was not doubled, even though the equation has been multiplied by two. The voltage of a cell does not depend on how many moles take part in a reaction. Voltage is a measure of electrical pressure. Thinking of the analogy with water helps us understand this. The pressure caused by water does not depend on how much is present. Pressure depends on potential energy, which is determined by the height of the water. The voltage caused by a cell does not depend on how many moles are present. Voltage depends on potential energy, which is determined by the bonding arrangement in the chemicals. Changing the number of moles does not change the voltage for an electrochemical reaction.

Since E° is a measure of the tendency for a reaction to occur, E° at equilibrium will be zero. Once equilibrium is reached, the tendency to go in one direction equals the tendency to go in the other. The net tendency is zero.

EXERCISE 15-2

Calculate the potential expected for the following combinations of half-reactions. Assume all ions are 1 M.

(a) $Co + Fe^{3+}$ gives $Co^{2+} + Fe^{2+}$

(b) $H_2 + Cl_2$ gives $H^+ + Cl^-$

(c) $I^- + MnO_4^-$ in acid solution gives $I_2 + Mn^{2+}$

Answer: $+ 0.99$ volt

(d) Will $Ag + Cl^-$ produce $Ag^+ + Cl_2$?

Although Ag does not dissolve in 1 M HCl, it dissolves readily in 1 M HNO_3. This suggests that NO_3^- ion rather than H^+ ion must be the oxidizing agent. The equations we want to consider are:

$$4\,H^+ + NO_3^- + 3\,e^- \longrightarrow NO + 2\,H_2O \qquad E^\circ = +0.96 \text{ volt}$$

$$3\,Ag \longrightarrow 3\,Ag^+ + 3\,e^- \qquad\qquad E^\circ = -0.80 \text{ volt}$$

$$\overline{4\,H^+ + NO_3^- + 3\,Ag \longrightarrow 3\,Ag^+ + NO + 2\,H_2O \qquad E^\circ = +0.16 \text{ volt}}$$

Experiments show that products are favored. The $E°$ value for the net reaction is positive. These ideas are always found together. There are other ways to express the same regularity:

A substance in the left column in Table 15-2 tends to react spontaneously with any substance in the right column that is *lower* in the table.

or conversely

A substance in the right column of the table tends to react spontaneously with any substance *higher* in the left column.

In Table 15-2 the strong oxidizing agents are at the top left side of the half-reaction list. The fluorine molecule is the strongest oxidizing agent shown. The strong reducing agents are at the bottom right side of the half-reaction list. The aluminum atom is the strongest reducing agent shown. Qualitative predictions about redox reactions can be made using these guides. For example, Br_2 and HNO_3 are above $Cu(s)$ in Table 15-2, and therefore we expect that $Cu(s)$ would be oxidized by Br_2 or HNO_3. On the other hand, Fe^{2+} and Zn^{2+} are below $Cu(s)$ and we expect that $Cu(s)$ would not react with Fe^{2+} or Zn^{2+}.

EXERCISE 15-3

Use $E°$ values in Table 15-2 to predict whether cobalt metal will dissolve in 1 M HCl solution. Then predict whether cobalt metal will dissolve in 1 M zinc sulfate solution.

EXERCISE 15-4

Use Table 15-2 to decide which substances in the following list tend to oxidize bromide ion, Br^-.

$$Cl_2, H^+, Ni^{2+}, Ni, O_2$$

EXERCISE 15-5

Use Table 15-2 to decide which substances in the following list tend to reduce bromine, Br_2.

$$Cl^-, H_2, Ni, Fe^{2+}$$

15-7 Storage Batteries and Electrochemical Cells

Electrochemical cells have great practical importance. They can supply energy at any time we want. Two familiar examples are the cells used in flashlights and the lead storage battery used in starting automobiles. Recently there has been renewed interest in developing an electrochemical cell that might replace the internal-combustion engine.

The most common flashlight cell is shown in Figure 15-10. A zinc container, the anode, is filled with a paste of ammonium

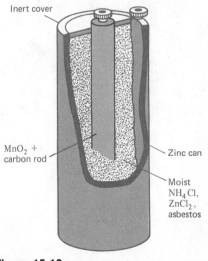

Inert cover

MnO_2 + carbon rod

Zinc can

Moist NH_4Cl, $ZnCl_2$, asbestos

Figure 15-10
A cutaway view of a dry cell.

chloride, zinc chloride, water, and an inert filler such as asbestos. This medium acts as a salt bridge. The central electrode, the cathode, is a mixture of carbon and manganese dioxide, MnO_2. The chemical reactions taking place in this cell depend on the amount of electric current drawn. When small currents are involved, these reactions probably occur:

$$2 MnO_2 + 2 NH_4^+ + 2 e^- \longrightarrow Mn_2O_3 + 2 NH_3 + H_2O$$

$$Zn + 4 NH_4^+ \longrightarrow Zn(NH_3)_4^{2+} + 4 H^+ + 2 e^-$$

The lead storage battery contains several cells, one of which is shown schematically in Figure 15-11. The reactions during discharge of this electrochemical cell can be represented in this manner:

$$PbO_2 + SO_4^{2-} + 4 H^+ + 2 e^- \longrightarrow PbSO_4 + 2 H_2O \qquad E° = +1.68 \text{ volt}$$

$$Pb + SO_4^{2-} \longrightarrow PbSO_4 + 2 e^- \qquad E° = +0.36 \text{ volt}$$

$$PbO_2 + Pb + 4 H^+ + 2 SO_4^{2-} \longrightarrow 2 PbSO_4 + 2 H_2O \qquad E° = +2.04 \text{ volts}$$

The net equation shows that H_2SO_4 is consumed when the battery is used. In addition, H_2O is formed. This means that as a battery becomes discharged, the electrolyte becomes more dilute. Measuring the density of the sulfuric acid electrolyte provides a simple way to know when your battery should be recharged. High density for the electrolyte indicates the sulfuric acid concentration is high, which means the battery is charged. Low density means the sulfuric acid concentration is low and the battery needs to be recharged. In areas where the winter temperatures go below 0 °C, it is important to keep a car battery charged. As the battery acid becomes more dilute, its freezing temperature rises and it is more likely to freeze.

Several other cells are used for special purposes. The AgO-Cd cell has been used in satellites. This cell can produce a large supply of electric power, and yet it can be made quite small. The electrolyte solution contains KOH. The equations for the half-reactions are:

$$2 AgO + H_2O + 2 e^- \longrightarrow Ag_2O + 2 OH^- \qquad E° = +0.57 \text{ volt}$$

$$Cd + 2 OH^- \longrightarrow Cd(OH)_2 + 2 e^- \qquad E° = +0.81 \text{ volt}$$

The net equation is:

$$2 AgO + Cd + H_2O \longrightarrow Cd(OH)_2 + Ag_2O \qquad E° = +1.38 \text{ volts}$$

Miniature batteries are used in watches, movie cameras, and hearing aids to give self-contained power. These batteries often are made of HgO–Zn or Ag_2O–Zn. As a last example of cells, we mention fuel cells. These are systems that convert the potential energy of chemicals like H_2 or CH_4 directly to electrical energy.

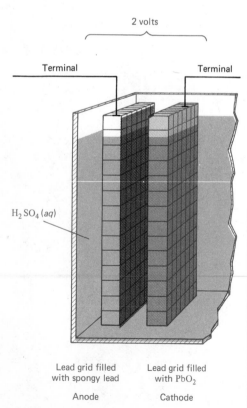

2 volts

Terminal — Terminal

H_2SO_4 (aq)

Lead grid filled with spongy lead — Lead grid filled with PbO_2

Anode — Cathode

Figure 15-11
View into a single lead storage cell.

Such cells can operate at about 70 percent efficiency. The usual process of burning a fuel and using that heat energy to form steam for driving turbines is about 30 percent efficient.

Lead storage batteries may power more cars in the near future.

15-8 Corrosion of Iron, an Undesirable Redox Reaction

All of us know that an object made of iron soon shows signs of rusting if it is left outside, exposed to the air. Rusting or corrosion of iron is a serious economic problem. In fact, one out of every four men in the steel industry works to replace the iron lost by rusting! This shows how important control of corrosion is. What is the chemical nature of rusting, and how can it be controlled? The observed facts are:

> H_2O and O_2 are necessary.
> H^+ speeds up the reaction.
> Some metals such as zinc and magnesium retard rusting.
> Corrosion occurs rapidly where there are the greatest strains in the object.

How can these observations be interpreted? A possible mechanism requires a series of steps that corresponds to the operation of an electrochemical cell.

(1) Iron acts as an anode to release two electrons, forming Fe^{2+}. This process seems to start most often at a strain point in the metal.

(2) Electrons move through the external circuit (in this case, the iron bar itself). Hydrogen ions, H^+, in water on the surface of the bar accept electrons. Neutral H atoms form.

(3) Oxygen in air reacts rapidly with H to form H_2O.

(4) Fe^{2+} ions are oxidized by oxygen, in the presence of water, to form rust.

It takes about 100 years for an iron can (a common "tin" can) to degrade completely, about 400 years for an aluminum can, and about 100 000 years for a glass bottle. Think about that the next time you throw a bottle or can away.

(5) To complete the electric circuit, electric charge must be carried back to the initial point of corrosion. A film of moisture on the iron bar serves as an effective salt bridge.

The comparison between the steps in corrosion and an electrochemical cell suggests a number of ways to minimize corrosion. If we interrupt the circuit at any point, electric charge cannot move from the anode to the cathode and back to the anode. Excluding O_2 would interfere with step 3; excluding H_2O would prevent steps 2, 4, and 5. The most effective way to exclude O_2 and H_2O is to cover the iron bar with grease, paint, or a metal like tin which is a weaker reducing agent than iron. Any break in the tin covering, however, gives rise to faster rusting than before. A "tin can," which is tin-covered steel, rusts rapidly after it once starts to corrode.

A much better way to prevent corrosion of iron involves bringing a stronger reducing agent than iron into the system. A metal such as zinc or magnesium in close contact with iron becomes the anode, forcing iron to act as the cathode. The zinc or magnesium piece is oxidized, releasing electrons. The iron bar does not corrode. Ship hulls are protected in this fashion. Large blocks of zinc metal are bolted to the steel hulls. The zinc oxidizes, largely preventing loss of iron from the hull.

15-9 The Electrolytic Process, a Nonspontaneous Redox Reaction

Until now, we have been concerned with redox reactions that proceed spontaneously. But the same ideas can be applied to reactions that are forced to take place, against their natural tendency. We do this by supplying energy with an externally applied electric current. Such a process is termed *electrolysis*. In Chapter 3 electrolysis of water was discussed. With proper controls the voltage can be gradually increased. At low voltages there is no current flowing through the circuit and there is no visible change in the solution. But when the voltmeter reads 1.23 volts, bubbles of gas begin to form at each electrode. The ammeter indicates that electric current is flowing through the circuit. As the voltage is increased further, the current increases. The evolution of gas at each electrode also increases. Chemical tests show that the gas formed at the cathode is H_2 and the gas formed at the anode is O_2. The equation for the reaction is

$$2\,H_2O \longrightarrow 2\,H_2 + O_2$$

Since this is an oxidation-reduction reaction, we can write equations for the two half-reactions:

$$
\begin{array}{ll}
4\,H^+ + 4\,e^- \longrightarrow 2\,H_2 & E^\circ = +0.00 \text{ volt} \\
2\,H_2O \qquad\quad \longrightarrow O_2 + 4\,H^+ + 4\,e^- & E^\circ = -1.23 \text{ volts} \\
\hline
2\,H_2O \longrightarrow 2\,H_2 + O_2 & E^\circ = -1.23 \text{ volts}
\end{array}
$$

The negative voltage tells us that the reaction is not spontaneous. No electrode reactions take place until the voltage from the battery in the external circuit reaches at least 1.23 volts. That much electrical pressure is necessary to oppose the voltage that the electrochemical cell can generate.

An important electrolytic method converts copper from 98–99 percent to 99.9+ percent purity. Copper is second only to silver as a conductor of electricity and is widely used in electrical circuits. However, small amounts of impurities sharply reduce the conductivity of copper. An electrolytic cell can remove the impurities. Figure 15-12 shows this process in use. The impure copper is made the anode, and a thin sheet of very pure copper serves as the cathode. The solution in the cells contains copper sulfate. As soon as any voltage is applied to the cells, current flows. The less pure copper anode is oxidized to Cu^{2+} ions. Pure copper deposits on the cathode as Cu^{2+} ions are reduced. The equations for the electrode reactions show what happens during this electrolysis:

$$2\,e^- + Cu^{2+} \longrightarrow Cu\,(\text{cathode}) \qquad E° = +0.34\ \text{volt}$$

$$Cu\,(\text{anode}) \longrightarrow Cu^{2+} + 2\,e^- \qquad E° = -0.34\ \text{volt}$$

$$Cu\,(\text{anode}) \longrightarrow Cu\,(\text{cathode}) \qquad E° = 0.00\ \text{volt}$$

Here is an interesting situation. Apparently the only change during this electrolysis is the transport of copper from the anode to the cathode. The zero voltage is a theoretical value. It does

Figure 15-12
Electrolysis cells for purifying copper. Utah Copper Division, Kennecott Copper Corporation.

not mean the process is free. Some electrical energy is lost as heat and in reacting with impurities. Common impurities in copper are iron and silver. The first is an element which is more easily oxidized than copper, and the second is an element which is less readily oxidized than copper. If the voltage is controlled, only iron and copper are oxidized at the anode. The silver is not oxidized. It drops to the bottom of the electrolytic cell and is recovered by other means. At the cathode, copper is more readily reduced and iron stays in solution. Only high-purity copper plates out on the cathode.

A number of other substances are made commercially by electrolysis. Some of them are illustrated in the next section as part of the study of how much electricity is needed to produce a given mass of material.

EXERCISE 15-6

The electrolysis of fused NaCl produces sodium metal at the cathode and chlorine gas at the anode. Write equations for the two half-reactions that occur in this electrolysis.

15-10   Quantitative Relations in Electrolysis

A British scientist, Michael Faraday, was the first chemist who tried to explain electrolysis. His experiments during the 1830's offered support for Dalton's atomic theory. Electricity, like atoms, seemed to come only in packages. Today electrolysis can be treated in a quantitative fashion in terms of half-reactions and their $E°$ values.

Figure 15-13 shows three electrolytic systems of great industrial importance. In this illustration these cells are connected in series.

The figure shows the production of Na(l) and $Cl_2(g)$ from NaCl(l). If NaOH is wanted as a product, a solution of NaCl, rather than molten salt, is electrolyzed. Sodium hydroxide, chlorine gas, and hydrogen gas are produced.

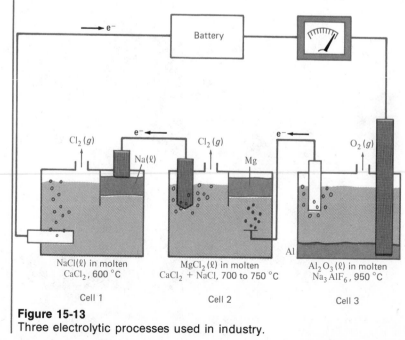

Figure 15-13
Three electrolytic processes used in industry.

These spoons were made the cathode and silver-plated in this large electrolytic cell.

When the switch is closed, electrons flow in the circuit. The current entering the cell on the right will be the same as the current leaving the cell on the left. The same number of electrons move through each cell per unit of time. The total electric charge carried through this circuit can be calculated. Millikan's oil drop experiment (Section 6-5) showed that the charge on the electron equals 1.6×10^{-19} coulomb. One mole of electrons would carry a total charge of

$$\left(1.6 \times 10^{-19} \frac{\text{coulomb}}{\text{electron}}\right)\left(6.0 \times 10^{23} \frac{\text{electrons}}{\text{mole}}\right) = 9.6 \times 10^4 \frac{\text{coulombs}}{\text{mole}}$$

More precise measurements lead to a value of 96 454 coulombs per mole of electrons. This number is sometimes referred to as "one Faraday" in recognition of Michael Faraday's contributions to electrochemistry. The equations for the half-reactions indicate what is taking place in each cell:

	Cathode reactions	Anode reactions
Cell 1	$Na^+ + e^- \longrightarrow Na(s)$	$Cl^- \longrightarrow \frac{1}{2}Cl_2(g) + e^-$
Cell 2	$\frac{1}{2}Mg^{2+} + e^- \longrightarrow \frac{1}{2}Mg(s)$	$Cl^- \longrightarrow \frac{1}{2}Cl_2(g) + e^-$
Cell 3	$\frac{1}{3}Al^{3+} + e^- \longrightarrow \frac{1}{3}Al(s)$	$\frac{1}{2}H_2O \longrightarrow \frac{1}{4}O_2(g) + e^- + H^+$

When 9.6×10^4 coulombs of electricity pass through this circuit, one mole of electrons moves through each of the three cells. The net chemical reactions produce

Cell 1   1 mole Na   plus $\frac{1}{2}$ mole Cl_2

Cell 2 $\frac{1}{2}$ mole Mg   plus $\frac{1}{2}$ mole Cl_2

Cell 3 $\frac{1}{3}$ mole Al   plus $\frac{1}{4}$ mole O_2

The total number of coulombs moving through an electrical circuit measures the total flow of electricity. The rate of flow, or the current passing a point, is specified by coulombs per second. A rate of one coulomb per second is called one *ampere*.

$$\text{amperes} = \text{coulombs/second}$$

Suppose a constant current of 2.0 amperes flows through each of the three electrolytic cells for 10 hours. The number of coulombs can be calculated:

$$\text{coulombs} = \text{amperes} \times \text{seconds}$$

$$= 2.0 \text{ amp} \times 10 \text{ hr} \times 60 \frac{min}{hr} \times 60 \frac{s}{min}$$

$$= 7.2 \times 10^4 \text{ amp} \cdot \text{s}$$

$$\text{moles of electrons} = 7.2 \times 10^4 \text{ coulombs} \times \frac{1 \text{ mole } e^-}{9.6 \times 10^4 \text{ coulombs}}$$

$$= 0.75 \text{ mole } e^-$$

Now you can calculate the mass of each substance by the usual use of moles.

EXERCISE 15-7

Calculate how many grams of Na, Mg, Al, Cl_2, and O_2 can be produced for each 0.75 mole of electrons through the series of cells.

15-11   Balancing Oxidation-Reduction Equations

A balanced equation shows that mass and electric charge are conserved in a chemical reaction. For many reactions, a bit of trial and error quickly leads to the assignment of the proper coefficients. Sometimes oxidation-reduction reactions are not readily balanced by this approach. There are systematic ways to balance redox equations. We will discuss three methods.

Method 1   Balance by Inspection

In Experiment 2 you observed the reaction between metallic aluminum and cupric chloride solution. Although several chemical reactions were occurring simultaneously, the principal one was the formation of copper metal as aluminum dissolved. It is not difficult to balance the equation for this reaction. It can be done by inspection. Here are the steps:

1. Write reactants and products:

$$Al + Cu^{2+} \longrightarrow Al^{3+} + Cu$$

(Atoms balanced; charges *not* balanced)

2. Balance electric charges:

$$Al + 3\,Cu^{2+} \longrightarrow 2\,Al^{3+} + Cu$$

(Charges balanced; atoms *not* balanced)

3. Balance atoms:

$$2\,Al + 3\,Cu^{2+} \longrightarrow 2\,Al^{3+} + 3\,Cu$$

(Charges balanced; atoms balanced)

The equation is now balanced: two moles of aluminum metal will reduce three moles of cupric ion.

EXERCISE 15-8

Write balanced equations for these redox reactions by inspection:

	Reactants	Products
(a)	$Zn + Ag^+$	$\longrightarrow Ag + Zn^{2+}$
(b)	$Cr^{2+} + I_2$	$\longrightarrow I^- + Cr^{3+}$
(c)	$Ti + Fe_2O_3$	$\longrightarrow TiO_2 + Fe$

Method II   Use the Table of Half-Reactions

In Experiment 23 you observed that ferrous ions reacted with permanganate ions in acid solution. It is too laborious to balance the equation for this reaction by inspection, particularly since there is another, much easier, way to balance it. First write the reactants and products:

$$Fe^{2+} + MnO_4^- \longrightarrow Mn^{2+} + Fe^{3+}$$

Then look in the table of reduction potentials, Appendix 4, for the two half-reactions containing these substances. Arrange them so that Fe^{2+} and MnO_4^- appear on the left as reactants:

$$Fe^{2+} \longrightarrow Fe^{3+} + e^-$$

$$5\,e^- + 8\,H^+ + MnO_4^- \longrightarrow Mn^{2+} + 4\,H_2O$$

There must be the same number of electrons in each half-reaction equation, since electric charge does not build up in a redox system. Multiplying the first equation by 5 provides the electrons that the permanganate gains:

$$5\ Fe^{2+} \longrightarrow 5\ Fe^{3+} + 5\ e^-$$

$$\underline{5\ e^- + 8\ H^+ + MnO_4^- \longrightarrow Mn^{2+} + 4\ H_2O}$$

$$8\ H^+ + 5\ Fe^{2+} + MnO_4^- \longrightarrow Mn^{2+} + 5\ Fe^{3+} + 4\ H_2O$$

The electric charge for the reactants $[+8 + (5 \times 2) - 1 = +17]$ is equal to the electric charge for the products $[+2 + (5 \times 3) = +17]$.

EXERCISE 15-9

Write balanced equations for these reactions by using the half-reaction equations in Appendix 4:

(a) $Cr_2O_7^{2-} + Hg \longrightarrow Cr^{3+} + Hg^{2+}$

(b) $MnO_4^- + H_2O_2 \longrightarrow Mn^{2+} + O_2$

(c) $H_2O_2 + SO_2 \longrightarrow H^+ + SO_4^{2-}$

Method III   Devise Half-Reactions

Many examples of redox reactions are too complicated to balance by the inspection method. Yet if the needed half-reaction equations are not in the table in Appendix 4, then another method is needed to balance the equation. Consider the reaction between zinc metal and sodium vanadate. As usual, write the reactants and products.

$$Zn + VO_3^- \longrightarrow VO^{2+} + Zn^{2+}$$

The equation for the zinc half-reaction can be written easily either by inspection or by looking in Appendix 4:

$$Zn \longrightarrow Zn^{2+} + 2\ e^-$$

The equation for the vanadate half-reaction does not appear in Appendix 4. Here is a simple procedure to find the equation for a half-reaction:

Step 1   Begin writing the half-reaction equation by showing reactant going to product. Balance the number of V atoms (in this example one vanadium atom appears both in reactant and in product):

$$VO_3^- \longrightarrow VO^{2+}$$

Step 2   *Oxygen balance* Add H_2O to balance the number of oxygen atoms. In this example the right side is lacking two oxygen atoms. Add two water molecules.

$$VO_3^- \longrightarrow VO^{2+} + 2\ H_2O$$

Step 3 *Hydrogen balance* Add H^+ to balance the number of hydrogen atoms. Here the left side is lacking 4 hydrogens.

$$4\,H^+ + VO_3^- \longrightarrow VO^{2+} + 2\,H_2O$$

Step 4 *Charge balance* Add e^- to balance the charge. In Step 3 the charge for the reactants equals $+4 - 1 = +3$ and for the products $+2$. We must add one electron to the reactants to achieve charge balance:

$$e^- + 4\,H^+ + VO_3^- \longrightarrow VO^{2+} + 2\,H_2O$$

This is the required half-reaction equation. Combine it with the equation for the Zn-Zn^{2+} half-reaction. Remember that the number of electrons must be the same in each equation.

$$Zn \longrightarrow Zn^{2+} + 2\,e^-$$
$$\underline{2\,e^- + 8\,H^+ + 2\,VO_3^- \longrightarrow 2\,VO^{2+} + 4\,H_2O}$$
$$8\,H^+ + Zn + 2\,VO_3^- \longrightarrow 2\,VO^{2+} + Zn^{2+} + 4\,H_2O$$

Final check on charge balance

$$(+8 - 2) = +6 = (+4 + 2)$$

Here is a much more complicated example in which both half-reaction equations must be generated. The same series of steps will lead to the balanced half-reaction equations.

$$P_4 + IO_3^- \longrightarrow H_2PO_4^- + I^-$$

Step 1 Begin writing the half-reaction equations by showing reactants going to products; then balance the P and I atoms.

$$P_4 \longrightarrow 4\,H_2PO_4^-$$
$$IO_3^- \longrightarrow I^-$$

Step 2 *Oxygen balance* Add H_2O as needed to balance the number of O atoms:

$$16\,H_2O + P_4 \longrightarrow 4\,H_2PO_4^-$$
$$IO_3^- \longrightarrow I^- + 3\,H_2O$$

Step 3 *Hydrogen balance* Add H^+ as needed to balance the number of H atoms:

$$16\,H_2O + P_4 \longrightarrow 4\,H_2PO_4^- + 24\,H^+$$
$$6\,H^+ + IO_3^- \longrightarrow I^- + 3\,H_2O$$

Step 4 Charge balance Add e^- as needed to balance the charge:

$$16\,H_2O + P_4 \longrightarrow 4\,H_2PO_4^- + 24\,H^+ + 20\,e^-$$

$$6\,e^- + 6\,H^+ + IO_3^- \longrightarrow I^- + 3\,H_2O$$

These are the required half-reaction equations. Combine them after making the number of electrons the same in each equation. In this example we need 60 e^- in each equation.

$$48\,H_2O + 3\,P_4 \longrightarrow 12\,H_2PO_4^- + 72\,H^+ + 60\,e^-$$

$$\underline{60\,e^- + 60\,H^+ + 10\,IO_3^- \longrightarrow 10\,I^- + 30\,H_2O}$$

$$18\,H_2O + 3\,P_4 + 10\,IO_3^- \longrightarrow 10\,I^- + 12\,H_2PO_4^- + 12\,H^+$$

Final check on charge balance

$$0 + 0 - 10 = -10 - 12 + 12$$

$$-10 = -10$$

EXERCISE 15-10

Write balanced equations for these redox reactions, using Method III.

(a) $N_2H_5^+ + PuO_2^{2+} \longrightarrow Pu^{4+} + N_2$

(b) $Zn + NO_3^- \longrightarrow NH_4^+ + Zn^{2+}$

(c) $S_2O_6^{2-} + BiO_3^- \longrightarrow Bi^{3+} + SO_4^{2-}$

15-12 Oxidation Numbers

When metallic iron is oxidized, two electrons are given up as a ferrous ion, Fe^{2+}, forms. Then when the ferrous ion is oxidized, another electron must be given up as a ferric ion, Fe^{3+}, forms. Chemists have found it useful to assign *oxidation numbers* to atoms or ions that enter into redox reactions.

Fe	oxidation number = 0
Fe^{2+}	oxidation number = +2
Fe^{3+}	oxidation number = +3

Iron as the element is electrically neutral. Therefore, the oxidation number assignment of zero is easy to understand. Since negative charge is carried away by the electrons, positive oxidation numbers are given to ferrous and ferric ions.

When chlorine is reduced to a chloride ion, each atom in the molecule gains one electron. The oxidation numbers for chlorine and chloride are zero and −1. Often, the oxidation number for an element is not quite as obvious as in these examples. Manganese and some of its compounds can serve to illustrate the problem.

What would the oxidation number be for Mn in each of these substances?

Mn	oxidation number $=$ 0
Mn^{2+}	oxidation number $= +2$
MnO_2	oxidation number $=$?
$KMnO_4$	oxidation number $=$?

There is no difficulty in assigning oxidation numbers for manganese as the element, Mn, or as the ion, Mn^{2+}. How do we assign oxidation numbers to manganese and oxygen in MnO_2? Since MnO_2 is a neutral compound, the oxidation numbers for the three atoms must add up to zero. If an oxidation number is assigned to oxygen in MnO_2, the oxidation number for manganese can be calculated quite readily.

If oxidation number of oxygen is	Oxidation number of manganese is
0	0
-1	$+2$
-2	$+4$
-3	$+6$

Since oxidation numbers of 0 and $+2$ have already been assigned to Mn metal and Mn^{2+}, the first two values for manganese in MnO_2 do not seem reasonable. Manganese dioxide, MnO_2, does not have the chemical properties exhibited by metallic manganese or by Mn^{2+} ion. How can we decide whether $+4$ or $+6$ (or some other value) is a reasonable oxidation number for manganese in MnO_2? A large amount of experimental evidence has been used to formulate a set of rules that give useful oxidation numbers:

Rule 1   The oxidation number for any atom in its elementary state is zero.

Rule 2   The oxidation number for any monatomic species is the net charge on the atom or ion.

Rule 3   The oxidation number for oxygen is -2 in all its compounds (except in peroxides, where it is -1).

Rule 4   The oxidation number for hydrogen is $+1$ in all its compounds (except in metallic hydrides, where it is -1).

Rule 5   All other oxidation numbers are assigned so that the sum of oxidation numbers equals the net charge on the molecule or ion.

With Rule 3 we can see that the oxidation number of Mn in MnO_2 is $+4$.

A few examples will illustrate further the use of these rules. What will be the oxidation number for manganese in potassium permanganate, $KMnO_4$? This salt ionizes to form K^+ and MnO_4^- ions. Apply Rule 5 to find the oxidation number (Ox. No.) of manganese in MnO_4^-.

$$\text{Ox. No. Mn} + 4(\text{Ox. No. O}) = -1$$

Rule 3 helps us:

$$\text{Ox. No. Mn} + 4(-2) = -1$$

$$\text{Ox. No. Mn} = +7$$

The dichromate ion has the formula $Cr_2O_7{}^{2-}$. What is the oxidation number for Cr in this ion? The sum of the oxidation numbers for the two Cr and seven O atoms must equal -2, the charge on the dichromate ion.

$$2(\text{Ox. No. Cr}) + 7(\text{Ox. No. O}) = -2$$

$$2(\text{Ox. No. Cr}) + 7(-2) = -2$$

$$2(\text{Ox. No. Cr}) = +12$$

$$\text{Ox. No. Cr} = +6$$

EXERCISE 15-11

Nitrogen forms a large number of compounds with hydrogen and oxygen. Calculate the oxidation numbers for N in these compounds:

$$NH_3, \ N_2O, \ NO_2, \ N_2O_4, \ NO_2{}^-, \ HNO_3$$

EXERCISE 15-12

Calculate the oxidation numbers for P in these acids:

$$H_3PO_2, \ H_3PO_3, \ H_3PO_4$$

Chemists sometimes use oxidation numbers in naming compounds. For example, iron forms two different compounds with chlorine. It is important to distinguish one from the other, both with chemical symbols and with words. In this book the four systems indicated in this example are used at various times. You are already familiar with the first system.

$FeCl_2$	$FeCl_3$
ferrous chloride	ferric chloride
iron dichloride	iron trichloride
iron(II) chloride	iron(III) chloride

The endings -*ous* and -*ic* survive from the early days of chemistry when fewer compounds were known. This system is suitable when only two compounds are known for the pair of elements. In such cases, the endings -*ous* and -*ic* are used to modify the element name and indicate lower and higher oxidation numbers. Cuprous chloride is $CuCl$; cupric chloride is $CuCl_2$.

The prefixes *di-* and *tri-* distinguish between the two iron chlorides. Some other examples using prefixes to name compounds are shown below:

NO	nitrogen monoxide
NO_2	nitrogen dioxide
N_2O_4	dinitrogen tetraoxide
N_2O_5	dinitrogen pentaoxide

The fourth approach to naming compounds is called the Stock system, after the chemist who first suggested this method. Roman numerals are used to indicate the oxidation number for the principal element or ion. For rather complex substances the Stock system provides an unambiguous name. Here are two examples:

$Fe(SCN)(H_2O)_5^{2+}$ pentaaquothiocyanoiron(III) ion

$CrCl_2(NH_3)_4^+$ dichlorotetraamminechromium(III) ion

Pickling, Polishing, and Part-Making

Electrolysis is useful for many purposes besides decomposing water, purifying copper, and producing chemicals such as sodium, aluminum, chlorine, sodium hydroxide, and magnesium. These processes depend on using the electric current to break chemical bonds and then to remake them in some desired new substance.

In another group of processes the object is just to remove material. The interest is focused on the final form of the electrode remaining, not on the material removed. Thus the surface of a steel auto bumper can be cleaned by electropickling. Or a sterling silver spoon has the final finish put on by electropolishing. A more dramatic and more modern use is electromachining. Electromachining is the controlled dissolving of metal to achieve a desired shape. Figure 1 shows the general setup. The cathode is shaped to cause preferential electrolysis. By this means we create the desired shape in the anode, which is the product.

When the process starts, the protruding bar on the cathode in Figure 1 will be closer to the flat anode than are other parts of the cathode. The electrical resistance will be lower in this region and the dissolving action greater. A channel will be machined in the anode. In actual practice, several additional features are needed. The separation of cathode and anode is usually rather small, so the effect of cathode contour is magnified. If the "cutting" is to be deep, the cathode or anode is normally moved to keep the working surfaces close. Finally, some cooling is necessary to prevent boiling of the electrolyte solution. Stirring the solution accomplishes this.

Figure 2 shows some more realistic machining operations. In these just the anode and cathode are shown. The rest of the system is omitted for simplicity. You can see one of the prime advantages of electrochemical machining. Complex shapes are made in one "pass" of the "tool," or cathode. Electromachining has other impressive advantages over cutting and grinding operations. It produces a fine, smooth finish requiring no further polishing. It does not harden the metal being formed. It works on metals too hard or brittle to machine. It works on thin foils. It can do otherwise impossible jobs, such as making a square hole or a blind (nonpiercing), flat-bottomed hole. Finally, it can be controlled to high precision, since metal removal is literally atom by atom, and the amount of electrolysis depends on current flow, which is easily regulated. There are limitations. Electromachining is not suitable for working large areas (too much current is required) or for metals that react with the electrolyte. The special cathode shape means the method is expensive if only one or two pieces are to be made. For aircraft turbines and aerospace needs where high-strength, high-temperature alloys are common it is the only possible way to do many jobs. All these achievements are based on the oxidation-reduction principles we have studied.

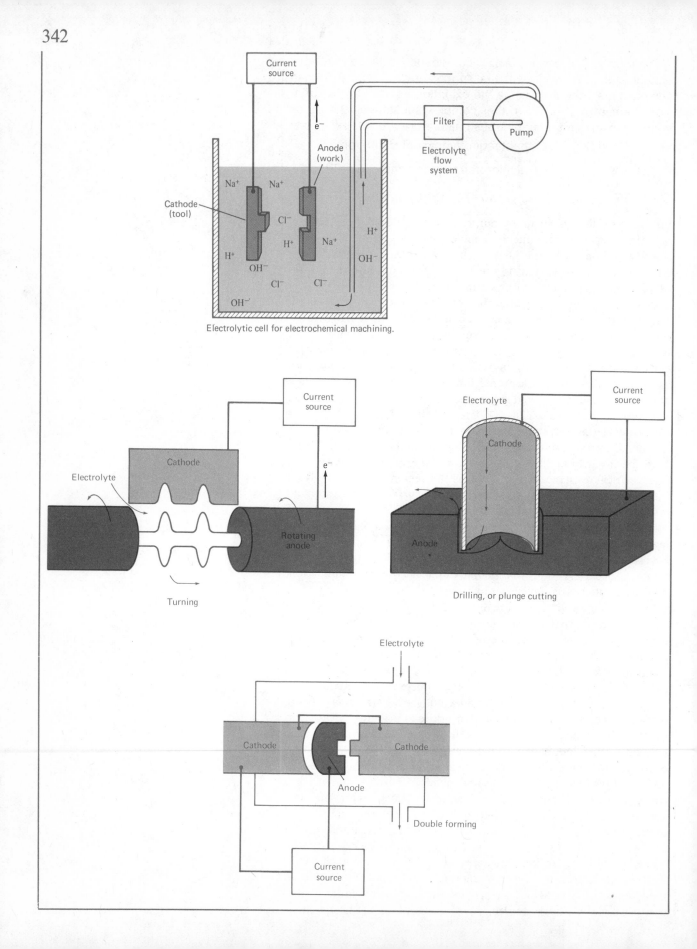

Electrolytic cell for electrochemical machining.

Turning

Drilling, or plunge cutting

Double forming

15-13 Review

An understanding of what chemists mean by the words *oxidation* and *reduction* has been developed in this chapter. The operation of an electrochemical cell brings out the essential features of oxi-. dation-reduction reactions.

Oxidation takes place at the anode of an electrochemical cell as electrons are released to the external circuit. Oxidation corresponds to the *loss of electrons.*

Reduction takes place at the cathode of an electrochemical cell as electrons are accepted from the external circuit. Reduction corresponds to the *gain of electrons.*

Oxidation and reduction always take place together. Electrons lost when oxidation occurs are gained when reduction occurs. Recognition that redox reactions can be interpreted as the sum of two half-reactions provides a systematic method for comparing the strength of oxidizing and reducing agents. In the discussion of Brønsted-Lowry acids and bases in Chapter 14, a quantitative measure of acid strength was obtained by determining the tendency for an acid to donate a proton to the reference base, H_2O. The strength of a reducing agent can be measured by determining the tendency for a reducing agent to donate an electron to the reference oxidizing agent H^+.

The quantitative scale on which reducing agents are ranked is expressed in terms of volts. The voltage of any electrochemical cell is a measure of the potential energy of the redox system. *A positive value for the voltage* means that, at equilibrium, the concentration of the products will be greater than the concentration of reactants. *A negative value for the voltage* means that, at equilibrium, the concentration of reactants will exceed the concentration of products.

Spontaneous electrochemical systems are important sources of energy. The lead storage battery and the cells used in flashlights are two examples. Nonspontaneous electrochemical systems are important for the preparation of a number of essential chemical substances; chlorine, sodium hydroxide, magnesium, aluminum, and bromine are a few examples. The word *electrolysis* is used when energy forces an electrochemical reaction in the nonspontaneous direction.

Methods of balancing oxidation-reduction equations include inspection, use of the table of half-reactions, and devising the needed half-reactions. Oxidation numbers and chemical nomenclature are reviewed briefly.

Questions and Problems for Chapter 15

1

(a) If a neutral atom becomes positively charged, has it been oxidized or reduced? Write a general equation using M for the neutral atom.

(b) If an ion X^- acquires a 2^- charge, has it been oxidized or reduced? Write a general equation.

2

If you wished to replate a silver spoon, would you make it the anode or cathode in a cell? Use half-reactions in your explanation. How many moles of electrons are needed to plate out 1.0 gram of Ag?

3

Figure 15-2 shows electrons leaving the $Cu(s)$ electrode and going to the $Ag(s)$ electrode. Experimentally, both half-cells are found to be electrically neutral before current flows and to remain so as the cell operates. Explain this.

4

Equations for two half-reactions taking place in an electrochemical cell are:

$$Fe \longrightarrow Fe^{2+} + 2\,e^- \qquad 2\,e^- + Sn^{2+} \longrightarrow Sn$$

Which metal serves as the anode? Which the cathode?

5

Equations for two half-reactions taking place in an electrochemical cell are:

$$Cr \longrightarrow Cr^{3+} + 3\,e^-$$

$$2\,e^- + Pb^{2+} \longrightarrow Pb$$

This cell is similar to the one discussed in Section 15-1. How many grams of Pb will deposit on the cathode when 1.56 grams of Cr dissolve from the anode?

6

One method of obtaining copper metal is to let a solution containing Cu^{2+} ions trickle over scrap iron. Write the equations for the two half-reactions. Assume Fe^{2+} forms. Indicate in which half-reaction oxidation is taking place.

7

Aluminum metal reacts with acidic solutions to liberate hydrogen gas. Write equations for the two half-reactions and the net ionic reaction.

8

When copper is placed in concentrated nitric acid, vigorous bubbling takes place as a brown gas is evolved. The copper disappears and the solution changes from colorless to a greenish-blue. The brown gas is nitrogen dioxide, NO_2, and the solution's color is due to the formation of cupric ion, Cu^{2+}. Using half-reactions from Appendix 4, write the net equation for this reaction.

9

In an acid solution the following are true: Oxygen gas will react with H_2S to give sulfur, S_8, and H_2O. Selenium and tellurium will not react in the corresponding reaction with H_2S. Sulfur will react with H_2Se, giving H_2S and selenium, but tellurium

will not react with H_2Se. Arrange the elements O_2, S_8, Se_8, and Te_8 in order of their tendency to gain electrons to form the hydrides H_2O, H_2S, H_2Se, and H_2Te. Place the one with the greatest tendency at the top of the list. Write a reduction half-reaction for each of these elements.

10

How many coulombs are needed to form 1 mole of Ag from a 1 M $AgNO_3$ solution?

$$Ag^+ + e^- \longrightarrow Ag$$

11

A 100-watt light bulb, when operated in a 110-volt household circuit, has a current of 0.9 ampere flowing through it. In one minute how many electrons pass through the light bulb?

12

A flashlight bulb will burn out almost instantly if connected to a 110-volt household circuit. This does not happen if a $1\frac{1}{2}$-volt dry cell is connected to the bulb. Explain.

13

If a copper wire carries a 0.1 ampere current, how many moles of electrons pass through the wire each second?

14

The $E°$ for the reduction of a substance is independent of the amount of substance present. Give two other properties of matter that are independent of the amount.

15

Consider this equation:

$$Mg + Co^{2+} \longrightarrow Co + Mg^{2+}$$

Determine

(a) which substance is oxidized
(b) which substance is reduced
(c) which substance acts as the reducing agent
(d) which substance acts as the oxidizing agent

16

Suppose chemists had assigned zero potential to the reaction shown by

$$I_2 + 2\,e^- \longrightarrow 2\,I^-$$

(a) Determine what $E°$ would have been for

$$Na^+ + e^- \longrightarrow Na$$

(b) Determine how much the net potential would have been changed for the reaction

$$2\,Na + I_2 \longrightarrow 2\,Na^+ + 2\,I^-$$

17

The four elements W, X, Y, and Z form diatomic molecules and also form singly charged negative ions. The following observations are made in a series of experiments:

$X^- + Y_2$	gives $Y^- + X_2$
$W^- + Y_2$	no reaction
$Z^- + X_2$	gives $X^- + Z_2$

Use these observations to write equations for each reduction half-reaction. Arrange them in a short reduction potential series. Place the easiest to reduce at the top. Which ion is the strongest reducing agent? Which molecule is the strongest oxidizing agent?

18

Complete the following equations. Determine the net voltage of each cell and decide whether reactants or products are favored at equilibrium.

(a) $Zn + Ag^+ \longrightarrow$
(b) $Cu + Ag^+ \longrightarrow$
(c) $Sn + Fe^{2+} \longrightarrow$
(d) $Hg + H^+ \longrightarrow$

19

For each of the following reactions,

(i) write the equations for the half-reactions,
(ii) determine the net equation,
(iii) predict whether the reactants or products are favored at equilibrium. Give the basis for your prediction.

(a) $Mg(s) + Sn^{2+} \longrightarrow$
(b) $Mn(s) + Cs^+ \longrightarrow$
(c) $Cu(s) + Cl_2(g) \longrightarrow$
(d) $Zn(s) + Fe^{2+} \longrightarrow$
(e) $Fe(s) + Fe^{3+} \longrightarrow$

20

A half-cell consisting of a palladium rod dipping into a 1 M $Pd(NO_3)_2$ solution is connected with a standard hydrogen half-cell. The cell voltage is 0.99 volt and the platinum electrode in the hydrogen half-cell is the anode. Determine $E°$ for the reaction

$$Pd \longrightarrow Pd^{2+} + 2\,e^-$$

21

If a piece of copper metal is dipped into a solution containing Cr^{3+} ions, what will happen? Explain, using $E°$ values.

22

What will happen if an aluminum spoon is used to stir an $Fe(NO_3)_2$ solution? What will happen if an iron spoon is used to stir an $AlCl_3$ solution?

23

Can a 1 M $Fe_2(SO_4)_3$ solution be stored in a container made of nickel metal? Explain your answer.

24

Will the reaction

$$2\,Fe^{2+} + Ni^{2+} \longrightarrow 2\,Fe^{3+} + Ni$$

occur? What is the net voltage?

25

Most of the bromine produced in the United States is made by oxidizing Br^- to Br_2 using Cl_2. What is $E°$ for this reaction?

26

Which of the half-reactions will spontaneously reduce Cu^{2+} to $Cu(s)$?

(a) Sn^{2+} to Sn^{4+}
(b) Cl^- to $Cl_2(g)$
(c) Au to Au^{3+}
(d) MnO_4^- to Mn^{2+}
(e) Ag to Ag^+

27

Which of the half-reactions will spontaneously oxidize Fe^{2+} to Fe^{3+}?

(a) Ag^+ to Ag
(b) Pb^{2+} to Pb
(c) Al^{3+} to Al
(d) MnO_4^- to Mn^{2+}
(e) Li to Li^+

28

Consider this half reaction:

$$Ag^+ + e^- \longrightarrow Ag \qquad E° = 0.80\ volt$$

Using Table 15-2 would you add Fe^{3+}, Br^-, or Co to cause silver metal to form spontaneously from a 1 M silver nitrate solution?

29

A 6-volt lead storage battery contains 700 grams of pure $H_2SO_4(l)$ dissolved in water.

(a) How many grams of solid sodium carbonate, Na_2CO_3, would be needed to neutralize this acid (giving CO_2 gas and H_2O) if it was spilled?
(b) How many liters of 2.0 M Na_2CO_3 solution would be needed?

30

In the electrolysis of aqueous cupric bromide, $CuBr_2$, 0.500 gram of copper is deposited at one electrode. How many grams of bromine are formed at the other electrode? Write the anode and cathode half-reactions.

31

Iodine is recovered from iodates in Chile saltpeter by the reaction

$$HSO_3^- + IO_3^- \text{ gives } I_2 + SO_4^{2-} + H^+ + H_2O$$

(a) How many grams of sodium iodate, $NaIO_3$, react with 1.00 mole of $KHSO_3$?
(b) How many grams of iodine, I_2, are produced?

32

The chlorine used to purify your drinking water was probably made by electrolyzing molten $NaCl$ to produce liquid sodium and gaseous chlorine.

(a) How many grams of sodium chloride are needed to produce 355 grams of chlorine gas?
(b) What volume would this gas occupy at STP?

33

Nitric acid, HNO_3, is made by the process

$$3\,NO_2(g) + H_2O(l) \rightleftharpoons 2\,HNO_3(l) + NO(g)$$

Commercial concentrated acid contains 68% by weight HNO_3 in water. The solution is 15 M. How many liters of concentrated acid are needed to react with 0.100 kg of copper metal?

$$Cu + H^+ + NO_3^- \text{ gives } Cu^{2+} + NO_2 + H_2O$$

34

How many grams of silver metal will react with 2.0 liters of 6.0 M HNO_3? The reactants and products are

$$Ag + H^+ + NO_3^- \text{ gives } Ag^+ + NO + H_2O$$

35

How many ml of a 0.050 M $KMnO_4$ solution are required to oxidize 2.00 g of $FeSO_4$ in a dilute acid solution?

36

Steel screws and bolts are often cadmium-plated to minimize rusting. From this net equation

$$Cd^{2+} + Ni \longrightarrow Ni^{2+} + Cd \qquad E° = 0.15 \text{ volt}$$

deduce the reduction half-cell potential for $Cd^{2+} - Cd$. How much Cd is plated if a current of 10 amperes flows for 10 hours?

37

Write a balanced equation for the reaction between stannous ion, Sn^{2+}, and permanganate ion, MnO_4^-, in acid solution to produce stannic ion, Sn^{4+}, and manganous ion, Mn^{2+}.

38

Use Appendix 4 to write a balanced equation for each of the following reactions:

(a) $H_2O_2 + I^- + H^+ \text{ gives } H_2O + I_2$
(b) $Cr_2O_7^{2-} + Fe^{2+} + H^+ \text{ gives }$
$$Cr^{3+} + Fe^{3+} + H_2O$$
(c) $Cu + NO_3^- + H^+ \text{ gives } Cu^{2+} + NO + H_2O$

39

Give a balanced equation for each of the following reactions:

(a) $HBr + H_2SO_4 \text{ gives } SO_2 + Br_2 + H_2O$
(b) $NO_3^- + Cl^- + H^+ \text{ gives } NO + Cl_2 + H_2O$
(c) $Zn + NO_3^- + H^+ \text{ gives } Zn^{2+} + NH_4^+ + H_2O$
(d) $BrO^- \text{ gives } Br^- + BrO_3^-$

40

Produce balanced equations for the following reactions:

(a) $ClO_2^- + MnO_2 \text{ gives } ClO^- + MnO_4^- + OH^-$
(b) $Tl + NO_3^- \text{ gives } Tl^+ + NO_2^- + OH^-$
(c) $Zn + S_4O_6^{2-} \text{ gives } Zn^{2+} + S_2O_3^{2-}$
(d) $S_2O_8^{2-} + S_2O_3^{2-} \text{ gives } SO_4^{2-} + S_4O_6^{2-}$

41

Give balanced equations for these reactions:

(a) $In + BiO^+ \text{ gives } In^{3+} + Bi$
(b) $V^{2+} + H_2SO_3 \text{ gives } V^{3+} + S_2O_3^{2-}$
(c) $Te^{2-} + C_2N_2(g) \text{ gives } Te + HCN$
(d) $Mn + IrCl_6^{3-} \text{ gives } Mn^{2+} + Ir + Cl^-$

42

Determine the oxidation number of uranium in each of these known compounds: UO_3, U_3O_8, U_2O_5, UO_2, UO, K_2UO_4, and MgU_2O_7.

The Chemistry of Carbon Compounds 16

The compounds of carbon furnish one of the most intriguing subjects of chemistry, because they play a dominant role in the chemistry of living things, both plant and animal. In addition, there are innumerable carbon compounds useful to man: dyes, drugs, detergents, plastics, perfumes, fibers, fabrics, foods, flavors, and fuels. These useful substances must be obtained from coal, petroleum, natural gas, plants, or animals. How have chemists changed crude petroleum or abundant plant and animal products into drugs that relieve our suffering, dyes that brighten our surroundings, or plastics that conserve scarce metals? These are some of the questions considered in this chapter.

". . . at its essence, life can be understood only in the language of chemistry."

Philip Handler
Biology and the Future of Man

347

16-1   Sources of Carbon Compounds

Coal is a black mineral of vegetable origin. Its production began during prehistoric eras when warm, wet climatic conditions led to rapid growth of plants. As the plants died, they accumulated on the forest floor or in swamps and marshes. The cycles of decay, new growth, and decay caused vast deposits of plant material to build up. Enormous pressures were exerted on the lower levels of this material, and gradually many of the atoms in the original cellulose were chemically reduced. In time the layers were pressed into hard beds composed chiefly of the carbon that was present in the original plants. Appreciable amounts of oxygen, hydrogen, nitrogen, and sulfur compounds are also present in coal. When coal is heated to a high temperature *in the absence of air,* it decomposes. Volatile products, coal gas and coal tar, are driven off and a residue called *coke* remains. This valuable industrial material is almost pure carbon. In Chapter 11 the formation of "water gas" from coke was discussed. One ton of coal yields about eight gallons of coal tar. Over 200 different carbon compounds have been isolated from it. While the great value of coal to mankind has been as a fuel, the many substances in the gas and tars make coal a very important source of chemical raw materials.

Another source of carbon compounds is petroleum, a complex mixture which may range from a volatile liquid to a viscous, tarry substance. Petroleum also had its origin in living matter that underwent chemical changes over the course of geological time. It is found underground between the grains of sandstone left from ancient seas. Natural gas is found in similar types of rock. Huge oil refineries daily change millions of gallons of crude oil into useful products.

Plants and animals are themselves highly effective chemical factories, and they synthesize many other carbon compounds useful to man. These include proteins, sugars, cellulose, starches, vitamins, plant oils, waxes, fats, gelatin, dyes, drugs, and fibers.

Because all these sources of carbon compounds had their origin in living matter, plant or animal, the chemistry of carbon is called **organic chemistry**. This name came from the belief, now discarded, that living materials were organized in a unique way or contained some special ingredient not present in nonliving matter. Compounds containing carbon are called organic compounds.

Although each of the sources mentioned accounts for thousands of tons of material, it is interesting that most of the carbon of our planet is not in these forms. It has been estimated that the CO_2 in the earth's atmosphere contains about 40 times as much carbon as in all the fossil fuels and the forests—this in spite of the fact that only 0.03 percent of the atmosphere is CO_2. But the largest store of all is the carbonates in limestone and other minerals. These rocks contain about 400 000 times as much carbon as the coal, oil, and wood reserves. Perhaps future chemists will find an economical way to convert the carbon in such minerals to more useful forms.

Each metric ton of coal yields
8 liters benzene
2 liters toluene
2 liters larger molecules

16-2 Naming Organic Compounds

There are several million different carbon compounds known. Over 300 000 new organic compounds are synthesized each year; this is more than the total number of compounds known that contain no carbon! The number of organic compounds is very large because each carbon atom has an outstanding ability to form covalent bonds to other carbon atoms. With the formation of many carbon-carbon bonds goes the possibility of having isomers.

Thus, each molecular formula can represent many compounds. For example, you learned in Chapter 10, Exercise 10-6, that three different compounds have the formula C_5H_{12}. There are 75 different compounds with the formula $C_{10}H_{22}$, and the 92 atoms in $C_{30}H_{62}$ can be arranged in about *four billion* different ways. Chemists need a system for naming each organic compound. This is necessary so that a chemist can figure out the structure from the name or write down the name by looking at the structural formula. A system has been worked out, and we will learn some of its parts.

The system is based on the simplest kind of organic compounds. This type contains only hydrogen and carbon, so the compounds are called *hydrocarbons.* The simplest hydrocarbons are *unbranched*—i.e., no carbon atom is connected to three or four other carbons—and *saturated* i.e., each carbon atom forms four single bonds to four other atoms. The first four compounds in the family have names that must be memorized. For compounds with more than four carbon atoms in the chain, the name is based on the Greek word for the number of carbons. In these formulas and through the next few pages we have adopted the shortcut of not showing all the hydrogen atoms. A complete formula would show a hydrogen atom at the open end of each line from carbon.

Note that each name in Figure 16-1 ends with *-ane.* This suffix indicates that the hydrocarbon contains only single bonds and that the general formula for chain structures is C_nH_{2n+2}.

There are many saturated hydrocarbon compounds that have branched chains—for instance, Example I. Clearly the black portion of this structure is almost the same as *n*-heptane and the colored portion is nearly the same as methane. We might call it methane-heptane, but that is a bit awkward to say. More important, it does not distinguish that compound from other isomers which are also methane-heptane. See Examples II and III. So chemists agreed to modify the name for the *smaller* portion or group. The group name is made by using *-yl* to replace *-ane.* Thus, Example I is a *methylheptane.* But which one? There are three. Well, the methyl group is on the third carbon atom (or the fifth if you count from the other end) of the long chain. Chemists always use the lowest "address" number. Example I is 3-methylheptane; II is 2-methylheptane; and III is 4-methylheptane.

Scientific librarians are important members of every science activity.

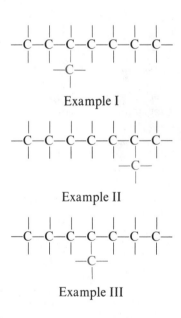

Example I

Example II

Example III

EXERCISE 16-1

Convince yourself that there are only three methylheptanes.

350

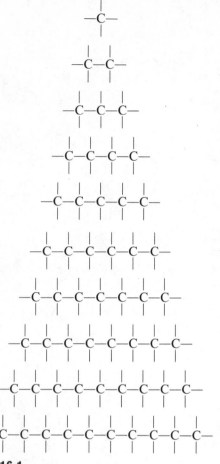

methane — from Greek "wood"

ethane — from Greek "to burn"

propane — from Greek "fat"

n-butane — from Latin "butter"

n-pentane — penta — five — pentagon

n-hexane — hexa — six — hexagon

n-heptane — hepta — seven

n-octane — octa — eight — octopus, octave

n-nonane — nona — nine

n-decane — deca — ten — decade

Figure 16-1
The first ten saturated straight chain hydrocarbons

TABLE 16-1
Naming Organic Hydrocarbons

Number, *n*	Name of Chain with *n* Carbon Atoms	Name of Group with *n* Carbon Atoms	Multiplier*
1	methane	methyl	mono (rarely used)
2	ethane	ethyl	di
3	propane	propyl	tri
4	*n*-butane	butyl	tetra
5	*n*-pentane	pentyl	penta
6	*n*-hexane	hexyl	hexa
7	*n*-heptane	heptyl	hepta
8	*n*-octane	octyl	octa
9	*n*-nonane	nonyl	nona
10	*n*-decane	decyl	deca

*Multipliers can be used with any group—not just the one with the same value of *n*. Thus tetramethyl and dihexyl are valid parts of names.

Now consider a slightly more complicated example (IV) in which two methyl groups are present. There are seven carbon atoms in the longest unbranched chain. This fact is shown by using heptane as the last part of the name. In this example the two methyl groups could be shown by the name 2-methyl-4-methylheptane. It is descriptive and unique, but there is a shorter way of showing the presence of two methyl groups. The Greeks had a word for it; *dyo,* meaning two. We use the shorter form *di.* Example IV is properly named 2,4-dimethylheptane. Table 16-1 summarizes the system so far.

EXERCISE 16-2

Draw as many structural formulas as you can for the dimethylheptanes. Name them.

EXERCISE 16-3

The formulas and names have been jumbled. Pair them up correctly.

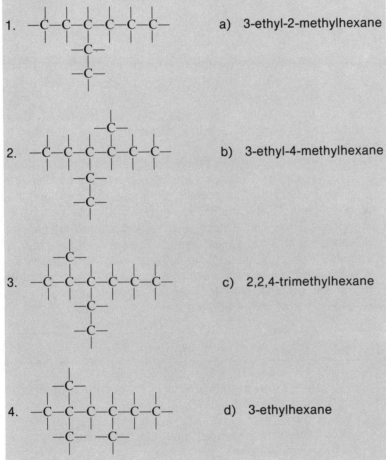

1.   a) 3-ethyl-2-methylhexane

2.   b) 3-ethyl-4-methylhexane

3.   c) 2,2,4-trimethylhexane

4.   d) 3-ethylhexane

Note from Exercise 16-3 that the group names are listed alphabetically, *not* according to the location numbers.

Many stable hydrocarbons contain double or triple bonds between carbon atoms. These are called *unsaturated compounds.* Picture just one of the 75 different isomers of decane. For this one isomer shown in Example V there are five different locations where two hydrogen atoms could be removed to produce a double bond. One of these $C_{10}H_{20}$ molecules is given in Example VI.

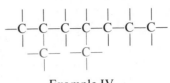

Example IV

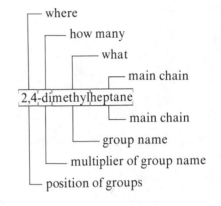

where
how many
what
main chain
2,4-dimethylheptane
main chain
group name
multiplier of group name
position of groups

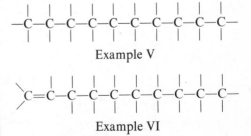

Example V

Example VI

EXERCISE 16-4

Draw structural formulas for the four other possible unbranched isomers of $C_{10}H_{20}$. Why are there not nine?

The name of a hydrocarbon containing double bonds is made by changing the name ending from -ane to -ene. A number is used to specify the position of a double bond in a molecule. As before, the lowest possible number is used. In VI the double bond is said to be between atoms 1 and 2, not 9 and 10. The compound is 1-decene, Example V is decane. Be sure you understand the names assigned to the following compounds:

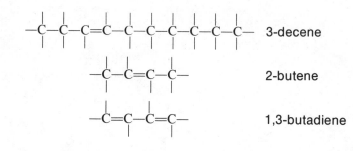

Notice how the multiplier *di* is used to show two double bonds in the last example, which happens to be an important ingredient in some synthetic rubbers.

The simplest molecule with a triple bond between carbon atoms is C_2H_2, or $H—C\equiv C—H$. Since it has two carbon atoms, its name should start with *eth-*. The correct, systematic name does. It is ethyne. In general, the ending -yne shows a triple bond. The compound C_2H_2 is called acetylene, an old name that has become entrenched in chemical usage. Acetylene is an example of a trivial name, one that does not tell you much about the structure. Acetylene is used for welding and for making other more complex compounds. Now that we can name compounds, we want to know how the structures were determined.

16-3   Determination of Different Kinds of Formulas

There are always three questions a chemist hopes to answer when he has synthesized a new compound:

Which elements, in what amounts, are present in this compound?

How many atoms of each element occur in one molecule?

How are the atoms arranged in the molecule?

During the 19th century, methods of chemical analysis were developed that led to answers to the first question. In order to answer the second question the molar mass of the new substance must be determined. Avogadro's hypothesis provided the first method to find the molar mass for a gas. The mass of a particular volume of a gas is compared with the mass of the same volume

Analytical technicians are able to test for the presence of elements and compounds.

of a reference gas, such as oxygen, at the same temperature and pressure.

Finding how the atoms in a molecule are arranged is the most difficult and also the most important problem in identifying an unknown compound. The search for an answer to this question can be as exciting as a detective story, with the chemical and physical properties of the compound furnishing the clues. With the right collection of clues, the chemist can establish the molecular structure of the substance he has synthesized. This phase of chemistry has developed slowly and carefully over the last one hundred years. First, the structure of simple molecules had to be established. One great step in arriving at an understanding of molecular structure was the proposal made in 1858 by a German chemist, August Kekulé. He knew that carbon atoms form compounds such as methane and carbon tetrachloride, CH_4 and CCl_4. Kekulé generalized when he suggested that carbon atoms form four bonds in all carbon compounds. He also proposed that many carbon compounds contained rings of carbon atoms. These two ideas helped chemists determine the structures of many molecules. Since Kekulé's time, a large number of structures have been established. Today the immense store of known molecular structures helps chemists to determine the structures of very complex molecules, many of great importance in biological systems.

Let us repeat the three questions posed above:

Which elements, in what amounts, are present in this
    compound?
How many atoms of each element occur in one
    molecule?
How are the atoms arranged in the molecule?

The steps a chemist follows to find answers to these questions are illustrated with ethane and ethanol.

16-4   Determination of the Structure of Ethane

Ethane is a gas that is often contained in the household gas used for heating and cooking. Its chemistry is almost wholly restricted to the combustion reaction. Ethanol is a liquid that has great value in the manufacture of chemicals, and it bears little chemical resemblance to ethane. Yet, the similarity of the two names, *ethane* and *ethanol,* suggests that these compounds are related. This is true. Their molecular structures will help us understand how they are related and, at the same time, why their properties are so different. We must find out *what kinds of atoms* are present in each substance, *how many atoms* there are per molecule, and their *bonding arrangement.* Usually many experiments need to be performed before the molecular structure of a compound is known with certainty. This fascinating problem involves three basic experimental steps: to determine the *empirical formula,* then the *molecular formula,* and finally, the *structural formula.* First the information conveyed by each of these formulas will be reviewed, with ethane as the example. Then we will consider the experiments used in the determination of each type of formula, with ethanol as the example.

Step 1   Which elements, in what amounts, are present in ethane?

The **empirical formula** tells the *relative number* of atoms of each element in a molecule. Analysis of ethane shows that this is a compound of carbon and hydrogen. For each 3 g of hydrogen, there are 12 g of carbon.

$$\text{number of moles of H atoms} = 3 \cancel{\text{ grams}} \text{ hydrogen}$$

$$\times \frac{1 \text{ mole hydrogen}}{1.00 \cancel{\text{ gram}}}$$

$$= 3 \text{ moles hydrogen}$$

$$\text{number of moles of C atoms} = 12 \cancel{\text{ grams}} \text{ carbon}$$

$$\times \frac{1 \text{ mole carbon}}{12.0 \cancel{\text{ grams}}}$$

$$= 1 \text{ mole carbon}$$

Therefore the empirical formula for ethane is CH_3.

Step 2   How many atoms of each element occur in one molecule of ethane?

The **molecular formula** shows the *total number* of each kind of atom in the molecule. Measurements similar to those you carried out in Experiment 7 indicate that the molar mass of ethane is 30 grams. This molar mass together with the empirical formula tells us the molecular formula. The molecular formula must be some multiple of the empirical formula:

$(CH_3)_1$	corresponds to a molar mass of 15 grams
$(CH_3)_2$	corresponds to a molar mass of 30 grams
$(CH_3)_3$	corresponds to a molar mass of 45 grams

Ethane has the molecular formula of $(CH_3)_2$, usually written C_2H_6.

EXERCISE 16-5

Write the molecular formula for the carbon-hydrogen compound having the empirical formula CH_2 and a molar mass of 28 grams.

Step 3   How are the atoms arranged in ethane?

The proposals Kekulé made can be used to obtain the **structural formula** from the molecular formula, C_2H_6:

A carbon atom forms four bonds and may bond to another carbon atom.
A hydrogen atom forms only one bond.

How can these eight atoms be arranged in the molecule C_2H_6? There is only one way to do this using the above regularities.

Several different representations of the structural formula for ethane are shown in Figure 16-2. The choice of which formula to use depends upon the structural feature to be emphasized. The first and second drawings emphasize the three-dimensional nature of ethane. The third is a simpler way of doing the same thing. The last formula merely shows that three hydrogens are attached to each carbon atom.

16-5 The Determination of the Structure of Ethanol

The three steps used to establish the structure of ethane are repeated for ethanol:

Step 1 Which elements, in what amounts, are present in ethanol?

Analysis of ethanol shows that it contains C, H, and O. A known mass of this compound is burned in oxygen. The products are CO_2 and H_2O, showing that carbon and hydrogen were present in ethanol. The mass of the carbon dioxide reveals how much carbon was in the sample. The mass of water reveals how much hydrogen was in the sample. The remainder of the sample is assumed to be oxygen, since no other elements occur in the products.

Suppose 46 grams of ethanol are burned. The reaction produces 88 grams of carbon dioxide and 54 grams of water. We want to know the relative numbers of carbon, hydrogen, and oxygen atoms in the compound. Again the relative numbers of each kind of atom can be obtained by first calculating the number of moles of carbon dioxide and water produced by the combustion of the 46-gram sample. From these answers we can obtain moles of C and H atoms:

$$\text{number of moles CO}_2 = 88 \; \text{grams CO}_2 \times \frac{1 \text{ mole CO}_2}{44 \text{ grams}}$$

$$= 2.0 \text{ moles CO}_2$$

$$\text{number of moles H}_2\text{O} = 54 \; \text{grams H}_2\text{O} \times \frac{1 \text{ mole H}_2\text{O}}{18 \text{ grams}}$$

$$= 3.0 \text{ moles H}_2\text{O}$$

Now the following statements can be made about ethanol:

46 grams of ethanol contain:

2 moles of CO_2 and three moles of H_2O;

or

2 moles of carbon atoms and 6 moles of hydrogen atoms;

or

24 grams of carbon and 6 grams of hydrogen.

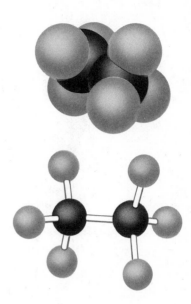

Figure 16-2
Various representations of ethane, C_2H_6.

U.S. industry produces about 1 billion liters of synthetic ethanol each year. It sells for about $0.29/liter in tank-car lots.

Thirty grams of the original 46 grams are accounted for. The remainder of the sample (46 − 30, or 16, grams) is assumed to be oxygen. This corresponds to:

$$\text{number of moles O atoms} = 16 \cancel{\text{ grams}} \text{ oxygen} \times \frac{1 \text{ mole O atoms}}{16 \cancel{\text{ grams}}}$$

$$= 1.0 \text{ mole O atoms}$$

Summarizing, 46 grams of ethanol contain

2 moles of carbon atoms
6 moles of hydrogen atoms
1 mole of oxygen atoms

These results give the empirical formula C_2H_6O.

EXERCISE 16-6

Automobile antifreeze often contains a compound called ethylene glycol. Analysis of pure ethylene glycol shows that it contains only carbon, hydrogen, and oxygen. A sample of ethylene glycol was burned and the following results were obtained:

mass of sample burned = 15.5 mg
mass of CO_2 formed   = 22.0 mg
mass of H_2O formed   = 13.5 mg

What is the empirical formula of ethylene glycol?

Step 2   How many atoms of each element occur in one molecule of ethanol?

We know that the relative numbers of atoms in ethanol are two carbon to six hydrogen to one oxygen. But is the molecular formula C_2H_6O or $C_4H_{12}O_2$ or $C_6H_{18}O_3$ or some other multiple of the empirical formula C_2H_6O?

An experiment to measure the molar mass will help in answering this question. Ethanol is a liquid at room temperature, but ethanol vapor is needed to determine the molar mass by the method used in Experiment 7. A weighed amount of liquid is placed in a gas-collecting device held at an easily regulated temperature. For example, a steam condenser around the device provides a convenient way of holding the temperature at 100 °C. When the substance has vaporized completely, its pressure and volume are measured. This measurement gives the mass per unit volume of gaseous ethanol at a known temperature and pressure. The mass is then compared with the mass of the same volume of a reference gas (usually O_2) at the same temperature and pressure.

Such a measurement shows that a given volume of ethanol at 100 °C and one atmosphere weighs about 1.5 times as much as the same volume of oxygen gas at the same conditions. Avogadro's hypothesis states that equal volumes of gases at the same temperature and pressure contain equal numbers of molecules. Therefore, the molar mass for ethanol is 1.5 times the molar mass of oxygen:

molar mass (ethanol) $= 1.5 \times$ molar mass O_2
$$= 1.5 \times 32$$
$$= 48 \text{ grams}$$

Even though this number may not have been measured with high precision, it shows clearly what multiple of the empirical formula to choose.

Molecular Formula	Molar Mass	Experimental Value for Molar Mass
C_2H_6O	46.07 grams	48 grams
$C_4H_{12}O_2$	92.14 grams	
$C_6H_{18}O_3$	138.21 grams	

For ethanol the molecular formula is C_2H_6O, the same as the empirical formula.

EXERCISE 16-7

Ethylene glycol, the example treated in Exercise 16-6, has an empirical formula of CH_3O. A sample weighing 0.49 gram is vaporized completely at 200 °C and at one atmosphere pressure. The volume measured under these conditions is 291 ml. The same volume of oxygen gas at the same conditions weighs 0.240 gram. Is the molecular formula for ethylene glycol CH_3O or $C_2H_6O_2$ or $C_3H_9O_3$ or some higher multiple of CH_3O?

Step 3 How are the atoms arranged in ethanol?

The determination of the bonding arrangement in a molecule is the most important problem in identifying an unknown compound. How can we proceed? Each molecule of ethanol contains two carbon, one oxygen, and six hydrogen atoms. In proposing a molecular structure, a good guide is that carbon will form four bonds, oxygen two bonds, and hydrogen one bond. Finally, the proposed formula must fit the chemical behavior of ethanol.

We can start with the oxygen atom and see how a molecule might be built around it. There are two carbon atoms and six hydrogen atoms at our disposal. The gradual construction of possible structures is shown in Figure 16-3. The atoms remaining to be connected are listed below each stage of the construction. Two possible structures result and are shown in Figure 16-4. Compounds with the same molecular formula but different structural formulas are called **isomers**. The existence of both compounds 1 and 2 was known long before their structures were clarified. Hence, the existence of these isomers perplexed chemists for decades.

EXERCISE 16-8

Ethylene glycol has the empirical formula CH_3O and the molecular formula $C_2H_6O_2$. Using the usual bonding rules, draw some of the possible structural formulas for this compound.

The problem now is to decide whether ethanol has structure 1 or structure 2. How can we tell which is correct? What preliminary ideas can be obtained from an examination of the structural formulas?

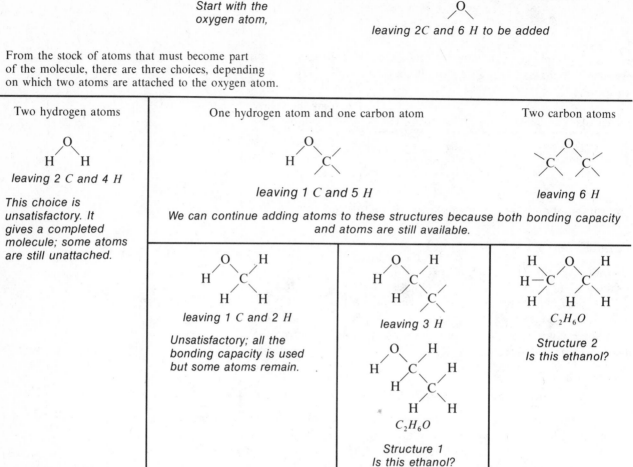

Start with the oxygen atom, leaving 2C and 6 H to be added

From the stock of atoms that must become part of the molecule, there are three choices, depending on which two atoms are attached to the oxygen atom.

Two hydrogen atoms

leaving 2 C and 4 H

This choice is unsatisfactory. It gives a completed molecule; some atoms are still unattached.

One hydrogen atom and one carbon atom

leaving 1 C and 5 H

We can continue adding atoms to these structures because both bonding capacity and atoms are still available.

leaving 1 C and 2 H

Unsatisfactory; all the bonding capacity is used but some atoms remain.

leaving 3 H

C_2H_6O

*Structure 1
Is this ethanol?*

Two carbon atoms

leaving 6 H

C_2H_6O

*Structure 2
Is this ethanol?*

Figure 16-3
Development of possible structures for a compound with the molecular formula C_2H_6O.

In structure 2 all the hydrogen atoms are the same. Each hydrogen atom is bonded to a carbon atom, which is, in turn, bonded to the oxygen atom. In structure 1 one of the hydrogen atoms is quite different from any of the others. It is bonded to oxygen and not to carbon. Of the remaining five hydrogen atoms, two are placed on the carbon which is bonded to oxygen, and three are on the other carbon. Structures 1 and 2 should have quite different properties. Which structure agrees with the chemistry of ethanol?

There are several kinds of evidence. Some evidence comes from the behavior of ethanol in chemical reactions and some from the determination of certain physical properties. Consider the chemical reactions first.

Sodium metal reacts vigorously with ethanol, giving hydrogen gas. An ionic compound, sodium ethoxide, with empirical formula $NaOC_2H_5$, also forms in the reaction. Sodium metal also reacts vigorously with water to produce hydrogen gas and an ionic compound, sodium hydroxide, NaOH. This similarity in reaction suggests that ethanol has some structural relation to water. In water there are two hydrogen atoms bonded to one oxygen atom. In structure 1 there is one hydrogen atom bonded to oxygen. This chemical evidence suggests ethanol has structure 1.

Quantitative evidence can be obtained by carrying out the reaction between an excess of sodium and a weighed amount of ethanol, measuring the amount of hydrogen gas evolved. It is found that one mole of ethanol produces one half mole of hydrogen gas. A balanced chemical equation can be written for the reaction of sodium with ethanol:

$$Na + C_2H_6O \longrightarrow \frac{1}{2}H_2 + C_2H_5ONa$$

Apparently one molecule of ethanol contains one hydrogen atom that is capable of reacting with sodium and five that are not. Consider structures 1 and 2 in the light of this information. In structure 2 all six of the hydrogen atoms are structurally equivalent. In structure 1 there is one hydrogen atom in the molecule different from the other five. One hydrogen is bonded to the oxygen atom; five hydrogen atoms are bonded to carbon atoms. Structure 1 agrees with the interpretation that only one hydrogen atom in ethanol will react with sodium. Structure 2 does not.

There is further evidence that CH_3CH_2OH is the correct structural formula for ethanol. Compounds containing only carbon and hydrogen do not react readily with metallic sodium to produce hydrogen gas. In these compounds, called hydrocarbons, the hydrogen atoms are bonded to carbon atoms. The deduction can be made that hydrogen atoms bonded to carbon atoms do not react with sodium to produce hydrogen gas. In structure 2, CH_3OCH_3, all the hydrogen atoms are bonded to carbon atoms. We do not expect a compound with this structure to react with sodium. Ethanol reacts with sodium. Therefore, it is unlikely that ethanol has structure 2.

Consider one other reaction of ethanol. If ethanol is heated with aqueous HBr, a volatile compound is formed. This compound is only slightly soluble in water and contains bromine. From chemical analysis and determination of the molar mass, the molecular formula is found to be C_2H_5Br, ethyl bromide. With the aid of the bonding rules, it can be seen that there is only one possible structure for this compound. See Figure 16-5. This result is verified by the fact that only one isomer of C_2H_5Br has ever been discovered.

How does this chemical reaction furnish a clue to the structure of ethanol? Structure 1 could give the structural formula shown in Figure 16-5 merely by breaking the carbon-oxygen bond. It is difficult to conceive of a simple way to go from structure 2 to the structure shown for ethyl bromide.

No one fact by itself gives absolute proof of the molecular structure of a substance. In our example results of many different experiments show that structure 1 is the correct structure

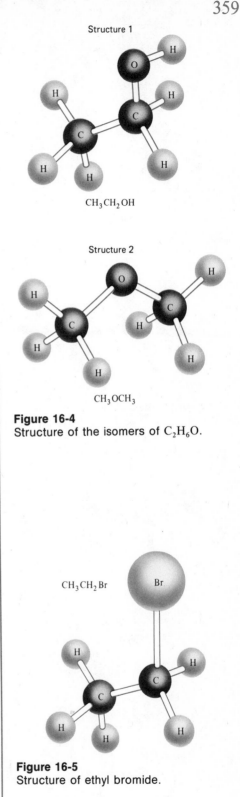

Figure 16-4
Structure of the isomers of C_2H_6O.

Figure 16-5
Structure of ethyl bromide.

for ethanol. A comparable set of experiments shows that another compound with the formula C_2H_6O has properties consistent with structure 2. This compound is called dimethyl ether.

EXERCISE 16-9

Find the possible structures for a compound with molecular formula C_2H_7N. Nitrogen has three unpaired electrons.

16-6   Hydrocarbons and Their Reactions

In Chapter 10 hydrocarbons were used as examples to illustrate covalent bonding. Ethane, ethylene, and acetylene are examples of hydrocarbons:

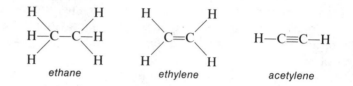

Ethane contains only carbon and hydrogen atoms connected by single bonds. Such compounds are called saturated hydrocarbons. Ethylene and acetylene are unsaturated hydrocarbons. There is a carbon-carbon double bond in ethylene and a triple bond in acetylene.

Saturated hydrocarbons are widely used as fuels to heat our homes and to move our automobiles. As you know, these compounds are not very reactive at low temperature. They are unreactive to strong acids and bases and to many oxidizing or reducing agents. At high temperatures saturated hydrocarbons undergo oxidation with oxygen or with the halogens, X_2. A few reactions with methane can serve as illustrations:

$$CH_4 + 2 O_2 \longrightarrow CO_2 + 2 H_2O$$
$$6 CH_4 + O_2 \longrightarrow 2 C_2H_2 + 2 CO + 10 H_2$$
$$CH_4 + X_2 \longrightarrow CH_3X + HX$$

(Further reactions give CH_2X_2, CHX_3, and CX_4.)

These high-temperature reactions are difficult to control, and mixtures of products arise. Therefore, it is important to transform the saturated hydrocarbons into other substances which are much more reactive at low temperature. Then we can use synthetic procedures which can be controlled, to make a great variety of useful substances. Ethylene and acetylene, with their multiple carbon-carbon bonds, are much more reactive than ethane. Their reactions with water are important industrial routes to ethyl alcohol and acetaldehyde.

Refinery operators have to make unsaturated hydrocarbons for polyethylene or polypropylene polymers. Crude oil contains few unsaturated hydrocarbon molecules.

Synthetic organic chemists are those who make new molecules to try as medicines, glues, plastics, insecticides, paints, or many other products.

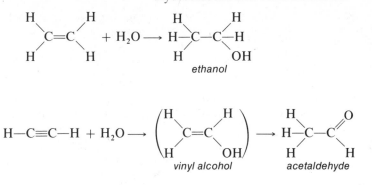

ethanol

vinyl alcohol   acetaldehyde

In the previous section the reactions of ethanol were explained on the basis of the behavior of the —OH group in CH_3CH_2OH. For many of the reactions of ethanol it is the OH group that reacts. The rest of the molecule has the saturated hydrocarbon structure, $CH_3CH_2—$, which is relatively unreactive. It is helpful to regard ethanol as containing two parts, the $C_2H_5—$, or ethyl, group, which is unchanged during many reactions, and the —OH, or hydroxyl, group, which can change more easily.

Such a division can be made of many organic molecules. There is a good reason to do so. In that way the millions of compounds can be reduced to a few hundred types according to the reactive group they contain. Those groups that most frequently change during reaction are called **functional groups**. Through study of the chemical behavior of a few alcohols we can learn the main reactions of hundreds of compounds which contain the —OH group as the only functional one.

In order to focus attention on the group that is reacting, a simplified formula is used. In it the part of the molecule other than the functional group is represented by **R**. Thus the general formula for **alcohols** is **R—OH**. When the group represented by **R** contains only chains of carbon and hydrogen atoms, it is called an **alkyl** group. The ethyl group, $C_2H_5—$, is a specific example of an alkyl group.

In Section 16-5 it was mentioned that ethyl bromide forms when ethanol reacts with hydrogen bromide. Similar treatment of ethanol with hydrogen chloride or hydrogen iodide gives the corresponding ethyl halides:

$$CH_3CH_2OH + HCl \longrightarrow CH_3CH_2Cl + H_2O$$

$$CH_3CH_2OH + HI \longrightarrow CH_3CH_2I + H_2O$$

EXERCISE 16-10

Write the equation for the general reaction between alcohols and HCl. Use —R to represent the hydrocarbon part of the molecules.

The hydroxyl group has been displaced and the halogen atom substituted. The group $CH_3CH_2—$ has not changed. Indeed, this group has appeared in most of our discussion so far. Sometimes it was attached to oxygen, as in ethanol and sodium ethoxide, and sometimes attached to other atoms, as in the ethyl halides.

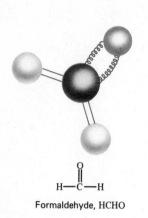

$$H-\overset{\overset{\displaystyle O}{\|}}{C}-H$$

Formaldehyde, HCHO

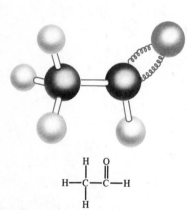

$$H-\overset{\overset{\displaystyle H}{|}}{\underset{\underset{\displaystyle H}{|}}{C}}-\overset{\overset{\displaystyle O}{\|}}{C}-H$$

Acetaldehyde, CH₃CHO

Figure 16-6
The structure of two aldehydes, formaldehyde, and acetaldehyde.

Cheese makers must study and understand the reactions of milk with various molds and bacteria.

Looking at the structural formula of ethane, you see that it is simply the CH_3CH_2- group attached to hydrogen:

$$CH_3CH_2-H, \quad \text{or} \quad CH_3CH_3$$

Because ethyl bromide and ethyl alcohol can be thought of as being derived from ethane by the substitution of —Br or —OH for one of its hydrogens, they are called derivatives of ethane. Ethane is the parent hydrocarbon for a series of related compounds, some of which will be discussed in the next section.

EXERCISE 16-11

Give the structural formula for two derivatives of propane.

16-7 Oxidation of Organic Compounds

By far the majority of the several million known compounds of carbon also contain hydrogen and oxygen. There are several types of oxygen-containing organic compounds, and they can be studied as an oxidation series. For instance, the compound methanol, CH_3OH, is very closely related to methane, as their structural formulas show. Methanol can be regarded as the first step in the complete oxidation of methane to carbon dioxide and water.

Alcohols react with inorganic oxidizing agents such as potassium dichromate, $K_2Cr_2O_7$. When an acidic solution of potassium dichromate reacts with methanol, the solution turns from bright orange to muddy green because of the production of green chromic ion, $Cr^{3+}(aq)$. The solution then has a strong odor easily identified as that of formaldehyde, CH_2O. The structure for this compound is shown at the top in Figure 16-6. Notice that the bond between carbon and oxygen has become a double bond. All the atoms in formaldehyde lie in the same plane.

Acetaldehyde can be made from ethanol by the same type of oxidation that yields formaldehyde from methanol. Acetaldehyde contains a methyl group attached to a

portion, called a **carbonyl group**. In this compound the carbonyl group also has a hydrogen atom bonded to it. You might correctly predict that there would be a series of such compounds with different alkyl groups connected to the carbonyl group. There is such a series. The compounds are called **aldehydes**.

EXERCISE 16-12

Write the formula of the aldehyde made from normal pentane.

Another oxidation product can be obtained from the reaction of an acidic solution of potassium permanganate with methanol.

The product has the formula HCOOH and is called formic acid. The structural formula of formic acid is shown in Figure 16-7. The structure of formic acid is also related to the structure of formaldehyde. If one of the hydrogen atoms of formaldehyde is replaced by an —OH group, the resulting molecule is formic acid.

Just as methanol can be oxidized to formic acid, ethanol can be oxidized to an acid, CH_3COOH, called acetic acid. The molecular structure of acetic acid is also shown in Figure 16-7. The atomic grouping

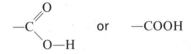

is called the **carboxyl group**, and acids containing this group are called **carboxylic acids**. Their general formula is

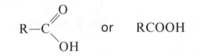

The oxidation of acetic acid is difficult to accomplish. It does not react in solutions of $K_2Cr_2O_7$ or $KMnO_4$. Vigorous treatment, such as burning, causes its complete oxidation to carbon dioxide and water. Formic acid also can be oxidized to carbon dioxide and water by combustion with oxygen.

EXERCISE 16-13

Butanol is an alcohol with the structural formula $CH_3CH_2CH_2CH_2OH$. If it is oxidized carefully, an aldehyde called butyraldehyde is obtained. Vigorous oxidation gives an acid called butyric acid. Draw structural formulas of these compounds.

The series alcohol-aldehyde-carboxylic acid represents the stepwise oxidation path taken when the —OH group in the alcohol is on an end carbon of a chain. Figure 16-8 illustrates the series for a three-carbon compound.

There are some alcohols having the —OH group on a carbon atom other than the end one. When 2-propanol is oxidized, a carbonyl group forms from the hydroxyl group. This is just what happened before. But the product, acetone, has a new feature not present in acetaldehyde. In Figure 16-9 you can see that the carbonyl group in acetone has no hydrogen attached to it. It cannot be oxidized to an acid. It will react with oxygen, giving CO_2 and water.

Acetone is the simplest member of a class of compounds called **ketones**. They are quite similar in structure to the aldehydes, since each contains a carbonyl group. The general formula for ketones is

$$R-\overset{\overset{\displaystyle O}{\|}}{C}-R'$$

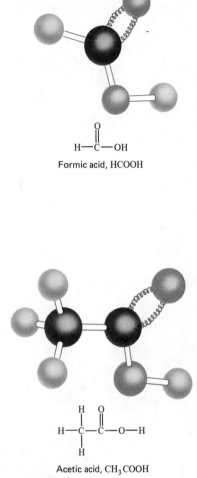

Formic acid, HCOOH

Acetic acid, CH_3COOH

Figure 16-7
The structure of carboxylic acids, formic and acetic.

364

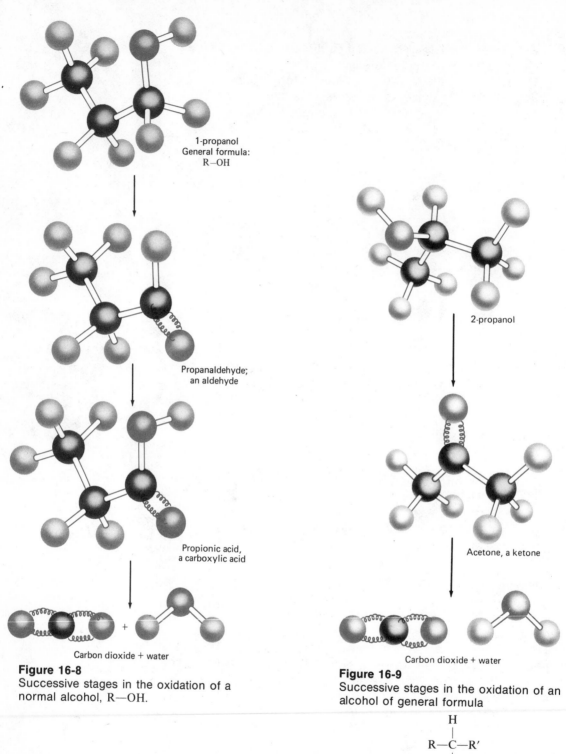

1-propanol
General formula:
R—OH

Propanaldehyde;
an aldehyde

Propionic acid,
a carboxylic acid

Carbon dioxide + water

2-propanol

Acetone, a ketone

Carbon dioxide + water

Figure 16-8
Successive stages in the oxidation of a
normal alcohol, R—OH.

Figure 16-9
Successive stages in the oxidation of an
alcohol of general formula

$$R—\underset{\underset{OH}{|}}{\overset{\overset{H}{|}}{C}}—R'$$

Huge amounts of aldehydes and ketones are used industrially in
a variety of chemical processes. Furthermore, these functional
groups are important in chemical synthesis of medicines, dyes,
plastics, and fabrics.

16-8 Amines (Organic Bases)

Alcohols can be related to water by imagining that an alkyl group (such as —CH_3) has been substituted for one of the two hydrogen atoms of water. In the same way a group of compounds called *amines* is related to ammonia:

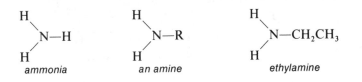

Amines can be prepared by direct reaction of ammonia with an alkyl halide, such as CH_3Br or CH_3CH_2I. Iodides react with the highest rate:

$$CH_3CH_2I + 2\,NH_3 \longrightarrow CH_3CH_2NH_2 + NH_4I$$

This equation represents a net change that occurs when an excess of ammonia reacts with an alkyl iodide. The mechanism of the reaction is thought to involve two steps. The first is analogous to the attack of the hydroxide ion on an alkyl halide (see Figure 12-14):

$$NH_3 + RI \longrightarrow RNH_3{}^+ + I^-$$

The second step is a proton transfer reaction:

$$NH_3 + RNH_3{}^+ \longrightarrow RNH_2 + NH_4{}^+$$

Although natural odors are usually due to complex mixtures of chemicals, some are easily associated with a single chemical. Some common odors and the chemicals mainly responsible are given below:

pineapple	ethyl butyrate
banana	isoamyl acetate
Concord grape	methyl anthranilate
apple	isoamyl isovalerate
Delicious apple	ethyl 2-methylbutyrate

16-9 Reactions of Acids and Amines

Oxidation of an aldehyde gives an organic acid. All such acids contain the functional group —COOH, the carboxyl group. The bonding in this group is shown in Figure 16-8. The carboxyl group releases a proton, acting as a Brønsted acid.

In addition to this acidic behavior, an important characteristic of carboxylic acids is that the entire OH group can be replaced by other groups. The resulting compounds are called **acid derivatives**. Only two types of acid derivatives, esters and amides, will be considered.

Compounds in which the —OH of an acid is transformed into —OR (such as —OCH_3) are called **esters**. They can be prepared by the direct reaction between an alcohol and the acid. For example,

Flavor and odor specialists use esters and other compounds to simulate natural products or create new ones.

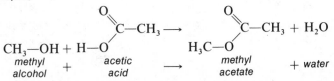

Esters are important substances. The esters of low molar mass have fragrant, fruitlike odors and are used in perfumes and artificial flavorings. Esters are useful solvents. This is the reason they are commonly found in "model airplane dope" and fingernail polish remover.

EXERCISE 16-14

Write equations for the reaction of (a) ethanol and formic acid, (b) propanol and propionic acid, (c) methanol and formic acid. Name the esters produced.

Another class of acid derivatives has been given the name **amides**. Amides are formed when the —OH group of an acid is replaced by an —NH₂ group. An amide can be made by reacting ammonia or an amine with an ester.

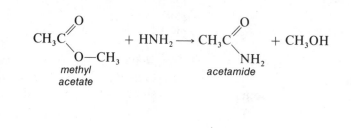

methyl
acetate

acetamide

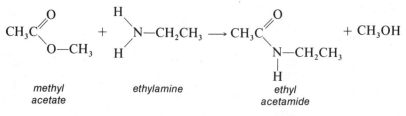

methyl   ethylamine   ethyl
acetate   acetamide

Note the similarity of the two reactions. Amides are of special importance because the amide grouping, at the left, is the basic structural element in the long-chain molecules that make up proteins and enzymes in living matter. Hydrogen bonding between two amide groups helps determine the protein structure, a topic that will be dealt with later, in Section 16-15.

Although we have treated only a small sample of the known functional groups, perhaps you can see how the possibility of adding them to organic compounds increases the number of compounds.

16-10   Benzene and Its Derivatives

There is another important class of hydrocarbons, sometimes referred to as aromatic hydrocarbons. The simplest example is the compound benzene, a cyclic compound with the formula C_6H_6 and with six carbon atoms in a ring. The benzene ring is found to be planar, with 120° angles between pairs of bonds formed by a given carbon atom. Experiment tells us the atoms of one molecule lie in a plane, with a regular arrangement shown at the left. We can easily decide how the carbon and hydrogen

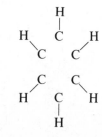

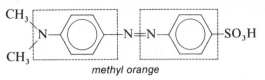

methyl orange

The portions of the methyl orange molecule set off by the broken lines come from aromatic amines like aniline. Aniline is indeed the starting material from which methyl orange and related dyes are made.

Another aniline derivative is acetanilide, which is the amide formed from aniline and acetic acid. Acetanilide is used medicinally as a pain-killing drug.

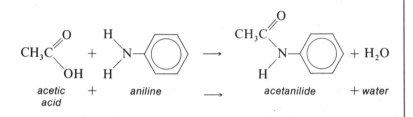

acetic + aniline ⟶ acetanilide + water
acid

Another important compound that can be obtained from coal tar is hydroxybenzene, more commonly called phenol.

Most phenol is now made industrially from benzene, which is chlorinated as a first step. Reaction of chlorobenzene with a base gives phenol:

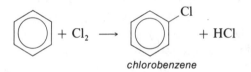

chlorobenzene

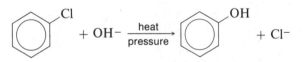

OH

phenol

Phenol is a germicide and disinfectant. It was first used by Lister in 1867 as an antiseptic in medicine. More effective and less toxic antiseptics have since been discovered.

Perhaps the most widely known compound prepared from phenol is aspirin. If phenol, sodium hydroxide, and carbon dioxide are heated together under pressure, the sodium salt of salicylic acid is formed:

Figure 16-10
Part of a modern aspirin plant.

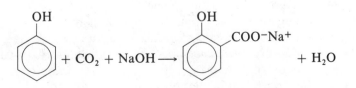

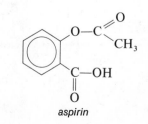

aspirin

$$+ \; H^+ \longrightarrow \qquad\qquad + \; Na^+$$

salicylic acid

Salicylic acid is quite useful. Its methyl ester has a sharp, characteristic odor and is called "oil of wintergreen." The acid itself (or the sodium salt) is a valuable drug in the treatment of arthritis. But the most widely known derivative of salicylic acid is aspirin, which has the structure shown on page 369. You will see, by examining this structure, that aspirin is an ester of acetic acid. Aspirin is mankind's most widely used drug. Somewhat over 32 million pounds of aspirin are manufactured each year in the United States alone! This amounts to something like 200 five-grain tablets for every person in the country! Figure 16-10 shows a portion of the process.

Benzene derivatives account for thousands of the known carbon-containing compounds. A few of them are listed in Table 16-2.

16-12 Polymers

The melting temperatures of the normal alkanes tend to increase as the number of carbon atoms in the chain is increased. Ethane, C_2H_6, is a gas under normal conditions; octane, C_8H_{18}, is a liquid; octadecane, $C_{18}H_{38}$, is a solid. Desired physical properties can be obtained by controlling the length of the chain. Functional groups attached to the chain provide additional variability, including chemical reactivity. In fact, by adjusting the chain length and composition of compounds with high molar mass, chemists have produced a multitude of organic solid substances called plastics. These have been tailored for a wide variety of uses, giving rise to an enormous chemical industry.

The key to this chemical treasure chest is the process by which extended chains of atoms are formed. It is necessary to begin with a relatively small chemical molecule—with carbon chains involving only a few atoms. Many of these small units, called **monomers**, must be bonded together until the appropriate chain length is reached. Often the desired properties are obtained only with giant molecules, each containing hundreds or even thousands of monomers. These giant molecules are called **polymers**, and the process by which they are formed is called **polymerization**.

Polymerization involves the chemical combination of many molecules to form a substance of high molar mass. Reactions that combine many small molecules are referred to as addition polymerization or condensation polymerization.

Addition polymers are formed by the reaction of monomeric units without the elimination of atoms. The monomer is usually an unsaturated organic molecule such as ethylene, $H_2C=CH_2$. In the presence of a suitable catalyst, ethylene undergoes an addition reaction to form a long chain molecule, polyethylene. A general equation for the first stage of such a process can be written

TABLE 16-2
Some Benzene Derivatives

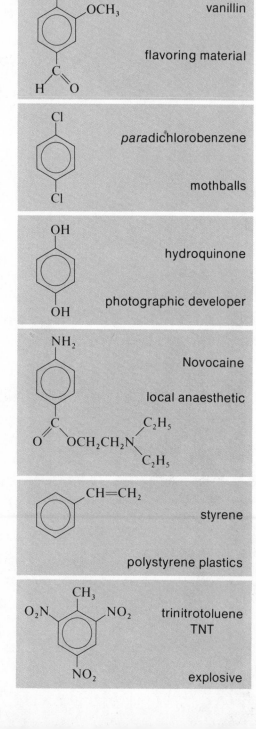

Structure	Name & Use
	vanillin flavoring material
	*para*dichlorobenzene mothballs
	hydroquinone photographic developer
	Novocaine local anaesthetic
	styrene polystyrene plastics
	trinitrotoluene TNT explosive

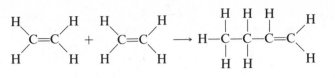

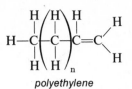

polyethylene

The same addition process continues, and the final product is the polymer polyethylene, in which *n* is a very large number.

One or more of the hydrogen atoms in ethylene can be replaced by groups such as —F, —Cl, —CH₃, and —COOCH₃. The synthetic polymers with trade names such as Teflon, D Saran, Lucite, and Plexiglas result. It is possible to create molecules with custom-built properties for various uses as plastics or fibers.

The second major class of polymers, **condensation polymers**, is produced by reactions in which monomers join and a simple molecule such as water is eliminated. In order to form long chain molecules, two or more functional groups must be present in each of the reacting units. For example, when ethylene glycol, $HOCH_2CH_2OH$, reacts with *para*phthalic acid,

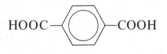

Adhesive compounders vary the composition of glues to bond the substances being joined.

Curiosity Makes the Difference

Teflon is an unusually inert material of many uses. Its discovery in 1938 was almost accidental. Here is how Roy J. Plunkett described it:

. . . gaseous tetrafluoroethylene ($F_2C{=}CF_2$) . . . was passed . . . into the reacting chambers where the tetrafluoroethylene was to be reacted with other chemicals.

On this particular day, soon after the experiment started, my helper called to my attention that the flow of tetrafluoroethylene had stopped. I checked the weight of the cylinder and found that it still contained a sizable quantity of material which I thought to be tetrafluoroethylene. I opened the valve completely and ran a wire through the valve opening but no gas escaped. When I shook the cylinder and found there was some solid material inside, I then removed the valve . . . to pour the white powder from the cylinder. Finally, with the aid of a hack saw, the cylinder was opened and a considerably greater quantity of white powder was obtained.

It was obvious immediately . . . that the tetrafluoroethylene had polymerized and the white powder was therefore a polymer of tetrafluoroethylene.*

Teflon proved to have outstanding properties. It does not burn, rot, or corrode. No liquid has been found to dissolve it. It is useful over a wide temperature range. Tin can be melted in a Teflon beaker, yet the beaker is unchanged at −270 °C. It forms such weak bonds to other molecules that few things will stick to it. It is so slippery it could be used as artificial "ice" in a skating rink. Teflon is an unusually stable substance.

All this because an alert technician noted a discrepancy and a chemist was not satisfied with a quick, obvious, wrong conclusion.

*Quoted from "The Flash of Genius, 2" by A. B. Garrett, *J. Chem. Ed. 39,* 288 (1962).

Did you ever wonder why the adhesive on self-sealing envelopes sticks to itself but to little else? A film of rubber is applied to the envelope and to the flap. The rubber film is coated with a protein which keeps the rubber clean and prevents accidental sticking. If a piece of paper is pressed on this, not much happens. However, when the two films are pressed together, the protein cracks enough to let the rubber layers touch and interlock.

a polyester of high molar mass called Dacron is produced. The equation below shows the first stages of this process:

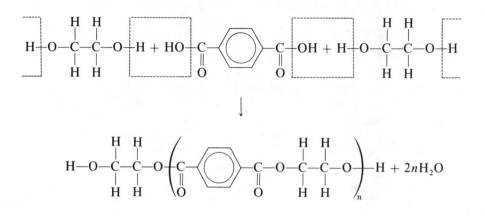

16-13   Nylon, a Polymeric Amide

Nylon, the material widely used in plastics and fabrics, is a condensation polymer. It consists of molecules with extremely long chains. The reaction by which monomer units become bonded together is by amide formation between reactants with two functional groups. Polyamides can be made from a compound with two acid groups, adipic acid, and another with two amine groups, 1,6-diaminohexane.

$$HOOC—CH_2—CH_2—CH_2—CH_2—COOH$$
$$HOOC—(CH_2)_4—COOH$$
adipic acid

$$H_2N—CH_2—CH_2—CH_2—CH_2—CH_2—CH_2—NH_2$$
$$H_2N—(CH_2)_6—NH_2$$
1,6-diaminohexane

These molecules combine to form long chains. For each new bond formed, one water molecule is removed. Reaction of three amine and three acid molecules gives

The creation of permanent-press clothing was based on an understanding of bonding. Consider cotton clothing. The fibers are a form of cellulose in which hundreds of glucose molecules join to form long chains having many OH groups on the surface. To form the permanent press, a chemical containing two reactive groups is added to the cloth. The heat produced by pressing the cloth to the desired form increases the rate of reaction between the added chemical and the OH groups. The bonds that are formed hold adjacent chains, and hence the crease, in place.

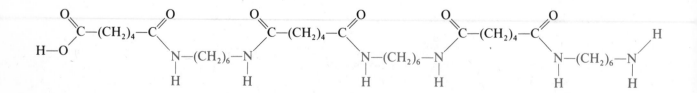

A usable Nylon molecule would contain hundreds of these monomers. Such linear structures are characteristic of polymers that produce fibers.

Discovery of Nylon

The discovery of Nylon is a good example of planned research coupled with unexpected observations. Man had used silk for many years. This natural product made wonderful cloth, but its production required so much manual labor that the cost was beyond the reach of most people. In Roman times it was literally worth its weight in gold.

Silk is a protein. Most protein molecules contain thousands of atoms. Such molecules are called polymers. The atoms occur in groups that come from amino acids. Silkworms combine these acids into long chains to form silk fibers. Two other common natural polymers are cellulose, made of glucose molecules, and rubber, made of isoprene molecules. Unfortunately chemists did not know how to make smaller units combine into long chains.

In 1927 the Du Pont company decided to finance a research program to learn more about the characteristics of polymers and to learn to make them—hopefully on an industrial scale. This would reduce the cost and make them available to more people. A young American chemist, Wallace Carothers, was employed and organized the research program.

He knew that silk contains several different amino acids, but for the sake of simplicity we will consider only the simplest, glycine,

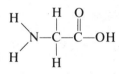

Glycine molecules can form a polymer by combining and eliminating water:

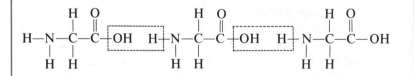

or after elimination of the water:

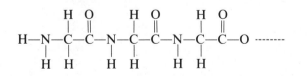

Since chemists had difficulty making molecules join each other in long chains, Carothers decided to use longer starting molecules. Two that led to success were these:

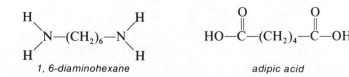

1, 6-diaminohexane   adipic acid

Other nylons are formed having different numbers of CH_2 units between the amide groups. Some are used for making thin fibers, others for casting (for example, bearings and gears).

One of the largest molecules is a chromosome from the fruit fly *Drosophila melanogaster*. It is about 2 centimeters long but only 0.000 002 centimeter in diameter. Its formula is approximately

$$C_{614\,000\,000}H_{759\,000\,000}N_{217\,000\,000}P_{62\,000\,000}O_{496\,000\,000}$$

or a little over 2 billion atoms! Its molar mass is about 23 100 tons!

These combine to form the polymer called Nylon 66:

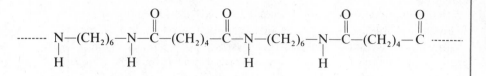

The unexpected occurred when Julian Hill, Carothers' associate, lifted a stirring rod out of a beaker of viscous product. Long threads formed but did not break. They solidified on cooling. When pulled, the threads stretched like rubber but did not snap back. The first man-made fiber had been found.

Today there are not only several different kinds of Nylon made from different starting monomers, but also many other polymers such as Dacron, polyethylene, Orlon, poly(vinyl chloride), Teflon, etc.

16-14 Simple Biological Compounds: Sugars

Living organisms—bacteria, fungi, mosses, algae, plants, animals—are highly organized systems of chemical compounds. All organisms derive the energy for their activities, and produce the substances of which they are built, by means of chemical reactions.

A century and a half ago men regarded the chemistry of living organisms as something quite distinct from the chemistry of rocks, minerals, and other nonliving things. Indeed, there was in their minds at that time the inclination to believe that living things were imbued with some mysterious "vital force" that was beyond the power of men to define and understand.

As time went on, it became apparent that the mystery in the chemistry of living things was due to ignorance of the details of what went on. With an increased understanding of chemical principles, the mystery gradually began to disappear. Compounds that were earlier known only as the products of plants and animals were produced in the laboratory from inorganic substances. By the middle of the 19th century the superstitious belief in a "vital force" had disappeared, and now there are few chemists who believe that the chemistry of living organisms is beyond the power of men to understand. We still, however, mark off a large area of chemical study by the term *biochemistry*. Biochemists are chiefly concerned with the chemical processes that go on in living organisms. These scientists must use information from all branches of chemistry to answer the questions they ask. Their questions are usually something like "What kind of molecules make up living systems?" or "How does a living system produce the energy it needs?"

Three classes of compounds that have great importance in biochemistry will be considered. Sugars are simple molecules which provide energy when they are oxidized. Cellulose and proteins are polymers that serve a double function, as foods and as structural elements in plants and animals. The word *sugar* brings to mind the sweet, white, crystalline grains found on a dinner table. The chemist calls this substance sucrose. It is only one of many "sugars," which are classed together because they have related composition and similar chemical reactions. Sugars are part of the larger family of **carbohydrates**, a name given because many such compounds have the empirical formula CH_2O.

EXERCISE 16-15

Glucose, a sugar simpler than sucrose, has a molar mass of 180 g and empirical formula CH_2O. What is its molecular formula?

The structure of the glucose molecule was deduced by a series of steps somewhat like those described in Sections 16-4 and 16-5 for ethanol. Glucose was found to contain one aldehyde group and five hydroxyl groups.

If all the oxygen-containing groups are reduced, *n*-hexane results. This test helps establish that the glucose molecule has a chain structure. One representation of the structural formula of glucose, $C_6H_{12}O_6$, is shown at the right.

Another naturally occurring sugar is fructose, also $C_6H_{12}O_6$. It is an isomer of glucose. The carbon of the

$$>C=O$$

group is at the second position in the carbon chain instead of at the end. It is a ketone.

EXERCISE 16-16

Draw a structural formula for the fructose molecule (remember that fructose is an isomer of glucose).

Both glucose and fructose exist as straight chain molecules and as cyclic structures. For each substance the two forms are in equilibrium. In solutions the latter form prevails. The equilibrium is shown for glucose:

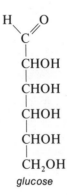

glucose

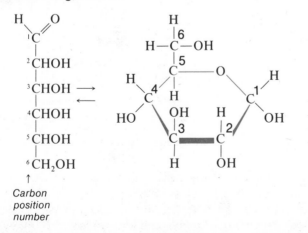

The cyclic form can be written in a simpler way as at the right. The hydrogen atoms attached to carbon atoms are represented by lines only, and the symbols for the carbons in the ring are omitted.

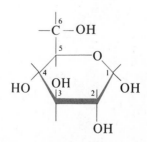

EXERCISE 16-17

At equilibrium in a 0.1 *M* solution of glucose in water, only 1 percent of the glucose is in the straight chain form. What is *K* for the reaction chain ⇌ ring?

The two sugars glucose and fructose are **monosaccharides**. They have a single sugar unit as the molecule. Table sugar is a disaccharide. It has two sugar units in the molecule. Sucrose contains one molecule of glucose and one of fructose joined together. Fructose has a slightly different ring structure because the carbonyl group, $\diagdown C{=}O$ is not on the end carbon. The structure of sucrose is shown in Figure 16-11.

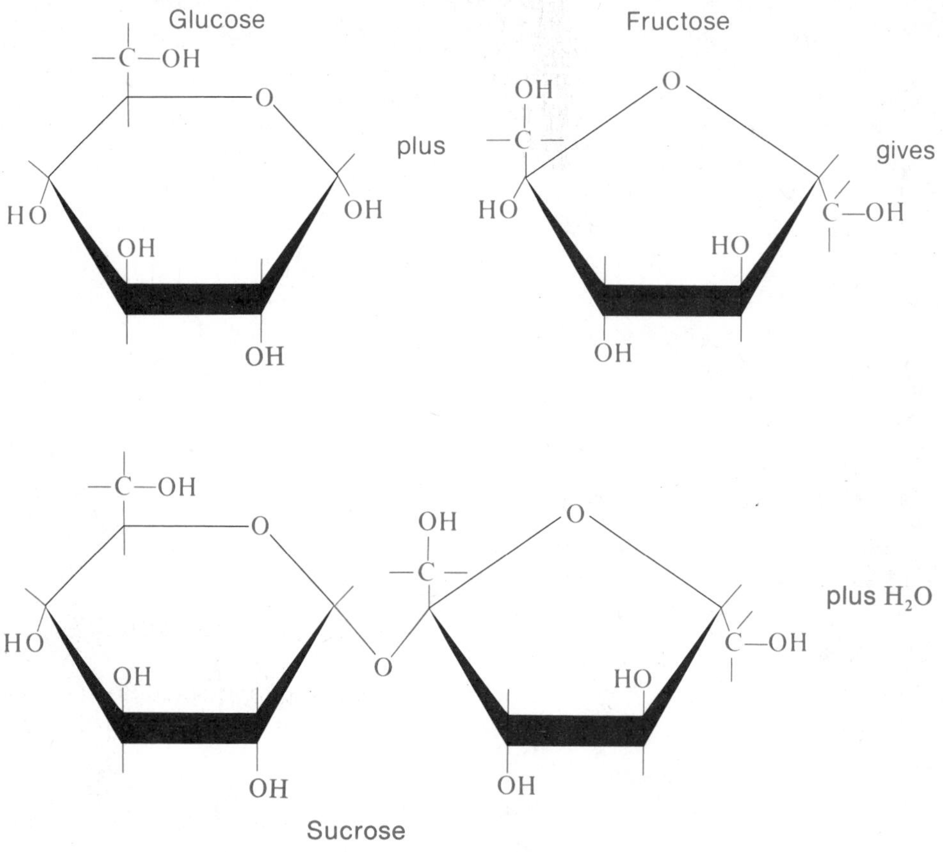

Glucose   plus   Fructose   gives

Sucrose   plus H₂O

Figure 16-11
The condensation of two simple sugars to form the disaccharide sucrose.

Sugars occur in many plants. Major commercial sources are sugarcane (a large, specialized grass which stores sucrose in the stem) and sugar beet (as much as 15 percent of the root is sucrose). In addition, fruits, some vegetables, and honey contain sugars. On the average every American eats almost 100 pounds of sugar per year. Sugar, at about 30 cents a pound retail, is one of the cheaper pure chemicals produced.

The Eyes Have It

Sight is probably the most valuable sense a human has. It is truly chemical in nature. "Seeing" depends directly on chemical reactions in the eye. The human eye is a spherical organ, open in the front to admit light and lined on the inside back surface with rod and cone cells. These cells are specialized nerve cells named for their general shape. See the figure. Each eye has 7 000 000 cones to detect color, whereas there are 120 000 000 rods to detect only black and white. However, the large number of rods gives acuity, or sharpness, to all vision. The tops of these cells consist of a stack of thin discs to which are attached the molecules responsible for vision. The molecules, called visual pigments, are of several types. We will illustrate only one, rhodopsin.

Rhodopsin has two parts: (1) a protein section of partially known structure, called opsin, to which (2) a simpler part, called retinal, joins and disconnects during vision. This action is caused by a structure change from a *cis* to a *trans* form. Retinal is an aldehyde, shown below in the all-*trans* form. *Trans* means that the two groups (CH_3 and H or two hydrogen atoms) that are not part of the main carbon chain are on opposite sides of the double bonds.

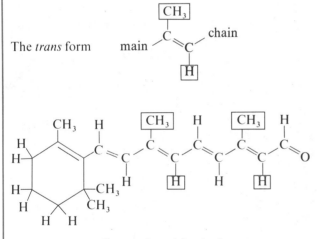

all *trans* form of retinal
There is a trans
configuration at every
C=C bond.

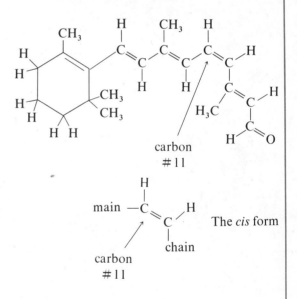

11-*cis* form of retinal
There is a *cis* configuration
between the 11th and 12th carbon
atoms—count ring carbons first.

The chain with alternating double and single bonds is responsible for absorption of visible light quanta. You can understand why vitamin A might aid our vision by noting that it has almost the same structure as retinal. The —C=O group at the end of the chain is —CH_2OH in vitamin A. Vitamin A is an alcohol; retinal is an aldehyde.

Some molecules of retinal will be in other isomeric forms, one of which is called the 11-*cis* form. *Cis* means that the two non-chain

As the number of daylight hours decreases from summer to fall, photosynthesis in the leaves of trees and plants is reduced. The chlorophyll content of leaves which accounts for their green color is diminished. The colors of other compounds which were there all the time begin to show. The brilliant display of fall colors is the result.

Papermakers require a knowledge of cellulose and the plants it comes from.

groups (two hydrogen atoms in this case) are on the same side of the chain. The number 11 means that the *cis* arrangement starts at the 11th carbon.

In this form, retinal is joined to the protein opsin to make rhodopsin. Rhodopsin has a red-purple color. When a single quantum of energy is absorbed by rhodopsin, it changes to the all-*trans* form, and the bond between retinal and opsin is weakened. The two separate, the red color is lost or bleached, and the nerve cell is now in an excited state. Somewhat later, up to 0.2 second, the excited receptor cell stimulates other cells, sending an impulse to the brain. Normally about five closely spaced receptor cells must be activated for you to be aware of "seeing" something. The energy needed is very small. For green light of 5000 Å wavelength, each quantum has about 9×10^{-20} calorie of energy. Five times that, or about 5×10^{-19} calorie, can be detected by the eye.

The regeneration of the 11-*cis* form and the rejoining to opsin are fairly slow and account for some of the time needed for dark adaptation. Intensely bright lights cause complete bleaching, and we are blinded because there is no retinal in the proper form to absorb quanta.

Color discrimination is accounted for by the recent discovery (1964) that the cone cells are of three classes, which are most receptive to frequencies of 4300 Å (blue), 5400 Å (green), and 5700 Å (yellow-red). Each type of cone also absorbs to a lesser degree over a range around its most sensitive frequency. Thus a blue-green light ray has photons that excite two types of cones, whereas a yellow-green ray excites other cones. These findings fit nicely with the trichromatic theory of color first proposed by Thomas Young (1800) and refined by Helmholtz in the mid-1800's. Your art teacher can discuss this theory.

So when it comes to valuable, complex light-chemical-electrical transformations, the eyes really do have it.

16-15 Some Biological Polymers: Starch, Cellulose, and Protein

Cellulose is an important part of woody plants, occurring in cell walls which make up part of the structural material of stems and trunks. Cotton and flax are almost pure cellulose. Chemically, cellulose is a polysaccharide. It is a polymer made by successive reactions of glucose molecules to give a high molar mass, approximately 600 000 grams. This polymer is quite similar to the polymers that were discussed in Sections 16-12 and 16-13.

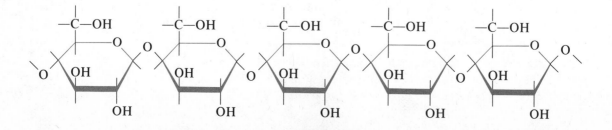

Starch is a mixture of glucose polymers, some of which are water-soluble. This soluble portion consists of comparatively short chains with molar mass near 4000 grams. The portion of low solubility involves much longer chains.

EXERCISE 16-18

The monomer unit in starch and that in cellulose both have the empirical formula $C_6H_{10}O_5$. These units are about 5.0 Å long. Approximately how many units occur and how long are the molecules of cellulose and of soluble starch?

A striking example of the effect of structure is shown by cellulose and water-soluble starch. Both contain the same monomer, since hydrolysis gives only glucose in each case. But the glucose ring has two slightly different arrangements of the —OH groups. These isomers give two different polymers. To show this we will represent the glucose ring in an even more simplified form. Only the two hydroxyl groups that take part in polymerization are shown.

Starch is the polymer formed when a large number of glucose molecules with the α-form react. On the other hand, a chain of the β-form of glucose gives the polymer called cellulose:

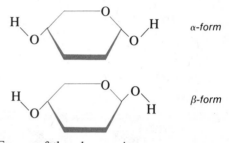

Forms of the glucose rings. Only the ring atoms and two —OH groups are shown for simplicity. Each ring is like that shown earlier for glucose.

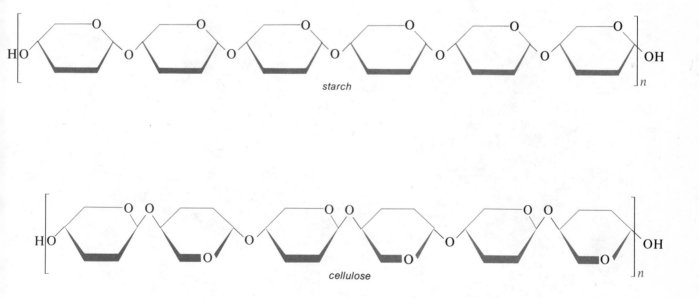

starch

cellulose

The different geometry in starch and cellulose causes these two polymers to have different chemical properties.

A most important class of compounds is that of proteins, the essential structure of all living matter. Man needs protein in his

Food technologists analyze the protein content in foods to make special diets or check labeling claims.

diet as a source of amino acids. From these acids the body synthesizes different types of proteins, which are used to build various parts of the body.

Proteins are polyamides that are formed by the polymerization, through amide linkages, of α-amino acids. Three important α-amino acids are shown in Figure 16-12. Each acid has an amine group, $-NH_2$, attached to the α-carbon, the carbon atom immediately adjacent to the carboxylic acid group. The protein molecule may involve hundreds of such amino acid molecules connected through the amide linkages. A portion of this chain is represented in Figure 16-13.

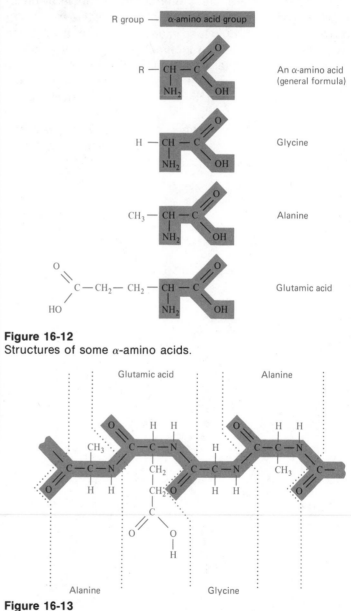

Figure 16-12
Structures of some α-amino acids.

Figure 16-13
A portion of an amide chain in a protein.

X-ray diffraction studies have led to the recognition of a coiled form of the chain in some natural proteins (Figure 16-14). This form has a great deal of regularity. It is not at all a random shape.

Figure 16-14
The coiled form of a protein.

But order is not achieved without some energy to maintain it, and this comes mainly from the formation of hydrogen bonds. The hydrogen bonds can be broken by heating or by putting the protein in alcohol. The order disappears and the coiled form loses its shape. Often this damage cannot be repaired, and the coil is permanently deformed. Cooking an egg destroys the coiled form of the proteins it contains. A few moments of thought concerning the profound differences between the physical form and chemical potentialities of an egg before and after it is cooked will suggest the very great importance of molecular structure in biochemistry.

Foresters study the interaction of plants, insects, fertilizers, and insecticides.

16-16 Biological Catalysts: Enzymes

Proteins act as catalysts for many of the reactions that take place in our bodies. The name **enzymes** has been given to these catalytic protein molecules. Usually enzyme molecules are very large, with a molar mass of about 100 000 grams being average. Compared with most chemicals that you have studied, these are enormous molecules. There are some important biochemical molecules that are considerably larger. The molar mass of hemoglobin in your red blood cells is about 500 000 grams, and some plant viruses have molar masses as high as 40 000 000 grams, or 40 metric tons!

A single living cell may contain as many as 1000 enzymes, each controlling a specific reaction.

An enzyme molecule causes its catalytic action by forming weak bonds to a smaller molecule, called the substrate. In the form produced by this combination, the substrate molecule reacts faster than it would without the enzyme present. In 1965 the detailed structure of an enzyme, lysozyme, was determined for the first time. This enzyme increases the rate at which polysaccharides in bacterial walls are broken into smaller units.

Lysozyme is a chain of 129 amino acids. Portions of the polyamide chain are coiled as in Figure 16-14, whereas other portions are not coiled. The molecule as a whole has 1940 atoms and is about 40 Å across its largest dimension. Each lysozyme molecule has a shape somewhat like a cupped hand. A slot or valley in the molecule is the site that can hold the polysaccharide molecule. The shape of the valley and placement of the functional groups in it mean that only certain molecules can fit. These are the ones whose reactions are catalyzed by the enzyme. Again, molecular structure has a vital part in chemical behavior.

Enzymes are added to some detergents. They help clean fabrics by increasing the rate of decomposition of proteins and fats, such as blood, body oils, and spilled gravy.

16-17 Energy Sources in Nature

Man and other animals use energy continuously, to maintain body temperature and for muscular activities such as breathing and moving around. The chief source of the needed energy is the oxidation of carbon compounds to CO_2. We can illustrate the process with sugar, one of the most important foods of animals. Man eats sugar either directly or as starch, the polymeric form in which sugar is stored in many plants, such as the potato. Cellulose, although a glucose polymer, is not useful to humans because our digestive systems cannot break the large molecules into glucose fast enough.

The process by which glucose is oxidized to yield CO_2, H_2O, and energy is very complex, but it has been confirmed by many experiments. We will present only the major points. First consider these three steps:

Glucose is converted to pyruvic acid.
Pyruvic acid is changed to acetic acid.
Acetic acid is oxidized to carbon dioxide, water, and
    energy.

We can picture the series of reactions in the following, much simplified manner:

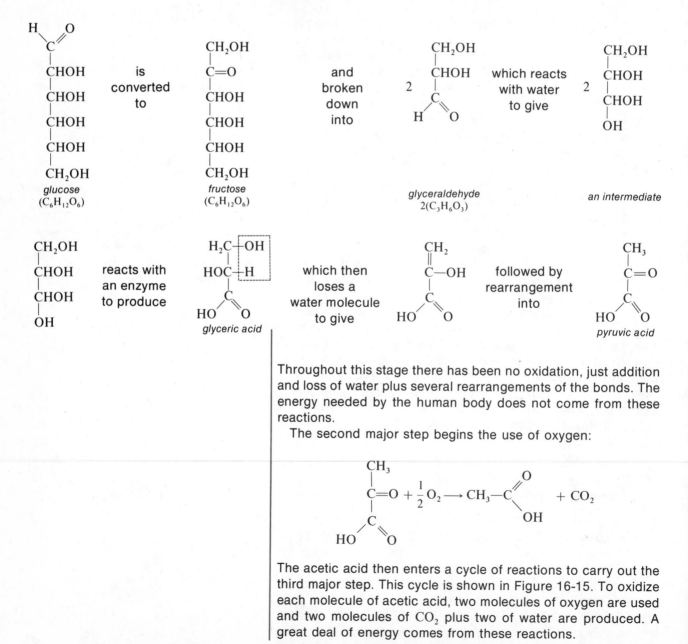

Throughout this stage there has been no oxidation, just addition and loss of water plus several rearrangements of the bonds. The energy needed by the human body does not come from these reactions.

The second major step begins the use of oxygen:

The acetic acid then enters a cycle of reactions to carry out the third major step. This cycle is shown in Figure 16-15. To oxidize each molecule of acetic acid, two molecules of oxygen are used and two molecules of CO_2 plus two of water are produced. A great deal of energy comes from these reactions.

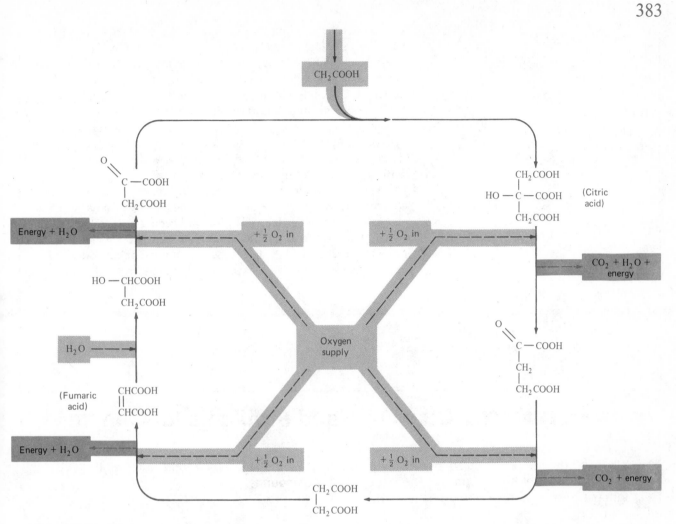

Figure 16-15
The cycle by which acetic acid provides energy.

Chemical Communication

You can communicate with people in many ways—from a soft "Hi, honey" to a sock on the nose. You can use sign language, a facial expression, a shake of the head, or a song.

Did you ever wonder how insects transfer information? They also have several ways. Maybe you have heard of the worker bee's "dance" that tells other bees the direction and distance to some nectar-laden flower. Chemicals are also used to give messages. The most common, perhaps most important, use of these substances is to find a mate. Many species, particularly of flying insects, use such attractants, called *pheromones*. Different species use different chemicals.

Various types of functional groups occur in attractants. Here are a few: Moths use alcohols $C_{12}H_{25}OH$ to $C_{16}H_{33}OH$

and esters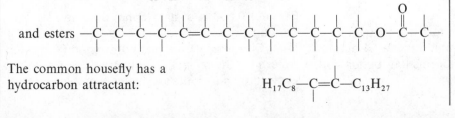

The common housefly has a
hydrocarbon attractant: $H_{17}C_8 - C = C - C_{13}H_{27}$

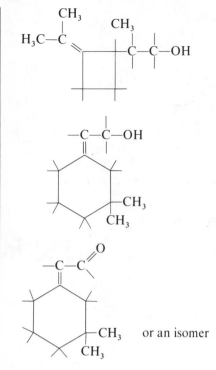

or an isomer

Boll weevils use a mixture of alcohols and aldehydes: Amazingly small amounts are needed. Silkworm moths (*Bombyx mori*) require only 200 molecules per cubic centimeter of air! This means there are a billion billion other molecules for each molecule of the attractant. One molecule is sufficient to trigger a nerve impulse, though it takes about 200 impulses to get a message to the moth's brain.

Such powerful and specific chemicals are clearly useful as lures in traps or as a "gas" to confuse the insects as to the source. In either case, the population of an undesired species is lowered by "jamming," or confusing the chemical communication system.

Other uses include: the queen bee's control of which bees will be workers, drones, etc.; "alarm" or warning signals of ants; ant trails leading to food or, in the case of slave-keeping ants, to nests to be raided. Pheromone communication by means of chemicals is not limited to insects, though that is the best-studied area. Crabs, at least one fish, and some monkeys have been found to secrete odor messages.

Questions and Problems for Chapter 16

1

What information is revealed by the empirical formula? The molecular formula? The structural formula? Demonstrate, using propane, C_3H_8.

2

A 100-mg sample of a compound containing only C, H, and O was found by analysis to give 149 mg CO_2 and 45.5 mg H_2O when burned completely. Calculate the empirical formula.

3

When 0.601 gram of a sample having an empirical formula CH_2O was vaporized at 200 °C and 1 atmosphere pressure, the volume occupied was 388 ml. This same volume was occupied by 0.301 gram of ethane under the same conditions. What is the molecular formula of CH_2O?

One mole of the sample, when reacted with zinc metal, liberated (rather slowly) ½ mole of hydrogen gas. Write the structural formula.

4

Butane has the molecular formula C_4H_{10}. Draw two different ways of arranging these 14 atoms. Remember, carbon usually forms *four* bonds and hydrogen *one*.

5

Draw the structural formulas for all the $C_2H_3Cl_3$ compounds.

6

Draw the structures of two isomeric compounds corresponding to the empirical formula C_3H_8O.

7

Draw the structural formulas for the four isomers of C_4H_9Cl.

8

What angle would you expect to be formed by the C, O, and H nuclei in an alcohol molecule? Explain

9

It is possible to obtain 10.3 g CO_2, 1.50 g H_2O, 1.53 g NO_2, and 2.13 g SO_2 by burning 6.1 g of the sweetener saccharin. What is its empirical formula?

10

Burning 0.600 g of an alcohol obtained by processing petroleum gave 1.32 g CO_2 and 0.72 g H_2O. One mole of the alcohol weighs 60 grams. Determine the molecular and structural formulas. Draw formulas for the two isomers of this alcohol?

11

How much ethanol can be made from 50 grams of ethyl bromide? What assumptions do you make in answering this question?

12

Give the empirical formula and the molecular formula and draw the structural formulas of the isomers of butene. This hydrocarbon contains four carbon atoms and one double bond.

13

Ethane, C_2H_6, reacts with chlorine to substitute first one chlorine for hydrogen, then two, and so on until C_2Cl_6 is formed. How many different ethane derivatives form in this series of reactions?

14

Write the balanced equation for the production of pentanone from pentanol, using dichromate ion as the oxidizing agent.

15

Knowing the possible oxidation products of ethanol and 2-propanol, predict the oxidation products of

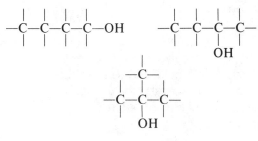

16

One mole of an organic compound is found to react with ½ mole of oxygen to produce an acid. To what class of compounds does this starting material belong?

17

Using the information given in Table 11-2, determine the reaction heat for the complete combustion of 1 mole of ethane, $C_2H_6(g)$.

18

An aqueous solution containing 0.10 mole/liter of chloroacetic acid, ClH_2CCOOH, is tested with indicators, and the concentration of $H^+(aq)$ is found to be 1.2×10^{-2} M. Calculate the value of K_A. Compare this value with K_A for acetic acid. The change is caused by the substitution of a halogen atom near a carboxylic acid group.

19

In an acid solution benzaldehyde is oxidized to benzoic acid:

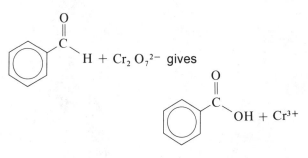

Write a balanced equation by generating the half-reactions.

20

Consider the half-cell reaction

$$CH_3COOH + 2\,H^+ + 2\,e^- \longrightarrow CH_3C\begin{smallmatrix}O\\\\H\end{smallmatrix} + H_2O$$

$E° = -0.13$ volt

Can acetaldehyde be oxidized to acetic acid by Br_2, Cu^{2+}, or Co^{2+}?

21

Give simple structural formulas of

(a) an alcohol
(b) an aldehyde
(c) an acid

each derived from methane, from ethane, from butane, and from octane.

22

Write the equations for the preparation of methylamine from methyl iodide.

23

Show a two-stage synthesis for the formation of butylamine starting with n-butyl alcohol, HI, and NH_3.

24

Suggest a formula for

(a) triethyl amine
(b) triethyl ammonium chloride

25

Write equations using structural formulas, and name the products for the reaction of acetic acid with

(a) ethyl alcohol

(b) ethylamine
(c) *isopropylamine*

26

Write equations to show the formation of the esters methyl butyrate and butyl propionate.

27

Given the structural formula

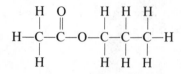

for an ester, write the formula of the acid and the alcohol from which it might be made.

28

When 0.01 mole of an organic acid is dissolved in distilled water and titrated to phenolphthalein equivalence point using 0.1 M NaOH solution, 200 ml of base solution were needed. How many ionizable hydrogen atoms are there in each molecule?

29

In the preparation of methyl acetate, the yield of ester is rather low at equilibrium. What can be done to increase the yield? Study the equation and apply Le Châtelier's principle.

$$\text{methyl alcohol} + \text{acetic acid} \rightleftharpoons \text{methyl acetate} + \text{water}$$

30

How much acetamide can be made from 3.1 grams of methyl acetate? See the equation on page 366. Assume the ester is completely converted.

31

An acid, RCOOH, and an alcohol, R′OH, react to form an ester RCOOR′ and water. The reaction is carried out in an inert solvent.

(a) Write the equilibrium law expression. Include the concentration of the product water.
(b) Calculate the equilibrium concentration of the ester if $K = 10$ and the concentrations *at equilibrium* of the other constituents are
    [RCOOH] = 0.1 M [H$_2$O] = 1.0 M
    [R′OH] = 0.1 M
(c) Repeat the calculation of part (b) if the equilibrium concentrations are
    [RCOOH] = 0.3 M [H$_2$O] = 1.0 M
    [R′OH] = 0.3 M

32

Draw structural formulas for the three isomers of dichlorobenzene, $C_6H_4Cl_2$.

33

Consider the compound phenol,

(a) Predict the angle formed by the nuclei of C, O, and H. Explain your choice in terms of the orbitals used by oxygen in its bonds.
(b) Predict qualitatively the boiling temperature of phenol. (The boiling temperature of benzene is 80 °C.) Explain your answer.
(c) Write an equation for the reaction of phenol as a proton donor in water.
(d) In a 1.0 M aqueous solution of phenol. [H$^+$] = 1.1 × 10^{-5}. Calculate K_A.

34

Name these compounds or write structural formulas:

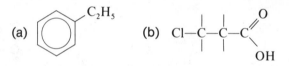

(c) dimethyl glutamate
(d) oxalic acid (the simplest possible compound with two carboxyl groups)
(e) 1, 4-diaminopentane

35

Work out a possible structural formula for the polymer of 1,3-butadiene,

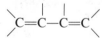

36

Lucite is an addition polymer of methylmethacrylate, shown below:

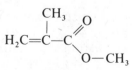

Draw a portion of the Lucite structure.

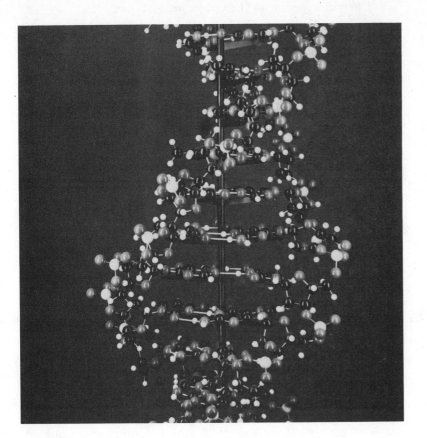

Chemical Bonding in Gases, Liquids, and Solids 17

The nature of the chemical bond was discussed in Chapter 10. Although it was convenient to introduce the two words *covalent* and *ionic* in describing chemical bonding, the formation of any chemical bond has only one cause. When bonding electrons are simultaneously attracted by two nuclei, a state of lower potential energy is achieved and a chemical bond forms. In this chapter bonding will receive more detailed study and will be extended to show that the shapes of molecules can be explained qualitatively using the orbital view of atomic structure. You may find it helpful to read Sections 10-1 and 10-2 again before continuing with this chapter.

17-1 Polar Molecules in the Gas Phase

The fluorine molecule is stable, because the potential energy is decreased when two fluorine atoms approach each other and the bonding electrons become concentrated between them. The electrons are distributed within the molecule, so the probability of finding the electrons is highest midway between the nuclei. Because the nuclei are the same, the distribution of electrons around one nucleus is the mirror image of the distribution around the other.

In the gaseous lithium fluoride molecule, the bonding pair of electrons is again concentrated between the lithium and fluorine nuclei. Now, however, the electrons move so that they spend more time near the fluorine nucleus, on the average, than they do near the lithium nucleus. The fluorine nucleus attracts the bonding electrons more than the lithium nucleus does.

The shifting of negative electric charge towards the fluorine atom in the LiF molecule causes a charge separation. The molecule has an excess of negative electric charge at the fluorine end and a deficiency of negative electric charge at the lithium end. To indicate this charge separation, the Li—F bond is called a **polar bond**. In LiF, the polar bond makes the whole molecule polar, and this **polar molecule** is said to have an **electric dipole**.

Table 17-1 summarizes some of the information on bonding that was presented in Chapter 10. The presence or absence of an electric dipole in the gaseous molecules is indicated in the last column. This information about electric dipoles, derived from many experiments, will be important in the discussion of molecular geometry.

TABLE 17-1

Bonding Arrangements and Polar Nature of Second-Row Fluorides

Compound with Fluorine		Electron Configuration			Orbitals Used in Bonding	Electric Dipole Present in Gaseous Molecule?
Formula	Number of Bonds		$1s$	$2s$	$2p$	
LiF	1	Li	$\otimes$	$\oslash$	$\bigcirc\bigcirc\bigcirc$	s	yes
BeF_2	2	Be	$\otimes$	$\oslash$	$\bigcirc\bigcirc\bigcirc$	sp	no
BF_3	3	B	$\otimes$	$\oslash$	$\bigcirc\bigcirc\bigcirc$	sp^2	no
CF_4	4	C	$\otimes$	$\oslash$	$\bigcirc\bigcirc\bigcirc$	sp^3	no
NF_3	3	N	$\otimes$	$\oslash$	$\bigcirc\bigcirc\bigcirc$	p^3	yes
OF_2	2	O	$\otimes$	$\otimes$	$\otimes\bigcirc\bigcirc$	p^2	yes
F_2	1	F	$\otimes$	$\otimes$	$\otimes\otimes\bigcirc$	p	no
—	0	Ne	$\otimes$	$\otimes$	$\otimes\otimes\otimes$	none	no

17-2 Molecular Architecture: The Shapes of the Second-Row Fluoride Molecules

Crime laboratory technicians use the structure of molecules to identify material found at the scene of a crime or on the suspect.

Lithium fluoride in the gas phase is a linear diatomic molecule. The bond can be described in terms of the overlap of the $2s$ orbital in lithium with the half-filled $2p$ orbital in fluorine. Experiments reveal that LiF(g) has a very large electric dipole, showing the separation of charge in the molecule.

The beryllium atom in gaseous BeF_2 uses the 2s and one of the 2p orbitals in bonding. Just as with the Li—F bond, it is reasonable to expect there would be appreciable charge separation in the Be—F bond. However, electric dipole measurements show *the absence of a molecular dipole* in BeF_2. This result is the clue to the geometry of the beryllium fluoride molecule. There are two Be—F bonds, and the electrical properties of the entire molecule depend on how these bonds are oriented relative to each other. To see how charge separation can occur without yielding a polar molecule, we need a method of representing electron shifting. Chemists have several, some of which are shown in Figure 17-1. The arrow is the simplest way to depict the charge separation. The arrowhead points to the region of excess negative charge. The arrow indicates a polar bond, also called a **bond dipole**.

The arrangement of two bond dipoles to give zero molecular dipole is illustrated in Figure 17-2. The molecule must be linear, with the two bond dipoles pointing in opposite directions. This geometry leads to cancellation of the effects of bond dipoles.

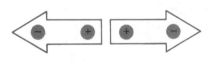

Zero molecular dipole results from two equal bond dipoles only when they are opposed.

Structure suggested by opposing bond dipoles.

Figure 17-2
The absence of molecular dipole in BeF_2 suggests a linear molecule.

The bonding in BeF_2 makes use of one s and one p orbital in beryllium. A linear arrangement of bonds in a molecule is expected when the available bonding orbitals on the central atom are an s and a p. Chemists refer to this as **sp bonding**.

In gaseous BF_3 the boron atom uses the 2s and two 2p orbitals in bonding. The zero electric dipole found for molecules of BF_3 can be explained by a symmetrical geometry for the three B—F bonds. The only way to achieve this is with the structure shown in Figure 17-3. The boron trifluoride molecule is planar, with the three fluorine atoms at the corners of an equilateral triangle. The lower part of the figure shows the method of deciding the net effect of the arrows. This method is called vector addition. The bonding in BF_3 is called sp^2 (read $s\ p\ two$). A planar, triangular arrangement is expected around an atom which uses one s and two p bonding orbitals.

For carbon, the bonding in CF_4 involves four valence orbitals, the 2s and three 2p orbitals. The zero value for the molecular dipole of CF_4 can be explained by several different structures. Two of them are shown in Figure 17-4. Additional experiments indicate that carbon compounds have the tetrahedral structure at the top in Figure 17-4. The fluorine atoms occupy the corners of

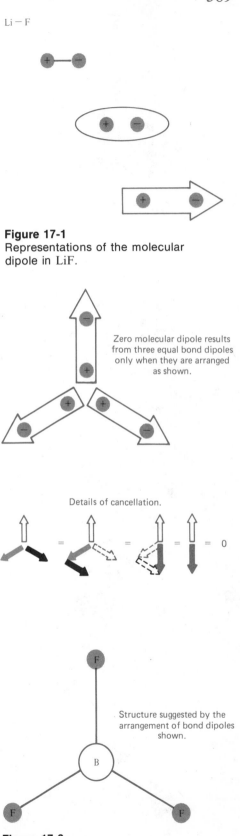

Li — F

Figure 17-1
Representations of the molecular dipole in LiF.

Zero molecular dipole results from three equal bond dipoles only when they are arranged as shown.

Details of cancellation.

Structure suggested by the arrangement of bond dipoles shown.

Figure 17-3
The absence of a molecular dipole in BF_3 suggests a symmetric planar molecule.

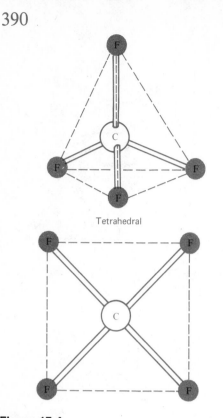

Figure 17-4
Two arrangements that would give a zero molecular dipole for CF_4.

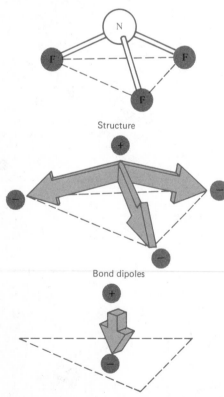

Structure

Bond dipoles

Molecular dipole resulting from bond dipoles

Figure 17-5
Structure and molecular dipole in NF_3.

a tetrahedron, with carbon at its center. The angle between any two C—F bonds is the tetrahedral angle, 109° 28′. The bonding in CF_4 is called **sp³** (*s p three*). Tetrahedral geometry is expected around any atom that makes use of one *s* and three *p* orbitals. This is the most common arrangement of bonds around a carbon atom.

EXERCISE 17-1

Molecules that have the same electron configuration often have similar molecular geometry. Comment on the bond angles you would expect in the molecules or ions listed. They are like CH_4.

$$NH_3, NH_4^+, NH_2^-, H_2O, H_3O^+$$

EXERCISE 17-2

In Exercise 17-1 you suggested a bond angle in NH_3 and H_2O. Compare those with the experimental values of 107° and 105° respectively.

Nitrogen is the next element in the second row. The bonding in its fluoride, NF_3, involves the three 2*p* orbitals of the nitrogen atom. The fact that there *is* a net, or molecular, electric dipole for NF_3 indicates that this molecule *does not* have the symmetrical geometry exhibited by BF_3. Since *p* orbitals are perpendicular to each other, NF_3 might have the structure shown in Figure 17-5. Other experiments confirm this structure. The molecule NF_3 can be thought of as a pyramid, with the nitrogen atom above the triangular base. Approximately 90° bond angles would be expected for the bonding arrangement around any atom using three *p* orbitals. Experiments indicate that the bond angle in NF_3 is about 102°. In NH_3 the bond angles are 107°.

Oxygen difluoride, OF_2, makes use of the two 2*p* orbitals of the oxygen atom to bond to fluorine. The electric dipole for the molecule is not zero. Because of this experimental evidence, the structure of OF_2 *cannot be* linear as BeF_2 is. Other measurements agree with the structure shown in Figure 17-6. One might expect that the F—O—F bond angle would be approximately 90°, the angle between the two 2*p* orbitals of oxygen used in bonding. Experimental measurements give this angle as 103°.

The last molecule to be discussed in this section on elements of the second row is F_2. There is no reason to expect separation of electric charge in this molecule, and the measured electric dipole is zero. There is no question of geometry for a diatomic molecule. Bond formation makes use of the last half-filled 2*p* orbital on each fluorine atom.

A summary of this discussion is presented in Table 17-2. The correlation of molecular geometry with the orbitals used in bonding is one of the most helpful regularities that chemists have discovered.

17-3 The Bonding in Liquids and Solids

Our discussion of molecules in the gas phase focused on the forces *within* molecules. Now we will discuss the forces *between*

TABLE 17-2

Bonding Orbitals, Bonding Capacity, and Molecular
Shape for Second-Row Fluorides

Element	Bonding Orbitals	Bonding Capacity	Molecular Shape of the Fluoride	Chemical Formula
He	none	0		He
Li	s	1	linear	LiF
Be	sp	2	linear	BeF_2
B	sp^2	3	planar, Y-shaped	BF_3
C	sp^3	4	tetrahedral	CF_4
N	p^3	3	pyramidal	NF_3
O	p^2	2	bent	OF_2
F	p	1	linear	F_2
Ne	none	0		Ne

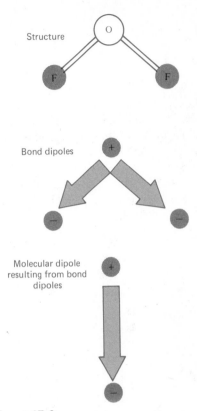

Figure 17-6
Structure and molecular dipole in OF_2.

molecules. When sufficient energy is removed from any gas, it condenses to a liquid. It then forms a solid if enough additional energy is removed. The forces that bring about formation of liquids and solids are *between* molecules. The temperature at which these phase changes occur varies from one substance to another, as shown by three examples in Figure 17-7.

Lithium fluoride gas at one atmosphere pressure liquefies when the heat of condensation is removed. It becomes liquid at 1949 K. When the temperature is lowered to 1143 K and the heat of crystallization is removed, the liquid forms a crystal made up of ions Li^+ and F^-.

In contrast, *lithium* gas at this pressure must be cooled to 1609 K before it can form a liquid, and this liquid does not solidify until its temperature reaches 459 K. The solid is a white, soft metallic crystal which does not resemble lithium fluoride. The metal contains lithium atoms.

Fluorine gas is equally distinctive. At one atmosphere pressure fluorine must be cooled far below room temperature before liquefaction can occur at only 85 K. The liquid is pale yellow in color and can be solidified to a crystal at 50 K. X-ray studies show that the crystal contains diatomic molecules of F_2.

Why do these three materials behave so differently? Is there some explanation to help us understand these differences? Several times in this book the statement has been made that attractive forces between atoms arise when electrons can be close to two or more nuclei at the same time. This is found to be true in liquids and solids as well as in gases. The three examples above show that the magnitude of the attractive forces in liquids and solids varies greatly, depending on how close electrons can approach these nuclei. This *approach distance* is fixed by the electron occupancy of the valence orbitals. The occupancy of valence orbitals can be used to help predict whether a substance will form a high-melting ionic crystal, a metallic crystal, or a low-melting molecular crystal. In the next sections, explanations for the observed properties will be presented in terms of the molecular structure of solids.

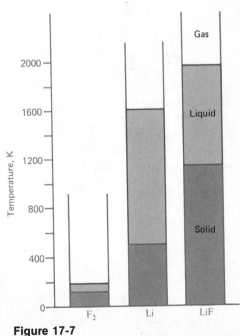

Figure 17-7
Temperature ranges for phases of molecular, metallic, and ionic solids.

A change in the concentration of CO_2 induces a resting mosquito to start flying. The mosquito then moves in a random fashion until it detects either infrared energy from a warm surface or water vapor. It then aims straight for the back of your hand. A useless bit of information? Well . . .

chemists have discovered that molecules of good mosquito-repellents are spherical in shape rather than long and thin. These molecules do not actually repel a mosquito but instead seem to block the sensory nerves in the mosquito's antennas which respond to warmth and moisture. The mosquito continues its random flight instead of homing in on your hand.

(Both figures from J. E. Amoore, *Molecular Basis of Odor,* 1st ed., 1970. Courtesy of Charles C. Thomas, Publisher, Springfield, Illinois.)

Smell

According to the stereochemical theory of odor, many odors can be explained on the basis of molecular shape. This theory suggests that there are seven primary odors: camphor, pungent, floral, ethereal, peppermint, musky, and putrid. The first five seem to depend on how a molecule fits into a receptor site in the nasal cavity. Here are two examples:

The camphor odor is associated with football-shaped molecules of length about 9 Å and diameter at the wide part of about 7 Å. The proposed receptor site is an oval basin 9 × 7 Å by about 4 Å deep. Below are some examples, together with diagrams of how a model of such molecules fits a model of the receptor:

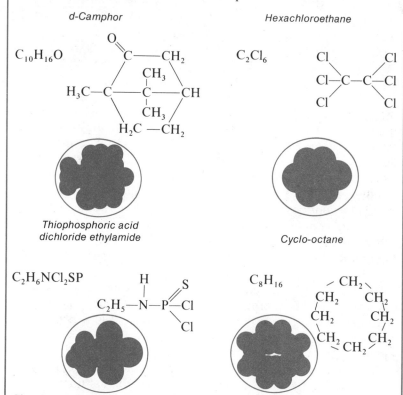

Clearly the composition, types of atomic groupings, and chemical behaviors are quite different for these molecules. Shape and size are remarkably similar, and they all have the odor of camphor.

The floral odor site is rather oddly shaped, somewhat like a deep slot connected to a shallow, round pan.

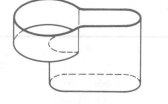
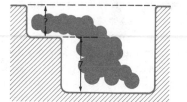

It is large, about 16 Å across the top the long way and 10 Å or so deep.

An interesting final note is that different proteins have been isolated that seem to contain the sweet taste site, the bitter taste receptor, or the floral odor detecting ability. These proteins may have crevices or indentations that act as receptor sites. Similar receptor sites are well known in enzymes. For example, crystal structure determinations of lysozyme have shown a clearly defined cleft of just the right size to hold a certain molecule. Sure enough, it is just this molecule that the enzyme acts on during digestion.

There is still much to learn about our senses and the chemistry of their action. Successful solution of these remaining problems can lead to medical remedies for the inability to detect odors, (odor blindness), better perfumes and flavors, the removal of polluting odors, and a better understanding of the odors insects use to attract mates or repel predators.

17-4 Van der Waals Forces

Polar molecules have relatively strong attraction for each other, resulting from the molecular dipoles present. However, even for molecules having no electric dipole there are attractive forces. For example, two noble gas atoms must attract each other slightly to explain the fact that the noble gases liquefy and form crystalline solids under suitable conditions. These forces are named *van der Waals forces,* after the Dutch scientist who studied them. Quantum mechanics helps us understand the origin of these forces. Electron locations inside an atom or a molecule are best described by the probability of finding them. For a noble gas the electron distribution *on the average* is symmetrical, so it has no permanent dipole. But *at any given instant,* the electron distribution may not be symmetrical. The atom would then have a *momentary electric dipole.* The weak attractive forces in the noble gases arise from interaction between such dipoles.

Atoms of fluorine form diatomic molecules with the formula F_2. In the fluorine molecule there are enough electrons close to each nucleus to fill the valence orbitals. Under these circumstances the diatomic molecule behaves like a noble gas toward other fluorine molecules. Momentary dipoles provide a weak attractive force. Molecular fluorine condenses to a liquid at 85 K due to these weak van der Waals forces.

Although charge separation is possible in a compound, there are many substances that do not have appreciable electric dipoles. When all the valence orbitals of such a molecule are filled, giving noble gas electron configurations, then the electrons of a second molecule cannot get very close to the nuclei of the first molecule. The decrease in potential energy is only a few tenths of a kilocalorie per mole when molecules of this sort approach each other. This very weak interaction between molecules is typical of van der Waals forces. It gives rise to low-melting solids and low-boiling liquids that retain many of the properties of the gaseous molecules. Such solids are called molecular solids, because they are made of molecules loosely held together.

There are three factors that are important in determining the magnitude of van der Waals forces: the number of electrons, the molecular size, and the molecular shape. These factors can be illustrated with carbon compounds. In Figure 17-8 the melting and boiling temperatures of compounds with the formula CX_4 are shown. (These compounds do not have a permanent electric dipole.) The horizontal axis shows the periodic table row number

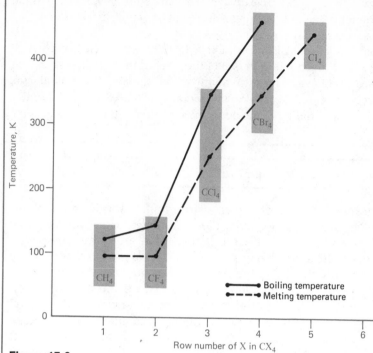

Figure 17-8
Melting and boiling temperatures of carbon-halogen compounds, CX_4.

for the outermost atoms in the molecule. These are the atoms which "rub shoulders" with neighboring molecules. As far as van der Waals interactions are concerned, the number of electrons on the outermost atoms is most important in fixing intermolecular forces.

The other two factors are closely related to each other. As the size of a molecule increases, its contact surface increases. The trend in boiling temperatures for the hydrocarbon molecules listed in Table 17-3 serves to illustrate this factor. Molecular shape sometimes determines the number of electrons that are "exposed" to other molecules. Notice the three isomers of pen-

TABLE 17-3
The Boiling Temperature of Some Hydrocarbons

Compound	Formula	Boiling Temperature, °C
Methane	CH_4	−161.5
Ethane	CH_3CH_3	−88.6
Propane	$CH_3CH_2CH_3$	−42.1
n-butane	$CH_3CH_2CH_2CH_3$	−0.5
n-pentane	$CH_3CH_2CH_2CH_2CH_3$	36.1
iso-pentane	$\begin{array}{c} CH_3 \\ \diagdown \\ CHCH_2CH_3 \\ \diagup \\ CH_3 \end{array}$	27.9
neo-pentane	$\begin{array}{c} CH_3 \\ | \\ CH_3-C-CH_3 \\ | \\ CH_3 \end{array}$	9.5

tane in Figure 17-9. (Chapter 10, p. 208, has some discussion of isomers.) The extended molecule, *n*-pentane, has a zigzag shape. The van der Waals forces between the external envelope of *n*-pentane molecules would lead to a relatively high boiling temperature. By contrast, the highly compact and symmetrical shape for *neo*-pentane offers much less surface contact with its neighbors. Lower van der Waals interaction and therefore lower boiling temperature are expected.

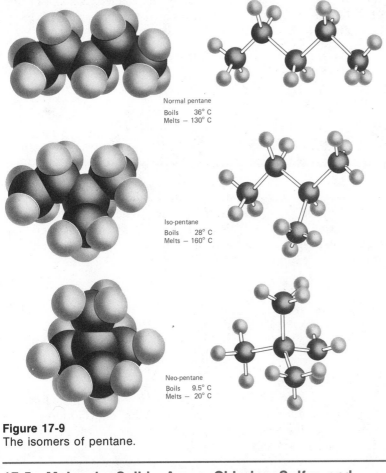

Normal pentane
Boils   36° C
Melts − 130° C

Iso-pentane
Boils   28° C
Melts − 160° C

Neo-pentane
Boils   9.5° C
Melts − 20° C

Figure 17-9
The isomers of pentane.

17-5 Molecular Solids: Argon, Chlorine, Sulfur, and Phosphorus

Argon, chlorine, sulfur, and phosphorus form molecular solids, with only van der Waals forces acting between the molecules. Argon molecules consist of the single atom. Chlorine forms the diatomic molecule Cl_2. The electron configuration of the chlorine atom provides a satisfactory explanation for the molecular form of this element. The single half-filled $3p$ orbital can be used to form one covalent bond.

In sulfur the electron configuration in the valence orbitals suggests that each sulfur atom will form two covalent bonds with other atoms. Sulfur molecules take on the geometrical form of an eight-membered puckered ring. The S_8 molecules have the structure shown in Figure 17-10, with each sulfur atom bonded to two other sulfur atoms.

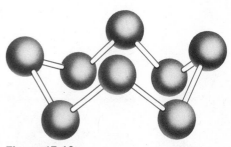

Figure 17-10
The structure of S_8.

Polymers with Inorganic Backbones

The commercial polymers—such as Bakelite, celluloid, Nylon, Dacron, polyethylenes, and polyurethanes—have mostly carbon in the main chain. Only occasionally is there an oxygen, nitrogen, or sulfur atom. These are organic polymers. However, there are several candidates for the name "inorganic polymer."

One true inorganic polymer is ancient and well known to you—glass. It has no carbon atoms. Glass is mainly interconnected chains or rings of SiO_2^{2-} ions. The symbol Si means a silicon atom with an oxygen atom above or below the paper.

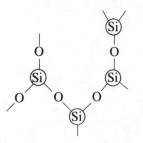

Glass has many useful properties, but it is fragile.

Another well-known family of examples, somewhat related to glass, is the silicone polymers. This family has a main chain of alternating silicon and oxygen atoms. Each silicon atom also has two organic alkyl groups attached to it.

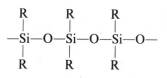

These are usually methyl, ethyl, or phenyl. Here is a simplified scheme of their preparation. Sand is changed to silicon tetrachloride, reacted with compounds containing the desired R group, and then hydrolyzed with water and condensed:

$$SiO_2 \longrightarrow SiCl_4$$

$$SiCl_4 + 2RMgCl \longrightarrow R_2SiCl_2 + 2MgCl_2$$

$$R_2SiCl_2 + 2H_2O \longrightarrow [R_2Si(OH)_2] + 2HCl$$

This process can continue to form long Si-O chains.

The silicone polymers can be oily liquids, varnishes, lacquers, rubbery substances, or transparent slabs, depending on the R group and the length of the chain. In all forms silicones are very temperature-resistant, giving better performance at both high and low temperatures than carbon-chain polymers. Thin layers of silicone provide water repellency. Silicones are neutral to the human body and are often used for implantation materials.

More Inorganic Polymers

A new class of inorganic polymers is just beginning to be made commercially. These are the polyphosphazenes. Their main chain is made of phosphorus and nitrogen atoms, with each phosphorus having two alkyl groups (R groups). In this

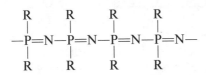

case the R groups usually have a non-carbon first atom, most commonly O or N. Thus alkoxy groups, such as butoxy, $CH_3CH_2CH_2CH_2O—$, or amino linkages,

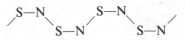

could be present as R.

These polymers are water-repellent, highly flexible at low temperatures, resistant to solvents, and do not burn well. Some applications are for fuel hoses in the Arctic, gaskets, O-rings, truck tires, and wire insulation. Phosphazenes are expected to find many applications as coatings for textiles or, when formed into fibers, as fabrics of very low flammability. Researchers are hopeful that R groups with an amine nitrogen connecting the carbon side chain to the phosphazene backbone will be biodegradable. The current price is very high, up to $100 per pound. However, the first aluminum produced was worth as much as gold.

Still another unusual polymer without carbon in the long chain is polythiazyl, with $(—S—N—)_x$ chains. This material forms long chains

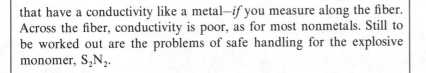

that have a conductivity like a metal—*if* you measure along the fiber. Across the fiber, conductivity is poor, as for most nonmetals. Still to be worked out are the problems of safe handling for the explosive monomer, S_2N_2.

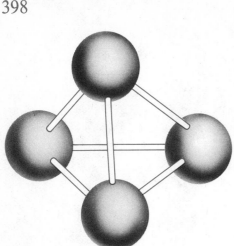

Figure 17-11
The structure of P_4.

The valence orbitals for phosphorus indicate that each atom should form three covalent bonds to other phosphorus atoms. The geometry around the phosphorus atom is like that around nitrogen in ammonia. Three bonds radiate from each phosphorus atom to form a pyramid with triangular faces. As shown in Figure 17-11, each phosphorus atom makes three bonds in the molecule. The white form of phosphorus is made up of individual P_4 molecules, held in the crystal by weak van der Waals forces.

In these four substances there is strong directional character to the bonds within each molecule. In addition, the valence electrons are completely used in bonding to other atoms in that particular molecule. Such molecules are said to have localized electrons because the electrons do not move from one molecule to another. The van der Waals forces in substances such as these four are not strongly directed. Because of this, molecular crystals are usually soft and easily distorted. Two planes of these crystals can move past each other easily because the intermolecular forces are so weak and diffuse. These substances are very poor conductors of electricity. The electrons are localized, or held, in a particular molecule, with a noble gas electron configuration for each atom. Electrons cannot readily move through the crystal because neighboring molecules have filled valence orbitals. Since the molecules do not have an electric charge, there are no charged particles to move and conduct electricity through molecular crystals.

The elements that form molecular solids are presented in Figure 17-12. These are the elements with high ionization energies. They are usually called nonmetals. There are many compounds with zero charge difference or a small electric dipole that form molecular solids similar to the ones discussed in this section. The large proportion of carbon compounds discussed in Chapter 16 form low-melting solids. Each atom in these molecules has a noble gas electron configuration.

EXERCISE 17-3

The compounds ClF and $S_4N_4H_4$ have been synthesized. What would you expect their molecular structures to be? Predict what their melting temperatures might be relative to ice and to salt.

EXERCISE 17-4

Convince yourself that each atom in the three molecules C_2H_6 (ethane), C_2H_4 (ethylene), and C_2H_2 (acetylene) has the electron configuration of a noble gas.

EXERCISE 17-5

In Table 10-7, page 207, there are nine molecules with the same electron configuration as F_2. Explain why these substances have low melting and boiling temperatures.

17-6   Network Solids: Silicon and Carbon

Silicon has four electrons in the valence orbitals, the $3s$ and the $3p$ orbitals. Silicon tends to form four covalent bonds with tetra-

Dentists make use of plastics, ceramics, and alloys.

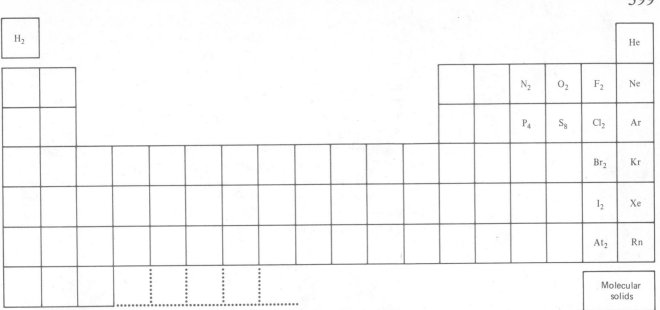

Figure 17-12
Elements that solidify as molecular solids.

hedral geometry around each silicon atom. In the element each silicon atom is surrounded by and is bonded to four other silicon atoms. This structure is shown in Figure 17-13. It is the same as the diamond structure of carbon. The crystal of silicon can be regarded as a giant three-dimensional molecule. Solids with an extensive web of covalent bonds are called **network solids**. One can readily understand why silicon has a very high melting temperature. A large number of strong covalent bonds must be broken before melting can occur. The hardness and brittle nature of silicon crystals can be explained in terms of this structure.

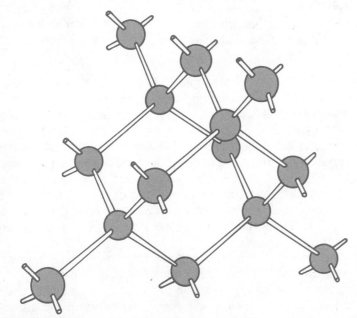

Figure 17-13
Silicon, a network solid.

Hafnium carbide, HfC, is one of the highest-melting-temperature compounds known, 3870 °C. For comparison, melting temperature of Pt is 1773 °C and of Fe is 1535 °C.

A very large force is required before the crystal can be deformed. The electrical conductivity of silicon is quite low because the electrons are localized in the covalent bonds between the atoms.

Carbon in the form of graphite is another example of a network solid. In contrast to the arrangement in diamond or silicon in which each atom is equidistant from its neighbors, graphite has the layered structure shown in Figure 17-14. There are strong covalent bonds between the carbon atoms in any plane. Only weak van der Waals forces exist between the layers, accounting for the ease with which graphite crystals can be cleaved. This property, so apparent from the structure, explains why graphite is useful as a lubricant. The elements which form network solids are indicated in Figure 17-15. These elements have properties intermediate between metals and nonmetals.

EXERCISE 17-6

When silica (SiO_2) is heated with carbon, the substance known as Carborundum is formed. The empirical formula for Carborundum is SiC. This material is important because it is almost as hard as diamond but is much less expensive. What would you expect the structure of SiC to be? How can you account for its hardness?

EXERCISE 17-7

The compound boron nitride, BN, has been known for many years. It has a structure very similar to that of graphite. Recently, it has been possible to convert this material to the diamond structure, using very high temperatures and pressures. Draw one layer of the graphitelike structure and a portion of the diamond structure for boron nitride.

EXERCISE 17-8

Show that boron nitride and carbon have the same electron configuration. Compare the total configuration for one boron atom plus one nitrogen atom with the total configuration for two carbon atoms.

Silica, with the empirical formula SiO_2, is a network solid. Silica and other silicon-oxygen compounds make up about 85 percent of the earth's crust. Almost all common minerals contain large amounts of silicates, the general term for the silicon-oxygen solids. These are network solids but with interesting and important variations. Three types of network solids are shown schematically in Figure 17-16. Silicon always forms four bonds, but in some compounds there are infinite silicon-oxygen-silicon chains; in some there are infinite sheets, with weak van der Waals forces between the layers; and in still others, an infinite three-dimensional structure occurs.

Many properties of the silicates can be understood in terms of the structure at the molecular level. In the one-dimensional chains the atoms within the chain are strongly linked with covalent bonds, but much weaker forces exist between the chains. This is consistent with the threadlike properties of many of these silicates. The asbestos minerals have this type of structure.

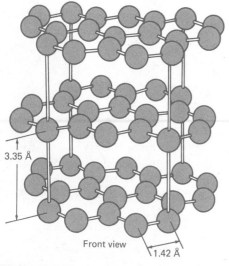

Top view — top layer

3.35 Å

Front view

1.42 Å

Figure 17-14
Structure of graphite.

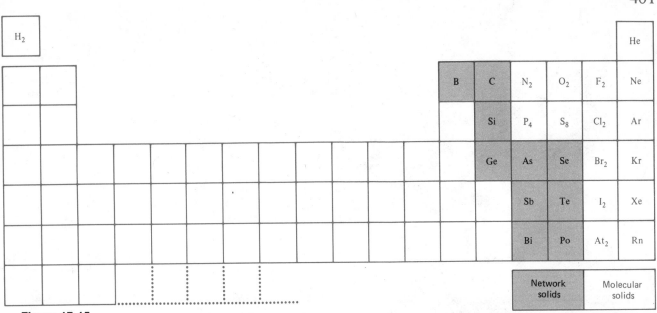

Figure 17-15
Elements that solidify as network solids.

In a similar way the sheets of the two-dimensional silicates are held together by weak forces. These minerals cleave readily into thin but strong sheets. The silicates called micas have this structure. Clays also have this molecular arrangement in microscopic flakes, accounting for their slipperiness when wet.

The three-dimensional network shown in Figure 17-16 occurs in silica or quartz. Like silicon and carbon, quartz has a very high melting temperature and is one of the hardest substances known.

Dental technicians must understand the properties of the materials they use.

Potters and ceramics engineers are quite interested in the structure and properties of clays and glazes.

17-7 Metallic Solids: Aluminum, Magnesium, and Sodium

The remaining elements of the third row are classed as metals. Their properties are strikingly different from those of the other elements in this row. All metals have high luster or reflectivity. Metals are good conductors of heat and electricity. They can be drawn into thin wires or hammered into very thin sheets without breaking. These properties suggest that the electron configurations of all metals have something in common.

Structural determinations show that each atom in aluminum or magnesium has 12 neighboring atoms. In sodium each atom has eight neighboring atoms. This is a strange situation! From silicon to argon the number of covalent bonds each atom forms decreases from four to zero. These numbers are in agreement with the number of vacancies in the valence orbitals, and therefore the number of neighboring atoms, in the elements.

For sodium there is one valence electron to be shared with eight other sodium atoms in the metal. Each sodium atom has four valence orbitals (one $3s$ and three $3p$) available for its electron and for the valence electrons of the neighboring sodium

● Silicon atoms   ○ Oxygen atoms   X Other atoms

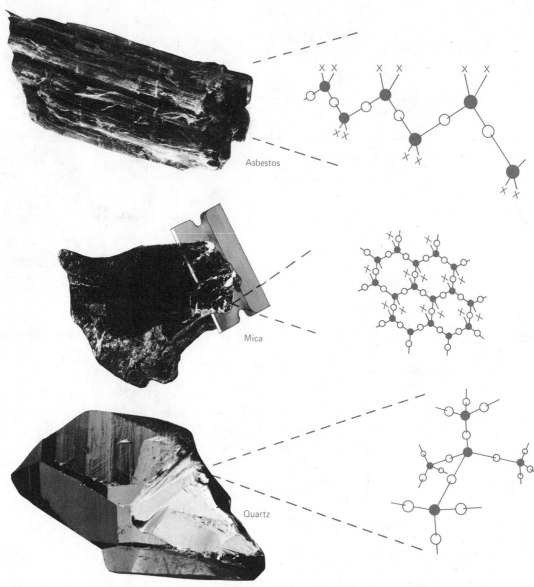

Asbestos

Mica

Quartz

Figure 17-16
Silicate structures.

atoms. Each atom has an abundance of valence orbitals but a shortage of bonding electrons. The valence electron is free to move in the many valence orbitals around its parent nucleus. There are many places around such an atom where its electrons can be between two or more positive nuclei. This situation is described as a **metallic bond**.

What is the nature of the metallic bond? This bond, like all others, forms because the electrons can move in such a way that they are simultaneously near two or more positive nuclei. The space around an atom in a metal is a region of almost uniformly low potential energy. Under these circumstances it is not surprising that an electron can move easily from place to place. Each valence electron is virtually free to make its way throughout the crystal.

A metal is pictured as an array of positive ions located at the crystal lattice sites, immersed in a "sea" of mobile electrons. The idea of a more or less uniform sea emphasizes an important difference between metallic and covalent bonding. In covalent bonds the electrons are localized in a way that fixes the positions of the atoms quite rigidly. In contrast, the valence electrons in a metal are spread throughout the crystal. Chemists talk about *nonlocalized electrons* in a metal.

The location of the metals in the periodic table is shown in Figure 17-17. The metals are found on the left side of the table while the nonmetals are on the right. Furthermore, the elements on the left side of the table have relatively low ionization energies. The low ionization energies of the metallic elements aid in explaining many of the features of metallic behavior.

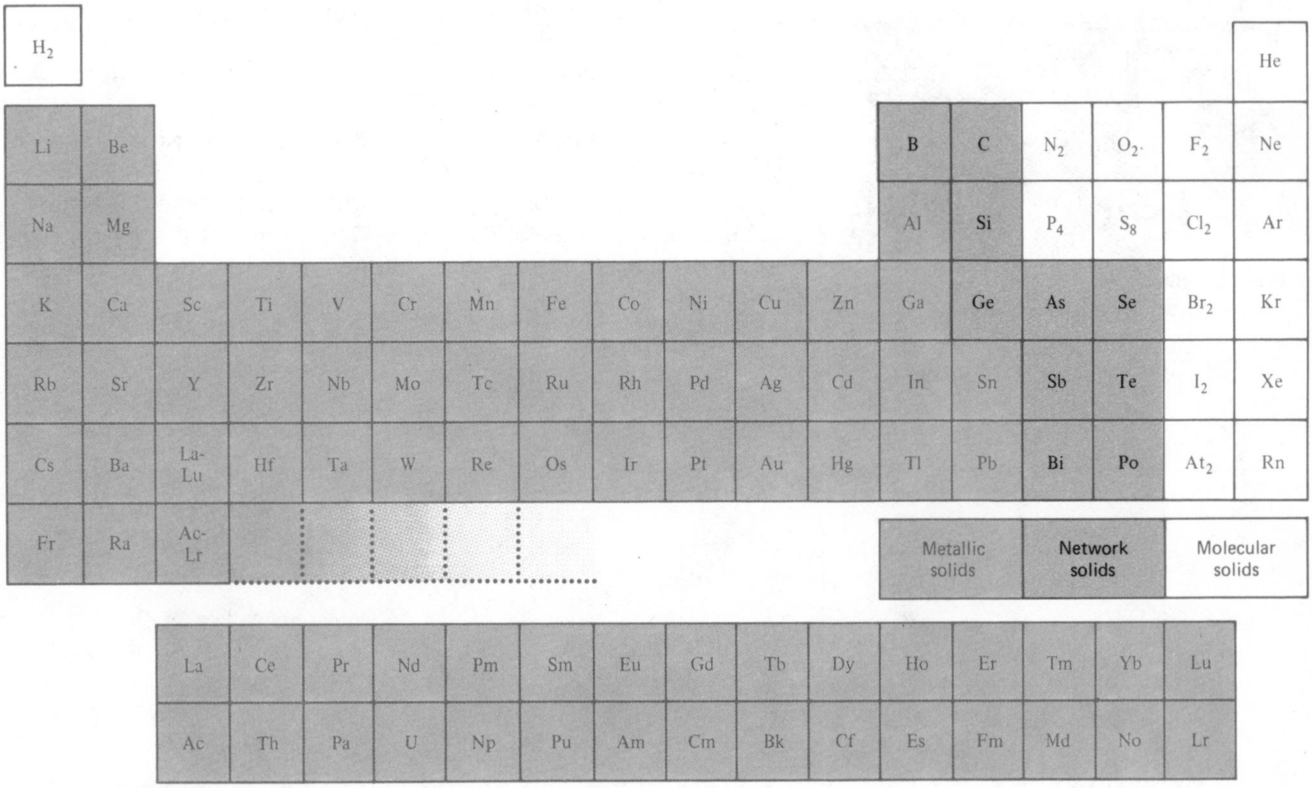

Figure 17-17
Periodic table showing crystal types in which elements solidify.

17-8 Crystal Structure of Metals

There are many ways in which atoms can be arranged in repeating units to form crystals of the elements. In a crystalline solid where all atoms are identical, the state of minimum energy is often achieved when atoms are packed together as efficiently as possible. This condition is referred to as *closest-packing*. Most metals form crystals with a closest-packed structure.

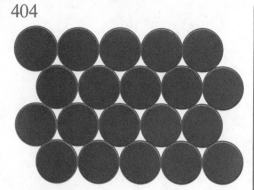

Figure 17-18
A layer of close-packed spheres.

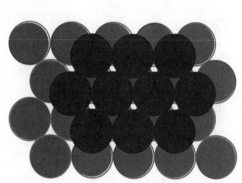

Figure 17-19
Two layers of close-packed spheres.

In Figure 17-18, closest-packing in two dimensions is shown. Each atom, represented by the sphere, is surrounded by and is in contact with six other spheres. These are called *nearest neighbors.* (The wax honeycomb in a beehive is very similar in appearance, with hexagons rather than spheres packed together.) To help you keep track of different layers, these spheres are colored gray. There are holes between the spheres.

A second closest-packed layer can be placed on top of the first. The most compact arrangement places the second group of spheres in one of the two sets of holes in the first layer. This is illustrated in Figure 17-19, in which the second layer is black. Now you can notice two types of openings in the second layer. Some are white because they are over holes in layer one. Some are gray; they are over spheres in layer one. A third closest-packed layer can be placed in two ways, either above the original set of spheres in layer one (over the "gray" holes) or above the alternate set of "white" holes. The first possibility is illustrated in Figure 17-20. This pattern of layers, numbered 12121212 . . . , is called the *hexagonal closest-packed structure.* The other arrangement is illustrated in Figure 17-21. Here, the number pattern, 123123 . . . , emphasizes the placement of the layers. This structure is called *cubic closest-packed.* Rotation of the grouping in Figure 17-21 brings out the cubic structure, accounting for the name. There are spheres at the eight corners of the cube and a sphere at the center of each face. This is one of the most important crystal structures. It is often referred to by the name *face-centered cubic.*

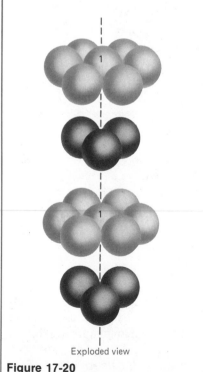

Exploded view

Figure 17-20
Hexagonal closest-packing of spheres.

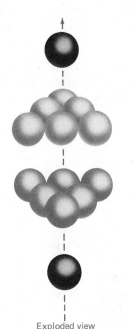

Exploded view

Figure 17-21
Cubic closest-packing of spheres.

In either of the closest-packed arrangements, each sphere is in contact with 12 other spheres. This is easy to see in Figure 17-20, where a sphere labeled "1" would have six spheres surrounding it in a plane, with three spheres above it and three spheres below it. Solids whose molecules or atoms are approximately spherical and are linked by nondirectional bonds often crystallize with one of the closest-packed structures. The noble gases form crystals with either cubic or hexagonal closest-packing. The hydrogen halides and molecular hydrogen are very nearly spherical molecules. These substances crystallize in one of the closest-packed structures.

In metallic magnesium and aluminum, each atom has twelve nearest neighbors. X-ray studies show that magnesium metal exhibits hexagonal closest-packing and aluminum metal crystallizes in the cubic closest-packing structure. What about sodium metal? Each atom has eight nearest neighbors. Sodium must crystallize in some other pattern than the hexagonal or cubic closest-packed structure.

The crystal structure for metallic sodium is shown in Figure 17-22. There are eight sodium atoms at the corners of a cube and one more in the center. This structure has been given the name *body-centered cubic*. The efficiency of packing atoms in this crystal pattern is slightly less than the two closest-packed forms. A number of metals, including iron and the alkali metals, exhibit body-centered cubic structures at room temperature.

Figure 17-22
Body-centered cubic packing of spheres.

EXERCISE 17-9

In Figure 17-23 the X-ray patterns for aluminum, copper, and sodium metal are shown. What type of crystal structure would you expect for copper?

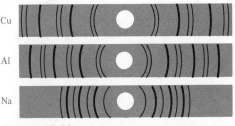

Cu

Al

Na

Figure 17-23
X-ray diffraction patterns from metallic copper, aluminum, and sodium powders.

Figure 17-24
Atomic view of metal planes sliding over one another.

Surgeons and naval architects need alloys that will not corrode.

Gas turbine designers are constantly looking for strong, high-temperature alloys.

17-9 An Explanation for Metallic Properties

Nonlocalized or mobile electrons account for many unique features of metals. Since metallic bonds do not have strong directional character, it is not surprising that most metals are soft and can be easily deformed into thin foils and very fine wire without shattering. Under the influence of a stress, one plane of atoms may slip by another. As this occurs, the electrons maintain some degree of bonding between the two planes. Figure 17-24 illustrates what happens. Metals can often be hardened by adding small amounts of carbon or nitrogen or sulfur. These elements have the property of forming directed covalent bonds. As a result, much more energy is required to move one plane of atoms past another, accounting for the increase in hardness. At the same time, the brittleness of the metal is increased when these elements are added, even in small amounts. Fracture of the crystal may occur when the covalent bonds are broken.

Metals are good conductors of electricity and heat because valence electrons are free to move throughout the solid. In regions of high temperature, electrons can acquire large amounts of kinetic energy. This energy can be transferred through the crystal rapidly as electrons interact with other free electrons. Metallic bonding occurs when two circumstances arise:

(1) the ionization energy is low and valence electrons are not held strongly;

(2) there are more unfilled valence orbitals than valence electrons.

In contrast, the electrons in covalently bonded solids are localized in the space between a particular pair of atoms. There are essentially no vacant valence orbitals available. In these unfavorable circumstances, a large amount of energy must be supplied to move electrons. Hence, covalent compounds are poor conductors.

17-10 Alloys

When two or more metals are heated above their melting temperatures and then allowed to cool, the solid that is obtained is called an *alloy*. Sometimes an alloy has properties very similar to those of the original metals, and other times the alloy may have very different properties. Often alloys are more useful than the starting metals. The many kinds of steel that have been developed are examples. Some important alloys are listed in Table 17-4.

The tensile strength of iron can be increased tenfold by the addition of small amounts of carbon, nickel, manganese, and other metals. The tensile strength of brass is more than twice that of copper and four times that of zinc. The hardness and strength of alloys can be explained in terms of bonding. The impurity atom may form localized and rigid bonds. Such bonds tend to prevent the slippage of atoms past each other, which results in a loss in malleability and an increase of hardness.

TABLE 17-4

Some Useful Alloys

Name	Composition of Alloy (percent by mass)	Uses
Stainless steel	16 Cr 8 Ni 76 Fe	In corrosive environments and where appearance is important
Nichrome	60 Ni 15 Cr 25 Fe	Resistance wire in electric heaters and toasters
Alnico	12 Co 10 Al 17 Ni 61 Fe	Permanent magnets
Brass	60-90 Cu 40-10 Zn	Hardware, pipes, ornaments
Bronze	80 Cu 15 Sn 5 Zn	Naval hardware
Gold (16 karat)	67 Au 33 Cu	Jewelry
Soft solder	50 Sn 50 Pb	Low-melting alloy that bonds to many metals and provides structural and electrical continuity

Electrical conductivity in metals apparently depends upon the smooth and uninterrupted movement of electrons through the crystal lattice. Small amounts of impurities in a metal such as copper may seriously affect its ability to conduct electricity. In Section 15-9, page 333, the electrolytic method of purifying copper was discussed. The importance of this method is directly related to the gain in electrical conductivity. Table 17-5 shows how the conductivity of copper can be reduced by even small amounts of impurities.

TABLE 17-5

Conductivity of Some Copper Alloys

Composition of Alloy (percent by mass)			Temperature °C	Conductivity (ohm-cm)$^{-1}$
100	Cu		25	5.9×10^6
99	Cu 1	Mn	0	2.1×10^6
95.8	Cu 4.2	Mn	25	0.56×10^6
97	Cu 3	Al	0	1.2×10^6
90	Cu 10	Al	0	0.79×10^6
88	Cu 12	Sn	25	0.56×10^6

17-11   Ionic Solids

In Section 10-1 we discussed the decrease in potential energy as positive and negative ions approached one another to form an ionic lattice. Each positive ion has only negative ions as nearest neighbors, and each negative ion has only positive ions as nearest neighbors.

Earlier in this chapter the bonding in gaseous lithium fluoride was examined. Although the diatomic molecule is held together because the bonding electrons are near both nuclei, the electron distribution is concentrated toward the fluorine atom. A stable and polar molecule is formed. Stable, but also highly reactive! The valence orbitals of the lithium atom are almost vacant. But each fluorine atom has three pairs of valence electrons not used in bonding. If these filled orbitals of fluorine overlap the vacant lithium orbitals, additional chemical bonding can occur. Lithium fluoride molecules are more stable when each lithium atom, with its vacant valence orbitals, is placed near several fluorine atoms. This is achieved by the formation of a solid. As in metals, an atom with vacant orbitals is more stable when it has several neighbors. There is, however, a significant difference between ionic solids and metals. In lithium fluoride half of the atoms have high ionization energies. Fluorine atoms hold their electrons tightly. Therefore, the characteristic electron mobility of metals is not present in an ionic solid. The absence of mobile electrons implies that metallic properties are not expected.

Ionic solids form regularly shaped crystals with well-defined crystal faces. Most ionic solids have high melting temperatures because a large amount of energy is needed to overcome the electrostatic forces that hold the crystal together. Ionic crystals cleave along certain directions only. Figure 17-25 suggests cleavage planes in a crystal such as $NaCl$.

Ionic solids do not conduct electricity because electrons are localized in the vicinity of the negative ions. However, when these solids are melted, the charged ions can move under the influence of an external electric field. The electrical conductivity of molten salts is generally lower than that of a typical metal. It is easy to understand why. In a metal, movement of electrons is responsible for the transport of electric charge. In a molten salt, ionic migration carries electric charge. Since ions have much greater mass than electrons, they move at much lower velocities. The rate at which electric charge is transported by ions is relatively low.

17-12   Structure of Ionic Solids

Ionic solids are found with many different crystal patterns. There is an interesting similarity between some of these structures and the structures of metals. In metals where the atoms do not carry an electric charge, atoms often pack together in the most efficient way possible. In an ionic solid such as sodium chloride, ions pack together in the most efficient way, too. But there is a new factor arising from the presence of electric charges. Ions

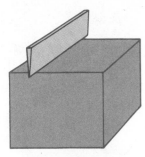
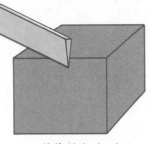

Knife blade placed
on cleavage plane

Knife blade placed
on noncleavage plane

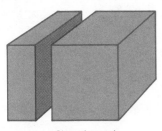
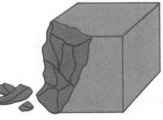

Cleaved crystal

Shattered crystal

Figure 17-25
Cleavage planes in sodium chloride.

of like charge would give rise to large repulsive forces, driving the ions apart. However, the negative ions and the positive ions can alternate and provide attractive forces. The result is shown in Figure 17-26. Positive ions with vacant valence orbitals are surrounded by negative ions with filled valence orbitals, and vice versa.

17-13 Solubility of Electrolytes in Water

The dissolving of electrolytes in water is one of the most important solvent effects that can be attributed to electric dipoles. Crystalline sodium chloride is quite stable, as shown by its high melting temperature. Yet sodium chloride dissolves readily in water. There must be strong interaction between water molecules and the ions formed in solution. This effect can be explained in terms of the polar nature of the interacting substances.

When an electric dipole (as in water molecules) is brought near an ion, the energy is lower if the dipole is oriented to place unlike charges near each other. This process, called *hydration,* is shown in Figure 17-27. In earlier sections of this book, the notation $Na^+(aq)$ was used to indicate interaction between the solvent, water, and the sodium ion. The structure of liquid water and of the aquated ions, $H^+(aq)$ and $OH^-(aq)$, are a consequence of the electric dipole of water.

17-14 The Hydrogen Bond

Section 10-7, page 211, presented some of the observations that led chemists to suggest that a hydrogen atom can form two

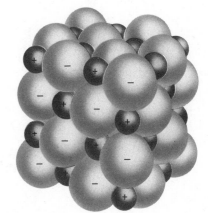

Figure 17-26
Close-packed ions in a sodium chloride crystal.

The water molecule can be represented as a molecular dipole

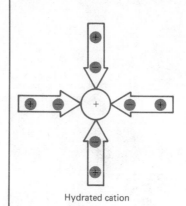
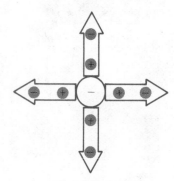

Hydrated cation

Hydrated anion

Figure 17-27
Hydration of ions.

bonds in some compounds. Substances which contain hydrogen attached to oxygen, nitrogen, or fluorine often have abnormally high melting and boiling temperatures.

The data in Figures 10-6 and 10-7 show that the interaction must be much stronger than van der Waals forces. Experiments show that formation of most hydrogen bonds releases between 3 kcal/mol and 10 kcal/mol. The energy of this bond places it between van der Waals and covalent bonds. Roughly speaking, the energies are in the ratio

van der Waals attractions : hydrogen bonds : covalent bonds
1   :   10   :   100

Hydrogen bonds have also been found in solid phases. The most familiar example is solid H_2O, or ice. Ice has a crystal structure in which the oxygen and hydrogen atoms are distributed in a regular hexagonal crystalline lattice that somewhat resembles the diamond lattice (see Figure 17-13). Each oxygen atom is surrounded by four other oxygen atoms in a tetrahedral arrangement. The hydrogen atoms are found on the lines extending between the oxygen atoms:

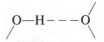

One of the factors connected with the formation of strong hydrogen bonds is the acidic character of the hydrogen atom involved. Thus, the hydrogen bond formed by hydrogen fluoride is one of the strongest known. Acetic acid, CH_3COOH, is a representative of an important class of acidic hydrogen bonding compounds. All the members of this class possess the carboxylic acid group:

For this type of compound the formation of hydrogen bonds can lead to the coupling of the molecules in pairs, to form a cyclic structure:

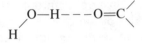

The molecular pair, or dimer, is more stable than two separate molecules.

Hydrogen bonds play an important part in determining such properties as solubility and phase change temperatures. They affect the form and stability of crystal structures. They play a crucial role in biological systems. For example, water is so common in living matter that it must influence the chemical behavior of many biological molecules, most of which can also form hydrogen bonds. Water can attach itself by hydrogen bonding, either by providing the proton, as in

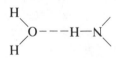

or in accepting the proton, as in

$$\underset{H}{\overset{H}{\diagdown}} O---H-N\diagup$$

Furthermore, intramolecular hydrogen bonding is one of the chief factors in determining the structure of such important biological substances as proteins. These substances were discussed in Chapter 16.

17-15 Review

Electrons in a chemical bond may be distributed in a symmetrical fashion between the atoms forming the bond. Whenever two different atoms bond, there is the possibility that electrons will be found more often near one atom than the other. This shift of negative charge gives rise to an electric dipole in the bond. The overall electric dipole for a molecule arises from combination of all the bond dipoles.

The presence or absence of a net electric dipole for the second-row fluorides guides us in understanding the geometrical shapes of simple molecules. The correlation between orbitals used for bonding and the resulting molecular geometry is one of the most useful generalizations chemists have proposed. Here is a summary of the examples discussed in this chapter:

Bonding orbitals used by central atom	Resulting molecular geometry
s	linear
sp	linear
sp^2	planar, Y-shaped
sp^3	tetrahedral
p^3	pyramidal
p^2	bent
p	linear

The bonding *between* molecules, atoms, or ions accounts for the formation of liquids and solids. It has been convenient in this chapter to classify solids under four headings: molecular solids, covalent or network solids, metallic solids, and ionic solids. The melting and boiling temperatures, the physical properties associated with different types of solids, and the electrical conductivity are interpreted in terms of the type of structure in the solid. The significance of *van der Waals forces* in the formation of liquids and solids is presented in this chapter. The hydration of ions in a solvent such as water is outlined as an electrostatic reaction between a dipole (H_2O) and an ion (Na^+ or Cl^-). Hydrogen bonding is also discussed.

Although chemists develop different models and words in talking about the nature of the chemical bond, it is important to state once more the single reason for all atomic and molecular interactions:

Chemical bonding arises from the decrease in energy that occurs when electrons can interact strongly with two or more nuclei simultaneously. The different names applied to bonds reflect chemists' attempts to specify variations in the arrangement of the electrons.

Questions and Problems for Chapter 17

1

Ethylene, C_2H_4, has a zero molecular dipole, whereas hydrazine, N_2H_4, has a large one. Explain. The atoms in each follow normal bonding rules.

2

Would you expect SiH_3F to have a molecular dipole? Explain your answer.

3

Consider the two compounds CH_3CH_3 (ethane) and CH_3NH_2 (methylamine). Why does CH_3NH_2 have an electric dipole, whereas CH_3CH_3 does not?

4

Consider the following series: CH_4, CH_3Cl, CH_2Cl_2, $CHCl_3$, CCl_4. In which cases will the molecules have electric dipoles? Support your answer by considering the bonding orbitals of carbon, the molecular shape of the molecules, and the resulting symmetry.

5

Draw the three isomers of dichloroethylene. Which will be polar molecules?

6

Would you expect liquid ammonia to be a good solvent for ionic compounds?

7

Considering comparable oxygen compounds, predict the shape of H_2S and H_2S_2 molecules. What bonding orbitals are used?

8

Predict the type of bonding and the shape of the ion BF_4^-.

9

Predict the structure of the compound N_2F_2 from the electron dot representation of the atoms and the molecule.

10

Compare PI_3 and BI_3 in terms of shape, electric dipole, and reaction with NH_3.

11

Suggest structures for:

(a) P_2I_4 diphosphorus tetraiodide
(b) $Se(SCN)_2$ selenium dithiocyanate
(c) H_2NCN cyanamide

12

Sulfur is made up of S_8 molecules; each molecule has a cyclic (crown) structure. Phosphorus contains P_4 molecules; each molecule has a tetrahedral structure. On the basis of molecular size and shape, which would you expect to have the higher melting temperature?

13

Suggest why SO_2 has a low boiling temperature but compounds containing SO_4^{2-} do not.

14

Would you expect van der Waals forces to be more evident in covalent or ionic compounds?

15

What type of solid do most organic substances form? Why?

16

The elements carbon and silicon form oxides with similar empirical formulas: CO_2 and SiO_2. The former sublimes at $-78.5\,°C$, and the latter melts at about $1700\,°C$ and boils at about $2200\,°C$. From this large difference, propose the types of solids involved. Draw an electron dot or orbital representation of the bonding in CO_2 that is consistent with your answer.

17

The heat of vaporization of four elements is given below:

$$\begin{array}{cccc} B & C & N & O \\ 129 & 170 & 0.7 & 0.8 \end{array} \text{ kcal/mol}$$

Suggest reasons for the abrupt change between carbon and nitrogen.

18

Silicon sulfide forms a polymer of empirical formula $(SiS_2)_n$. Draw a possible structure.

19

Digermane is the name for Ge_2H_6, an analog of ethane, C_2H_6. Draw structures for tetramethylgermane and octamethyltrigermane.

20

Which of these compounds would you think are unlikely to form?

(a) H_3GeSiH_3
(b) $GeSe_2$
(c) SnI_4
(d) PbO_3
(e) $(C_2H_5)_4Pb$

21

In a crystal the SiF_4 molecules are in a body-centered cubic arrangement. Draw a possible structure of the crystal. (Hint: Draw a cube and place the Si atoms as in Figure 17-22.)

22

There are compounds called polyamines. They have a repeating structure such as:

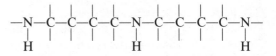

Show how such molecules could be linked together to form a network solid. Assume a linking molecule

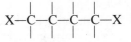

where $-X$ will react with $-NH$ groups in the polyamines. Use a line to represent

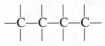

23

Considering the polyamines described in the preceding problem, what would a "ladder polymer" look like? Draw a structure. Which silicate mineral type would it be like?

24

Why are there so few halogen chains in network solids?

25

Discuss the conduction of heat by copper (a metal) and by glass (a network solid) in terms of the valence orbital occupancy and electron mobility.

26

Contrast the bonds between atoms in metals, in molecular solids, and in network solids in regard to:

(a) bond strength
(b) orientation in space
(c) number of orbitals available for bonding

27

What crystal structures would you expect for Cs and Be?

28

Explain these facts: There are many alloys in which metal atoms are mixed in the crystal. There are few molecular solids containing mixtures of molecules.

29

Calculate the distance between the centers of the corner spheres along a cube diagonal in Figure 17-22. Take r as the radius of each sphere.

30

How do you account for the following properties in terms of the structures of the solids?

(a) Graphite and diamond both contain only carbon. Both have high melting temperatures, yet diamond is very hard, whereas graphite is a soft, greasy solid.
(b) When sodium chloride crystals are shattered, plane surfaces are produced on the fragments.
(c) Silicon carbide (Carborundum) is a very high-melting temperature, hard substance, used as an abrasive.

31

If you were given a sample of a white solid, describe some simple tests you would perform to help you classify the solid as molecular, network, ionic, or metallic.

32

If elements A, D, E, and J have atomic numbers 6, 9, 10, and 11 (in order), write the formula for a substance you would expect to form between the following:

(a) D and J   (d) E and E
(b) A and D   (e) J and J
(c) D and D

In each case describe the forces involved between the building blocks in the solid state.

33

Predict the order of the melting temperatures of these substances containing chlorine: HCl, Cl_2, $NaCl$, CCl_4. Explain the basis of your prediction.

34

Identify all the types of bonds you would expect to find in each of the following crystals:

(a) argon   (f) Al
(b) water   (g) $CaCl_2$
(c) methane   (h) $KClO_3$
(d) carbon monoxide (i) $NaCl$
(e) Si   (j) HCN

35

Aluminum, silicon, and sulfur are close together in the same row of the periodic table, yet their electrical conductivities are widely different. Aluminum is a metal; silicon has much lower conductivity and is called a semiconductor; sulfur has such low conductivity it is called an insulator. Explain these differences in terms of valence orbital occupancy.

36

Discuss the bonding in NH_4AlF_4.

37

What is the meaning of "molar mass" applied to either ionic or network solids?

38

Which of these substances would you rate as likely candidates to dissolve salt, NaCl?

(a) carbon tetrachloride, CCl_4

(b) acetone,

$$CH_3-\overset{\displaystyle O}{\underset{\displaystyle \|}{C}}-CH_3$$

(c) benzene,

(d) hydrogen peroxide, H_2O_2

(e) carbon disulfide, CS_2

39

The labels have been lost from three bottles containing white powders. It is known they contain LiCl, GeO_2, and p-dichlorobenzene. From the following data decide which sample is which. Specify the type of solid suggested for each sample.

Sample	Melting Temperature (°C)	Density (g/m)
I	1100	4.70
II	53	1.46
III	614	2.07

Solubility in Water (g/100 g H_2O)
0.40
none
67

40

Olive oil can be heated to 285 °C without boiling. The melting temperature of tin is 505 K. Which is higher? What would cause it to be so high?

41

Salt and sugar (sucrose) have almost identical solubilities in water at room temperature, 0.62 mol/100 g H_2O at 25 °C. Explain why the sugar solution is viscous and syrupy, whereas the salt solution is not.

42

DNA (deoxyribonucleic acid) is the information-bearing part of a cell. DNA chains are held together by H bonds between groups such as these:

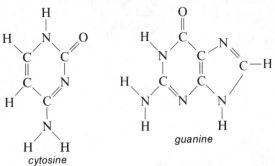

cytosine   guanine

Show how these can bond to form three hydrogen bonds.

43

What hydrogen bonding arrangement would you suggest in a solution of acetone

$$CH_3\overset{\displaystyle O}{\underset{\displaystyle \|}{C}}CH_3$$

in chloroform, $CHCl_3$?

44

Why is hydrogen bonding essentially limited to hydrogen?

45

HCN melts at -13.3 °C. Draw the electron configuration or dot formula, and decide what shape it has, whether it is hydrogen-bonded, and if so what shape the complex molecule has.

46

Cyanamide, H_2NCN, readily polymerizes at 150 °C to form a cyclic trimer.

$$3\ H_2NCN \longrightarrow (H_2NCN)_3\ \text{(cyclic trimer)}$$

Suggest a structure for the trimer. What type of solid would it be? Would it hydrogen-bond?

47

Consider each of the following in the solid state: sodium, germanium, methane, neon, potassium chloride, and water. Which would be an example of

(a) a solid held together by van der Waals forces that melts far below room temperature?

(b) a solid with a high degree of electrical conductivity that melts near 100 °C?

(c) a high melting, network solid involving covalently bonded atoms?

(d) a nonconducting solid which becomes a good conductor upon melting?

(e) a substance in which hydrogen bonding is pronounced?

18

The Halogens

On many occasions in this book you have encountered the halogens and their compounds, both in your laboratory program and in class discussions. Some of the most important and most useful substances are derived from the elements fluorine, chlorine, bromine, and iodine. Element 85, astatine, is a member of the halogen family, but it is so rare that it will not be included in our discussion. Perhaps better than any other group of elements, the halogens show remarkable similarities and trends in chemical behavior.

In the 19th century chemists studied the halogens and wondered about these striking similarities. This family of elements provided many important clues to the periodic relations among the elements. Later, with an understanding of atomic structure, the long-sought explanation for periodic properties was obtained. Today it is easy for us to correlate a large body of experimental information with the electron populations of the elements. The trends within a family such as the halogens can be understood in terms of the increase in nuclear charge, number of electrons, and atomic size in going from fluorine to iodine. With all the information available today we sometimes forget that observations of chemical systems came first and that explanation came second. Figure 18-1 highlights the place of the halogens in the periodic table.

1 H																Halogens	2 He
3 Li	4 Be											5 B	6 C	7 N	8 O	9 F	10 Ne
11 Na	12 Mg											13 Al	14 Si	15 P	16 S	17 Cl	18 Ar
19 K	20 Ca	21 Sc	22 Ti	23 V	24 Cr	25 Mn	26 Fe	27 Co	28 Ni	29 Cu	30 Zn	31 Ga	32 Ge	33 As	34 Se	35 Br	36 Kr
37 Rb	38 Sr	39 Y	40 Zr	41 Nb	42 Mo	43 Tc	44 Ru	45 Rh	46 Pd	47 Ag	48 Cd	49 In	50 Sn	51 Sb	52 Te	53 I	54 Xe
55 Cs	56 Ba	57-71 La-Lu	72 Hf	73 Ta	74 W	75 Re	76 Os	77 Ir	78 Pt	79 Au	80 Hg	81 Tl	82 Pb	83 Bi	84 Po	85 At	86 Rn
87 Fr	88 Ra	89-103 Ac-Lr	104	105	106												

Figure 18-1
The halogen family.

The halogens are very reactive elements. The pure elements exist as diatomic molecules in which the atoms are held together by a covalent bond. Fluorine and chlorine are gases at room temperature. Bromine is a liquid. Iodine is a solid with sufficient vapor pressure that a thin layer of crystals left out overnight will sublime away by morning. Halogen molecules absorb light in the visible region of the spectrum, and consequently the halogens are colored substances. Fluorine is light yellow, chlorine is yellowish-green, bromine is reddish-brown, and crystalline iodine is black (in the gas phase, iodine is purple). In their elementary state the halogens are toxic and dangerous substances. Fluorine is the most hazardous. The danger *decreases* as the atomic number of the halogen *increases*. Nevertheless, even iodine, I_2, should be handled with care. However, the halogens form part of many compounds that are quite safe to handle. A fluorocarbon, dichlorodifluoromethane (CCl_2F_2), is used widely as a refrigerant and as the gas in aerosol cans.

18-1 Preparation and Properties of the Elements

The halogens are so reactive that they do not occur uncombined in nature. They must be made from halogen-containing compounds. Electrolytic oxidation is used to prepare fluorine and chlorine. Chlorine, for example, is made by electrolysis of molten

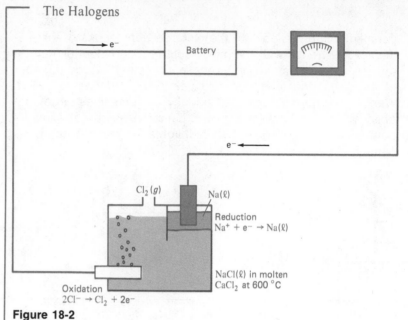

Figure 18-2
Production of Cl_2 by electrolysis of molten NaCl.

sodium chloride. Figure 18-2 shows the components of the electrolytic cell. Molten sodium is produced at the cathode, and chlorine gas is collected at the anode.

Gaseous fluorine is prepared by electrolysis of molten KHF_2, using a copper vessel. Copper, like most metals, is attacked by fluorine. However, a layer of copper(II) fluoride forms, protecting the metal from rapid corrosion.

Chemical oxidation, usually with chlorine as the oxidizing agent, provides bromine and iodine economically because chlorine is a relatively inexpensive chemical. Most of the bromine in the United States comes from seawater, which contains about 0.005 percent by weight of bromide ion.

A brief look at the production of iodine will show examples of the commercial use of many of the principles you have studied. Iodine now comes from three main sources. The French and Japanese recover it from seaweed; the Chileans as a by-product from nitrate fertilizer preparation; and the Americans from salt brines produced by some California oil wells.

Seaweed is dried and burned, with the temperature kept as low as possible so that NaI will not vaporize and leave the oven. The ashes are leached with hot water to produce a solution containing about 8 g of iodine (as salts) per liter. Cooling causes Na_2SO_4 and NaCl to precipitate. Evaporation raises the concentration of NaI to around 50 g/liter. Sulfuric acid is added to decompose sulfites and sulfides and give an acidic solution. Then the elemental iodine is produced by an oxidation-reduction reaction with MnO_2:

$$4\ H^+ + 2\ I^- + MnO_2 \rightleftharpoons I_2 + Mn^{2+} + 2\ H_2O$$

In Chile sodium nitrate is prepared in huge quantities for fertilizer. The mineral when mined has 0.05–0.3 percent iodine as $NaIO_3$. The salts are dissolved in hot water; and on cooling, $NaNO_3$ precipitates, leaving a solution with about 10 g of iodine

Beauticians must understand the chemistry of bleaches, dyes, and pigments and how these substances affect hair and skin.

(still $NaIO_3$) per liter. A different redox reaction releases elemental iodine, which is then purified by sublimation.

$$NaIO_3 + NaHSO_3 \text{ gives } I_2 + NaHSO_4 + H_2O$$

EXERCISE 18-1

(a) Write a balanced equation for the liberation of I_2 from $NaIO_3$.
(b) Suggest why the amount of $NaHSO_3$ must be carefully controlled?

Many oil wells produce salt water. Some wells in California have about 50 parts per million of iodine in the water as NaI. That is about 0.005 percent iodine as a soluble salt. Reaction with $NaNO_2$ produces a dilute solution of I_2. The iodine is adsorbed and concentrated on carbon black, then removed in a step that gives NaI again. The final reaction is by oxidation with Cl_2:

$$2\,I^- + Cl_2 \rightleftharpoons I_2 + 2\,Cl^-$$

Some properties of the halogens are summarized in Table 18-1.

TABLE 18-1
Comparison of the Halogens

Property	F	Cl	Br	I
Melting temperature, °C	−223	−102	−7.3	113
Boiling temperature, °C	−188	−35	58	183
Color of gas	light yellow	yellowish-green	reddish-brown	purple
Valence electrons	$2s^22p^5$	$3s^23p^5$	$4s^24p^5$	$5s^25p^5$
Ionic radius of X^-, (Å)	1.36	1.81	1.95	2.16
Van der Waals radius of X in X_2, (Å)	1.35	1.80	1.95	2.16
Covalent radius of X in X_2, (Å)	0.72	0.99	1.14	1.33
$E°$ in volts for $X_2 + 2e^- \longrightarrow 2\,X^-$	+2.87	+1.36	+1.06	+0.53
Ionization energy for atom X, kcal/mol $X(g) \longrightarrow X^+(g) + e^-$	401.8	300	273	241
Ionization energy for ion X^- kcal/mol $X^-(g) \longrightarrow X(g) + e^-$	80	83	78	71
Bond dissociation energy, kcal/mol $X_2(g) \longrightarrow 2\,X(g)$	37	59	46.1	36.1

The first four properties listed in Table 18-1 have been discussed several times in earlier sections of this book. The remaining properties illustrate trends within a family of elements. The significance of the three kinds of radii will be outlined first.

18-2 The Sizes of Halogen Atoms and Ions

The "size" assigned to an atom or ion requires a decision about where an atom "stops." According to the orbital model an atom has no sharp boundaries or surfaces. However, chemists find it convenient to assign sizes to atoms according to the observed distances between them. Atomic size is defined operationally. It is determined by calculating the distance between atoms.

For example, Figure 18-3 contrasts the dimensions found for the halogens in the elementary state. One-half the measured internuclear distance is called the **covalent radius**. This distance indicates how close a halogen atom approaches another atom to which it is bonded. To atoms with which it is not bonded, a halogen atom seems to be larger. One-half the average distance between neighboring molecules in the solid state defines the **van der Waals radius**, shown by the lower lines in Figure 18-3. This radius indicates how closely nonbonded atoms approach.

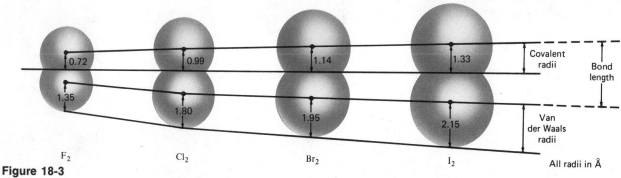

Figure 18-3
Covalent and van der Waals radii of the halogens.

Covalent radii aid in explaining and predicting bond lengths in other covalent halogen compounds. For example, when a chlorine atom is bonded to a carbon atom (as in carbon tetrachloride), it seems reasonable to expect the C—Cl bond length to be the sum of the covalent radii of the two elements, carbon and chlorine. From the diamond structure, the covalent radius for carbon is 0.77 Å. Combining this value with 0.99 Å, the covalent radius of chlorine, leads to a calculated C—Cl bond length of 1.76 Å. Experiment shows that each bond in CCl_4 is 1.77 Å.

EXERCISE 18-2

Use the carbon atom covalent radius 0.77 Å and the covalent radii given in Figure 18-3 to predict C—X bond length in each of the following molecules: CF_4, CBr_4, CI_4. Compare your values with the experimental ones:

$$C—F \ \text{in} \ CF_4 = 1.32 \ \text{Å}$$
$$C—Br \ \text{in} \ CBr_4 = 1.94 \ \text{Å}$$
$$C—I \ \text{in} \ CI_4 = 2.15 \ \text{Å}$$

Figure 18-4 contrasts the sizes of the halide ions. Each of these dimensions is obtained from the examination of crystal structures of many halide salts. The size found for a given halide ion is called its **ionic radius**. These radii are larger than the covalent radii but close to the van der Waals radii of neutral atoms.

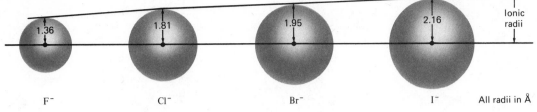

Figure 18-4
Ionic radii of the halogens.

The covalent, van der Waals, and ionic radii are presented in Table 18-1. We see some interesting trends. For each type of radius there is a gradual increase from fluorine to iodine. The increase in size reflects the fact that as the atomic number increases, higher energy levels are used to accommodate the electrons. In addition, Table 18-1 shows a trend of increasing melting and boiling temperatures from fluorine to iodine. This trend is appropriate for a series of molecular solids in which van der Waals forces are the principal forces holding the molecules in their positions in the crystal.

18-3 The Oxidation-Reduction Properties of the Halogens

Most of the reactions of the halogens are oxidation-reduction reactions. The oxidizing abilities of the halogens vary in a regular manner, fluorine being the strongest and iodine the weakest. The equations and $E°$ values for the half-reactions are:

$$F_2 + 2e^- \longrightarrow 2\,F^- \qquad E° = +2.87 \text{ volts}$$
$$Cl_2 + 2e^- \longrightarrow 2\,Cl^- \qquad E° = +1.36 \text{ volts}$$
$$Br_2 + 2e^- \longrightarrow 2\,Br^- \qquad E° = +1.06 \text{ volts}$$
$$I_2 + 2e^- \longrightarrow 2\,I^- \qquad E° = +0.53 \text{ volt}$$

The halogens react quite vigorously with most of the metals to produce simple halide salts. Here are a few examples:

$$2\,Na + Br_2 \longrightarrow 2\,NaBr$$
$$Mg + F_2 \longrightarrow MgF_2$$
$$2\,Fe + 3\,Cl_2 \longrightarrow 2\,FeCl_3$$

18-4 The Importance of the Halogens and Their Compounds

There are many ways in which the halogens and their compounds are important. Table 18-2 summarizes a few examples:

TABLE 18-2

Major Uses for the Halogens

Halogen	Used to Prepare:
Fluorine	Plastics such as Teflon Catalysts in some petroleum processes SnF_2 for fluoride toothpastes NaF, an insecticide
Chlorine	Br_2 and I_2 HCl, an important acid $CaOCl_2$ for bleaching and disinfecting Chlorates and perchlorates for matches, fireworks, explosives
Bromine	$C_2H_4Br_2$, an important gasoline additive (to remove Pb produced from tetraethyl lead) AgBr for photographic emulsions
Iodine	Disinfectants Dyes and other organic compounds AgI for photographic emulsions Iodized salt, to prevent and cure goiter and other thyroid disorders

Prize-winning photographers often make their own developers, toners, and special-effect solutions.

18-5 Photography

One of the major uses of the halogens, particularly bromine, is in photographic emulsions. The silver salts of the halogens are light-sensitive. They decompose to form metallic silver and the free halogen when exposed to light and later developed. Black-and-white photography is based on this property of the silver halides. A photographic film is a sheet of transparent plastic covered with a thin layer of gelatin. Very fine crystals of AgBr are suspended in the gelatin. The process of changing unexposed film into a finished print can be outlined in four steps.

Exposure. When the film is exposed by opening the camera shutter, an image is produced in the film by light reflected from the object being photographed. The whiter the object, the larger the amount of reflected light. Crystals of AgBr, in the areas where light strikes the film, are sensitized by some process not yet well understood. Sometimes the words *latent image* and *hidden image* are used to describe the film at this stage. In a darkroom, using red light that does not affect the film, this latent image is not visible.

Development. The film is developed by placing it in a solution that contains a weak reducing agent such as hydroquinone. The sensitized AgBr crystals react at a much faster rate than do AgBr crystals not struck by light. The rate of this reaction is related to the intensity of light that struck the crystals. The chemical reaction that takes place can be represented as

$$AgBr + \text{reducing agent} \longrightarrow Ag + Br^- + \text{oxidized products from the reducing agent}$$

Metallic silver forms in the emulsion. Development of the latent image is carefully timed to produce black, white, and gray regions that have the desired relative intensities. The white areas of the object photographed show up as dark regions of silver in the film. When the developing process reaches the proper stage, the film is removed from the developing solution and put into a "stop bath" to destroy the unused reducing agent. It is then washed and placed in the "fixing" solution.

Fixation. Some AgBr crystals have been reduced to metallic silver. The remaining AgBr crystals must now be removed from the emulsion. Otherwise the entire negative will turn black when exposed to light. This is done by reaction with sodium thiosulfate, often called "hypo," to dissolve the AgBr.

$$AgBr + 2\,S_2O_3^{2-} \longrightarrow Ag(S_2O_3)_2^{3-} + Br^-$$

The film is thoroughly washed with water and then allowed to dry. At this stage, the film is called the *negative*. The white areas of the object have been recorded in the emulsion as black metallic silver regions; the dark areas of the object appear as transparent regions in the emulsion because AgBr has been removed.

Printing. A positive print is made by passing light through the negative onto a piece of print paper. This paper contains a layer of AgBr crystals, too. After exposing, developing, and fixing this print, one has a *positive* which duplicates the light and dark portions of the original object. Figure 18-5 shows schematically what takes place.

About 25 percent of the silver used in the United States each year is used to make AgBr for use in photographic films.

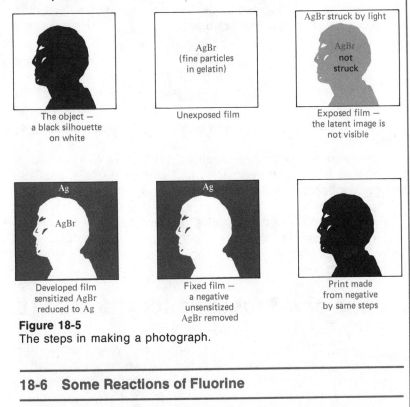

The object —
a black silhouette
on white

Unexposed film

Exposed film —
the latent image is
not visible

Developed film
sensitized AgBr
reduced to Ag

Fixed film —
a negative
unsensitized
AgBr removed

Print made
from negative
by same steps

Figure 18-5
The steps in making a photograph.

18-6 Some Reactions of Fluorine

Because of the small size of the atom, fluorine is rather special in the halogen group. It is a very strong oxidizing agent in an aqueous solution. One special property of fluorine is revealed when hydrogen fluoride is compared with the other hydrogen halides. See Figure 10-6. These properties can be explained in terms of the strong hydrogen bonding which occurs because of the small size of fluorine. Also, in an aqueous solution hydrogen fluoride, HF, is a weak acid, whereas HCl, HBr, and HI are strong acids. The equilibrium constant for HF is 6.7×10^{-4}; so hydrofluoric acid is less than 10 percent ionized in a 0.1 M HF solution.

Another unusual property of HF is its reactivity with glass. Hydrofluoric acid cannot be kept in glass bottles because it reacts with the silica, SiO_2, in glass. On the other hand, even the most concentrated hydrochloric acid solutions can remain indefinitely in glass without any evidence of a comparable reaction. Polyethylene or wax containers are often used to store HF solutions. Silicon bonds more strongly to fluorine than to oxygen, and therefore silica dissolves in a solution of HF. The equation is

$$SiO_2 + 6\,HF \longrightarrow SiF_6{}^{2-} + 2\,H_3O^+$$

In many cities in the United States, a very small amount of fluoride ion, F^-, is added to the drinking water supply. The presence of fluoride ion has been shown to reduce tooth decay in children.

The carbon-fluorine bond is a very stable bond. The strength of the C—F bond is comparable to the strength of the C—H bond. This fact has led chemists to synthesize a series of compounds known as *fluorocarbons.* These are analogous to the hydrocarbons and can be imagined as derived from them by substituting F atoms for H atoms. For example,

is the fluorocarbon analogue of ethylene. It is called tetrafluoroethylene.

Polymeric fluorocarbons, such as Teflon, are being used in many new ways each year. They find extensive use in gaskets, valves, stopcocks, and fittings for handling corrosive chemicals. Teflon-coated cooking pans have become popular because foods do not stick to these pans. In the "protective coating," fluorine atoms are bonded so strongly to the carbon chain of these polymer coatings that they show almost no tendency to react with other substances.

Questions and Problems for Chapter 18

1

Give the electron configuration for each of the trio F^-, Ne, Na^+. How do the trios Cl^-, Ar, K^+ and Br^-, Kr, Rb^+ differ from the above?

2

Table 18-1 contains values for the covalent radii and the ionic radii of the halogens. Plot the radii versus the row numbers. What systematic changes are evident in the two curves?

3

Using the data from Table 18-1, plot on one set of axes the melting and boiling temperatures of the halogens versus row numbers.

4

For astatine, use your graphs from Problems 2 and 3 as a basis for a prediction of its covalent radius, ionic radius of the At^- ion, and melting and boiling temperatures.

5

Explain in terms of nuclear charge why the K^+ ion is smaller than the Cl^- ion, even though they have the same number of electrons.

6

Predict the molecular structures and bond lengths for SiF_4, $SiCl_4$, $SiBr_4$, and SiI_4, assuming the covalent radius of silicon is 1.16 Å.

7

Can aqueous bromine, Br_2, be used to oxidize ferrous ion, Fe^{2+}, to ferric ion, Fe^{3+} (use Appendix 4)? Can aqueous iodine, I_2, be used instead of bromine?

8

What will happen if F_2 is bubbled into 1 M NaBr solution? Justify your answer using $E°$ values.

9

Use $E°$ values to predict what will happen if chlorine is added to 1 M solutions of Br^- and of I^-. What will happen if Br_2 is added to 1 M I^-? Which halogen is oxidized and which is reduced in each case?

10

Write a balanced equation for the reaction of dichromate and iodide ions in acid solution. Determine $E°$ for the reaction

$$Cr_2O_7^{2-} + I^- + H^+ \quad gives \quad Cr^{3+} + I_2 + H_2O$$

11

Balance the equation for the reaction of iodine with thiosulfate ion:

$$I_2 + S_2O_3^{2-} \quad gives \quad S_4O_6^{2-} + I^-$$

thiosulfate	tetrathionate
ion	ion

What is the oxidation number of sulfur in the tetrathionate ion?

12

How many grams of iodine can be formed from 20.0 grams of KI by oxidizing it with ferric chloride ($FeCl_3$)? Determine $E°$.

13

Balance the equation for the reaction between SO_2 and I_2 to produce SO_4^{2-} and I^- in acid solution. Calculate $E°$. From Le Châtelier's principle predict the effect on the $E°$ in this reaction if $[H^+] = 10^{-7}$ M is used instead of $[H^+] = 1$ M.

14

What is the oxidation number of the halogen in each of the following: HF, $HClO_2$, HIO_3, BrO_3^-, F_2, ClO_4^-?

15

Comparable half-reactions for iodine and chlorine are shown below:

$$IO_3^- + 6\,H^+ + 5\,e^- \longrightarrow \tfrac{1}{2}I_2 + 3\,H_2O$$
$$E° = 1.195 \text{ volts}$$

$$ClO_3^- + 6\,H^+ + 5e^- \longrightarrow \tfrac{1}{2}Cl_2 + 3\,H_2O$$
$$E° = 1.47 \text{ volts}$$

(a) Which is the stronger oxidizing agent, iodate, IO_3^-, or chlorate, ClO_3^-?
(b) Balance the equation for the reaction between chlorate ion and I^- to produce I_2 and Cl_2.

16

Two half-reactions involving chlorine are

$$Cl_2 + 2\,e^- \longrightarrow 2\,Cl^-$$
$$E° = 1.36 \text{ volts}$$

$$2\,HOCl + 2\,H^+ + 2\,e^- \longrightarrow Cl_2 + 2\,H_2O$$
$$E° = 1.63 \text{ volts}$$

(a) Balance the reaction in which self-oxidation-reduction of Cl_2 occurs to produce chloride ion and hypochlorous acid, $HOCl$.
(b) What is the oxidation number of chlorine in each species containing chlorine?
(c) What is $E°$ for the reaction?
(d) Explain, using Le Châtelier's principle, why the self-oxidation-reduction reaction occurs in 1 M OH^- solution instead of 1 M H^+.

17

From each of the following sets, select the substance which best fits the requirement specified.

(a) Biggest atom	F, Cl, Br, I
(b) Smallest ionization energy	F, Cl, Br, I
(c) Best reducing agent	F^-, Cl^-, Br^-, I^-
(d) Weakest acid	HF, HCl, HBr, HI
(e) Strongest hydrogen bonding	HF, HCl, HBr, HI

18

Describe two properties that the halogens have in common and give an explanation of why they have these properties in common.

19

How many grams of SiO_2 would react with 5.00×10^2 ml of $1.00\ M$ HF to produce SiF_4?

20

The HF in a $0.10\ M$ aqueous solution is 8% dissociated. What is the value of K_A?

21

Some seaweed, when dry, contains 0.10% by weight of iodine. How many grams of $KMnO_4$ are needed to produce the pure I_2 from a metric ton of seaweed? Mn^{2+} is formed. (1 metric ton = 1000 kilograms)

22

There are some combinations of atoms that behave like halogens and are called *pseudohalogens*. Use electron dot diagrams to explain why CN^- and NCO^- ions are pseudohalogens.

23

There are some substances that behave as though they were halogens. The best known example is $(CN)_2$, cyanogen. Use your book as a library of chemical facts to decide what characteristics a substance should have to qualify as a pseudohalogen. List at least three characteristics.

24

Use the periodic table and your answers to Problem 23 to suggest some properties of $(CN)_2$ and its compounds. List at least three.

25

Here are some pseudohalogens. (See Problems 22 and 24.)

$(OCN)_2$ oxycyanogen
N_3^- azide ion
$(SCN)_2$ thiocyanogen

Decide which of these formulas are reasonable. Give reasons for your decisions.

(a) CH_3SeCN (d) HN_3
(b) $SiCl_3(SCN)$ (e) CH_3OCNCH_3
(c) $Na(N_3)_2$

26

$(CN)_2$ is colorless. What color would you expect $(SeCN)_2$ to be?

27

Many azides are dangerously explosive. Balance the equation for sodium azide decomposing to liquid metal and nitrogen gas. Calculate the volume of gas formed at 300 °C and 2 atm from 650 g of NaN_3.

28

Iodine dissolves only slightly in water, about 0.30 g/liter at 20 °C. Calculate the value of K for this reaction.

29

At 60 °C a saturated solution of I_2 in water holds 0.96 g/liter. How many liters must be cooled to 20 °C to precipitate 0.100 mole of I_2? (See Problem 28 for data.)

30

Bromine is less soluble in warm water than in cold water. When bromine dissolves, is the reaction endothermic or exothermic?

31

Naturally occurring bromine contains ^{79}Br and ^{81}Br. Calculate the percentage of each.

32

Astatine occurs rarely in nature. ^{211}At was first made in 1940 by bombarding a ^{209}Bi with alpha particles. Write a balanced equation for this reaction.

33

The isotope ^{211}At has a half-life of 7.5 hours. What part of a sample would remain after 30 hours?

34

Cl_2O is an explosive yellow-red gas which liquefies at about 3 °C and freezes at −20 °C. Discuss the bonding, the structure of the molecule, and the type of crystalline solid formed.

35

Hypochlorous acid, HOCl, can be made by this method:

$Cl_2 + HgO + H_2O$ $HgO \cdot HgCl_2 + HOCl$

Write a balanced equation and calculate the grams of acid formed using 64.8 g of HgO.

36

K_A for the acid HOBr is equal to 2×10^{-9}. (a) Calculate the H^+ ion concentration for a $1\ M$ solution. (b) What will the addition of a strong acid do to the ionization of HOBr?

The Fourth-Row
Transition Elements

19

In preceding chapters the chemical properties of many of the elements across the top of the periodic table and down the two sides have been presented. Now some of the elements in the middle section will be considered. These elements are often referred to as the **transition elements**. Chemists once believed that these elements behaved in a fashion intermediate between the extremes shown by the chemical families on the left and right sides of the periodic table. Figure 19-1 shows this intermediate position. Today the term "transition element" is still a useful way to designate elements in the middle of the periodic table.

When the elements in families such as the alkali metals or the halogens are compared, the similarities in chemical properties are very striking. The electronic designations and the ionization

Transition elements

1 H																	2 He
3 Li	4 Be											5 B	6 C	7 N	8 O	9 F	10 Ne
11 Na	12 Mg											13 Al	14 Si	15 P	16 S	17 Cl	18 Ar
19 K	20 Ca	21 Sc	22 Ti	23 V	24 Cr	25 Mn	26 Fe	27 Co	28 Ni	29 Cu	30 Zn	31 Ga	32 Ge	33 As	34 Se	35 Br	36 Kr
37 Rb	38 Sr	39 Y	40 Zr	41 Nb	42 Mo	43 Tc	44 Ru	45 Rh	46 Pd	47 Ag	48 Cd	49 In	50 Sn	51 Sb	52 Te	53 I	54 Xe
55 Cs	56 Ba	57-71 La-Lu	72 Hf	73 Ta	74 W	75 Re	76 Os	77 Ir	78 Pt	79 Au	80 Hg	81 Tl	82 Pb	83 Bi	84 Po	85 At	86 Rn
87 Fr	88 Ra	89-103 Ac-Lr	104	105	106												

Figure 19-1
The transition elements.

energies for these elements help explain this similarity of properties. On the other hand, when the elements sodium through chlorine are compared, the contrasts in chemical properties are equally striking. The trends in acid-base and redox properties can be explained in terms of the great differences in electronic structure and ionization energy as we move horizontally across a row in the periodic table.

In this chapter the first group of transition elements, scandium through zinc, will be examined. In Chapter 9, when the electron configurations for the elements were being discussed, it was pointed out that the regular pattern of filling *s* and *p* orbitals was interrupted when the 21st element, scandium, was reached. The electron configuration for calcium is shown in Figure 19-2. Let us examine the electron configurations for Sc and the next nine elements.

19-1 Electron Configurations

The element scandium contains one more electron than calcium. The 21st electron enters the lowest-energy orbital that is not fully occupied. Figure 19-2 shows that this is a 3*d* orbital. There are five 3*d* orbitals. Putting a pair of electrons in each of these orbitals means that ten electrons can be accommodated before the higher-energy 4*p* orbitals are needed. The fourth-row transition elements have the electron configurations shown in Table 19-1. Valence electrons for the transition elements include *d* electrons, whereas *s* and *p* electrons were the only ones needed for nontransition elements.

Catalyst manufacturers use many transition-element compounds.

Notice that chromium and copper provide interruptions to the regular buildup. In chromium, the gas-phase atom has lower energy if one of the 4*s* electrons moves into the 3*d* set. This gives chromium a half-filled set of 3*d* orbitals and a half-filled 4*s* orbital. In copper, the atom has lower energy if the 3*d* set is completely filled with ten electrons and the 4*s* orbital is half-filled.

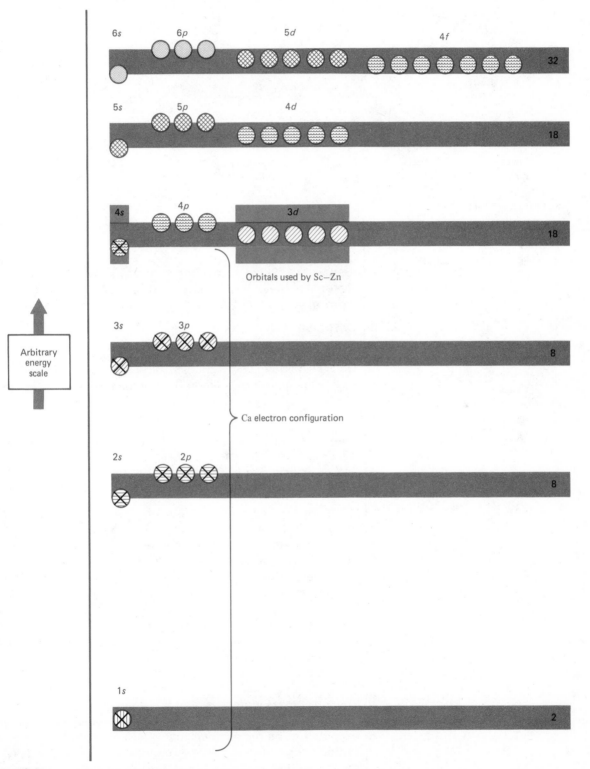

Figure 19-2
The fourth-row transition elements use the 3*d* orbitals beyond the Ca configuration.

TABLE 19-1

The Electron Configurations of the Fourth-Row
Transition Elements

Element	Symbol	Atomic Number	Argon Core	Electron Configuration Beyond an Argon Core	
				3d	4s
Scandium	Sc	21	$1s^2$ $2s^2 2p^6$ $3s^2 3p^6$	1	2
Titanium	Ti	22		2	2
Vanadium	V	23	Each	3	2
Chromium	Cr	24	fourth-row	5	1
Manganese	Mn	25	transition	5	2
Iron	Fe	26	element	6	2
Cobalt	Co	27	has these	7	2
Nickel	Ni	28	orbitals	8	2
Copper	Cu	29	filled.	10	1
Zinc	Zn	30		10	2

EXERCISE 19-1

Use Figure 19-2 to decide which orbital would be used after the 3d orbitals have been filled. What element has this configuration? In which family does this element occur?

EXERCISE 19-2

Use Figure 19-2 to write the electronic configuration for yttrium, Y. Would you expect yttrium to have chemical properties more like aluminum or scandium? Yttrium has atomic number 39.

19-2   Some Properties and Regularities of the Fourth-Row Transition Elements

What trends in properties can be observed for the transition elements scandium through zinc? What kinds of compounds do they form? How can their properties be related to the electron configurations of these elements?

All the transition elements are metals, with high melting and boiling temperatures. They are good conductors of heat and electricity. Copper is widely used in electrical circuits because of its exceptionally high conductivity and relatively low cost. Some of the properties of these elements are summarized in Table 19-2, where several regularities can be observed.

Molar Mass

The molar mass increases regularly across the row except for the inversion at cobalt and nickel. The molar mass of Ni might be expected to be higher than that of Co because there are more protons (28) in the Ni nucleus than in the Co nucleus (27). The reason for the inversion lies in the abundance of the naturally

TABLE 19-2
Some Properties of the Fourth-Row Transition Elements

Property	Sc	Ti	V	Cr	Mn	Fe	Co	Ni	Cu	Zn
Atomic number	21	22	23	24	25	26	27	28	29	30
Molar mass (g)	45.0	47.9	51.0	52.0	54.9	55.9	58.9	58.7	63.5	65.4
Abundance* (% by mass)	0.005	0.44	0.015	0.020	0.10	5.0	0.0023	0.008	0.0007	0.01
Melting temperature (°C)	1400	1812	1730	1900	1244	1535	1493	1455	1083	419
Boiling temperature (°C)	3900	3130**	3530**	2480**	2087	2800	3520	2800	2582	907
Density (g/cm³)	2.4	4.5	6.0	7.1	7.2	7.9	8.9	8.9	8.9	7.1
First ionization energy (kcal/mol)	154	157	155	155	171	180	180	175	176	216
2+ ion radius (Å)	—	0.90	0.88	0.84	0.80	0.76	0.74	0.72	0.72	0.74
3+ ion radius (Å)	0.81	0.76	0.74	0.69	0.66	0.64	0.63	0.62	—	—
$E°$ (volt) $M^{2+} + 2e^- \longrightarrow M$	-2.1***	-1.75	-1.2	-0.90	-1.18	-0.44	-0.28	-0.25	+0.34	-0.76

*In the Earth's crust. **Estimated. ***$M^{3+} + 3e^- \longrightarrow M$.

occurring isotopes of these elements. Natural cobalt consists entirely of the single isotope Co—59. Natural nickel consists primarily of two isotopes, Ni—58 and Ni—60, with the isotope of mass number 58 about three times as abundant as the isotope having mass number 60.

Abundance

With the exception of iron and titanium, the transition elements are not very abundant in the earth's crust. There is evidence that the center of the earth is predominantly iron and nickel. One theory for the formation of the earth suggests that the temperature rose to several thousand degrees during the early stages of development. Metals such as iron would have been present as liquids of fairly high density. These liquids would have moved toward the center of the earth. The silicate rocks which make up the outer levels of the earth's crust would have floated on the top of the liquid metals.

Melting Temperature

Except for zinc at the end of the transition element group, the melting temperatures are quite high. This is reasonable, since these elements have a large number of valence electrons and also a large number of vacant valence orbitals. Toward the end of this group of elements, the 3d orbitals become filled and the melting temperature is relatively low.

During the last decade oceanographers discovered black nodules, ranging in size from pebbles to grapefruit, on some areas of the ocean floor. The concentration of manganese in these nodules is high enough that it may be economical to mine the ocean floors. The metal manganese is used in manufacturing some steels and dry-cell batteries. The nodules appear to grow about 1 mm in diameter every 1000 years.

The Fourth-Row Transition Elements

Density

The density increases in a regular manner for the transition metals, with some leveling off at Co, Ni, and Cu. This trend is closely tied to the approximately constant size of the atoms. The main effect producing density change is the increasing nuclear mass.

Ionization Energy

The ionization energies for the transition elements are rather similar in magnitude. The values are intermediate between low values for the alkali metals and high values for the noble gases. The increasing nuclear charge which tends to increase the ionization energy seems to be almost offset by the extra screening of the nucleus provided by the added electrons.

Ionic Radius

The ionic radii for the transition elements do not change appreciably from scandium to zinc. There seem to be two factors that are balanced. First, an increasing nuclear charge should pull the electrons more strongly towards the nucleus. But second, as more electrons enter the $3d$ orbitals, these electrons repel each other, increasing the size of the ion. As expected, the radii of the $3+$ ions are smaller than the radii of the $2+$ ions.

Color

Many compounds of the transition metals and their aqueous solutions absorb light in the visible region of the spectrum. The energy levels that account for this absorption are relatively close together and involve unoccupied d orbitals. The environment of the ion changes the spacing of these levels, thereby influencing the color. An example is the Ni^{2+} ion, which changes from green when surrounded by water molecules to blue when ammonia is added to replace the water.

$E°$

The last row in Table 19-2 gives the values for the reduction potentials for the transition metals. Except for scandium the potentials correspond to the reaction

$$M^{2+} + 2e^- \longrightarrow M$$

All the elements except copper have negative $E°$ values. This means that they will dissolve in HCl solutions, liberating H_2. The positive $E°$ for copper indicates why it is one of the few elements found in the metallic state in the earth's crust. The existence of deposits of metallic copper suggests why man evolved through the Bronze Age before the Iron Age. Copper, the essential ingredient of bronze, did not require the difficult smelting process needed for iron.

EXERCISE 19-3

The densities for metallic K and Ca are 0.86 g/cm³ and 1.55 g/cm³, respectively. Use information from Table 19-2 to draw a graph of density versus atomic number for the elements K through Zn. Does your graph suggest a regularity?

19-3 Some Compounds of Chromium

Suppose we go into a chemical stockroom to see what kinds of compounds can be found for a particular transition element, chromium. First, there might be a bottle of green powder labeled Cr_2O_3, chromic oxide or chromium(III) oxide. Next to it there might be a bottle containing a red powder, CrO_3, chromium(VI) oxide. We might also find some black powder marked CrO, chromous oxide or chromium(II) oxide. There would be other compounds such as $CrCl_3$, chromic chloride, and maybe some green CrF_2, chromous fluoride. Elsewhere in the stockroom there would be bright-yellow potassium chromate, K_2CrO_4, next to a bottle of orange potassium dichromate, $K_2Cr_2O_7$. Chromium has an oxidation number of $+6$ in both compounds.

Metal-plating chemists (chromium bumpers, silverware, rustproof nails) must know the properties of metal compounds and their solutions.

The anions in these last two compounds provide an interesting example of different structures containing the same oxidation number. You studied these ions and the equilibrium between them in Experiment 30. The chromate ion exhibits a tetrahedral arrangement of oxygen atoms around the central chromium ion. The dichromate ion may be visualized as two such tetrahedra, having one corner in common. Figure 19-3 shows the two structures. You found that the chromate ion can easily be converted to the dichromate ion by increasing $[H^+]$.

$$2\ CrO_4{}^{2-} + 2\ H^+ \rightleftharpoons Cr_2O_7{}^{2-} + H_2O$$

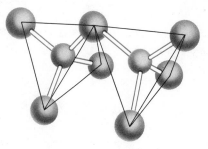

Ion with 2⁻ charge

Chromate ion

Dichromate ion

Figure 19-3
The structures of chromate and dichromate ions.

Returning to the stockroom search, we would conclude that chromium forms a number of stable compounds, most of them colored solids. We also would realize that chromium may have different oxidation numbers, including $+2$, $+3$, and $+6$, in its compounds. Similar conclusions would have resulted for most of the other transition elements. Table 19-3 summarizes some of the information chemists have found for the transition elements.

TABLE 19-3

Typical Oxidation Numbers Found for Fourth-Row
Transition Elements

Symbol	Representative Compounds							Number of Valence Electrons in Neutral Atom	
	Oxidation Number of Transition Element								
	+1	+2	+3	+4	+5	+6	+7	3d	4s
Sc			Sc_2O_3					1	2
Ti		TiO	Ti_2O_3	TiO_2				2	2
V		VO	V_2O_3	VO_2	V_2O_5			3	2
Cr		CrO	Cr_2O_3			CrO_3 K_2CrO_4 $K_2Cr_2O_7$		5	1
Mn		MnO	Mn_2O_3	MnO_2		K_2MnO_4	$KMnO_4$	5	2
Fe		FeO	Fe_2O_3					6	2
Co		CoO	Co_2O_3					7	2
Ni		NiO	Ni_2O_3					8	2
Cu	Cu_2O	CuO						10	1
Zn		ZnO						10	2

19-4 Complex Ions

$CrCl_3 \cdot 6\,NH_3$	$CrCl_3 \cdot 5\,NH_3$	$CrCl_3 \cdot 4\,NH_3$	$CrCl_3 \cdot 3\,NH_3$
Yellow	Purple	Green	Violet

These four labels are from bottles of brightly colored solids standing next to each other on the stockroom shelf. The dot in the formulas simply indicates that a certain number of moles of neutral NH_3 are bound to one mole of $CrCl_3$. Chromium has an oxidation number of $+3$ in each compound.

This series of compounds exhibits some behavior that is not suggested by the molecular formulas. Let us dissolve one mole of each in water. To these, add some silver nitrate solution in an attempt to precipitate the chloride as $AgCl$. The amount of chloride that can be precipitated varies from one compound to another.

Compound	Moles of Cl^- precipitated	Moles of Cl^- not precipitated
$CrCl_3 \cdot 6\,NH_3$	3	0
$CrCl_3 \cdot 5\,NH_3$	2	1
$CrCl_3 \cdot 4\,NH_3$	1	2
$CrCl_3 \cdot 3\,NH_3$	0	3

Apparently there are two ways in which chlorine is bound in these compounds. One allows chlorine to ionize and be precipitated; the other does not. In $CrCl_3 \cdot 6\,NH_3$ three Cl^- ions form and are precipitated; in $CrCl_3 \cdot 3\,NH_3$, no chloride forms. The explanation of this behavior was provided in the early 1900's by Alfred Werner, a Swiss chemist. He proposed that each chromium is bonded to six neighbors. In $CrCl_3 \cdot 6\,NH_3$, the cation consists of a central

Cr^{3+} surrounded by 6 NH_3 molecules at the corners of an octahedron. Octahedral geometry is illustrated in Figures 19-4 and 19-5. The three chlorine atoms form anions, Cl^-. In $CrCl_3 \cdot 5\,NH_3$, the cation consists of the central chromium ion surrounded by the five NH_3 molecules and one of the Cl^- ions. In $CrCl_3 \cdot 4\,NH_3$, the chromium is bound to four NH_3 and two Cl^-, while in $CrCl_3 \cdot 3\,NH_3$ all three Cl^- ions and three NH_3 molecules are bonded to the central Cr^{3+}. The formulas can be written in this way:

$$[Cr(NH_3)_6{}^{3+}]\,[Cl^-]_3$$
$$[Cr(NH_3)_5Cl^{2+}]\,[Cl^-]_2$$
$$[Cr(NH_3)_4Cl_2{}^+]\,[Cl^-]$$
$$[Cr(NH_3)_3Cl_3]$$

Werner demonstrated by experiment that only two compounds have the formula $CrCl_3 \cdot 4\,NH_3$. This is strong evidence for octahedral geometry around the central ion. Figure 19-4 shows the isomers of the cation. In one of them, the *cis*-isomer, two bonded chlorines occupy positions next to each other. In the other isomer, the *trans*-isomer, two bonded chlorines have positions on opposite sides of the metal atom.

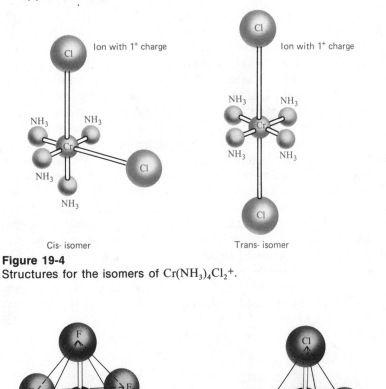

Figure 19-4
Structures for the isomers of $Cr(NH_3)_4Cl_2{}^+$.

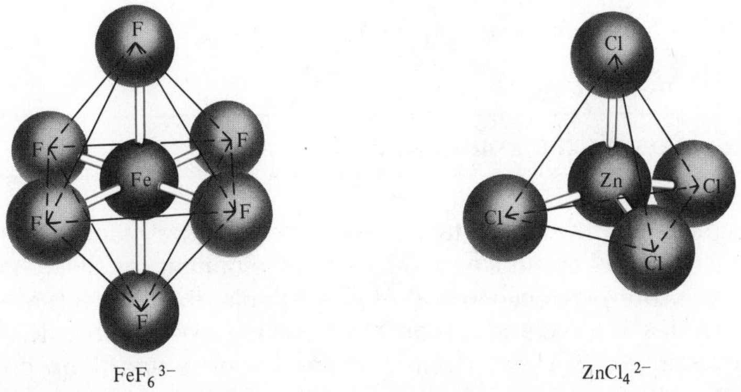

Figure 19-5
Complex ions with octahedral and tetrahedral geometry.

19-5 The Geometry of Complex Ions

The way in which atoms and molecules are arranged around a central atom has a great influence on the stability of the cluster. What kinds of arrangements are found in complex ions? What shapes do they have?

First, here is a concept useful in giving spatial descriptions. The **coordination number** *is the number of nearest neighbors that an atom has.* For example, in the complex ion FeF_6^{3-}, each iron atom is surrounded by six fluoride ions at the corners of an octahedron. We say that the iron atom has a coordination number of 6 in this ion. In the complex ion $ZnCl_4^{2-}$, the chloride ions are arranged around a central Zn^{2+} at the corners of a regular tetrahedron. The coordination number of Zn is 4 in this ion. Figure 19-5 shows these complex ions.

If more than simple atoms are bound to a central atom, then the coordination number still refers to the number of nearest neighbors. For example, in $Ni(NH_3)_6^{2+}$, the cation consists of a central nickel ion joined to six ammonia molecules arranged in an octahedral manner. The nitrogen atom in each NH_3 molecule is turned toward the central nickel and the hydrogen atoms point away. This ion is shown in Figure 19-6.

The complex ion $Fe(C_2O_4)_3^{3-}$ is formed when rust stains are bleached out with oxalic acid solution. The central iron(III) ion has a coordination number of 6, even though there are only three oxalate groups around each iron. Each oxalate ion, $C_2O_4^{2-}$, uses two of its oxygen atoms to bond with the central iron atom. The number of nearest neighbors, viewed from the iron ion, is six oxygen atoms at the corners of an octahedron. A group which can furnish simultaneously two atoms for coordination is said to be *bidentate,* which literally means double-toothed. The structure for $Fe(C_2O_4)_3^{3-}$ is drawn in Figure 19-7.

In addition to the tetrahedral and octahedral structures, there are two other geometrical arrangements often found. In square planar complexes, the central atom has four near neighbors at the corners of a square. An example is the nickel cyanide anion, $Ni(CN)_4^{2-}$. In a linear complex, the coordination number is 2, corresponding to one group on each side of the central atom. When copper(I) chloride dissolves in ammonia, the complex ion $Cu(NH_3)_2^+$ forms. The structures for $Ni(CN)_4^{2-}$ and for $Cu(NH_3)_2^+$ are shown in Figure 19-8.

Figure 19-6
The geometry of $Ni(NH_3)_6^{2+}$.

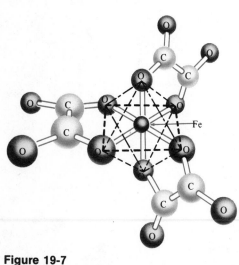

Figure 19-7
The structure of $Fe(C_2O_4)_3^{3-}$.

19-6 Complexes Found in Nature

Complex ions have important roles in many of the reactions that occur in plants and animals. Two of these complexes are hemin and chlorophyll. Hemin is part of hemoglobin, the pigment in red corpuscles in the blood. Chlorophyll provides the green coloring material in plants. Hemoglobin contains iron, whereas chlorophyll is a complex compound containing magnesium. As extracted from plants, chlorophyll is made up of two closely related compounds called chlorophyll A and chlorophyll B.

The structural formula for chlorophyll A is shown on the left in Figure 19-9. The most obvious thing to notice is that chlorophyll A is a large organic molecule with a magnesium atom at the center. Around the magnesium atom there are four nearest neighbor N atoms. Each N atom is a part of a five-membered ring. The overall shape of this molecule is planar.

Hemin is shown on the right in Figure 19-9. There is an astonishing similarity between these molecules. The portions within dotted lines identify the differences between the two molecules. Except for the central metal atoms, the differences are all on the outer edges of these cumbersome molecules. We cannot help wondering how nature adopted this molecular skeleton for molecules with such different functions. We cannot avoid a feeling of impatience as we await the clarification of the possible relation, a clarification that may be provided by scientists of the next generation.

Hemoglobin carries oxygen from the lungs to the tissue cells. The iron atom of hemin forms a complex with an oxygen molecule. The connection must be a rather loose one, since O_2 is readily released to the cells. The complex is bright red, the characteristic color of arterial blood. When O_2 is stripped off the hemin group, the color changes to a purplish red, the color of blood in the veins.

Other groups can be bound to the iron atom in hemoglobin. Carbon monoxide is more firmly bound to hemoglobin than

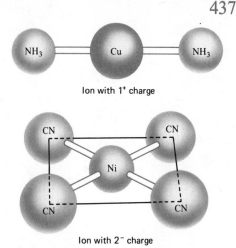

Figure 19-8
Square planar and linear structures.

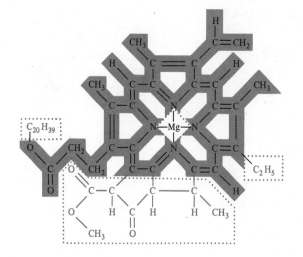

Chlorophyll A

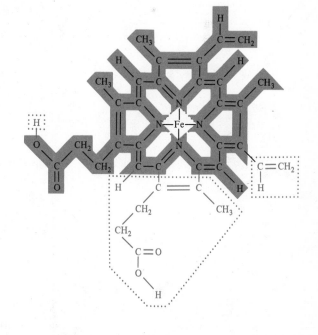

Hemin

Figure 19-9
The structures of chlorophyll A and hemin.

Medical researchers use complex ions to simulate natural processes.

oxygen is. If we breathe a mixture of CO and O_2, the carbon monoxide molecules are picked up by the red blood cells. The sites that are normally used to carry O_2 molecules are filled by CO molecules. The tissue cells starve for lack of oxygen. If caught in time, carbon monoxide poisoning can be treated by administering fresh air or oxygen.

19-7 Iron, Workhorse of the Metals

This chapter concludes with a discussion of iron, the most commonly used of the transition elements. Iron is quite abundant. It makes up about 5 percent of the earth's crust, ranking fourth of all elements and second of the metals. Iron has useful mechanical properties, especially when alloyed with other elements. Steel, one of the most useful construction materials, is iron with a small percentage of carbon. Often, small amounts of other elements are added in making special types of steel.

Workman dips sample cup into molten pig iron.

The most common iron ores are the oxides hematite, Fe_2O_3, and magnetite, Fe_3O_4. The important high-grade iron ore resources in northern Michigan, Wisconsin, and Minnesota are almost depleted now. However, methods have been developed to extract iron from a lower-grade ore (taconite), a very hard mixture of Fe_3O_4 in silicate rocks. One of the first steps is the concentration of Fe_3O_4, taking advantage of its magnetic properties. Other major deposits of iron oxides are found in Brazil, Venezuela, Canada, Sweden, and Russia.

Reduction of Iron Ore

The production of iron is an excellent example of chemical reduction on a massive scale. The process is carried out in a huge vertical reactor called a blast furnace. The three raw materials are iron ore, limestone, and coke. These are fed into the top of the furnace while air is blown in at the bottom. A simplified version of what goes on in a blast furnace is shown in Figure 19-10. As the mixture of ore, limestone, and coke moves down through the furnace, it encounters the updraft of oxygen. Carbon monoxide forms, and the heat energy released in this reaction maintains the high temperatures required in the furnace:

$$2\ C + O_2 \rightleftharpoons 2\ CO + 52.8\ kcal$$

As CO rises through the furnace, the iron oxide ore is reduced to metal, probably in three stages:

$$CO + 3\ Fe_2O_3 \longrightarrow 2\ Fe_3O_4 + CO_2$$
$$CO + Fe_3O_4 \longrightarrow 3\ FeO + CO_2$$
$$CO + FeO \longrightarrow Fe + CO_2$$

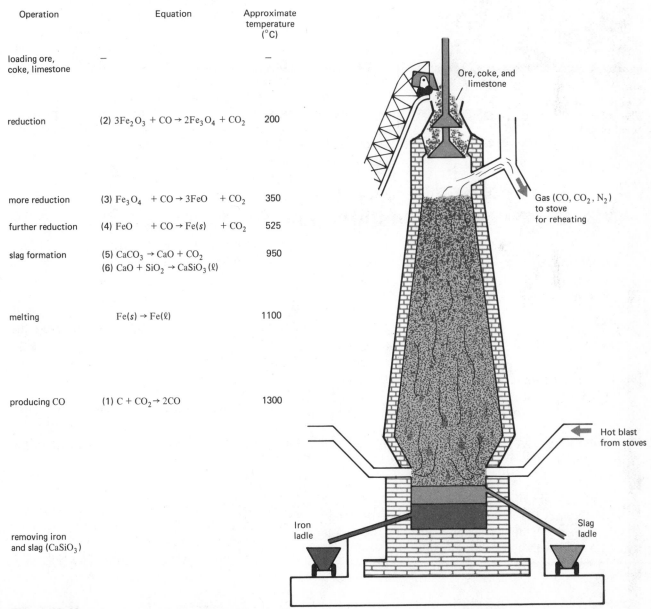

Operation	Equation	Approximate temperature (°C)
loading ore, coke, limestone	—	—
reduction	(2) $3Fe_2O_3 + CO \rightarrow 2Fe_3O_4 + CO_2$	200
more reduction	(3) $Fe_3O_4 + CO \rightarrow 3FeO + CO_2$	350
further reduction	(4) $FeO + CO \rightarrow Fe(s) + CO_2$	525
slag formation	(5) $CaCO_3 \rightarrow CaO + CO_2$ (6) $CaO + SiO_2 \rightarrow CaSiO_3 (\ell)$	950
melting	$Fe(s) \rightarrow Fe(\ell)$	1100
producing CO	(1) $C + CO_2 \rightarrow 2CO$	1300
removing iron and slag ($CaSiO_3$)		

Ore, coke, and limestone

Gas (CO, CO_2, N_2) to stove for reheating

Hot blast from stoves

Iron ladle

Slag ladle

Figure 19-10
Cross-section view of an operating blast furnace.

440

The temperature near the bottom of the furnace is sufficiently high that the impure iron collects as a molten liquid. Molten slag, formed when limestone reacts with silicates in the ore, floats on top of the more dense liquid iron. An average furnace that produces about 750 tons of iron per day will also yield about 400 tons of slag. The slag is sometimes used in the manufacture of cement. About 400 000 tons of iron are produced *daily* in the United States. A general view of a blast furnace is seen in Figure 19-11.

When the iron from a blast furnace cools, it is called pig iron. The high carbon content, about 4 percent, makes pig iron too brittle for most uses. Pig iron is made into steel by burning out most of the carbon, sulfur, and phosphorus impurities. Manganese, vanadium, and chromium are added in small amounts to produce steel alloys with particular properties. The important stainless steel alloys contain 10–20 percent chromium, up to 10 percent nickel, and sometimes 1 percent manganese. Stainless steels are free from one of the main deficiencies of iron, its tendency to rust. Corrosion of iron was discussed in Section 15-8 as a very undesirable redox reaction.

Iron is so well known as the major component of steel that its use in compounds is often overlooked. Iron oxides are important as pigments and as coating for magnetic tape. The compound ferrous sulfate is widely used as an inexpensive reducing agent in a number of industrial processes.

Figure 19-11
View of a blast furnace. (U.S. Steel photo)

Questions and Problems for Chapter 19

1

Why are the elements with atomic numbers 21 to 30 placed in a group and considered together in this chapter?

2

Write the orbital representation for

(a) chromium
(b) molybdenum
(c) tungsten

3

What properties of the transition elements are consistent with their being classified as metals?

4

Place a piece of paper over Figure 9-21 and trace it. Extend the x axis and add the ionization energies of the transition elements. Complete the row with the following ionization energies in kcal/mol: Ga, 138; Ge, 187; As, 242; Se, 225; Br, 273; Kr, 322; Rb, 96.

5

What is the oxidation number of manganese in each of the following: MnO_4^-; Mn^{2+}; Mn_3O_4; MnO_2; $Mn(OH)_2$; $MnCl_2$; MnF_3?

6

The first six ionization energies of vanadium in kcal/mol are 155, 335, 675, 1100, 1490, and 2950. Use these values to predict formulas for vanadium halides.

7

A uranium ore, carnotite, $K(UO_2)VO_4 \cdot \frac{3}{2}H_2O$, is also a source of vanadium. Calculate the amount of vanadium present in a ton of ore that assays 3.0% carnotite.

8

Vanadium reacts with both oxygen and nitrogen, forming V_2O_5 and VN. Assume only these products are formed in equal molar amounts. What is the percentage by weight of VN in the product?

9

Vanadium reacts with the dimer of nitrogen dioxide, N_2O_4, to form VO_2NO_3. Write a balanced equation for the decomposition of this compound into V_2O_5 and N_2O_5.

10

Write a balanced equation for these reactions of molybdenum:

(a) $MoO_3 + Zn$ gives $Mo_2O_3 + Zn^{2+}$
(b) $MoO_3 + KI + H^+$ gives $MoO_2I + K^+ + I_2$

11

Some metallic radii for fourth-row elements are

Metal	Radii (Å)
K	2.35
Sc	1.62
Ti	1.47
Mn	1.26
Ni	1.24
Zn	1.38
As	1.39

(a) Predict values for the radii of Fe, V, and Ga.
(b) Explain why there are many alloys containing combinations of the four elements Fe, Co, Mn, and Ni and few containing only Cu and Ca.

12

The ferrate ion is FeO_4^{2-}, and it is a powerful oxidizing agent. Write a balanced equation for the following reaction, and calculate the mass of ferrate needed to make 44.8 liters of nitrogen gas at STP.

$$FeO_4^{2-} + NH_3 \text{ gives } Fe^{3+} + N_2$$

13

MoF_6 is an octahedral molecule, melts at 17.5 °C (10.5 kcal/g), and boils at 36 °C (28.6 kcal/g). Estimate the electric dipole, and suggest the type of bonding present in the solid. Calculate the heat needed to vaporize 0.30 mole at 36 °C.

14

Write balanced equations for these reactions of transition elements:

(a) $V_2O_4 + K_3Fe(CN)_6 + KOH$ gives
$$V_2O_5 + K_4Fe(CN)_6$$
(b) $Na_2ZnO_2 + HCl$ gives $ZnCl_2 + NaCl + H_2O$
(c) $CoSO_4 + KI + KIO_3 + H_2O$ gives
$$Co(OH)_2 + K_2SO_4 + I_2$$

15

If manganese metal is put in a solution of Na_2ZnO_2 at pH 13, what will happen?

$$Mn(OH)_2 + 2\,e^- \longrightarrow Mn + 2\,OH^-$$
$$E° = 1.47 \text{ volts}$$

$$ZnO_2^{2-} + 2\,H_2O + 2\,e^- \longrightarrow Zn + 4\,OH^-$$
$$E° = 1.22 \text{ volts}$$

16

Suppose silver metal is put in a solution containing $CoCl_3$ and $CoCl_2$. What will happen?

$$Co^{3+} + e^- \longrightarrow Co^{2+} \qquad E° = 1.82 \text{ volts}$$

17

Vanadium pentoxide dissolves in water to the extent of 0.0070 g/liter. Calculate the solubility constant, K_{sp}, assuming it dissolves as a molecule of V_2O_5.

18

One way of making $CrCl_3$ is by the reaction (at 500–600 °C)

$$2\,Cr(s) + 3\,Cl_2(g) \rightleftharpoons 2\,CrCl_3(s) + 269.2 \text{ kcal}$$

What conditions would you use to get the greatest production of $CrCl_3$?

19

One test for alcohol on the breath involves this reaction:

$C_2H_5OH + K_2Cr_2O_7 + H_2SO_4$ gives
$$CH_3COOH + Cr_2(SO_4)_3$$

Write a balanced equation for the reaction.

20

Pure chromium is made in a multistep process using three main reactions as indicated below. Write balanced equations, and find the ratio of ore to carbon to aluminum needed to make one gram of chromium. List the oxidizing and reducing agent for each reaction:

$FeCr_2O_4 + Na(l) + O_2$ gives $Na_2Cr_2O_7 + Fe_2O_3$
$Na_2Cr_2O_7 + C$ gives $Cr_2O_3 + Na_2CO_3 + CO$
$Cr_2O_3 + Al$ gives $Al_2O_3 + Cr$

21

Use the following equations and constants to decide whether CrO_4^{2-} or $HCrO_4^-$ predominates in acid solution.

$$2\,CrO_4^{2-} + 2\,H^+ \rightleftharpoons Cr_2O_7^{2-} + H_2O$$
$$K = 4.2 \times 10^{14}$$

$$Cr_2O_7^{2-} + H_2O \rightleftharpoons 2\,HCrO_4^-$$
$$K = 3 \times 10^{-2}$$

22

Note these incomplete half-reactions:

$$Cr_2O_7^{2-} \longrightarrow Cr^{3+} \qquad E° = 1.33 \text{ volts}$$
$$CrO_4^{2-} \longrightarrow Cr(OH)_3 \qquad E° = -0.13 \text{ volt}$$

Write balanced half-reactions, and decide whether you would use an acidic or a basic solution of Cr^{3+} to produce Br_2 from KBr solution.

23

Chromic oxide, Cr_2O_3, is used as a green pigment and is often made by the reaction between $Na_2Cr_2O_7$ and NH_4Cl to give Cr_2O_3, $NaCl$, N_2, and H_2O. Write a balanced equation, and calculate how much pigment can be made from 1.0×10^2 kg of sodium dichromate.

24

Write balanced equations to show the dissolving of $Cu(OH)_2(s)$ on the addition of $NH_3(aq)$, and also the reprecipitation caused by the addition of an acid.

25

Ferric ions form halogen complexes. Here are a few examples:

$$Fe^{3+} + \quad Cl^- \longrightarrow FeCl^{2+} \quad \text{(yellow)} \; K = 30$$
$$Fe^{3+} + \quad F^- \longrightarrow FeF^{2+} \quad \text{(yellow)} \; K = 10^5$$
$$Fe^{3+} + SCN^- \longrightarrow FeSCN^{2+} \quad \text{(red)} \; K = 2 \times 10^2$$

Explain why the fluoride ion causes the red color of $FeSCN^{2+}$ to fade, whereas the chloride ion does not.

26

Ferrous ion, iron(II), forms a complex with six cyanide ions, CN^-; the octahedral complex is called ferrocyanide. Ferric ion, iron(III), forms a complex with six cyanide ions; the octahedral complex is called ferricyanide. Write the structural formulas for the ferrocyanide and the ferricyanide complex ions.

27

Draw the different structures for an octahedral cobalt complex containing four NH_3 and two NO_2 groups.

28

Draw the structures of the following compounds:

$$Cr(NH_3)_6(SCN)_3$$
$$Cr(NH_3)_3(SCN)_3$$

(SCN^- is the thiocyanate ion.) Consider the oxidation number of chromium to be $+3$ and the coordination number to be 6 in both compounds. Estimate

(a) the solubility of these compounds in water
(b) their relative melting temperatures
(c) the relative conductivity of the liquid phases

29

Why is it NH_3 readily forms complexes but NH_4^+ does not?

30

Manganese(III), Mn^{3+}, spontaneously reacts with water to form Mn^{2+} and MnO_2. Balance the equation for the reaction which occurs in an aqueous solution.

31

Ferrous ions usually form octahedral complexes. For instance, in a water solution they are hydrated and symbolized $[Fe(H_2O)_6]^{2+}$. When this ion reacts with ethylene diamine (abbreviated "en"),

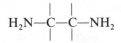

each nitrogen replaces a water molecule. Draw the structure for $[Fe(en)_3]^{2+}$.

32

$[Pt(NH_3)_2Br_2] [Pt(NH_3)_2Br_4]$ is a complex with a square planar cation and an octahedral anion. Find the total number of isomeric substances of this compound.

33

The ionic radii of Fe^{2+} and Fe^{3+} are 0.76 Å and 0.64 Å respectively. Explain why this is reasonable, and calculate the $Fe—Cl$ bond length in $[FeCl_6]^{4-}$ and Fe_2Cl_6.

34

Use the structure of $Cr_2O_7^{2-}$ to explain the structure of CrO_3 where there are infinite chains of tetrahedra. From your model of the chain, what kind of solid would CrO_3 form?

35

Suggest how three octahedra of a transition element, M, surrounded by six oxygen atoms might condense to form an ion. Assume that the octahedra share edges as $Cr_2O_7^{2-}$ shares corners of tetrahedra. Draw two possible combinations. Show that they are or are not isomers.

Appendices

443

1 Appendix

A DESCRIPTION OF A BURNING CANDLE

A drawing of a burning candle is shown[1] in the figure to the left. The candle is cylindrical[2] and has a diameter[3] of about $\frac{3}{4}$ inch. The length of the candle was initially about eight inches[4], and it changed slowly[5] during observation, decreasing about half an inch in one hour[6]. The candle is made of a translucent[7], white[8] solid[9] which has a slight odor[10] and no taste[11]. It is soft enough to be scratched with the fingernail[12]. There is a wick[13] which extends from top to bottom[14] of the candle along its central axis[15] and protrudes about half an inch above the top of the candle[16]. The wick is made of three strands of string braided together[17].

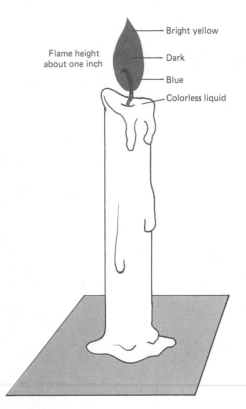

Flame height about one inch

Bright yellow

Dark

Blue

Colorless liquid

A candle is lit by holding a source of flame close to the wick for a few seconds. Thereafter the source of flame can be removed and the flame sustains itself at the wick[18]. The burning candle makes no sound[19]. While burning, the body of the candle remains cool to the touch[20] except near the top. Within about half an inch of the top the candle is warm[21] (but not hot) and sufficiently soft to mold easily[22]. The flame flickers in response to air currents[23] and tends to become quite smoky while flickering[24]. In the absence of air currents, the flame is of the form shown in the figure, though it retains some movement at all times[25]. The flame begins about $\frac{1}{8}$ inch above the top of the candle[26], and at its base the flame has a blue tint[27]. Immediately around the wick in a region about $\frac{1}{4}$ inch wide and extending about $\frac{1}{2}$ inch above the top of the wick[28] the flame is dark[29]. This dark region is roughly conical in shape[30]. Around this zone and extending about half an inch above the dark zone is a region which emits yellow light[31], bright but not blinding[32]. The flame has rather sharply defined sides[33] but a ragged top[34]. The wick is white where it emerges from the candle[35], but from the base of the flame to the end of the wick[36] it is black, appearing burnt, except for the last $\frac{1}{16}$ inch, where it glows red[37]. The wick curls over about $\frac{1}{4}$ inch from its end[38]. As the candle becomes shorter, the wick shortens too, so as to extend roughly a constant length above the top of the candle[39]. Heat is emitted by the flame[40], enough so that it becomes uncomfortable in 10 to 20 seconds if one holds his finger $\frac{1}{4}$ inch to the side of the quiet flame[41] or three or four inches above the flame[42].

The top of a quietly burning candle becomes wet with a color-less liquid[43] and becomes bowl shaped[44]. If the flame is blown, one side of this bowl-shaped top may become liquid, and the liquid trapped in the bowl may drain down the candle's side[45]. As it courses down, the colorless liquid cools[46], becomes trans-lucent[47], and gradually solidifies from the outside[48], attaching itself to the side of the candle[49]. In the absence of a draft, the candle can burn for hours without such dripping[50]. Under these conditions, a stable pool of clear liquid remains in the bowl-shaped top of the candle[51]. The liquid rises slightly around the wick[52], wetting the base of the wick as high as the base of the flame[53].

COMMENTS

Several aspects of this description deserve specific mention. Compare your own description in each of the following charac-teristics:

1. The description is comprehensive in *qualitative* terms. Did *you* include mention of appearance? Smell? Taste? Feel? Sound? (Note: A chemist quickly becomes reluctant to taste or smell an unknown chemical. A chemical should be con-sidered to be poisonous unless it is *known* not to be!)
2. Wherever possible, the description is stated *quantitatively*. This means the question "How much?" is answered (the quantity is specified). The remark that the flame emits yellow light is made more meaningful by the "how much" expression, "bright but not blinding." The statement that heat is emitted might lead a cautious investigator who is lighting a candle for the first time to stand in a concrete blockhouse one hun-dred yards away. The few words telling him "how much" heat would save him this overprecaution.
3. The description does not presume the importance of an observation. Thus the observation that a burning candle does not emit sound deserves to be mentioned just as much as the observation that it does emit light.
4. The description does not confuse observations with interpre-tations. It is an observation that the top of the burning candle is wet with a colorless liquid. It would be an interpretation to state the presumed composition of this liquid.

2 Appendix

NAMES, FORMULAS, AND CHARGES OF SOME COMMON IONS

POSITIVE IONS (CATIONS)		NEGATIVE IONS (ANIONS)	
aluminum	Al^{3+}	acetate	CH_3COO^-
ammonium	NH_4^+	bromide	Br^-
barium	Ba^{2+}	carbonate	CO_3^{2-}
cadmium	Cd^{2+}	hydrogen carbonate, bicarbonate	HCO_3^-
calcium	Ca^{2+}	chlorate	ClO_3^-
chromium(II),* chromous	Cr^{2+}	chloride	Cl^-
chromium(III), chromic	Cr^{3+}	chlorite	ClO_2^-
cobalt	Co^{2+}	chromate	CrO_4^{2-}
copper(I),* cuprous	Cu^+	dichromate	$Cr_2O_7^{2-}$
copper(II), cupric	Cu^{2+}	fluoride	F^-
hydrogen, hydronium	H^+, H_3O^+	hydroxide	OH^-
iron(II),* ferrous	Fe^{2+}	hypochlorite	ClO^-
iron(III), ferric	Fe^{3+}	iodide	I^-
lead	Pb^{2+}	nitrate	NO_3^-
lithium	Li^+	nitrite	NO_2^-
magnesium	Mg^{2+}	oxalate	$C_2O_4^{2-}$
manganese(II), manganous	Mn^{2+}	hydrogen oxalate, binoxalate	$HC_2O_4^-$
mercury(I),* mercurous	Hg_2^{2+}	perchlorate	ClO_4^-
mercury(II), mercuric	Hg^{2+}	permanganate	MnO_4^-
nickel	Ni^{2+}	phosphate	PO_4^{3-}
potassium	K^+	monohydrogen phosphate	HPO_4^{2-}
scandium	Sc^{3+}	dihydrogen phosphate	$H_2PO_4^-$
silver	Ag^+	sulfate	SO_4^{2-}
sodium	Na^+	hydrogen sulfate, bisulfate	HSO_4^-
strontium	Sr^{2+}	sulfide	S^{2-}
tin(II),* stannous	Sn^{2+}	hydrogen sulfide, bisulfide	HS^-
tin(IV), stannic	Sn^{4+}	sulfite	SO_3^{2-}
zinc	Zn^{2+}	hydrogen sulfite, bisulfite	HSO_3^-

*Aqueous solutions are readily oxidized by air.
Note: In ionic compounds the relative number of positive and negative ions is such that the sum of their electric charges is zero.

Appendix

RELATIVE STRENGTHS OF ACIDS IN AQUEOUS SOLUTION AT ROOM TEMPERATURE
All ions are aquated

$$HB \rightleftharpoons H^+(aq) + B^-(aq) \qquad K_A = \frac{[H^+][B^-]}{[HB]}$$

ACID	STRENGTH	REACTION	K_A
perchloric acid	very strong	$HClO_4 \longrightarrow H^+ + ClO_4^-$	very large
hydroiodic acid		$HI \longrightarrow H^+ + I^-$	very large
hydrobromic acid		$HBr \longrightarrow H^+ + Br^-$	very large
hydrochloric acid		$HCl \longrightarrow H^+ + Cl^-$	very large
nitric acid		$HNO_3 \longrightarrow H^+ + NO_3^-$	very large
sulfuric acid	very strong	$H_2SO_4 \longrightarrow H^+ + HSO_4^-$	large
orange IV		$H(Ind) \longrightarrow H^+ + Ind^-$	$\sim 10^{-2}$
oxalic acid		$HOOCCOOH \longrightarrow H^+ + HOOCCOO^-$	5.4×10^{-2}
sulfurous acid ($SO_2(g) + H_2O$)		$H_2SO_3 \longrightarrow H^+ + HSO_3^-$	1.7×10^{-2}
hydrogen sulfate ion	strong	$HSO_4^- \longrightarrow H^+ + SO_4^{2-}$	1.3×10^{-2}
phosphoric acid		$H_3PO_4 \longrightarrow H^+ + H_2PO_4^-$	7.1×10^{-3}
ferric ion		$Fe(H_2O)_6^{3+} \longrightarrow H^+ + Fe(H_2O)_5(OH)^{2+}$	6×10^{-3}
hydrogen telluride		$H_2Te \longrightarrow H^+ + HTe^-$	2.3×10^{-3}
methyl orange		$H(Ind) \longrightarrow H^+ + Ind^-$	$\sim 10^{-4}$
hydrofluoric acid	weak	$HF \longrightarrow H^+ + F^-$	6.7×10^{-4}
nitrous acid		$HNO_2 \longrightarrow H^+ + NO_2^-$	5.1×10^{-4}
hydrogen selenide		$H_2Se \longrightarrow H^+ + HSe^-$	1.7×10^{-4}
chromic ion		$Cr(H_2O)_6^{3+} \longrightarrow H^+ + Cr(H_2O)_5(OH)^{2+}$	10^{-4}
benzoic acid		$C_6H_5COOH \longrightarrow H^+ + C_6H_5COO^-$	6.6×10^{-5}
hydrogen oxalate ion		$HOOCCOO^- \longrightarrow H^+ + OOCCOO^{2-}$	5.4×10^{-5}
acetic acid	weak	$CH_3COOH \longrightarrow H^+ + CH_3COO^-$	1.8×10^{-5}
aluminum ion		$Al(H_2O)_6^{3+} \longrightarrow H^+ + Al(H_2O)_5(OH)^{2+}$	10^{-5}
carbonic acid ($CO_2(g) + H_2O$)		$H_2CO_3 \longrightarrow H^+ + HCO_3^-$	4.4×10^{-7}
hydrogen sulfide		$H_2S \longrightarrow H^+ + HS^-$	1.0×10^{-7}
dihydrogen phosphate ion		$H_2PO_4^- \longrightarrow H^+ + HPO_4^{2-}$	6.3×10^{-8}
hydrogen sulfite ion		$HSO_3^- \longrightarrow H^+ + SO_3^{2-}$	6.2×10^{-8}
phenolphthalein		$H(Ind) \longrightarrow H^+ + Ind^-$	$\sim 10^{-9}$
alizarin yellow R	weak	$H(Ind) \longrightarrow H^+ + Ind^-$	$\sim 10^{-10}$
ammonium ion		$NH_4^+ \longrightarrow H^+ + NH_3$	5.7×10^{-10}
hydrogen telluride ion		$HTe^- \longrightarrow H^+ + Te^{2-}$	10^{-11}
hydrogen carbonate ion		$HCO_3^- \longrightarrow H^+ + CO_3^{2-}$	4.7×10^{-11}
indigo carmine		$H(Ind) \longrightarrow H^+ + Ind^-$	$\sim 10^{-12}$
hydrogen peroxide	very weak	$H_2O_2 \longrightarrow H^+ + HO_2^-$	2.4×10^{-12}
monohydrogen phosphate ion		$HPO_4^{2-} \longrightarrow H^+ + PO_4^{3-}$	4.4×10^{-13}
hydrogen sulfide ion		$HS^- \longrightarrow H^+ + S^{2-}$	1.3×10^{-13}
water		$H_2O \longrightarrow H^+ + OH^-$	1.8×10^{-16}*
hydroxide ion		$OH^- \longrightarrow H^+ + O^{2-}$	$< 10^{-36}$
ammonia	very weak	$NH_3 \longrightarrow H^+ + NH_2^-$	very small

*$K_w = K_A(55.5) = 1.0 \times 10^{-14}$

4 Appendix

STANDARD REDUCTION POTENTIALS FOR HALF-REACTIONS
IONIC CONCENTRATIONS, 1 M IN WATER AT 25 °C

All ions are aquated

	HALF-REACTION		$E°$ (volts)	
Very strong oxidizing agents ↑ Oxidizing strength increases	$F_2(g)$	$+ 2\,e^- \longrightarrow 2\,F^-$	$+2.87$	**Very weak reducing agents**
	$H_2O_2 + 2\,H^+$	$+ 2\,e^- \longrightarrow 2\,H_2O$	$+1.77$	
	$4\,H^+ + SO_4^{2-} + PbO_2$	$+ 2\,e^- \longrightarrow PbSO_4 + 2\,H_2O$	$+1.68$	
	$MnO_4^- + 8\,H^+$	$+ 5\,e^- \longrightarrow Mn^{2+} + 4\,H_2O$	$+1.52$	
	Au^{3+}	$+ 3\,e^- \longrightarrow Au$	$+1.50$	
	$Cl_2(g)$	$+ 2\,e^- \longrightarrow 2\,Cl^-$	$+1.36$	
	$Cr_2O_7^{2-} + 14\,H^+$	$+ 6\,e^- \longrightarrow 2\,Cr^{3+} + 7\,H_2O$	$+1.33$	
	$MnO_2 + 4\,H^+$	$+ 2\,e^- \longrightarrow Mn^{2+} + 2\,H_2O$	$+1.28$	
	$\frac{1}{2}\,O_2(g) + 2\,H^+$	$+ 2\,e^- \longrightarrow H_2O$	$+1.23$	
	$Br_2(l)$	$+ 2\,e^- \longrightarrow 2\,Br^-$	$+1.06$	
	$AuCl_4^-$	$+ 3\,e^- \longrightarrow Au + 4Cl^-$	$+1.00$	Reducing strength increases ↓
	$NO_3^- + 4\,H^+$	$+ 3\,e^- \longrightarrow NO(g) + 2\,H_2O$	$+0.96$	
	$\frac{1}{2}\,O_2(g) + 2\,H^+(10^{-7}\,M)$	$+ 2\,e^- \longrightarrow H_2O$	$+0.81$	
	Ag^+	$+ \ e^- \longrightarrow Ag$	$+0.80$	
	$\frac{1}{2}\,Hg_2^{2+}$	$+ \ e^- \longrightarrow Hg(l)$	$+0.79$	
	Hg^{2+}	$+ 2\,e^- \longrightarrow Hg(l)$	$+0.78$	
	$NO_3^- + 2\,H^+$	$+ \ e^- \longrightarrow NO_2(g) + H_2O$	$+0.78$	
	Fe^{3+}	$+ \ e^- \longrightarrow Fe^{2+}$	$+0.77$	
	$O_2(g) + 2\,H^+$	$+ 2\,e^- \longrightarrow H_2O_2$	$+0.68$	
	I_2	$+ 2\,e^- \longrightarrow 2\,I^-$	$+0.53$	
	Cu^+	$+ \ e^- \longrightarrow Cu$	$+0.52$	
	Cu^{2+}	$+ 2\,e^- \longrightarrow Cu$	$+0.34$	
	$SO_4^{2-} + 4\,H^+$	$+ 2\,e^- \longrightarrow SO_2(g) + 2\,H_2O$	$+0.17$	
	Cu^{2+}	$+ \ e^- \longrightarrow Cu^+$	$+0.15$	
	Sn^{4+}	$+ 2\,e^- \longrightarrow Sn^{2+}$	$+0.15$	
	$\frac{1}{8}\,S_8 + 2\,H^+$	$+ 2\,e^- \longrightarrow H_2S(g)$	$+0.14$	
	$2\,H^+$	$+ 2\,e^- \longrightarrow H_2(g)$	0.00	
	Pb^{2+}	$+ 2\,e^- \longrightarrow Pb$	-0.13	
	Sn^{2+}	$+ 2\,e^- \longrightarrow Sn$	-0.14	
	Ni^{2+}	$+ 2\,e^- \longrightarrow Ni$	-0.25	

HALF-REACTION			$E°$ (volts)
Co^{2+}	$+ 2\,e^-$	$\longrightarrow Co$	-0.28
$PbSO_4$	$+ 2\,e^-$	$\longrightarrow Pb + SO_4^{2-}$	-0.36
$\frac{1}{8} Se_8 + 2\,H^+$	$+ 2\,e^-$	$\longrightarrow H_2Se$	-0.40
Cr^{3+}	$+ \quad e^-$	$\longrightarrow Cr^{2+}$	-0.41
$2\,H^+(10^{-7}\,M)$	$+ 2\,e^-$	$\longrightarrow H_2(g)$	-0.41
Fe^{2+}	$+ 2\,e^-$	$\longrightarrow Fe$	-0.44
Ag_2S	$+ 2\,e^-$	$\longrightarrow 2\,Ag + S^{2-}$	-0.69
$\frac{1}{8} Te_8 + 2\,H^+$	$+ 2\,e^-$	$\longrightarrow H_2Te$	-0.72
Cr^{3+}	$+ 3\,e^-$	$\longrightarrow Cr$	-0.74
Zn^{2+}	$+ 2\,e^-$	$\longrightarrow Zn$	-0.76
$2\,H_2O$	$+ 2\,e^-$	$\longrightarrow H_2(g) + 2\,OH^-$	-0.83
Mn^{2+}	$+ 2\,e^-$	$\longrightarrow Mn$	-1.18
Al^{3+}	$+ 3\,e^-$	$\longrightarrow Al$	-1.66
Ti^{2+}	$+ 2\,e^-$	$\longrightarrow Ti$	-1.75
Mg^{2+}	$+ 2\,e^-$	$\longrightarrow Mg$	-2.37
Na^+	$+ \quad e^-$	$\longrightarrow Na$	-2.71
Ca^{2+}	$+ 2\,e^-$	$\longrightarrow Ca$	-2.87
Sr^{2+}	$+ 2\,e^-$	$\longrightarrow Sr$	-2.89
Ba^{2+}	$+ 2\,e^-$	$\longrightarrow Ba$	-2.90
Cs^+	$+ \quad e^-$	$\longrightarrow Cs$	-2.92
K^+	$+ \quad e^-$	$\longrightarrow K$	-2.92
Rb^+	$+ \quad e^-$	$\longrightarrow Rb$	-2.92
Li^+	$+ \quad e^-$	$\longrightarrow Li$	-3.00

Oxidizing strength increases

Very weak oxidizing agents

Reducing strength increases

Very strong reducing agents

Symbols and Abbreviations

Page numbers refer to the first reference. See inside front cover for symbols for elements.

A	mass number, 150	Ox. no.	oxidation number, 339
Å	angstrom, 10^{-8} cm, 167	p	type of orbital, 174
(aq)	indicates an ion is aquated, 108	p or p^+	proton, 107
atm	atmosphere (pressure unit), 10	$\bar{p}$	partial pressure, 66
°C	Celsius degree, 10	P	pressure, 16
e	charge on electron, 142	PE	potential energy, 85
e^-	electron, 107	R	general alkyl group, 361
$E°$	electrical potential, 322	s	type of orbital, 174
(g)	indicates gas phase, 89	(s)	indicates solid phase, 87
h	Planck's constant, 166	STP	standard temperature and pressure (0°C and 1 atm), 10
IE	ionization energy, 185		
K	Kelvin, or absolute degree, 70	t	temperature, °C, 15
K	equilibrium constant, 276	T	temperature, K, 70
K_A	equilibrium constant for acid ionization, 300	$T_{1/2}$	half-life, 153
K_{sp}	solubility product, 278	V	volume, 16
K_w	[H⁺] [OH⁻], ion product of water, 277	Δ (delta)	change, 19
KE	kinetic energy, 73	λ (lambda)	wavelength, 164
(l)	indicates liquid phase, 87	ν (nu)	frequency, 164
m	mass of the electron, 142	α (alpha)	particles, He²⁺, 152
M	molarity, moles/liter, 102	β or β^- (beta)	particles, e^-, 152
n	neutron, 155	γ (gamma)	radiation, 152
n	principal quantum number, 172	◯	empty orbital, 178
N	Avogadro's number, particles/mole, 6.0×10^{23}, 40	⊘ ⊘	half-filled orbitals, 178
		⊗	filled orbital, 178
		[ ]	concentration, moles/liter, 274

Answers to Exercises and Some Problems

This appendix gives answers for the exercises and most of the odd-numbered problems.

CHAPTER 1

Exercise
1. 135 g/cm²
2. (a) 0.470, (b) 1.76, (c) 3.06, (d) 0.004 96, (e) 10 000, (f) 24 800 000
3. 66 ml
4. 1.80 g/ml

Problem
1. Route, speed, weather, load, mechanical condition
5. (a) When x grams of candle burn, y calories are released.
   (b) When x grams of aluminum react with y grams of copper chloride in z grams of water, the temperature rises by t degrees Celsius.
   (c) When 1 Alka-Seltzer tablet reacts with 1 glass of water, x ml of gas forms.
9. They are the squares of the first five odd integers— Number $= n^2$.
11. (a) They are 1 greater than the square of integer—Number $= n^2 + 1$.
    (b) 100 does not fit, 226 does $= (15)^2 + 1$.
13. (a) The column will tilt but show the same height difference.
    (b) The height difference will decrease.
    (c) The height difference will increase.
17. Man's shoe $\dfrac{120 \text{ lb}}{10 \text{ in}^2} = 12 \text{ lb/in}^2$

    Woman's shoe $\dfrac{120 \text{ lb}}{0.5 \text{ in}^2} = 240 \text{ lb/in}^2$
21. Item cost and the number you can buy with a fixed amount of money
25. (a) Car odometer
    (b) Surveying equipment or aerial photo
27. (a) 41.6, (b) 21, (c) 0.02
29. (a) Density $= \dfrac{497 \text{ g}}{(6.50)(2.30)(12.30)\text{cm}^3} = \dfrac{497}{184}$
    $= 2.70 \text{ g/cm}^3$
    (b) 313 g
31. 11.2 g/12.6 ml $= 0.892$ g/ml
33. 4.76 ml
35. No. Should weigh 27.5 g in water if solid, pure gold.
37. Volume $= 12.6$ ml; density $= 2.70$ g/ml.

CHAPTER 2

Exercise
1. 36.5 g
2. 20.2
5. CS_2, SO_2, SO_3
6. 5.3×10^{-17} g
8. Molar mass $S_8 = 257$ g, $NH_3 = 17.03$ g, $N_2 = 28.02$ g
9. 28.0 g
10. 1.8×10^{22} atoms in 1.67 g iron

11. Follow calculations in book.
12. Follow calculations in book.
13. NH_2, N_2H_4

Problem
1. Sell at a pressure lower by 2½ or more.
3. 3, 2, NH_3
5. Compound. Clearly, more than one substance came out of it.
7. (a) Hydrogen, oxygen
   (b) Iron, oxygen
   (c) Tungsten
   (d) Lead, carbon, hydrogen
   (e) Sodium, hydrogen, carbon, oxygen
   (f), (g) Carbon, hydrogen
9. Hydrogen
11. (a) HCl (f) SF_6
    (b) SCl_2 (g) N_2S_5
    (c) NF_3 (h) CS_2
    (d) AlF_3 (i) PCl_5
    (e) N_2F_2 (j) $ZnCl_2$
13. 6.0×10^{23} particles
15. 1500×10^9 \$/person
17. 1.3×10^{-6} sq in./person
19. (a) 3.0×10^{-23} g
    (b) 5.3×10^{-23} g
    (c) 0.17×10^{-23} g
    (d) 40×10^{-23} g
    (e) 18×10^{-23} g
    (f) 33×10^{-23} g
22. Molar mass: $SiF_4 = 104.1$ g, $HF = 20.0$ g, $Cl_2 = 71.0$ g, $Xe = 131.3$ g, $NO_2 = 46.0$ g
23. (a) CS_2, 76.2 g   (c) NCl_3, 120.5 g
    (b) SF_6, 146.1 g   (d) OsO_4, 254.2 g
25. (d) 88.0 g
29. 0.14 mole Cl_2, 0.097 mole SCl_2
31. 0.53 mole H_3PO_4
33. 10 moles of stones
35. 2.3×10^{-12} g
37. SO_2, SO_3
39. WC, W_2C

CHAPTER 3

Exercise
1. 10 molecules form, 5 oxygen molecules left
2. 2 million molecules form, 2 million hydrogen molecules consumed
3. 680 kcal, 6.8 kcal
6. Molar mass of paraffin $= 352.7$ g; we have 0.100 mole, requiring
   $38 \times 0.100 = 3.8$ moles O_2
7. 3.00 moles O_2
8. $3 \text{ Fe} + 2O_2 \longrightarrow Fe_3O_4$
   0.0067 mole O_2, 0.77 g Fe_3O_4

Problem
1. 2 g
3. (a) 2 molecules of NO_2
   (b) 4 moles of NO
   (c) 2 moles of oxygen atoms
   (d) 2 moles of oxygen atoms

(e)   4 moles of oxygen atoms
(f) $2 + 2 = 4$
5.   The coefficients, in order, are
(a)-(c) 2   1   2
(d)   1   ½   1
(e)   1   2   2
(f)   ½   1   1
7.   (a)   1 mole of N_2
(b)   22 kcal
(c)   66 kcal
(d)   34.07 g in two moles NH_3
Same as sum of 1 mole N_2 and 3 moles H_2
9.   (a) $S_8 + 8 O_2 \longrightarrow 8 SO_2$
(b)   One molecule of sulfur reacts with 8 molecules of O_2 to form 8 molecules of SO_2.
(c)   16 moles
11.   (a) $2 NaCl \longrightarrow 2 Na + Cl_2$
(b) 1.65×10^6 g NaCl needed
(c) 1.00×10^3 kg Cl_2 produced
13.   (a) $TiCl_4 + 2 Mg \longrightarrow Ti + 2 MgCl_2$
(b)   1000 g Mg required
15.   (a) $Fe + CuSO_4 \longrightarrow Cu + FeSO_4$
(b)   0.044 mole Cu
(c)   2.79 g Cu
17. $2 NH_3 + 22 \text{ kcal} \longrightarrow N_2 + 3 H_2$
$2 NF_3 + 54 \text{ kcal} \longrightarrow N_2 + 3 F_2$
$2 NCl_3 \longrightarrow N_2 + 3 Cl_2 + 109 \text{ kcal}$
NCl_3 is most likely to be explosive because of the
large heat release. It *is* explosive and very dangerous.
19.   (a) $CuSO_4 \cdot 5 H_2O \longrightarrow CuSO_4 + 5 H_2O$
(b)   1.80 g H_2O formed
(c)   13.9 g $CuSO_4 \cdot 5 H_2O$
21.   (a)   321 kg S_8 required
(b)   641 kg SO_2 needed
(c)   321 kg S_8 required
23.   (a) $CH_4 + 2 O_2 \longrightarrow CO_2 + 2 H_2O$
(b)   1 mole CH_4 produces 2 moles H_2O
(c)   0.50 mole H_2O produced
25.   (a) 3.1×10^2 moles O_2
(b)   200 moles, 8800 g, 8.8 kg
(c)   194 lbs, 88 kg
27.   (a)   42.0 g HNO_3
(b)   21.0 g more could be formed.
29.   (a)   1170 g NaCl used.
(b)   1060 g Na_2CO_3 made.
31. 2.12×10^3 g H_2O_2

CHAPTER 4

Exercise
1.   740 mmHg
2.   (a)   298 K   (d)   90 K
(b)   373 K   (e)   234 K
(c)   77 K   (f)   408 K
3.   An NH_3 molecule is lighter than an HCl molecule.
Therefore it must go faster to give the same $\frac{1}{2} mv^2$
value.
4.   The gas molecules are farther apart.

Problem
1.   729 mmHg
5.   1 atm
7.   7.50 liters
9. 6.0×10^{23}

11.   (a)   0.76 kg CO
(b) 6.0×10^2 liters CO
13.   22 liters
15.   (a)   32.7 g Zn
(b)   13.8 liters
(c)   same as (a)
17.   Molar volume at Earth conditions, 24.3 liters; at
Mars conditions, 3900 liters.
19.   0.78 mole O_2 remain
21.   (a)   greater
(b)
23.   44.8 g
25.   Volume and pressure vary directly with temperature in kelvins.
27.   (c)   103 ml
31.   Venus 62 liters, Jupiter 10 liters.
33.   The second one; 0.042 mole vs. 0.037 mole.
35.   As temperature goes up, K.E. increases, tire volume is constant so pressure goes up.
37.   (c)   Pressure drops to 380 mmHg.

CHAPTER 5

Exercise
2. 7×10^{18} molecules evaporate/sec
3.   Estimated b.t. of ethanol, 76 °C

Problem
1.   (a)   At the top of the flight
(b)   At the start of the flight
(c)   At the end of the flight
(d)   At the top of the flight
5.   The atoms or molecules change position relative
to each other. This gives a potential energy
change.
7.   1750 cal lost; 1300 cal gained. The difference is
the heat lost to surroundings.
9.   43 kcal
11.   (a)   0 °C
(b)   It goes to melt some ice.
(c)   1.6 kcal given up
13.   (a)   100 g
(b)   8 kcal
(c)   0.08 kcal/g ice melted
(d)   1.4 kcal/mol
17.   The gas
19.   Decomposing the water
21.   Evaporation
23.   (a)   0–100 °C
(b)   80 kcal/kg
(c)   538 kcal/kg
25.   (a)   13.2 moles benzene, 10 moles H_2O. Therefore heat of vaporization of benzene is less
than that of water.
(b)   7.3 kcal/mol benzene
27.   Plot heat *vs.* b.t. Get a fair, straight line.
28.   Soldering, casting jewelry or lead soldiers, car-
buretion of gasoline, glass blowing, wax melting.
31.   The atmospheric pressure is lower.
33.   (a)   55 mmHg
(b)   No effect
(c)   No effect
35.   Same
37.   Low-pressure evaporation occurs at low temperature.

CHAPTER 6

Exercise
1. 170 g
2. 34 g
3. 0.10 mole could make 0.10 l of 1 M solution.
4. $Ca \longrightarrow Ca^{2+} + 2\,e^-$
5. $Na_2SO_4 \longrightarrow 2\,Na^+ + SO_4{}^{2-}$
   $NH_4Cl \longrightarrow NH_4{}^+ + Cl^-$
   $(NH_4)_2CO_3 \longrightarrow NH_4{}^+ + CO_3{}^{2-}$
   $NaHCO_3 \longrightarrow Na^+ + HCO_3{}^-$
   $CuCl_2 \longrightarrow Cu^{2+} + 2\,Cl^-$

Problem
1. Concrete, wood
3. (e)
5. Yes. The ice is essentially pure water, so the salt is concentrated by the freezing.
7. (a), (b), (d), (e)
9. 64 g, 2.4×10^{24} molecules
11. 0.800 liter
13. Dissolve 5.7 g Na_2SO_4 in enough water to make 1.00×10^3 ml solution.
15. 0.400M
17. 1.53×10^{-4}M
19. Color, conductivity, density, boiling temp., freezing temp., viscosity and chemical reactivity.
21. This is an unexplained fundamental property.
23. (a) Yes, the smallest. All others are divisible by it a whole number of times.
    (b) The given data do not need 0.81×10^{-19} coulomb as the unit charge.
25. There are 10 e^- in F^-. $F_2 + 2\,e^- \longrightarrow 2\,F^-$. There are 2 negative charges on each side.
27. (a) $(NH_4)_2SO_4(s) \rightleftharpoons 2\,NH_4{}^+(aq) + SO_4{}^{2-}(aq)$
    (b) Zero charge on reactants. Two + and 2 − give zero net charge.
    (c) Concentration of $NH_4{}^+$ is 0.0400M and of $SO_4{}^{2-}$ is 0.0200M
29. (a) H^+, I^-
    (b) Ca^{2+}, Cl^-
    (c) Na^+, $CO_3{}^{2-}$
    (d) Ba^{2+}, OH^-
    (e) K^+, $NO_3{}^-$
    (f) $NH_4{}^+$, Cl^-
31. The ions and molarities are: (Cl^-, 0.535), (Na^+, 0.435), (Mg^{2+}, 0.0494).
33. H^+
35. Evaporate enough solvent or reduce the temperature or dissolve more solute.
37. $Os(IO_3)_2$
39. A precipitate of $MgSO_3$ would form.
    $Mg^{2+}(aq) + SO_3{}^{2-}(aq) \longrightarrow MgSO_3(s)$

CHAPTER 7

Exercise
1. $Cl_2 + 2\,Li \longrightarrow 2\,LiCl$, similar for K, Rb, Cs
2. $2\,Li + 2\,H_2O \longrightarrow 2\,Li^+ + 2\,OH^- + H_2$, similar for K, Rb, Cs
3. $2\,Li + F_2 \longrightarrow 2\,LiF$, similar for Cl_2, Br_2, I_2, At_2

Problem
1. (a) $SbBr_3$ (b) In_2S_3 (c) TeO

3.
	x	y
(a)	1	3
(b)	1	1
(c)	1	2
(d)	3	2

5. We could not find any. Did you?
7. The determinations of molar mass were so poor, the regularity seemed true.
9. (a) SrS   (d) ICl
   (b) GaF_3 (e) $AsBr_3$
   (c) BeTe
11. Plot values and predict Nb 135-145, Ru 125-130, Pd 75-90 kcal/mol. Actual values 166, 136, 90.
13. Plot density $vs.$ molar mass or atomic number. 11 g/ml estimate, actual value 11.3 g/ml.
15. Both properties increase. Attractive forces are increasing.
19. As you go down a column, boiling temperature and melting temperature increase; ionization energy goes down for both series of elements.
21. $M + X_2 \longrightarrow MX_2$
23. (d)
25. 810–820 °C.
29. Mo is a high melting metal.
31. Will concentrate in the bones and increase the dose of radioactivity.
33. $2F_2 + 2H_2O \longrightarrow O_2 + 4HF$

CHAPTER 8

Exercise
1. $\dfrac{1.008 \text{ g/mol H}}{5.5 \times 10^{-4} \text{ g/mol } e^-} = 1800$
2. $^{16}_{6}O$ $^{17}_{6}O$ $^{18}_{8}O$
3.
^{235}U	92 protons	143 neutrons	235
^{238}U	92 protons	146 neutrons	238
^{239}U	92 protons	147 neutrons	239
^{233}U	92 protons	141 neutrons	233

Problem
1. 2.7×10^{17} molecules/cm³ when glow starts
   2.7×10^{13} molecules/cm³ when glow stops
3. 96,000 coulombs/mole
5. Another pair of electrodes perpendicular to the first pair, and variable voltage on each.
7. No to both. The masses are different for F, Cl, and e^-.
8. 3.8×10^4 coulombs/cm³
9. 0.7×10^{-5} nucleus/atom ratio or 1.5×10^5 atom/nucleus ratio
13. 10^{15} = atomic volume/nuclear volume
17. More, because of the greater positive charge on the nucleus.
19. CCl_4 or $TiCl_3$
23. 3p, 4n, 3e⁻
25. Differ in mass and number of neutrons. They have the same number of p^+ and e^-, and their chemical behaviors are the same.
29. $^{35}_{16}S$. The other is too short-lived.
31. (a) $^{253}_{98}Cf \longrightarrow ^{253}_{99}Es + ^{0}_{-1}e$
    (b) $^{253}_{100}Fm \longrightarrow ^{249}_{98}Cf + ^{4}_{2}He$
    (c) $^{120}_{51}Sb \longrightarrow ^{120}_{50}Sn + ^{0}_{+1}e$
33. 1.5%
35. $^{86}_{33}As$
37. $^{93}_{41}Nb + ^{4}_{2}He \longrightarrow ^{96}_{43}Tc + ^{1}_{0}n$

CHAPTER 9

Exercise

3. 43.6, 58.8, 65.9 kcal/mol, etc.
   13.2, 22.2 kcal/mol, etc., Infrared.
4. The atom or ion has 9 electrons located 2 each in the $1s$ and $2s$ orbitals plus 5 in $2p$ orbitals.
5. Al $1s^2$ $2s^2$ $2p^6$ $\qquad$ $3s^23p$
   B $1s^2$ $\qquad$ $2s^22p$
   Ga $1s^2$ $2s^2$ $2p^6$ $3s^23p^63d^{10}$ $4s^24p$

Problem

3. AM 3.0×10^4 cm/cycle, FM 3.0×10^2 cm/cycle
5. $(n-1)n^2$
7. $(n-1)(n-2)(n-3)$
9. $\nu = 4.92 \times 10^{14}$ cycles/sec; visible
11. Make step sizes, reading from bottom:
    1, 2, 4 1, 4, 2 2, 1, 4 2, 4, 1 4, 1, 2 4, 2, 1
    Then only these combinations are possible:
    1, 2, 3, 4, 6, 7 1, 2, 4, 5, 6, 7 1, 2, 3, 4, 5, 7
15. There is the same probability for an electron to be found at any particular spot on that surface.
17. Advantages: Model is cheap and easy to get.
    Disadvantages: Is not zero at origin, shows boundary to probability distribution, appears empty inside and out, but probability is not the same inside and out.
19. (d)
21. (c)
23. He, Li, B, N, K
25. (a) $1s^2$ $\quad$ $2s^22p^5$
    (b) $1s^2$ $\quad$ $2s^22p^6$ $\quad$ $3s^23p^1$
    (c) $1s^2$ $\quad$ $2s^22p^6$ $\quad$ $3s^23p^6$ $\quad$ $4s^2$
    (d) $1s^2$ $\quad$ $2s^22p^3$
27. (a) Mg $\qquad$ (d) Cl
    (b) Te $\qquad$ (e) Sc
    (c) Ne $\qquad$ (f) Ba
29. It is one of the elements from Al to Ar.
31. (c)
33. C $\quad$ $1s^2$ $\quad$ $2s^22p^2$ $\qquad$ 4 valence e^-
    Si $\quad$ $1s^2$ $\quad$ $2s^22p^6$ $\quad$ $3s^23p^2$ $\quad$ 4 valence e^-
    P $\quad$ $1s^2$ $\quad$ $2s^22p^6$ $\quad$ $3s^23p^3$ $\quad$ 5 valence e^-
    H $\quad$ $1s^1$ $\qquad$ 1 valence e^-
37. Ca $\quad$ IE$_3$ $\quad$ 1200–1400 kcal/mol
    Sr $\quad$ IE$_2$ $\quad$ 260 kcal/mol
    Ba $\quad$ IE$_1$ $\quad$ 120 kcal/mol I E$_2$ 250 kcal/mol
    Ra $\quad$ IE$_1$ $\quad$ 100 kcal/mol I E$_2$ 200 kcal/mol
39. TlBr, TlBr$_2$, TlBr$_3$
41. Similarities: electromagnetic waves, contain energy, not visible
    Differences: X rays can penetrate farther; X rays have higher energy and shorter wave length.

CHAPTER 10

Exercise

1. Al $1s^2$ $2s^22p^6$ $3s^23p^1$,
   Al^{3+}, Al_2O_3

2.

Expect the first two to be very reactive. They each have an unpaired electron, thus more bonding capacity.

3. 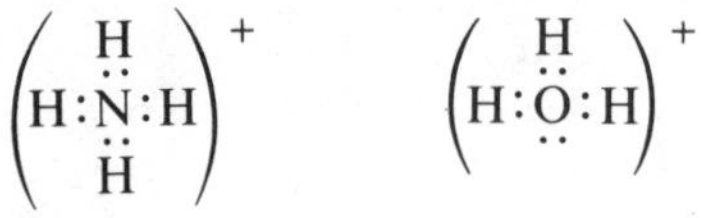 $\left(\text{H:N:H} \atop \text{H H} \right)^+$ $\qquad$ $\left(\text{H:O:H} \atop \text{H} \right)^+$

4. 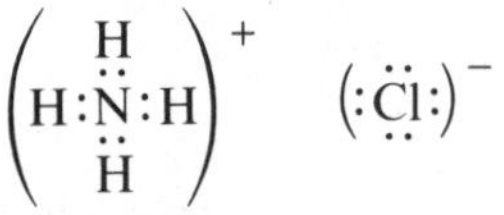 $\left(\text{H:N:H} \atop \text{H} \right)^+$ $\qquad$ $(:\ddot{C}l:)^-$

5. 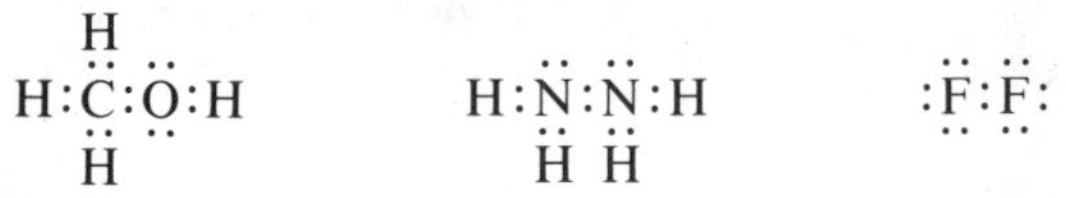 H:C:O:H $\qquad$ H:N:N:H $\qquad$:F:F:
   (with H below C) $\qquad$ (H H below)

6. Three $\quad$ $H_3C-CH_2-CH_2-CH_2-CH_3$

   $H_3C-CH_2-CH-CH_3$
   $\qquad\qquad\qquad |$
   $\qquad\qquad\quad CH_3$

   $\qquad\quad CH_3$
   $\qquad\qquad |$
   CH_3-C-CH_3
   $\qquad\qquad |$
   $\qquad\quad CH_3$

7. Each has progressively more electrons attracting the two nuclei.

Problem

1. (c) and (e)
3. Li with $3e^-$ loses one to become Li^+.
   F with $9e^-$ gains one to become F^-.
5. (a) Al_2S_3
   (b) Mg_3N_2
   (c) $BaAt_2$
   (d) Fr_2O
   (e) RaI_2
7. Check ionization energies. The two elements Mg and O are quite different. Ionic bonding likely.
9. Any bonding needs lower energy after bond forms, available valence e^-, and partially filled valence orbitals. In addition
   (a) covalent—nearly the same ionization energy.
   (b) ionic—quite different ionization energies.
11. Valence electrons must be available. Partially filled or vacant valence orbital must be available.

13. 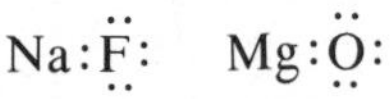 Na:F: $\quad$ Mg:O:

    MgO should melt higher, double charges attracting the two ions.

15. 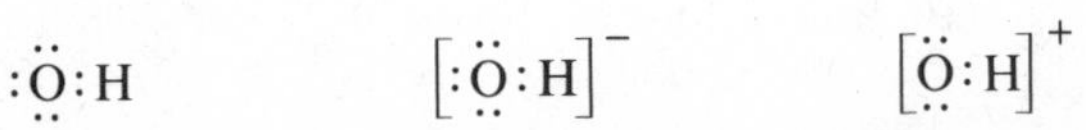 :O:H $\qquad$ $[:O:H]^-$ $\qquad$ $[O:H]^+$

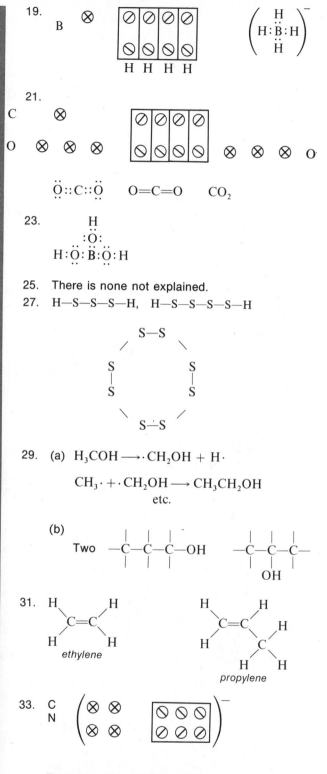

19. B
$$\left(H:\overset{\cdot\cdot}{\underset{\cdot\cdot}{B}}:H \right)^{-}$$
with H, H, and H arranged around B

21. C, O
$$\overset{\cdot\cdot}{O}::C::\overset{\cdot\cdot}{O} \qquad O=C=O \qquad CO_2$$

23.
$$H$$
$$:\overset{\cdot\cdot}{O}:$$
$$H:\overset{\cdot\cdot}{O}:\overset{\cdot\cdot}{B}:\overset{\cdot\cdot}{O}:H$$

25. There is none not explained.

27. H—S—S—S—H,   H—S—S—S—S—H

Ring of S atoms: S—S at top, S and S on sides, S and S below, S—S at bottom

29. (a) $H_3COH \longrightarrow \cdot CH_2OH + H\cdot$

$$CH_3\cdot + \cdot CH_2OH \longrightarrow CH_3CH_2OH$$
etc.

(b) Two
$$-\overset{|}{\underset{|}{C}}-\overset{|}{\underset{|}{C}}-\overset{|}{\underset{|}{C}}-OH \qquad -\overset{|}{\underset{|}{C}}-\overset{|}{\underset{OH}{C}}-\overset{|}{\underset{|}{C}}-$$

31.
ethylene structure $H_2C=CH_2$

propylene structure

33. C, N
$$\left(\text{structure} \right)^{-}$$

Triple bond   NaCN, Ba(CN)$_2$

35. Yes. See Figures 10-6 and 10-7.

37. Acetone, water, and ether provide oxygen atoms with unbonded electron pairs for the —OH group to bond to. Octane has none.

39. Hydrogen atoms on O, N, or S plus a source of unbonded electron pairs as on O, N, Cl, F, or S.

CHAPTER 11

Exercise

1. $C + O_2 \longrightarrow CO_2 + 94.0$ kcal
$C + O_2 \longrightarrow CO_2 + 94.0$ kcal
—————————————————
$2C + 2O_2 \longrightarrow 2CO_2 + 2(94.0)$ kcal

2. $C(s) + O_2(g) \longrightarrow CO_2(g) + 94.0$ kcal
$CO(g) \longrightarrow C(s) + \frac{1}{2}O_2(g) - 26.4$ kcal
—————————————————
$CO(g) + \frac{1}{2}O_2(g) \longrightarrow CO_2(g) + 67.6$ kcal

3.   (a) $4[NH_3(g) \longrightarrow \frac{1}{2}N_2(g) + \frac{3}{2}H_2(g) - 11.0$ kcal$]$
$6[H_2(g) + \frac{1}{2}O_2(g) \longrightarrow H_2O(g) + 57.8$ kcal$]$
—————————————————
$4NH_3(g) + 3O_2(g) \longrightarrow 2N_2(g) + 6H_2O(g) + 302.8$ kcal

$$\frac{302.8}{4} = 75.7 \text{ kcal/mol } NH_3$$

(b)   The reaction is exothermic.

4. $H_2(g) + \frac{1}{2}O_2(g) \longrightarrow H_2O(g) + 57.8$ kcal
$H_2O(l) \longrightarrow H_2(g) + \frac{1}{2}O_2(g) - 68.3$ kcal
—————————————————
$H_2O(l) \longrightarrow H_2O(g) - 10.5$ kcal
or $H_2O(l) + 10.5$ kcal $\longrightarrow H_2O(g)$

Problem

1.   Blow air through the coke. Some will burn and heat the rest.

3.   (a) Unburned match head (b) Potato
(c) Unused flashbulb (d) Freshly cut grass

5.   133 °C

7.   Left

9.   25.5 kcal

11.   6.83 kcal

13.   (c)

15. $C_2H_6 + \frac{7}{2}O_2 \longrightarrow 2CO_2 + 3H_2O + 341.2$ kcal

17. $2Al + \frac{3}{2}O_2 \longrightarrow Al_2O_3 + 400$ kcal
$Fe_2O_3 + 200$ kcal $\longrightarrow 2Fe + \frac{3}{2}O_2$
—————————————————
$2Al + Fe_2O_3 \longrightarrow 2Fe + Al_2O_3 + 200$ kcal

19.   2.00 kg

21.   65 kcal released/mol $SO_2(g)$ formed

23.   94 kcal released/mol $SO_3(g)$ formed

25.   (a) 174 g   (b) 147 g

27.   Ethane

29.   The heat liberated is 117, 72, 72 kcal as successive moles of H_2O are added. The first mole is most strongly held.

31. $I_2(s)$ if reaction is exothermic (vessel warms)
$I_2(g)$ if reaction is endothermic (vessel cools)

33.   Because it accurately correlates a large amount of data.

35.   Yes.

37.   The molecules move more rapidly and rotate more quickly.

39. 1.85×10^8 kcal/mol nuclear particles

41. $^{235}_{92}U + ^{1}_{0}n \longrightarrow ^{236}_{92}U \longrightarrow ^{137}_{52}Te + ^{97}_{40}Zr + 2\,^{1}_{0}n$

CHAPTER 12

Exercise

1.   (a) 1 M
(b) 2 M
(c) A reaction dependent on HI concentration would be faster in case (b).

2.   Faster in (c), less in (b), least in (a), because the surface area becomes lower in that order.

3. (a) Probably none
    (b) Speed up process
    (c) Probably none

Problem

1. Many answers are possible. Some are
    (a) frames/sec, feet of film/second
    (b) rev/min, rpm
    (c) ft/sec
    (d) qt/wk
    (e) autos/day
3. As concentration goes up, collisions/sec go up. The rate may rise if number of collisions was the limiting factor.
5. (1) Temperature. Increases collisions/sec and, more important, increases the average energy per collision.
    (2) Concentration. Increases collisions/sec.
    (3) Catalyst. Provides new mechanism requiring less activation energy.
7. (a) Exothermic
    (b) High temperature gives faster reaction. Low pressure means less expensive equipment.
    (c) 12 kcal released/mol NH_3 formed.
    (d) 4.85 g H_2
9. Since step 1 is rate-controlling, 10 more helpers would cause a big increase. They would not have much effect if used in step 2 or 3.
11. A glass gets many bumps that do not break it. A blow of sufficient energy will break it. A certain threshold energy is needed to break the glass.
13. Food spoils as the end result of many chemical reactions which are slowed by the low temperature.
15. Whether the collision has sufficient energy.
17.

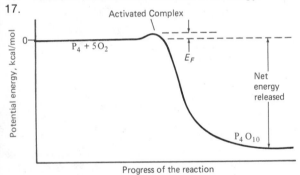

Progress of the reaction

19. The reactions of the burning match supply enough activation to start the reaction of oxygen with the wick.
21. (a) 54.1 kcal released/mol   CO reacted
     (b) 86.1 kcal/mol
     (c)

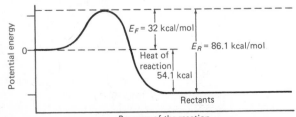

Progress of the reaction

23.

Progress of the reaction

25. Note that Cu^{2+} does cancel out. So does $CuSO_4$.
27. The large surface area of the dust gives a faster reaction.
29. 8.4×10^{23} particles/mole
31. 2 M
33. 0.100 mole
34. 0.000 010 mole KSCN
37. 0.080 M

CHAPTER 13

Exercise

1. (a) More $Cr_2O_7{}^{2-}$ forms and makes the solution color more orange.
    (b) Some $Cr_2O_7{}^{2-}$ is converted to $CrO_4{}^{2-}$; the solution becomes more yellow in color.
2. Decrease
3. $PCl_3 + Cl_2$ favored
    No effect
    $NO + H_2O$ favored
4. (a) 55.5 moles/liter
    (b) 55.4 moles/liter
5. $CaSO_4(s) \rightleftharpoons Ca^{2+} + SO_4{}^{2-}$
    $K_{sp} = [Ca^{2+}][SO_4{}^{2-}]$
6. $Ag_2CrO_4(s) \rightleftharpoons 2 Ag^+ + CrO_4{}^{2-}$
    $K_{sp} = [Ag^+]^2[CrO_4{}^{2-}]$
7. AgCl is most soluble, AgI least
8. 4.9×10^{-3} mole/liter

Problem

1. Yes. No, because sugar will leave solution faster. Equilibrium will be unaffected by solid added after equilibrium is established.
3. The rates of forward and reverse reactions
5. Because on a molecular level there is much "action."
7. (a) (1) $C_2H_6(g)$ increases
         (2) $CO_2(g)$ increases
         (3), (4), (5) little effect
    (b) Statements apply to species in the order listed in the equation.
         (1) Increase, increase, decrease
         (2) Increase, increase, decrease
         (3) Increase, decrease, increase
         (4) No change in concentration, but the amount of solid would increase; increase; increase; decrease.
         (5) No change
9. (a) $CH_3OH(g)$ will decrease, others increase.
    (b) $CH_3OH(g)$ will increase, others decrease.

11. (a) No effect
    (b) More H_2S produced
13. It does not.
15. (a) Chlorine concentration will decrease because equilibrium shifts to absorb heat.
    (b) Decrease
    (c) Increase
    (d) Decrease
    (e) No change
17. $\overline{p}H_2(g) = 1$ atm
    $\overline{p}O_2(g) = 0.5$ atm
    $K = 0.5$
19. $K = \dfrac{[HI]^2}{[H_2][I_2]} = 50.0$ (forward reaction)

    $K = \dfrac{[H_2][I_2]}{[HI]^2} = 0.0200$ (reverse reaction)

21. (a) $K = \dfrac{[\overline{p}(CO)][\overline{p}(H_2O)]}{[\overline{p}(CO_2)][\overline{p}(H_2)]}$

    (b) Trial 1 $K = 1.291$ ⎫
         2   $K = 1.290$ ⎬ = 1.29 to precision
         3   $K = 1.293$ ⎭ of experiment

25. (c)
27. $3 O_2(g) \rightleftharpoons 2 O_3(g)$
    $K = [O_3]^2/[O_2]^3$
29. Partial pressure of isobutane $= 25$ atm
    Partial pressure of butane $= 10$ atm
31. 8.5×10^{-14} M
33. The sulfides will precipitate in order as K gets bigger. You would see CuS (brown-black), then CdS (yellow), and then CoS (brown).
35. (a) Increase rate of dissolving   No effect on solubility
    (b) Increase rate   Increase
    (c) Increase rate   No effect
    (d) Increase at first, then no effect   No effect
37. (a) $K_{sp} = [Ca^{2+}][CO_3^{2-}]$
    (b) $K_{sp} = [Ag^+]^2[S^{2-}]$
    (c) $K_{sp} = [Al^{3+}][OH^-]^3$
39. 1.2×10^{-2} M

CHAPTER 14

Exercise
1. $1.00 \times \dfrac{10^3 \text{ g}}{\text{liter}} \times \dfrac{1 \text{ mol}}{18 \text{ g}} = 55.5 \dfrac{\text{mol}}{\text{liter}}$
    $= 55.5$ M

2. 55.5 M in each case
3. $[OH^-] = 0.010$ $M = 1.0 \times 10^{-2}$ M.
   NaOH is a strong electrolyte that dissociates 100%.
   Therefore,
   $[H^+] = \dfrac{1.0 \times 10^{-14}}{1.0 \times 10^{-2}} = 1.0 \times 10^{-12}$ M

4. $[H^+] = 1.00 \times 10^{-2}$ M
   $[OH^-] = 1.00 \times 10^{-12}$ M
5. (a) In H_2O $[H^+] = [OH^-]$
                   $= 1.0 \times 10^{-7}$ M
    or 6.0×10^{16} H^+ or OH^- ions/liter
    (b) In 0.1 M HCl
         $H^+ = 6.0 \times 10^{22}$ ions/liter
         $OH^- = 6.0 \times 10^{10}$ ions/liter

6. $[H^+] = 1 \times 10^{-3}$ M
   $[OH^-] = 1 \times 10^{-11}$ M
7. 0.05 M
8. H_2SO_3 is strongest; its K_A is largest.
   HNO_2 is weakest; its K_A is smallest.
9. Write the equilibrium constant for each equation. Observe that one is the reciprocal of the other.
10. Products

Problem
1. Possible answers include: Hydrogen-containing compounds; conducting solutions; solutions liberate H_2 (g) when reacted with Zn; solutions turn litmus red.
5. $Ba^{2+} + 2OH^- + 2H^+ + SO_4^{2-} \longrightarrow BaSO_4(s) + 2H_2O(l)$
   The ions are removed, so conductivity decreases.
7. $[H^+] = 5.0 \times 10^{-3}$, $[OH^-] = 2.0 \times 10^{-12}$
9. $H^+ + OH^- \longrightarrow H_2O$
   One mole of acid requires one mole of OH^-.
11. (a) 1.5×10^{-2} M
    (b) 1.0×10^{-7} M
    (c) 1.0×10^{-12} M
13. $[H^+] = 2 \times 10^{-4}$ M
    $[OH^-] = 5 \times 10^{-11}$ M
15. $[H^+] = 10^{-5}$ M; acidic solution
17. $pH = 4$ means $[H^+] = 10^{-4}$
    Takes 0.00084 g $NaHCO_3$
19. Lemon juice/$NH_3 = 1/10$
21. 0.0200 M
25. (a) Products
    (b) Reactants
    (c) K_1 is larger than K_2.
27. The acid donating the first proton is much stronger than that donating the second, which in turn is much stronger than that donating the third.
29. (a) $H_2S(aq) + CO_3^{2-}(aq) \rightleftharpoons$
                            $HS^-(aq) + HCO_3^-(aq)$
    (b) $HS^- + CO_3^{2-}$, hydrosulfide and carbonate ions
    (c) K_A for $H_2S = 1.0 \times 10^{-7}$
         for $HCO_3^- = 4.7 \times 10^{-11}$
    H_2S releases H^+ much more readily than HCO_3^- ($10^{-7} > 10^{-11}$). The reaction favors products.
31. (a) $H_2SO_3(aq) + HCO_3^-(aq) \rightleftharpoons$
                           $HSO_3^-(aq) + H_2CO_3(aq)$
    Products favored.

    (b) $H_2CO_3(aq) + SO_3^{2-}(aq) \rightleftharpoons$
                         $HCO_3^-(aq) + HSO_3^-(aq)$
    Products slightly favored.

    (c) $H_2SO_3(aq) + SO_3^{2-}(aq) \rightleftharpoons$
                             $2 HSO_3^-(aq)$
    Products favored.

33. 1.9×10^{-4}
35. 6.9×10^{-4}
37. 9.2×10^2 Products favored.

CHAPTER 15

Exercise
1. Below hydrogen but above zinc.

2. (a) $Co \longrightarrow Co^{2+} + 2 e^-$
        $2 Fe^{3+} + 2 e^- \longrightarrow 2 Fe^{2+}$

        $Co + 2 Fe^{3+} \longrightarrow Co^{2+} + 2 Fe^{2+}$

        $E° \quad = +0.28$ volt
        $E° \quad = +0.77$ volt

        $E°_{net} = +1.05$ volts

    (b) $H_2 \longrightarrow 2 H^+ + 2 e^-$
        $Cl_2 + 2 e^- \longrightarrow 2 Cl^-$

        $H_2 + Cl_2 \longrightarrow 2 H^+ + 2 Cl^-$

        $E° \quad = \quad 0.00$ volt
        $E° \quad = +1.36$ volts

        $E°_{net} = +1.36$ volts

    (c)

    $5(2 I^- \longrightarrow I_2 + 2 e^-)$
    $2(MnO_4^- + 8 H^+ + 5 e^- \longrightarrow Mn^{2+} + 4 H_2O)$

    $10 I^- + 2 MnO_4^- + 16 H^+ \longrightarrow 5 I_2 + 2 Mn^{2+} + 8 H_2O$

        $E° \quad = -0.53$ volt
        $E° \quad = +1.52$ volts

        $E°_{net} = +0.99$ volt

    (d) $Ag \longrightarrow Ag^+ + e^-$
        $2 Cl^- \longrightarrow Cl_2 + 2 e^-$
        The proposed reaction will not occur to any appreciable extent. Each half-reaction produces electrons.

3. Co will dissolve in 1 M H$^+$ but not in 1 M Zn^{2+}.
4. O_2, Cl_2
5. H_2, Fe^{2+}, Ni(s)
6. Cathode $Na^+ + e^- \longrightarrow Na$
    Anode $2 Cl^- \longrightarrow 2 e^- + Cl_2$
7. 17 g Na, 9.0 g Mg, 6.9 g Al,
    27 g Cl$_2$, 6.0 g O$_2$
8. (a) $Zn + 2 Ag^+ \longrightarrow 2 Ag + Zn^{2+}$
    (b) $2 Cr^{2+} + I_2 \longrightarrow 2 I^- + 2 Cr^{3+}$
    (c) $3 Ti + 2 Fe_2O_3 \longrightarrow 3 TiO_2 + 4 Fe$
9. (a) Find $Cr_2O_7^{2-}$ and Hg half-reactions, multiply the second by 3, and add to get
        $Cr_2O_7^{2-} + 14 H^+ + 3 Hg \longrightarrow$
        $2 Cr^{3+} + 7 H_2O + 3 Hg^{2+}$.
    (b) Find MnO_4^- and H_2O_2 half-reactions, multiply first by 2, add, then subtract 10 H$^+$ from each side to get
        $2 MnO_4^- + 6 H^+ + 5 H_2O_2 \longrightarrow$
        $2 Mn^{2+} + 8 H_2O + 5 O_2$.
    (c) Find the two half-reactions and add to get
        $H_2O_2 + SO_2 \longrightarrow 2 H^+ + SO_4^{2-}$.
10. (a) $N_2H_5^+ + 2 PuO_2^{2+} + 3 H^+ \longrightarrow$
        $N_2 + 2 Pu^{4+} + 4 H_2O$
    (b) $4 Zn + NO_3^- + 10 H^+ \longrightarrow$
        $4 Zn^{2+} + NH_4^+ + 3 H_2O$
    (c) $S_2O_6^{2-} + BiO_3^- + 2 H^+ \longrightarrow$
        $2 SO_4^{2-} + H_2O + Bi^{3+}$
11. In order listed, the oxidation numbers of N are −3, 1, 4, 4, 3, 5.
12. In order listed, the oxidation numbers of P are 1, 3, 5.

Problem
1. (a) Oxidized. $M \longrightarrow M^+ + e^-$
    (b) Reduced. $X^- + e^- \longrightarrow X^{2-}$
3. The ions move.
5. 9.3 g
7. (a) $Al \longrightarrow Al^{3+} + 3 e^-$
    (b) $2 H^+ + 2 e^- \longrightarrow H_2(g)$
        2(a) + 3(b) gives:
        $2 Al + 6 H^+ \longrightarrow 2 Al^{3+} + 3 H_2(g)$
9. Oxygen has the greatest tendency to gain e^-; S_8, Se_8, Te_8 have the least tendency.
11. 3×10^{20} e^-/min
13. 10^{-6} mole e^- per s.
15. (a) Magnesium
    (b) Co^{2+}
    (c) Magnesium
    (d) Co^{2+}
17. $W_2 + 2e^- \rightleftharpoons 2 W^-$
    $Y_2 + 2e^- \rightleftharpoons 2 Y^-$
    $X_2 + 2e^- \rightleftharpoons 2 X^-$
    $Z_2 + 2e^- \rightleftharpoons 2 Z^-$
    Z^- is the strongest reducing agent.
    W_2 is the strongest oxidizing agent.
19. (a) 2.23 volts—products favored
    (b) −1.74 volts—reactants favored
    (c) 1.02 volts—products favored
    (d) 0.32 volt —products favored
    (e) 1.21 volts—products favored
21. Practically nothing happens. $E_{net} = -1.08$ volts. Reactants are favored.
23. No, the container will dissolve.
25. +0.30 volt
27. (a) and (d)
29. (a) 757 g Na_2CO_3
    (b) 3.57 liter
31. (a) 79.2 g $NaIO_3$
    (b) 50.8 g I_2
33. 0.42 liter HNO_3
35. 53 ml $KMnO_4$ solution
37. $5 Sn^{2+} + 2 MnO_4^- + 16 H^+ \rightleftharpoons$
    $5 Sn^{4+} + 2 Mn^{2+} + 8 H_2O$
39. (a) $2 HBr + H_2SO_4 \rightleftharpoons Br_2 + SO_2 + 2 H_2O$
    (b) $2 NO_3^- + 8 H^+ + 6 Cl^- \rightleftharpoons$
        $2 NO + 3 Cl_2 + 4 H_2O$
    (c) $4 Zn + NO_3^- + 10 H^+ \rightleftharpoons$
        $4 Zn^{2+} + NH_4^+ + 3 H_2O$
    (d) $3 BrO^- \rightleftharpoons 2 Br^- + BrO_3^-$
41. (a) $In + BiO^+ + 2 H^+ \rightleftharpoons In^{3+} + Bi + H_2O$
    (b) $4 V^{2+} + 2 H_2SO_3 + 2 H^+ \rightleftharpoons$
        $4 V^{3+} + S_2O_3^{2-} + 3 H_2O$
    (c) $Te^{2-} + C_2N_2 + 2 H^+ \rightleftharpoons Te + 2 HCN$
    (d) $3 Mn + 2 IrCl_6^{3-} \rightleftharpoons 3 Mn^{2+} + 2 Ir + 12 Cl^-$

CHAPTER 16

Exercise
1. All formulas are rotations of the three given in the text. Kinks in the 7-carbon chain are not different formulas.
2. There are nine. The address of methyl groups will be 2, 2; 2, 3; 2, 4; 2, 5; 2, 6; or 3, 3; 3, 4; 3, 5; or 4, 4.
3. 1-d, 2-b, 3-a, 4-c
4. Beside 1-decene on p. 351 there are (hydrogens omitted).

C—C=C—C—C—C—C—C—C—C   2-decene

C—C—C=C—C—C—C—C—C—C   3-decene

C—C—C—C=C—C—C—C—C—C   4-decene

C—C—C—C—C=C—C—C—C—C   5-decene

No other *different* arrangements; "6-decene" is the same as 4-decene, etc.

5. $(CH_2)_2$ or C_2H_4
6. CH_3O
7. $C_2H_6O_2$
8. Answers which fit the empirical formula and the bonding rules are

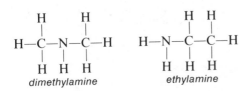

methyl hydroxymethyl ether

glycol

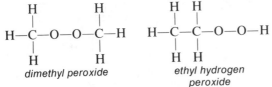

dimethyl peroxide   *ethyl hydrogen peroxide*

9.

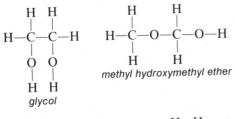

dimethylamine   *ethylamine*

10. $R—OH + HCl \longrightarrow R—Cl + H_2O$

11.

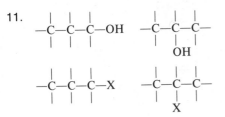

12.

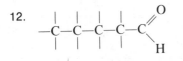

13.

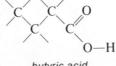

butyraldehyde   *butyric acid*

14. (a) $CH_3CH_2O\boxed{—H + HO—}C—H \longrightarrow$

ethanol   *formic acid*

$CH_3CH_2—O—C—H + H_2O$

ethyl formate

(b) $CH_3CH_2CH_2O\boxed{—H + HO—}C—CH_2CH_3 \longrightarrow$

propanol   *propionic acid*

$CH_3CH_2CH_2—O—C—CH_2CH_3 + H_2O$

propyl propionate

(c) $CH_3O\boxed{—H + HO—}C—H \longrightarrow$

methanol   *formic acid*

$CH_3—O—C—H + H_2O$

methyl formate

15. $C_6H_{12}O_6$

16.
```
CH_2OH
|
C=O
|
CHOH
|
CHOH
|
CHOH
|
CH_2OH
```

17. $K = 99$. The ring form is favored.
18. Starch 125 Å long
Cellulose 19 000 Å long

Problem

1. Empirical formula, C_3H_8, tells relative number of atoms.
Molecular formula, C_3H_8, tells total number of atoms.
Structural formula,

shows total number of atoms plus the arrangement of atoms.

3.

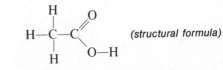

(structural formula)

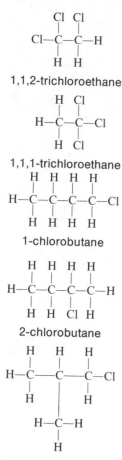

5.

1,1,2-trichloroethane

1,1,1-trichloroethane

7.

1-chlorobutane

2-chlorobutane

1-chloro-2-methyl propane

2-chloro-2-methyl propane

9. $C_7H_5O_3NS$

11. 20 g. Assume complete reaction to only one product.

13. Nine

15. 1-butanol can give butyraldehyde, then butyric acid, then $CO_2 + H_2O$.
2-butanol gives butanone, then $CO_2 + H_2O$.
2-methyl-2-propanol does not give four-carbon oxidation products.

17. 341.2 kcal/mol—exothermic

19.

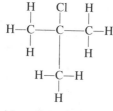

$$Cr_2O_7^{2-} + 14 H^+ + 6 e^- \longrightarrow 2 Cr^{3+} + 7 H_2O$$
Take 3 times the first and add.

3 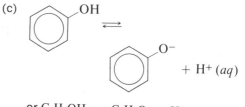 $+ Cr_2O_7^{2-} + 8H^+ \longrightarrow$

3

21.	Alcohol	Aldehyde	Acid
	CH_3OH	HCHO	HCOOH
	C_2H_5OH	CH_3CHO	CH_3COOH
	C_4H_9OH	C_3H_7CHO	C_3H_7COOH
	$C_8H_{17}OH$	$C_7H_{15}CHO$	$C_7H_{15}COOH$

23. $CH_3CH_2CH_2CH_2OH + HI \rightleftharpoons$
$\qquad\qquad CH_3CH_2CH_2CH_2I + H_2O$
$CH_3CH_2CH_2CH_2I + 2 NH_3 \rightleftharpoons$
$\qquad\qquad CH_3CH_2CH_2CH_2NH_2 + NH_4I$

27. $H_3C\,COOH$, $HO{-}CH_2CH_2CH_3$

29. Remove H_2O with a drying agent. Increase the concentration of a reactant.

31. (a) $K = \dfrac{[RCOOR'][H_2O]}{[RCOOH][R'OH]}$

    (b) $[RCOOR'] = 0.1\ M$

    (c) $[RCOOR'] = 0.9\ M$

33. (a) $90\text{–}105°$

    (b) Greater than benzene because phenol can form hydrogen bonds.

    (c)

$+ H^+ (aq)$

    or $C_6H_5OH \rightleftharpoons C_6H_5O^- + H^+$

    (d) $K_A = 1.2 \times 10^{-10}$

35.

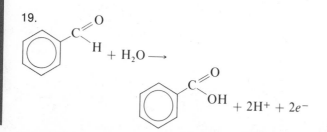

CHAPTER 17

Exercise

1. Probably near 109° as in CH_4.
2. Experimental angles are near the predicted 109°.
3. ClF should be a molecular solid melting below 0 °C. S and NH are quite similar. Might get a cyclic structure.
4. Draw structures. Each carbon has 8 e^-, as do atoms in a noble gas.
5. F_2 and molecules of similar electron configuration have all valence orbitals full. Thus only weak van der Waals forces exist and are easily broken at low temperatures.
6. Network solid

7.

A graphitelike sheet of BN

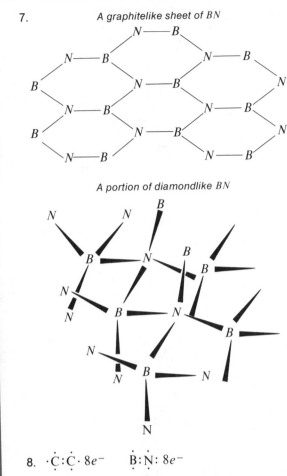

A portion of diamondlike BN

8. $\cdot \ddot{C} : \ddot{C} \cdot\ 8e^-$ $\ddot{B} : \ddot{N} :\ 8e^-$

9. Cubic closest packed. Same relative pattern as Al.

Problem

1. The double bond in ethylene maintains a symmetrical arrangement—no moment. Hydrazine has a pyramidal arrangement around each N atom. A molecular moment results.

3. Ethane is symmetric; methylamine is not.

5.

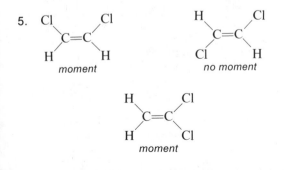

7. H_2S should be bent like H_2O. H_2S_2 is like H_2O_2.

9. $\cdot \ddot{F} \cdot\ \ddot{N} :: \ddot{N} \cdot \ddot{F} \cdot$

11. (a)

$$\begin{array}{c} I \\ | \\ I-P \\ \quad \diagdown P-I \\ \qquad | \\ \qquad I \end{array}$$

(b)
$$Se \diagup^{S-C \equiv N}_{\diagdown S-C \equiv N}$$

(c)
$$\begin{array}{c} H \\ \diagdown \\ \quad N-C \equiv N \\ \diagup \\ H \end{array}$$

13. SO_2 molecules are held together by van der Waals forces; $SO_4{}^{2-}$ compounds by ionic forces.

15. Molecular solids. The molecules are largely covalently bonded with van der Waals or H-bonding forces between them.

17. B and C are covalent, network solids. N and O form diatomic gases with van der Waals forces between molecules.

19.
$$\begin{array}{c} CH_3 \\ | \\ H_3C-Ge-CH_3 \\ | \\ CH_3 \end{array}$$

$$\begin{array}{c} CH_3\ CH_3\ CH_3 \\ |\quad\ |\quad\ | \\ H_3C-Ge-Ge-Ge-CH_3 \\ |\quad\ |\quad\ | \\ CH_3\ CH_3\ CH_3 \end{array}$$

23.
$$\begin{array}{c} -N-N-N-N- \\ |\ \ |\ \ |\ \ | \\ -N-N-N-N- \end{array}$$
It would be like asbestos.

25. Copper has many empty orbitals and free, mobile electrons. Glass has no empty orbitals, and the electrons are closely bound in covalent bonds.

27. Cs—body centered
Be—hexagonal

29. $2\sqrt{2}\,r$

33. $Cl_2 \approx HCl < CCl_4 < NaCl$

35. Al has more vacant orbitals than bonding electrons; thus it is a metal.
Si has the same number of each, so it forms a network solid.
S has only 2 half-vacant orbitals; it can form chains or rings but cannot cross-link into a network.

37. It is the mass of 6×10^{23} empirical formula units. The "molecule" is undefined.

39. I is GeO_2; network solid.
II is p-dichlorobenzene; molecular solid.
III is LiCl; ionic solid.

41. Sugar can H bond to the solvent. Salt cannot.

43. $Cl_3CH \cdots O = C \diagup^{CH_3}_{\diagdown CH_3}$

Since oxygen has two lone pairs of electrons, two $CHCl_3$ molecules can H bond if the concentration is high enough.

45.

$H : C ::: N :$

	C	$\otimes$						H

N $\otimes\ \otimes$

Linear, H bonded, linear complex.

47. (a) Ne, CH_4 (d) KCl
    (b) Na   (e) H_2O
    (c) Ge

CHAPTER 18

Exercise
1. (a) $2\,NaIO_3 + 5\,NaHSO_3 + 2\,H^+ \longrightarrow$
          $I_2 + 2\,Na^+ + 5\,NaHSO_4 + H_2O$
   (b) An excess of HSO_3^- will reduce I_2 to I^-.
2. CF_4 1.49 Å calc.   1.32 Å obs.
   CBr_4 1.91   1.94
   CI_4 2.10   2.15

Problem
1. The outermost groups of electrons are the same. There are more total electrons as atomic number goes up.
3. The two regularities give straight lines.
5. The greater charge on K^+ nucleus attracts the electrons more, making K^+ smaller than Cl^-.
7. Br_2 can oxidize Fe^{2+} to Fe^{3+}. I_2 cannot.
9. Cl_2 will be reduced to Cl^- by Br^- or I^-.
   Br_2 goes to Br^- with I^-.
11. $I^- + 2\,S_2O_3^{2-} \rightleftharpoons S_4O_6^{2-} + 2\,I^-$
   Oxidation number of S in $S_4O_6^{2-}$ is 2.5.
13. $SO_2 + 2\,H_2O + I_2 \rightleftharpoons SO_4^{2-} + 4\,H^+ + 2\,I^-$.
   $E^0 = +0.36$ volt. If $[H^+]$ is lowered, the reaction is favored. E^0 would be a larger positive number.
15. (a) ClO_3^- is a stronger oxidizing agent.
   (b) $10\,I^- + 2\,ClO_3^- + 12\,H^+ \rightleftharpoons$
                $5\,I_2 + Cl_2 + 6\,H_2O$
17. (a) I   (d) HF
   (b) I   (e) HF
   (c) I^-
19. 7.51 g SiO_2

22. $\cdot C \!::\! N \!:$ $\cdot N \!::\! C \!::\! \ddot{O}$ $\cdot \ddot{\underset{..}{Cl}} :$

   Each has one unpaired electron.
23. To be classed as a pseudohalogen, the substance (X) should:
      (1) form a 1^- ion.
      (2) be gaseous in dimer form.
      (3) form HX acid.
      (4) form only slightly soluble salts with Ag^+, Pb^{2+}, Hg_2^{++}, and Cu^+.
      (5) be an oxidizing agent.
      (6) react with other halogens or pseudo-halogens.
      (7) form covalent compounds with organic groups.
25. (a), (b), (c) Reasonable compared to halogens.
   (d) Unreasonable, would expect NaN_3 parallel with NaCl.
   (e) Unreasonable, OCN should form a single covalent bond as in (a).
27. 350 liter
29. 38 liter
31. ^{79}Br, 50.5%; ^{81}Br, 49.5%
33. 1/16
35. 15.8 g HOCl

CHAPTER 19

Exercise
1. $4\,p$, Ga
2. $1s^2\,2s^22p^6\,3s^23p^63d^{10}\,4s^24p^64d^1\,5s^2$ Sc
3. The graph shows a curve generally rising to the right. Density increases with atomic number in this set of elements. It does *not* for all the elements. Rather a "sawtooth" curve is found.

Problem
1. They have their valence electrons in the same orbitals ($4s$ and $3d$) and similar properties.
3. Good conductors of heat and electricity, lustrous and strong, and they have many orbitals for bonding.
5. The oxidation number of Mn in
   MnO_4^- is $+7$
   Mn^{2+} $+2$
   Mn_3O_4 $+8/3$ (or $+3$ for 2 Mn and $+2$ for the other)
   MnO_2 $+4$
   $Mn(OH)_2$ $+2$
   $MnCl_2$ $+2$
   MnF_3 $+3$
7. 6.8 lb.
9. $2\,VO_2NO_3 \longrightarrow V_2O_5 + N_2O_5$
11. (a) Fe 1.25 Å, V 1.40 Å, Ga 1.38 Å
   (b) Mn-Ni atoms are essentially of equal-size; they fit easily. Cu (1.30 Å) and Ca (1.95 Å) are quite different in size.
13. No dipole. Van der Waals bonding. 1800 cal to vaporize 0.30 mole.
15. Nothing
17. $K_{sp} = 3.8 \times 10^{-5}$
19. $3\,C_2H_5OH + 2\,K_2Cr_2O_7 + 8\,H_2SO_4 \longrightarrow$
   $3\,CH_3COOH + 2\,Cr_2(SO_4)_3 + 2\,K_2SO_4 + 11\,H_2O$
21. $HCrO_4^-$
23. $Cr_2O_7^{2-} + 2\,NH_4Cl \longrightarrow Cr_2O_3 + 2\,Cl^- + N_2$
                             $+ 4\,H_2O$
   58 kg Cr_2O_3
25. The K values show FeF^{2+} is more favored than $FeSCN^{2+}$, which in turn is more favored than $FeCl^{2+}$. The F^- can "steal" the Fe^{3+} from $FeSCN^{2+}$, but Cl^- cannot.
27. The two NO_2 groups can be next to each other or separated.
29. NH_3 has an orbital containing two electrons. They can be donated to an empty orbital, and a complex results. NH_4^+ does not have this feature. A proton (H^+) has already "used" the electron pair to form the ion.
31.

33. The fewer electrons in Fe^{3+} are attracted more strongly; hence, there is a smaller ion.
   Fe-Cl in $[FeCl_6]^{4-} = 2.57$ Å
         in $Fe_2Cl_6 = 2.45$ Å

35.   There are four possibilities:

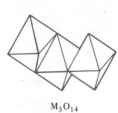

M_3O_{14}
Isomer

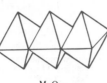

M_3O_{14}
Isomer

M_3O_{14}
Isomer

M_3O_{13}
Not an Isomer

Index

(Pr. 00) refers to problem number 00.

Index

Abundance of Elements in Earth's Crust
(percent of atoms)

O	Si	Al	Fe	Ca	Na	K	Mg	Ti
47	28	7.9	4.5	3.5	2.5	2.5	2.2	0.5

Row

Row 1

1
1.0080
H
Hydrogen

Row 2

3	4
6.941	9.012
Li	Be
Lithium	Beryllium

Row 3

11	12
22.990	24.30
Na	Mg
Sodium	Magne-sium

Row 4

19	20	21	22	23	24	25	26	27
39.098	40.08	44.96	47.90	50.94	52.00	54.94	55.85	58.93
K	Ca	Sc	Ti	V	Cr	Mn	Fe	Co
Potassium	Calcium	Scandium	Titanium	Vanadium	Chromium	Manganese	Iron	Cobalt

Row 5

37	38	39	40	41	42	43	44	45
85.47	87.62	88.91	91.22	92.91	95.94	(97)	101.1	102.91
Rb	Sr	Y	Zr	Nb	Mo	Tc	Ru	Rh
Rubidium	Strontium	Yttrium	Zirconium	Niobium	Molyb-denum	Techne-tium	Ruthe-nium	Rhodium

Row 6

55	56	57-71 *	72	73	74	75	76	77
132.90	137.34		178.49	180.95	183.85	186.2	190.2	192.2
Cs	Ba	La-Lu	Hf	Ta	W	Re	Os	Ir
Cesium	Barium	Below	Hafnium	Tantalum	Tungsten	Rhenium	Osmium	Iridium

Row 7

87	88	89-103 †	104	105	106
(223)	(226)		(261)	(262)	
Fr	Ra	Ac-Lr			
Francium	Radium	Below			

6 *LANTHANIDE SERIES

57	58	59	60	61	62	63
138.91	140.12	140.92	144.24	(145)	150.35	152.0
La	Ce	Pr	Nd	Pm	Sm	Eu
Lantha-num	Cerium	Praseo-dymium	Neody-mium	Prome-thium	Samarium	Europium

7 † ACTINIDE SERIES

89	90	91	92	93	94	95
(227)	232.04	(231)	238.03	(237)	(244)	(243)
Ac	Th	Pa	U	Np	Pu	An
Actinium	Thorium	Protac-tinium	Uranium	Neptu-nium	Plutonium	Ameri-cium